*Elementary Theory of
Electric and Magnetic Fields*

Elementary Theory of

Electric and Magnetic Fields

Warren B. Cheston

Professor of Physics
University of Minnesota
Minneapolis, Minnesota

John Wiley & Sons, Inc. New York · London · Sydney

Library of Congress Catalog Card Number: 64-17135
Printed in the United States of America

Preface

The theory of electric and magnetic fields is one aspect of classical physics. An author who chooses such a subject for a text can add little if anything to the fund of knowledge physicists possess of the structure of the physical world. Yet old theories, and physical theories age exceedingly rapidly in the twentieth-century world, bear re-examination from time to time, not with the intent of modification but rather of recasting in a form more suitable to the present era. In other words, a contemporary text on a classical subject is an attempt at style. This is a text written for students of physics who exist in the 1960's and who will shortly join the ranks of practicing physical scientists whose view of the physical world is particularly characteristic of the 1960's. It is a text written for a full year's course for upper division or senior college students; it presupposes some exposure to electricity and magnetism in a general physics course. It also presupposes a facility with mathematical concepts which ten years ago could only be assumed of beginning graduate students. Above all, as its title suggests, this is a text in fields, and little if any attention is paid to circuits and devices. There is some attempt, particularly in the final chapters, to discuss subjects of contemporary interest such as plasma physics, but serious students of these subjects will find the material in this text a limited introduction.

The underlying theme of the first half of the text, before the introduction of the Maxwell–Lorentz theory of electromagnetism, is the one-to-one correspondence between electrostatic and magnetostatic (steady-state) phenomena. For students who have read the chapters on electricity and magnetism, the transition to electromagnetism should be seen as an obvious outcome of the basic similarity between the separate theories of electricity and magnetism. Chapters 2–4 concern themselves with a discussion of the electrostatics of charges residing in vacuum or upon conducting surfaces. This discussion is based on Coulomb's law of force between two fixed charged particles. Chapter 5 is a discussion of the modifications brought about by the presence of nonconducting material media, and a macroscopic theory of the behavior of material media in the presence of static charges is developed. Chapters 6–8 concern themselves with a discussion of the magnetic effects produced by slowly moving

v

charges in approximately uniform motion.   The discussion of magnetostatics is based on the empirical law of force between slowly moving charged particles, and the discussion parallels that of electrostatics.   In Chapter 9 the effect of material media on steady-state magnetic phenomena is discussed, and a macroscopic theory of magnetism is introduced. Chapters 10 and 11 serve as an introduction to the Maxwell–Lorentz equations of electromagnetism, and emphasis is placed in these chapters on electromagnetic waves in free space and guided waves.   Chapter 12 is a brief discussion of the macroscopic Maxwell–Lorentz equations which are suitable for the discussion of material media, and the behavior of electromagnetic waves in conductors and insulators is discussed.   In Chapter 13 the radiation of electromagnetic waves from systems of charges and currents is introduced.   Chapter 14 concerns itself with two main topics: the motion of single charges in electric and magnetic fields and the behavior of an ensemble of charged particles, the latter being a brief discussion of magnetohydrodynamics and plasma physics.   The final chapter, Chapter 15, is an abbreviated discussion of those aspects of solid-state physics which are relevant to a text on electricity and magnetism.   Some of the subjects treated in this last chapter are electric and magnetic susceptibilities, ferromagnetism, and superconductivity.   The book begins, Chapter 1, with a very condensed treatment of the salient mathematical techniques to be used throughout the text.   It is assumed that this chapter will serve as a reference to the student and that the lecturer will begin his discussion with Chapter 2.   The text is supplemented by a mathematical appendix consisting of a list of useful formulas and identities, and an appendix in which the various systems of units are commented upon.

   Since the text aims at adopting a style consistent with the era in which it is written, attention should be called to a few of the topics of a strictly contemporary character.   Chapter 6 concludes with a comparison between electrostatics and magnetostatics as to the behavior of the quantities related in the two theories under time reversal and space inversions; Chapter 9 contains a discussion of the Meissner effect and superconductivity; Chapter 12 discusses a simplified version of Kramers' classical dispersion theory; Chapter 14 concerns itself to a large extent with a subject of contemporary interest, namely, the physics of plasmas; Chapter 15 attempts to present a modern point of view concerning the behavior of real materials in electric and magnetic fields.

   A text does not get written without the participation, some of it unintentional, of a large number of people.   Included among these are the students in the classes to which I have lectured during the past ten years, and my colleagues at the University of Minnesota who have been the subjects of my many questions concerning certain aspects of electricity and magnetism which appeared to me to be subject to particularly murky discussions in the existing texts. Finally, grateful acknowledgment is offered to the quantity and high quality of the work of Mrs. Joyce Fay and Mrs. Kay Kirwin who prepared the manuscript for publication.

Warren B. Cheston

University of Minnesota
June 1964

Contents

Elementary Theory of
Electric and Magnetic Fields

1 | *Mathematical and Mechanical Preliminaries*

In a discussion of electric and magnetic fields, the physical phenomena under investigation concern the interaction of charged objects and current-carrying elements among themselves. Such a discussion necessarily presumes a certain prior knowledge of the behavior of objects under the application of forces. The general ideas of analytical mechanics form the background to this discussion. In addition, a familiarity with the analytical tools employed in physics is essential. These analytical tools are the logic and techniques of mathematics, particularly those of the calculus, vector analysis, and vector calculus. A text in electric and magnetic fields cannot encompass a detailed discussion of analytical mechanics or mathematics, although certain ideas from these areas will be introduced as needed. Such mechanical or mathematical features will be handled in a rather cursory fashion. Nevertheless the discussion will be sufficiently complete to enable the student to understand the particular physical phenomenon under consideration. It is assumed that the student will be sufficiently curious to explore these ideas and techniques further in texts devoted entirely to the discussion of analytical mechanics or mathematics.

Although many mathematical techniques will be introduced as the physical ideas are developed, certain basic techniques will be set forth as a preliminary to the main discussion.

1.1 Vector Analysis

For the analytical description of certain physical entities, it is necessary to assign one number to represent the entity. For example, one number suffices to represent the mass of an object. An entity which can be described by giving one number is said to be a *scalar*. A scalar quantity may be restricted to take on positive values only (i.e., mass, temperature on the Kelvin scale, length, etc.) or it may assume both positive and negative values (i.e., mechanical energy, temperature on the centigrade

1

scale, electric charge, etc.). Since all physical quantities are of necessity real, scalar quantities are represented by real numbers.

A given scalar quantity may depend in some way on the value of another scalar quantity. For example, the temperature of an object may depend on the time at which it is measured. Here, the temperature would be represented by a *scalar function* of the time.

There are many physical quantities for which it is necessary to specify more than one number in order to determine the quantity completely. For example, to locate the position of a point on a plane, or on any physical surface, it is necessary to specify two numbers. To locate the position of a point in space, it is necessary to specify three numbers. Many of the physical entities of this type can be represented by *vectors*. In general, the vectors used to represent physical quantities are specified by three numbers.

All the vectors dealt with in this text represent physical quantities which have a *magnitude* and an *orientation* defined with respect to some arbitrarily fixed direction in space. Since it is customary to represent a vector by a directed line segment (see Fig. 1.1), the magnitude of a vector is represented by the length of the directed line segment. To define the direction of a vector, a set of three mutually perpendicular straight lines— a set of coordinate axes—is erected, and the orientation of the directed line segment with respect to these coordinate axes represents the direction of the vector. Any vector can be represented by the projection of the vector along the three coordinate axes. These projections are numerically equal to the magnitude of the vector multiplied by the *direction cosines*

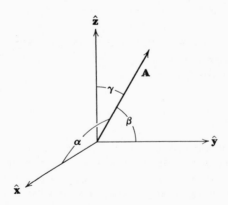

Fig. 1.1 A vector quantity **A** is represented by a directed line-segment. The orientation of the vector is given by the cosines of the angles between the vector and the x, y, z coordinate axes.

of the vector with respect to the coordinate axes (see Fig. 1.1). These projections are called the *components* of the vector and are a triad of numbers.

The three coordinate axes are customarily labelled the x-axis, the y-axis, and the z-axis, respectively. In this text, the axes (x, y, z) are always labelled in the right-hand sense. The components of the vector are consequently referred to as the x, y, and z components of the vector. This designation of a vector is called its *Cartesian representation*. An arbitrary vector $\mathbf{A}$ is therefore represented by three numbers (A_x, A_y, A_z). The magnitude of the vector is written as

$$|\mathbf{A}| = A = \sqrt{A_x^2 + A_y^2 + A_z^2} \tag{1.1}$$

and the orientation of the vector is specified by the three direction cosines as

$$\cos \alpha \equiv A_x/A, \qquad \cos \beta \equiv A_y/A, \qquad \cos \gamma = A_z/A \tag{1.2}$$

with the restriction implied by eq. 1.1, namely

$$\cos^2 \alpha + \cos^2 \beta + \cos^2 \gamma = 1.$$

A very useful concept is that of a *unit vector*. A unit vector is one whose magnitude is 1 (dimensionless). It is usually represented by affixing a "karat" symbol on top of the vector:

$$|\hat{\mathbf{A}}| \equiv 1; \qquad \hat{A}_x = \cos \alpha, \quad \hat{A}_y = \cos \beta, \quad \hat{A}_z = \cos \gamma. \tag{1.3}$$

The Cartesian components of a unit vector are simply the direction cosines of the vector. Any vector $\mathbf{A}$ can be written in terms of its magnitude A and the unit vector $\hat{\mathbf{A}}$ which is parallel to it; for example,

$$\mathbf{A} = A\hat{\mathbf{A}}. \tag{1.4}$$

A vector can be represented in terms of its components (A_x, A_y, A_z) and unit vectors along the coordinate axes $(\hat{\mathbf{x}}, \hat{\mathbf{y}}, \hat{\mathbf{z}})$. This representation can be obtained from the above and is written as

$$\mathbf{A} = A_x\hat{\mathbf{x}} + A_y\hat{\mathbf{y}} + A_z\hat{\mathbf{z}}. \tag{1.5}$$

Often several vector quantities are considered simultaneously. If the vectors are expressed in the same units or dimensions, the "sum" of the vectors is a well-defined concept. Consider three vectors $\mathbf{A}$, $\mathbf{B}$, $\mathbf{C}$. The sum of the vectors is also a vector and is uniquely defined as

$$\mathbf{A} + \mathbf{B} + \mathbf{C} \equiv \mathbf{D} = D_x\hat{\mathbf{x}} + D_y\hat{\mathbf{y}} + D_z\hat{\mathbf{z}} \tag{1.6}$$

where
$$D_x \equiv A_x + B_x + C_x$$
$$D_y \equiv A_y + B_y + C_y$$
$$D_z \equiv A_z + B_z + C_z$$

From eq. 1.6, it is obvious that vector addition is an *associative operation*, that is,

$$(\mathbf{A} + \mathbf{B}) + \mathbf{C} = \mathbf{A} + (\mathbf{B} + \mathbf{C}).$$

It is also a *commutative operation*, that is,

$$\mathbf{A} + \mathbf{C} + \mathbf{B} = \mathbf{B} + \mathbf{C} + \mathbf{A} = \cdots.$$

Sometimes it is necessary to know the relative orientation of two vectors **A** and **B** (see Fig. 1.2). The relative orientation of **A** and **B** is specified by the angle between them. Since ϑ is restricted to lie between 0 and 2π radians (or alternatively between $-\pi$ and π radians), it is necessary to specify both the sine and the cosine of ϑ to determine it completely. The cosine of the relative orientation of two vectors is involved in the "scalar" or "inner" product of two vectors. The scalar product of the vectors **A** and **B** is defined as

$$\mathbf{A} \cdot \mathbf{B} \equiv |\mathbf{A}| \, |\mathbf{B}| \cos \vartheta. \tag{1.7}$$

It is quite obvious from the definition of a scalar product that it is a commutative operation:

$$\mathbf{A} \cdot \mathbf{B} \equiv \mathbf{B} \cdot \mathbf{A}. \tag{1.8}$$

The scalar product of **A** and **B** can be written in terms of the Cartesian components of these vectors

$$\mathbf{A} \cdot \mathbf{B} = (A_x \hat{\mathbf{x}} + A_y \hat{\mathbf{y}} + A_z \hat{\mathbf{z}}) \cdot (B_x \hat{\mathbf{x}} + B_y \hat{\mathbf{y}} + B_z \hat{\mathbf{z}}).$$

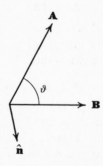

Fig. 1.2   The relative orientation of two vectors **A** and **B** is given by the angle ϑ between them. The angle ϑ in turn is determined by specifying its cosine and sine. The cosine of ϑ is involved in the scalar product of **A** and **B**; the sine of ϑ is involved in the vector product of **A** and **B**. The unit vector $\hat{\mathbf{n}}$ is perpendicular to the plane formed by the vectors **A** and **B**.

Since the unit vectors $\hat{\mathbf{x}}, \hat{\mathbf{y}}, \hat{\mathbf{z}}$ are mutually orthogonal (i.e., $\hat{\mathbf{x}} \cdot \hat{\mathbf{y}} = \hat{\mathbf{y}} \cdot \hat{\mathbf{z}} = \hat{\mathbf{z}} \cdot \hat{\mathbf{x}} = 0$), it follows that

$$\mathbf{A} \cdot \mathbf{B} = A_x B_x + A_y B_y + A_z B_z. \tag{1.9}$$

Use can be made of the concept of a scalar product to arrive at an expression for the Cartesian components of a vector alternative to that already employed. Taking cognizance of eqs. 1.2 and 1.9, it follows that

$$A_x = \mathbf{A} \cdot \hat{\mathbf{x}}, \, A_y = \mathbf{A} \cdot \hat{\mathbf{y}}, \, A_z = \mathbf{A} \cdot \hat{\mathbf{z}} \tag{1.10}$$

The sine of the relative orientation angle of two vectors is involved in the *vector product* of two vectors. This vector product is given the symbol $\mathbf{A} \times \mathbf{B}$ and is defined as

$$\mathbf{A} \times \mathbf{B} = |\mathbf{A}| \, |\mathbf{B}| \sin \vartheta \hat{\mathbf{n}} \tag{1.11}$$

where $\hat{\mathbf{n}}$ = unit vector perpendicular to the plane defined by $\mathbf{A}$ and $\mathbf{B}$. The direction of $\hat{\mathbf{n}}$ is arbitrarily chosen so that $\mathbf{A}$, $\mathbf{B}$, and $\hat{\mathbf{n}}$ form a right-handed triad of vectors. It is evident that the vector product of two vectors is a noncommutative operation. In fact,

$$\mathbf{A} \times \mathbf{B} = -\mathbf{B} \times \mathbf{A} \tag{1.12}$$

as can be seen directly from eq. 1.11. The vector product can be written in terms of the Cartesian components of the vectors involved and the unit vectors parallel to the Cartesian coordinate axes.

$$\mathbf{A} \times \mathbf{B} = (A_x \hat{\mathbf{x}} + A_y \hat{\mathbf{y}} + A_z \hat{\mathbf{z}}) \times (B_x \hat{\mathbf{x}} + B_y \hat{\mathbf{y}} + B_z \hat{\mathbf{z}})$$

using such relations as

$$\hat{\mathbf{x}} \times \hat{\mathbf{y}} = \hat{\mathbf{z}}, \,\, \hat{\mathbf{y}} \times \hat{\mathbf{z}} = \hat{\mathbf{x}}, \,\, \hat{\mathbf{z}} \times \hat{\mathbf{x}} = \hat{\mathbf{y}}$$
$$\hat{\mathbf{x}} \times \hat{\mathbf{x}} = \hat{\mathbf{y}} \times \hat{\mathbf{y}} = \hat{\mathbf{z}} \times \hat{\mathbf{z}} = 0,$$

it follows after some computation that

$$\mathbf{A} \times \mathbf{B} = (A_y B_z - A_z B_y)\hat{\mathbf{x}} + (A_z B_x - A_x B_z)\hat{\mathbf{y}} + (A_x B_y - A_y B_x)\hat{\mathbf{z}}. \tag{1.13}$$

There are many vector identities of some usefulness, some of which are listed below. They can all be developed in a straightforward manner by Cartesian expansion of the expressions involved.

$$\mathbf{A} \cdot (\mathbf{B} \times \mathbf{C}) = \mathbf{C} \cdot (\mathbf{A} \times \mathbf{B}) = \mathbf{B} \cdot (\mathbf{C} \times \mathbf{A}) \tag{1.14}$$

$$\mathbf{A} \times (\mathbf{B} \times \mathbf{C}) = (\mathbf{A} \cdot \mathbf{C})\mathbf{B} - (\mathbf{A} \cdot \mathbf{B})\mathbf{C} \tag{1.15}$$

$$(\mathbf{A} \times \mathbf{B}) \cdot (\mathbf{C} \times \mathbf{D}) = (\mathbf{A} \cdot \mathbf{C})(\mathbf{B} \cdot \mathbf{D}) - (\mathbf{A} \cdot \mathbf{D})(\mathbf{B} \cdot \mathbf{C}). \tag{1.16}$$

1.2 Coordinate Systems

All physical phenomena take place in space. Whether the phenomena under consideration are mechanical, electrical, etc., they take place at a given time at a given point in space. If one wishes to describe a point in space analytically, it is necessary to relate the point in some way to a given reference point. It is evident that it is not only necessary to specify "how far" the point under consideration is from the reference point but also in what "direction." It is clear therefore that it is possible to represent a point in space by a vector, called a *position vector* and given the symbol **r**. The position vector (or simply the position) can be given by the three Cartesian components of **r** defined by

$$\mathbf{r} = r_x\hat{\mathbf{x}} + r_y\hat{\mathbf{y}} + r_z\hat{\mathbf{z}}.$$

Without any danger of misinterpretation, a more common notation will be adopted:

$$\mathbf{r} = x\hat{\mathbf{x}} + y\hat{\mathbf{y}} + z\hat{\mathbf{z}} \tag{1.17}$$

where $\quad\quad x \equiv (\mathbf{r} \cdot \hat{\mathbf{x}}), \quad y \equiv (\mathbf{r} \cdot \hat{\mathbf{y}}), \quad z \equiv (\mathbf{r} \cdot \hat{\mathbf{z}}).$

The Cartesian axes to which **r** is referred is a set of axes whose origin is located at the reference point, but whose orientation is arbitrary but fixed *ab initio*.

Most physical quantities to be considered in this text fall into two classes: (1) scalar point functions, and (2) vector point functions. A scalar point function is a scalar function of the vector variable **r**. A scalar point function is sometimes called a *scalar field*. The electrostatic potential function $\varphi(\mathbf{r})$ is such a scalar field. A vector point function is a vector function of the variable **r**; for example, at every point in space there exists a given value for the vector quantity under consideration. A vector point function is sometimes referred to as a *vector field*. The electric field $\mathbf{E}(\mathbf{r})$ and magnetic field $\mathbf{B}(\mathbf{r})$ are vector fields.

A vector point function can also be decomposed into its components; the value of the vector function **G** at **r** may be written as

$$\mathbf{G}(\mathbf{r}) = G_x(\mathbf{r})\hat{\mathbf{x}} + G_y(\mathbf{r})\hat{\mathbf{y}} + G_z(\mathbf{r})\hat{\mathbf{z}} \tag{1.18}$$

where

$$G_x(\mathbf{r}) \equiv \hat{\mathbf{x}} \cdot \mathbf{G}(\mathbf{r}), \quad G_y(\mathbf{r}) \equiv \hat{\mathbf{y}} \cdot \mathbf{G}(\mathbf{r}), \quad G_z(\mathbf{r}) = \hat{\mathbf{z}} \cdot \mathbf{G}(\mathbf{r}).$$

Equation 1.18 may be interpreted as follows. At every point in space **r** is imbedded a set of Cartesian axes. The value of the vector point function at **r** is a *position vector* in this Cartesian space; the projections of **G** on the coordinate axes are the Cartesian components of the vector **G** in this Cartesian space.

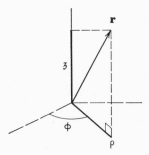

Fig. 1.3   In cylindrical coordinates, the position vector **r** is specified by the triad of numbers (ρ, ϕ, z).

Coordinate systems other than Cartesian may conveniently represent a vector point function.   The most widely used coordinate systems other than Cartesian are (1) cylindrical, and (2) spherical polar.   *Cylindrical coordinates* are defined as follows (see Fig. 1.3).   One of the three components of **r** is the projection of **r** on the Cartesian z-axis or the so-called *azimuthal* axis.   This axis is designated in cylindrical coordinates by a unit vector $\hat{z}$.   The other cylindrical components of **r** are obtained by projecting **r** onto the plane perpendicular to the azimuthal axis (the x-y plane).   The magnitude of this projection is given the symbol ρ.   A unit vector from the origin parallel to the projection of **r** is given the symbol $\hat{\rho}$. $\hat{\rho}$ is obviously perpendicular to $\hat{z}$.   The third orthogonal direction is defined by the unit vector $\hat{\phi}$ which is perpendicular to both $\hat{\rho}$ and $\hat{z}$. It is defined in such a way that ($\hat{\rho}$, $\hat{\phi}$, $\hat{z}$) form a right-handed orthogonal system.   It is obvious that $\hat{\phi}$ lies in the Cartesian x-y plane.   The position vector **r** can be written in cylindrical coordinates as

$$\mathbf{r} = \rho\hat{\rho} + z\hat{z} \qquad (1.19)$$

where $\qquad \rho \equiv (\mathbf{r} \cdot \hat{\rho}) \quad$ and $\quad z \equiv (\mathbf{r} \cdot \hat{z}).$

($\hat{\phi} \cdot \mathbf{r} = 0$ for *all* **r**.)   The position vector **r** is not defined by the numbers ρ and z alone; a third number is needed and that number is taken to be the angle ϕ that $\hat{\rho}$ makes with the Cartesian x-axis.   Evidently $\hat{\rho}$ is a function of ϕ.   Then **r** is specified by giving the triad (ρ, ϕ, z).   A vector point function can also be written in cylindrical coordinates, i.e.,

$$\mathbf{G}(\mathbf{r}) = \mathbf{G}(\rho, \phi, z).$$

and $\qquad \mathbf{G}(\mathbf{r}) = G_\rho(\mathbf{r})\hat{\rho} + G_\phi(\mathbf{r})\hat{\phi} + G_z(\mathbf{r})\hat{z} \qquad (1.20)$

with $\qquad G_\rho \equiv \hat{\rho} \cdot \mathbf{G}, \qquad G_\phi \equiv \hat{\phi} \cdot \mathbf{G}, \qquad G_z \equiv \hat{z} \cdot \mathbf{G}.$

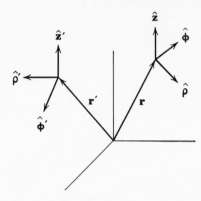

Fig. 1.4 The orientation of the triad of orthogonal unit vectors in cylindrical coordinates depends on the position vector **r**. In general, for two position vectors **r** and **r′**; the triad of unit vectors at **r** ($\hat{\rho}, \hat{\phi}', \hat{z}'$) has a different orientation from those at **r′** ($\hat{\rho}, \hat{\phi}', \hat{z}'$).

Equation 1.20 can be interpreted as follows. At each point **r**, a set of orthogonal unit vectors ($\hat{\rho}, \hat{\phi}, \hat{z}$) is constructed. The projections of **G(r)** on this set of orthogonal unit vectors are the *cylindrical components* of **G(r)** at **r**. The set of unit vectors ($\hat{\rho}, \hat{\phi}, \hat{z}$) so constructed at **r** and the set ($\hat{\rho}', \hat{\phi}', \hat{z}'$) constructed at some other point **r′** do not have the same orientation (see Fig. 1.4). In general,

$$\hat{\rho}' \times \hat{\rho} \neq 0, \quad \hat{\phi}' \times \hat{\phi} \neq 0, \quad \text{but} \quad \hat{z}' \times \hat{z} = 0 \quad \text{always.}$$

It is always possible to express the Cartesian components of a vector point function in terms of its cylindrical components and vice versa. This is accomplished, for example, as follows:

$$G_\rho \equiv \mathbf{G(r)} \cdot \hat{\rho} = G_x(\hat{x} \cdot \hat{\rho}) + G_y(\hat{y} \cdot \hat{\rho}) + G_z(\hat{z} \cdot \hat{\rho}).$$

However, $\hat{x} \cdot \hat{\rho} = \cos \phi$, $\hat{y} \cdot \hat{\rho} = \sin \phi$, $\hat{z} \cdot \hat{\rho} = 0$, and consequently

$$G_\rho = G_x \cos \phi + G_y \sin \phi. \tag{1.21a}$$

The expressions for the other two cylindrical components of **G** are obtained in a similar fashion:

$$G_\phi = -G_x \sin \phi + G_y \cos \phi, \tag{1.21b}$$

$$G_x = G_z. \tag{1.21c}$$

As a special application, consider $\mathbf{G(r)} \equiv \mathbf{r}$; then it follows from eq. 1.21a that $\rho = x \cos \phi + y \sin \phi$. (Equation 1.21b yields an identity, that is,

0 = 0.) The unit vectors in cylindrical coordinates can be expressed in terms of those in Cartesian coordinates as

$$\begin{aligned}
\hat{\rho} &= \hat{x} \cos \phi + \hat{y} \sin \phi, \\
\hat{\phi} &= -\hat{x} \sin \phi + \hat{y} \cos \phi, \\
\hat{z} &= \hat{z}
\end{aligned} \tag{1.22a}$$

It is possible to solve eq. 1.22a for the $(\hat{x}, \hat{y}, \hat{z})$ in terms of the $(\hat{\rho}, \hat{\phi}, z)$. The result is

$$\begin{aligned}
\hat{x} &= \hat{\rho} \cos \phi - \hat{\phi} \sin \phi, \\
\hat{y} &= \hat{\rho} \sin \phi + \hat{\phi} \cos \phi, \\
\hat{z} &= \hat{z}.
\end{aligned} \tag{1.22b}$$

Spherical polar coordinates are introduced in the following manner (see Fig. 1.5). One of the three components of **r** is its magnitude designated by r. One of the unit vectors that forms the triad of unit vectors in this system is the unit vector $\hat{r}$ parallel to **r**. A second member of this triad is obtained as follows: **r** and the z-axis of the Cartesian system (the polar direction) form a plane. A unit vector $\hat{\theta}$ is a vector lying in the plane and perpendicular to $\hat{r}$ pointing away from the polar axis. The third member of the triad is a vector $\hat{\phi}$ perpendicular to the plane defined by $\hat{r}$ and $\hat{\theta}$. Then $(\hat{r}, \hat{\theta}, \hat{\phi})$ form a right-handed triad of orthogonal unit vectors. The vector $\hat{\phi}$ (the azimuthal vector) is parallel to the x-y plane. The position vector **r** can be written in spherical polar coordinates as

$$\mathbf{r} = r\hat{r}, \tag{1.23}$$

$(\hat{\theta} \cdot \mathbf{r} = \hat{\phi} \cdot \mathbf{r} = 0$ for *all* **r**.) The position vector **r** is not defined by the number r alone; two others are needed. These are the polar angle θ, the angle that **r** makes with the polar axis, and the azimuthal angle ϕ, the angle that the projection of **r** on the x-y plane makes with the x-axis.

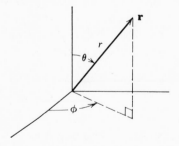

Fig. 1.5 In spherical polar coordinates, the position vector **r** is specified by the triad of numbers (r, θ, ϕ).

Evidently $\hat{\mathbf{r}}$ is a function of both θ and ϕ. Then $\mathbf{r}$ is specified by giving the triad (r, θ, ϕ). A vector point function can also be written in spherical polar coordinates, i.e.,

$$\mathbf{G(r)} = \mathbf{G}(r, \theta, \phi)$$

and
$$\mathbf{G(r)} = G_r(\mathbf{r})\hat{\mathbf{r}} + G_\theta(\mathbf{r})\hat{\boldsymbol{\theta}} + G_\phi(\mathbf{r})\hat{\boldsymbol{\phi}} \qquad (1.24)$$

with
$$G_r \equiv \hat{\mathbf{r}} \cdot \mathbf{G}, \qquad G_\theta \equiv \hat{\boldsymbol{\theta}} \cdot \mathbf{G}, \qquad G_\phi \equiv \hat{\boldsymbol{\phi}} \cdot \mathbf{G}.$$

Equation 1.24 can be interpreted as follows. At each point $\mathbf{r}$, a set of orthogonal unit vectors $(\hat{\mathbf{r}}, \hat{\boldsymbol{\theta}}, \hat{\boldsymbol{\phi}})$ is constructed. The projections of $\mathbf{G(r)}$ on this set of orthogonal unit vectors are the *spherical components* of $\mathbf{G(r)}$ at the position $\mathbf{r}$. The set of unit vectors $(\hat{\mathbf{r}}, \hat{\boldsymbol{\theta}}, \hat{\boldsymbol{\phi}})$ so constructed at $\mathbf{r}$ and the set $(\hat{\mathbf{r}}', \hat{\boldsymbol{\theta}}', \hat{\boldsymbol{\phi}}')$ constructed at some other point $\mathbf{r}'$ do not have the same orientation (see Fig. 1.6). In general,

$$\hat{\mathbf{r}} \times \hat{\mathbf{r}}' \neq 0, \qquad \hat{\boldsymbol{\theta}} \times \hat{\boldsymbol{\theta}}' \neq 0, \quad \text{and} \quad \hat{\boldsymbol{\phi}} \times \hat{\boldsymbol{\phi}}' \neq 0.$$

It is always possible to express the Cartesian components of a vector point function in terms of its spherical components and vice versa. This is accomplished, for example, as follows:

$$G_r \equiv \mathbf{G(r)} \cdot \hat{\mathbf{r}} = (\hat{\mathbf{x}} \cdot \hat{\mathbf{r}})G_x + (\hat{\mathbf{y}} \cdot \hat{\mathbf{r}})G_y + (\hat{\mathbf{z}} \cdot \hat{\mathbf{r}})G_z.$$

However,
$$\hat{\mathbf{x}} \cdot \hat{\mathbf{r}} = \sin \theta \cos \phi$$
$$\hat{\mathbf{y}} \cdot \hat{\mathbf{r}} = \sin \theta \sin \phi$$
$$\hat{\mathbf{z}} \cdot \hat{\mathbf{r}} = \cos \theta$$

and as a consequence

$$G_r = G_x \sin \theta \cos \phi + G_y \sin \theta \sin \phi + G_z \cos \theta. \qquad (1.25a)$$

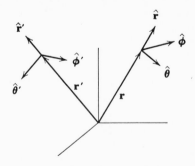

Fig. 1.6   The orientation of the triad of orthogonal unit vectors in spherical polar coordinates depends on the position vector $\mathbf{r}$. In general, for two position vectors $\mathbf{r}$ and $\mathbf{r}'$, the triad of unit vectors at $\mathbf{r}(\hat{\mathbf{r}}, \hat{\boldsymbol{\theta}}, \hat{\boldsymbol{\phi}})$ has a different orientation from those at $\mathbf{r}'(\hat{\mathbf{r}}', \hat{\boldsymbol{\theta}}', \hat{\boldsymbol{\phi}}')$.

The expressions for the other two spherical components of **G** in terms of its Cartesian components are obtained in a similar fashion:

$$G_\theta = G_x \cos \theta \cos \phi + G_y \cos \theta \sin \phi - G_z \sin \theta, \qquad (1.25b)$$

$$G_\phi = -G_x \sin \phi + G_y \cos \phi. \qquad (1.25c)$$

The unit vectors in spherical polar coordinates can be expressed in terms of those in Cartesian coordinates:

$$\hat{\mathbf{r}} = \hat{\mathbf{x}} \sin \theta \cos \phi + \hat{\mathbf{y}} \sin \theta \sin \phi + \hat{\mathbf{z}} \cos \theta$$
$$\hat{\boldsymbol{\theta}} = \hat{\mathbf{x}} \cos \theta \cos \phi + \hat{\mathbf{y}} \cos \theta \sin \phi - \hat{\mathbf{z}} \sin \theta \qquad (1.26a)$$
$$\hat{\boldsymbol{\phi}} = -\hat{\mathbf{x}} \sin \phi + \hat{\mathbf{y}} \cos \phi.$$

The relationships of eq. 1.26a can be solved for the unit Cartesian vectors with the result

$$\hat{\mathbf{x}} = \hat{\mathbf{r}} \sin \theta \cos \phi + \hat{\boldsymbol{\theta}} \cos \theta \cos \phi - \hat{\boldsymbol{\phi}} \sin \phi$$
$$\hat{\mathbf{y}} = \hat{\mathbf{r}} \sin \theta \sin \phi + \hat{\boldsymbol{\theta}} \cos \theta \sin \phi + \hat{\boldsymbol{\phi}} \cos \phi \qquad (1.26b)$$
$$\hat{\mathbf{z}} = \hat{\mathbf{r}} \cos \theta - \hat{\boldsymbol{\theta}} \sin \theta.$$

Other coordinate systems have occasional use. However, they will not be discussed here.

1.3   Vector Calculus

A calculus involving vectors, scalar functions of vectors, and vector functions of vectors can be developed. Consider, for example, a vector **A** which is a function of some parameter s. The derivative of **A** with respect to s is defined as

$$\frac{d\mathbf{A}}{ds} = \left(\frac{dA}{ds}\right)\hat{\mathbf{A}} + A\left(\frac{d\hat{\mathbf{A}}}{ds}\right), \qquad (1.27)$$

where, dA/ds = rate of change in the magnitude of **A** with respect to s,
     $d\hat{\mathbf{A}}/ds$ = rate of change in the direction of **A** with respect to s.

As an illustration of eq. 1.27, consider the velocity or the time rate of change of the position vector **r** of a particle. In Cartesian representation this is

$$\mathbf{v} \equiv \frac{d\mathbf{r}}{dt} = \left(\frac{dx}{dt}\right)\hat{\mathbf{x}} + \left(\frac{dy}{dt}\right)\hat{\mathbf{y}} + \left(\frac{dz}{dt}\right)\hat{\mathbf{z}}. \qquad (1.28)$$

There are no terms in $(d\hat{\mathbf{x}}/dt)$, etc., since the orientation of the Cartesian axes at every point is the same.   If this same derivative is evaluated in terms of spherical coordinates, the result is

$$\mathbf{v} = \frac{d\mathbf{r}}{dt} = \left(\frac{dr}{dt}\right)\hat{\mathbf{r}} + r\left(\frac{d\hat{\mathbf{r}}}{dt}\right)$$

where, from eq. 1.26*a*,

$$\frac{d\hat{\mathbf{r}}}{dt} = \hat{\mathbf{x}}\left[\cos\theta\cos\phi\left(\frac{d\theta}{dt}\right) - \sin\theta\sin\phi\left(\frac{d\phi}{dt}\right)\right]$$
$$+ \hat{\mathbf{y}}\left[\cos\theta\sin\phi\left(\frac{d\theta}{dt}\right) + \sin\theta\cos\phi\left(\frac{d\phi}{dt}\right)\right]$$
$$+ \hat{\mathbf{z}}\left[-\sin\theta\left(\frac{d\theta}{dt}\right)\right]$$

or

$$\frac{d\hat{\mathbf{r}}}{dt} = \frac{d\theta}{dt}\left[\hat{\mathbf{x}}\cos\theta\cos\phi + \hat{\mathbf{y}}\cos\theta\sin\phi - \hat{\mathbf{z}}\sin\theta\right]$$
$$+ \sin\theta\frac{d\phi}{dt}\left[-\hat{\mathbf{x}}\sin\phi + \hat{\mathbf{y}}\cos\phi\right],$$

yielding the result that

$$\frac{d\hat{\mathbf{r}}}{dt} = \hat{\mathbf{\theta}}\frac{d\theta}{dt} + \hat{\mathbf{\phi}}\sin\theta\frac{d\phi}{dt},$$

or finally

$$\frac{d\mathbf{r}}{dt} \equiv \mathbf{v} = \hat{\mathbf{r}}\left(\frac{dr}{dt}\right) + \hat{\mathbf{\theta}}\left(r\frac{d\theta}{dt}\right) + \hat{\mathbf{\phi}}\left(r\sin\theta\frac{d\phi}{dt}\right). \qquad (1.29)$$

A similar calculation can be carried out for $d\mathbf{r}/dt$ in cylindrical coordinates. This is left as an exercise.

The derivative of an arbitrary scalar function of position $\psi(\mathbf{r})$ is evaluated as follows. Since ψ is a function of three independent variables, the three components of $\mathbf{r}$, any derivative with respect to an *explicit* variable is a *partial derivative* of the kind

$$\frac{\partial\psi}{\partial x}, \qquad \frac{\partial\psi}{\partial y}, \qquad \frac{\partial\psi}{\partial z}.$$

On the other hand, it is possible to evaluate the *total derivative* of ψ with respect to a variable contained only *implicitly* in ψ.   For example, $\psi(\mathbf{r})$ may not depend explicitly on the time t but may change with time because of the variation of $\mathbf{r}$ with time.   The total derivative of ψ with respect to time is then

$$\frac{d\psi}{dt} = \left(\frac{\partial\psi}{\partial x}\frac{dx}{dt} + \frac{\partial\psi}{\partial y}\frac{dy}{dt} + \frac{\partial\psi}{\partial z}\frac{dz}{dt}\right). \qquad (1.30)$$

If ψ depends explicitly on t as well as on x, y, and z, an additional term $\partial\psi/\partial t$ appears on the right-hand side of eq. 1.30. The three Cartesian components of $\mathbf{v}$ appear explicitly in the above. In fact, it is useful to define a vector $\nabla\psi$ or *gradient* of ψ by the expression

$$\nabla\psi = \text{grad } \psi \equiv \left(\frac{\partial\psi}{\partial x}\right)\hat{\mathbf{x}} + \left(\frac{\partial\psi}{\partial y}\right)\hat{\mathbf{y}} + \left(\frac{\partial\psi}{\partial z}\right)\hat{\mathbf{z}}. \tag{1.31}$$

From eqs. 1.29–1.31 it is evident that $d\psi/dt$ can be written as the scalar product between two vectors $\nabla\psi$ and $\mathbf{v}$:

$$\frac{d\psi(\mathbf{r})}{dt} \equiv \nabla\psi \cdot \mathbf{v}. \tag{1.32}$$

It is not necessary to restrict the definition of grad ψ to a Cartesian representation. The defining eq. 1.31 can be transformed term by term to any other representation. For example, consider grad ψ in cylindrical coordinates: $(\hat{\mathbf{x}}, \hat{\mathbf{y}}, \hat{\mathbf{z}})$ can be expressed via eq. 1.22*b* in cylindrical co-ordinates. In addition, terms such as $\partial\psi/\partial x$ may be calculated from the rules for implicit differentiation of a function of several variables:

$$\frac{\partial\psi(\rho, \phi, z)}{\partial x} = \frac{\partial\psi}{\partial\rho}\frac{\partial\rho}{\partial x} + \frac{\partial\psi}{\partial\phi}\frac{\partial\phi}{\partial x} + \frac{\partial\psi}{\partial z}\frac{\partial z}{\partial x}.$$

Using the facts that

$$\rho \equiv \sqrt{x^2 + y^2} \quad \text{and} \quad \phi = \cos^{-1} x/\rho$$

it is straightforward to demonstrate that

$$\nabla\psi(\rho, \phi, z) = \hat{\boldsymbol{\rho}}\frac{\partial\psi}{\partial\rho} + \hat{\boldsymbol{\phi}}\frac{1}{\rho}\frac{\partial\psi}{\partial\phi} + \hat{\mathbf{z}}\frac{\partial}{\partial z}\psi. \tag{1.33}$$

Similarly in spherical polar coordinates

$$\nabla\psi(r, \theta, \phi) = \hat{\mathbf{r}}\frac{\partial}{\partial r}\psi + \hat{\boldsymbol{\theta}}\frac{1}{r}\frac{\partial}{\partial\theta}\psi + \hat{\boldsymbol{\phi}}\frac{1}{r\sin\theta}\frac{\partial}{\partial\phi}\psi. \tag{1.34}$$

The details of the calculations leading to the results of eqs. 1.33 and 1.34 are left as exercises.

The derivatives of vector point functions may be calculated, taking into account what has already been said about derivatives of vectors and derivatives of scalar point functions. Of special interest are the derivative operations called respectively the *divergence* and the *curl* of a vector point function. The divergence of a vector point function $\mathbf{A}$ is written variously as $\nabla \cdot \mathbf{A}$ and div $\mathbf{A}$ and is defined in Cartesian representation as

$$\nabla \cdot \mathbf{A} = \text{div } \mathbf{A} = \frac{\partial A_x}{\partial x} + \frac{\partial A_y}{\partial y} + \frac{\partial A_z}{\partial z}. \tag{1.35a}$$

It is once again a straightforward exercise in algebra and differentiation to show that

cylindrical

$$\text{div } \mathbf{A}(\rho, \phi, z) \equiv \frac{1}{\rho} \frac{\partial}{\partial \rho} (\rho A_\rho) + \frac{1}{\rho} \frac{\partial}{\partial \phi} A_\phi + \frac{\partial A_z}{\partial z}, \tag{1.35b}$$

and *spherical*

$$\text{div } \mathbf{A}(r, \theta, \phi) \equiv \frac{1}{r^2} \frac{\partial}{\partial r} (r^2 A_r) + \frac{1}{r \sin \theta} \frac{\partial}{\partial \theta} (\sin \theta A_\theta) + \frac{1}{r \sin \theta} \frac{\partial A_\phi}{\partial \phi}. \tag{1.35c}$$

The divergence of a vector point function plays a fundamental role in the discussion of the properties of a vector field. The usefulness of the divergence operation is based on Gauss's theorem, which may be stated as follows. Consider an arbitrary vector point function $\mathbf{A}(\mathbf{r})$ whose first derivatives with respect to the coordinate variables are defined everywhere within a volume τ. Assume further that the function is defined everywhere on the closed surface Σ enveloping τ (see Fig. 1.7). Gauss's theorem states that

$$\int_\tau d\tau \, \text{div } \mathbf{A} \equiv \oiint_\Sigma ds \, \mathbf{A} \cdot \hat{\mathbf{n}}. \tag{1.36}$$

The integral on the right-hand side of eq. 1.36 is called the *flux* of the vector $\mathbf{A}$ through the surface Σ. Gauss's theorem relates the flux of a vector point function through a closed surface to an integral of the spatial derivatives of the function over the volume enclosed by the surface. Since one often knows the value of vector point functions representing physical quantities on the boundary of a physical region, Gauss's law

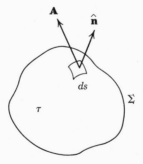

Fig. 1.7   The volume τ is enclosed by a closed surface Σ. ds is an element of the surface Σ and $\hat{\mathbf{n}}$ is a unit normal to ds pointing outward from τ.   According to Gauss's theorem, the flux of $\mathbf{A}$ through Σ is equal to the integral of div $\mathbf{A}$ throughout τ.

enables one to translate this knowledge on the boundary of the region to knowledge of the behavior of the physical quantity in the interior of the region.

Another vector derivative operator which appears quite frequently in a discussion of vector fields is the *curl* operator. This operator may be represented as $\nabla \times$ and is defined as follows:

$$\text{curl } \mathbf{A} \equiv \nabla \times \mathbf{A} \equiv \left(\frac{\partial}{\partial y} A_z - \frac{\partial}{\partial z} A_y\right)\hat{\mathbf{x}}$$
$$+ \left(\frac{\partial}{\partial z} A_x - \frac{\partial}{\partial x} A_z\right)\hat{\mathbf{y}} \qquad (1.37a)$$
$$+ \left(\frac{\partial}{\partial x} A_y - \frac{\partial}{\partial y} A_x\right)\hat{\mathbf{z}}.$$

Although the curl operation is somewhat complex, its definition can be remembered by the following device—the curl of **A** can be symbolically represented by the following determinant:

$$\text{curl } \mathbf{A} = \begin{vmatrix} \hat{\mathbf{x}} & \hat{\mathbf{y}} & \hat{\mathbf{z}} \\ \dfrac{\partial}{\partial x} & \dfrac{\partial}{\partial y} & \dfrac{\partial}{\partial z} \\ A_x & A_y & A_z \end{vmatrix}.$$

Of course, the definition of the curl is not restricted to the Cartesian representation. It is a straightforward exercise to convert the curl from its Cartesian representation to a representation characteristic of some other choice of the coordinate system. The results for cylindrical and spherical coordinates are listed below:

cylindrical

$$\text{curl } \mathbf{A} \equiv \left(\frac{1}{\rho} \frac{\partial A_z}{\partial \phi} - \frac{\partial A_\phi}{\partial z}\right)\hat{\boldsymbol{\rho}} + \left(\frac{\partial A_\rho}{\partial z} - \frac{\partial A_z}{\partial \rho}\right)\hat{\boldsymbol{\phi}}$$
$$+ \left(\frac{1}{\rho} \frac{\partial}{\partial \rho} (\rho A_\phi) - \frac{1}{\rho} \frac{\partial A_\rho}{\partial \phi}\right)\hat{\mathbf{z}}.$$

spherical

$$\text{curl } \mathbf{A} \equiv \frac{1}{r \sin \theta} \left[\frac{\partial}{\partial \theta} (\sin A_\phi) - \frac{\partial A_\theta}{\partial \phi}\right]\hat{\mathbf{r}}$$
$$+ \frac{1}{r} \left[\frac{1}{\sin \theta} \frac{\partial A_r}{\partial \phi} - \frac{\partial}{\partial r} (r A_\phi)\right]\hat{\boldsymbol{\theta}} \qquad (1.37c)$$
$$+ \frac{1}{r} \left[\frac{\partial}{\partial r} (r A_\theta) - \frac{\partial A_r}{\partial \theta}\right]\hat{\boldsymbol{\phi}}.$$

The usefulness of the curl operation stems from Stokes's theorem of the vector calculus. Suppose a vector point function **A** is defined everywhere

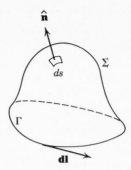

Fig. 1.8   A closed contour Γ is "capped" by an open surface Σ.   *ds* is an element of the surface Σ and $\hat{n}$ is a unit vector normal to *ds*.   **dl** is a vector element of Γ.   The direction of $\hat{n}$ is determined in the following manner: if the fingers of the right hand are curved to point in the direction of **dl**, the thumb of the right hand points in the direction of $\hat{n}$.   Stokes's theorem states that the line integral of **A** around Γ is equal to the flux of the curl **A** through Σ.

on a closed curve or contour Γ.   Suppose further that the first partial space derivatives are defined everywhere on an *open* surface Σ capping the contour (see Fig. 1.8).   Stokes's theorem states that

$$\oint_{\Gamma} \mathbf{A} \cdot \mathbf{dl} = \iint_{\Sigma} \text{curl } \mathbf{A} \cdot \hat{n} \, ds. \tag{1.38}$$

The right-hand side of eq. 1.38 is the *flux of the curl of* **A** through the open surface Σ.   Stokes's theorem relates the flux of the curl of **A** to the line integral of **A** around the contour which is capped by Σ.   (Throughout this text, the integral over an *open* surface will be represented by $\iint ds \ldots$,

whereas the integral over a *closed* surface will be represented by $\oiint ds \ldots$.)

The importance of the divergence and curl operations resides in the Helmholtz theorem, which states that a vector point function is completely determined when its divergence and curl are known everywhere.[1]   Therefore, in formulating a theory of electric and magnetic fields, it is necessary to establish relationships involving the divergence and curl of these fields and other prescribed physical quantities such as charge density and current density usually referred to as the "sources" of the fields.   The goal of any attempts to construct a theory of vector fields amounts to the construction of partial differential equations which involve the curl and divergence of the vector fields.

[1] For a sketch of a proof of this theorem, see A. P. Wills, *Vector Analysis*, Dover, New York, p. 121.

There are many useful mathematical identities involving the operators gradient, divergence, and curl. These are listed in the Mathematical Appendix.

1.4   Mechanical Preliminaries

Any description of physical phenomena relies heavily on a general knowledge of how particles and objects behave under the application of specified forces. Such forces are those acting between charged particles at rest and slowly moving. The behavior of the charged particles can be understood within the framework of Newton's laws of motion. Briefly, a particle of mass m subject to a force $\mathbf{f}$ experiences an acceleration $\mathbf{a}$ given by

$$\mathbf{f} = m\mathbf{a}. \tag{1.39}$$

Strictly, an equation more general than eq. 1.39 is valid which relates the force $\mathbf{f}$ to the time rate of change of the linear momentum of the particle designated by $\mathbf{p} \equiv m\mathbf{v}$.

$$\mathbf{f} = \frac{d}{dt}(m\mathbf{v}). \tag{1.40}$$

Equations 1.39 and 1.40 are equivalent if the mass of the particle is a constant.

If the agency of the force is another particle, then there are certain classes of forces which satisfy the following relationship. Consider the force on particle 1 due to particle 2 ($\mathbf{f}_{12}$); this force is related to the force exerted on particle 2 by particle 1 ($\mathbf{f}_{21}$) by the condition

$$\mathbf{f}_{12} + \mathbf{f}_{21} = 0. \tag{1.41}$$

The Coulomb or electrostatic force acting between two charged particles satisfies eq. 1.41. It is important to realize, however, that not all physical forces satisfy eq. 1.41. If the forces under consideration do satisfy eq. 1.41, then it is straightforward to show that the two-body system with internal forces can be replaced by an equivalent one-body system. This demonstration proceeds as follows. The equations of motion for the two particles are

$$\mathbf{f}_{12} = m_1 \frac{d\mathbf{v}_1}{dt}, \qquad \mathbf{f}_{21} = m_2 \frac{d\mathbf{v}_2}{dt}$$

where $\mathbf{v}_1 = d\mathbf{r}_1/dt$, $\mathbf{v}_2 = d\mathbf{r}_2/dt$. A change in variables is now made, defined by the relation

$$\mathbf{R} \equiv \frac{m_1\mathbf{r}_1 + m_2\mathbf{r}_2}{m_1 + m_2},$$

$$\mathbf{f}_{12} = \mathbf{f} = -\mathbf{f}_{21}$$

$$\mathbf{r} \equiv \mathbf{r}_1 - \mathbf{r}_2.$$

$\mathbf{R}$ is called the coordinate of the *center of mass*, whereas $\mathbf{r}$ is called the *relative coordinate*. In terms of the new variables and making use of eq. 1.41, it is straightforward to show that

$$\frac{d^2\mathbf{R}}{dt^2} = 0 \qquad (1.42)$$

$$\mathbf{f} = \frac{m_1 m_2}{m_1 + m_2}\left(\frac{d^2\mathbf{r}}{dt^2}\right). \qquad (1.43)$$

The quantity $m_1 m_2/(m_1 + m_2)$ is usually referred to as the *reduced mass* of the system. Equation 1.42 states that the center of mass of the system moves with uniform velocity. Equation 1.43 states that the relative motion of the two particles is that of one particle whose mass is the reduced mass of the system in the force field acting between the particles.

Many forces experienced in physics are so-called *conservative forces*. A conservative force $\mathbf{f}(\mathbf{r}, t)$ obeys the following relationships:

$$\frac{\partial \mathbf{f}(\mathbf{r}, t)}{\partial t} = 0, \quad \text{i.e., } \mathbf{f}(\mathbf{r}, t) = \mathbf{f}(\mathbf{r}) \qquad (1.44)$$

$$\text{curl } \mathbf{f}(\mathbf{r}, t) = 0. \qquad (1.45)$$

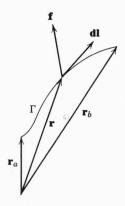

Fig. 1.9   A particle moves from position $\mathbf{r}_a$ to position $\mathbf{r}_b$ along the path Γ. The work done by an applied force $\mathbf{f}$ on the particle as it moves from $\mathbf{r}_a$ to $\mathbf{r}_b$ is: $W = \int_\Gamma \mathbf{f}(\mathbf{r}) \cdot d\mathbf{l}$.

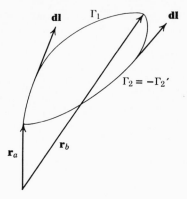

Fig. 1.10 Two arbitrary paths Γ_1 and Γ_2 connect points $\mathbf{r}_a$ and $\mathbf{r}_b$. The path Γ_2' is defined to be the same as Γ_2 except directed in the opposite sense. The composite path $\Gamma = \Gamma_1 + \Gamma_2'$ is a closed contour passing through $\mathbf{r}_a$ and $\mathbf{r}_b$. If the work done by a force $\mathbf{f}(\mathbf{r})$ is independent of path, then $\oint_\Gamma \mathbf{f} \cdot \mathbf{dl} = 0$, from which it follows that curl $\mathbf{f}(\mathbf{r}) = 0$.

To understand the physical implications of eq. 1.45, it is necessary to introduce the concept of the *work* done by a force in moving a particle from a position $\mathbf{r}_a$ to a position $\mathbf{r}_b$ along a path Γ (see Fig. 1.9). The work done is defined by

$$W = \int_\Gamma \mathbf{f} \cdot \mathbf{dl}, \tag{1.46}$$

where $\mathbf{dl}$ is a vector element of the path Γ.

Consider now the work done by the force $\mathbf{f}$, in moving the particle from $\mathbf{r}_a$ to $\mathbf{r}_b$ along two arbitrary but different paths Γ_1 and Γ_2 (see Fig. 1.10).

$$W_1 = \int_{\Gamma_1} \mathbf{f} \cdot \mathbf{dl}$$

$$W_2 = \int_{\Gamma_2} \mathbf{f} \cdot \mathbf{dl}.$$

If $W_1 = W_2$, then it follows that

$$\int_{\Gamma_1} \mathbf{f} \cdot \mathbf{dl} - \int_{\Gamma_2} \mathbf{f} \cdot \mathbf{dl} = 0. \tag{1.47}$$

If the sense of path Γ_2 is reversed (the reversed path called Γ_2'), then

$$\int_{\Gamma_1} \mathbf{f} \cdot \mathbf{dl} + \int_{\Gamma_2'} \mathbf{f} \cdot \mathbf{dl} = \int_{\Gamma_1 + \Gamma_2'} \mathbf{f} \cdot \mathbf{dl} = 0.$$

However, $\Gamma_1 + \Gamma_2'$ is a closed path or contour Γ passing through $\mathbf{r}_a$ and $\mathbf{r}_b$; hence

$$\oint_\Gamma \mathbf{f} \cdot \mathbf{dl} = 0. \tag{1.48}$$

Application of Stokes's theorem to eq. 1.48 yields

$$\iint_\Sigma ds(\hat{\mathbf{n}} \cdot \text{curl } \mathbf{f}) = 0. \tag{1.49}$$

However, Γ_1, Γ_2, Γ, and hence Σ are arbitrary, and consequently the integrand in eq. 1.49 must vanish; that is,

$$\text{curl } \mathbf{f} = 0.$$

Therefore, the vanishing of the curl of $\mathbf{f}$ implies that the work done by $\mathbf{f}$ in moving a particle from $\mathbf{r}_a$ to $\mathbf{r}_b$ is *independent of the path*. (The logic in the above discussion is not complete; using Stokes's theorem it is possible to show that the necessary and sufficient condition for the work to be independent of the path is curl $\mathbf{f} = 0$. To see that Stokes's theorem implies both the necessary and the sufficient conditions requires a deeper understanding of the theorem than is possible from the brief discussion of the theorem given in Sec. 1.3.)

The vanishing of the curl $\mathbf{f}$ means that $\mathbf{f}$ can be represented by a scalar function $V(\mathbf{r})$ through the definition

$$\mathbf{f}(\mathbf{r}) = -\text{grad } V(\mathbf{r}), \tag{1.50}$$

since curl grad $V(\mathbf{r}) \equiv 0$ for all sufficiently well-behaved functions $V(\mathbf{r})$. $V(\mathbf{r})$ is commonly called the *potential function*, and conservative forces are said to be "derivable from a potential." For a conservative force, it is possible to show that the *total mechanical energy* of a particle is a constant of the motion or is "conserved." To demonstrate this, consider the work done by a force $\mathbf{f}$ in moving a particle from position $\mathbf{r}_a$ to $\mathbf{r}_b$:

$$W = \int_\Gamma \mathbf{f} \cdot \mathbf{dl} = \int_\Gamma m \frac{d\mathbf{v}}{dt} \cdot \mathbf{dl}.$$

Now $\mathbf{dl}$ is an element of the *physical* path Γ over which the particle moves. Consequently $\mathbf{dl}/dt = \mathbf{v}$ and

$$\frac{d\mathbf{v}}{dt} \cdot \mathbf{dl} = \left(\frac{d\mathbf{v}}{dt} \cdot \frac{\mathbf{dl}}{dt} \right) dt = \left(\frac{d\mathbf{v}}{dt} \cdot \mathbf{v} \right) dt$$

or

$$\frac{d\mathbf{v}}{dt} \cdot \mathbf{dl} = \frac{1}{2} \left(\frac{d}{dt} v^2 \right) dt.$$

The work done can therefore be expressed as

$$W = \int_\Gamma \frac{d}{dt} \left\{ \frac{1}{2} mv^2 \right\} dt = \int_\Gamma d \left\{ \frac{1}{2} mv^2 \right\}. \tag{1.51}$$

The quantity $T \equiv \frac{1}{2}mv^2$, is called the *kinetic energy* of the particle. The work done by the applied force is equal to the change in the kinetic energy of the particle from eq. 1.51

$$W = T_b - T_a. \tag{1.52}$$

The work done can be calculated in terms of $V(\mathbf{r})$ if $\mathbf{f}$ is conservative. From eqs. 1.46 and 1.50, it follows that

$$W = \int_\Gamma \mathbf{f} \cdot \mathbf{dl} = - \int_\Gamma \operatorname{grad} V \cdot \mathbf{dl}.$$

However, according to the definition of grad V,

$$\operatorname{grad} V = \hat{\mathbf{x}} \frac{\partial}{\partial x} V + \hat{\mathbf{y}} \frac{\partial}{\partial y} V + \hat{\mathbf{z}} \frac{\partial}{\partial z} V$$

and $\qquad \mathbf{dl} = \hat{\mathbf{x}} \, dx + \hat{\mathbf{y}} \, dy + \hat{\mathbf{z}} \, dz.$

Hence

$$W = - \int_\Gamma \left\{ dx \frac{\partial}{\partial x} V + dy \frac{\partial}{\partial y} V + dz \frac{\partial}{\partial z} V \right\}. \tag{1.53}$$

However, the integrand of eq. 1.53 is the total differential of V; hence

$$W = - \int_\Gamma dV = - (V_b - V_a). \tag{1.54}$$

Combining eqs. 1.52 and 1.54

$$T_a + V_a = T_b + V_b$$

or since $\mathbf{r}_a$ and $\mathbf{r}_b$ are quite arbitrary, it follows that

$$T + V = \text{constant} = E. \tag{1.55}$$

The constant E is called the *total mechanical energy* of the particle. In deriving eq. 1.55 it was necessary to assume that $\mathbf{f}$ was conservative.

There is a certain class of conservative forces which is of special interest. Such forces are called *central forces* and are defined as

$$\mathbf{f}(\mathbf{r}) = f(r)\hat{\mathbf{r}} \quad \text{(central force)}. \tag{1.56}$$

The curl of $\mathbf{f}$ is identically zero for a central force. Since $\mathbf{f}(\mathbf{r})$ is parallel to $\hat{\mathbf{r}}$ and its magnitude depends only on the magnitude of $\mathbf{r}$, it follows immediately from eq. 1.34 that the potential associated with a central force satisfies

$$f(r) = -\frac{d}{dr} V(r). \tag{1.57}$$

In addition to the total energy E, the angular momentum l of a particle in a central force field is a constant of the motion. The angular momentum l of a particle about the origin is defined as

$$l = \mathbf{r} \times \mathbf{p} = m\mathbf{r} \times \mathbf{v}. \tag{1.58}$$

The time rate of change of l can be evaluated using Newton's equation of motion:

$$\frac{dl}{dt} = \frac{d\mathbf{r}}{dt} \times \mathbf{p} + \mathbf{r} \times \frac{d\mathbf{p}}{dt} = \mathbf{r} \times \mathbf{f}$$

since $d\mathbf{r}/dt$ is parallel to $\mathbf{p}$.

For a central field, $\mathbf{f} = f(r)\hat{\mathbf{r}}$ and, consequently, $\mathbf{r} \times \mathbf{f} \equiv 0$. Therefore l is a constant of the motion; that is,

$$\frac{dl}{dt} = 0. \tag{1.59}$$

Although there are many other aspects of analytical mechanics which are useful in a discussion of electric and magnetic phenomena, the discussion of mechanics will be ended here. Whenever other mechanical concepts are needed, they shall be developed at the appropriate time.

PROBLEMS

1.1   Two vectors **A** and **B** are defined by their Cartesian components in two coordinate systems a and b. Coordinate system b is obtained from coordinate system a by a rigid rotation through the angle β about the z-axis. Express the Cartesian components of **A** and **B** in coordinate system b in terms of those in a and show explicitly that $\mathbf{A} \cdot \mathbf{B}$ has the same value in both systems.

1.2   The vector **c** is defined by the relationship $\mathbf{c} = \mathbf{A} \times \mathbf{B}$. Calculate the direction cosines of **c** in terms of the direction cosines of **A** and **B**.

1.3   Prove the vector identities of eqs. 1.14–1.16.

1.4   Show that $\mathbf{A} \cdot (\mathbf{B} \times \mathbf{C})$ is the volume of a parallelepiped whose side lengths are A, B, and C.

1.5   Show that $(\mathbf{A} \times \mathbf{B}) \times (\mathbf{C} \times \mathbf{D}) = [(\mathbf{A} \times \mathbf{B}) \cdot \mathbf{D}]\mathbf{C} - [(\mathbf{A} \times \mathbf{B}) \cdot \mathbf{C}]\mathbf{D}$.

1.6   Using the expressions for $\hat{\boldsymbol{\rho}}$ and $\hat{\boldsymbol{\phi}}$ of eq. 1.22a, establish that $\hat{\boldsymbol{\rho}} \cdot \hat{\boldsymbol{\rho}} = \hat{\boldsymbol{\phi}} \cdot \hat{\boldsymbol{\phi}} = 1$ and $\hat{\boldsymbol{\rho}} \cdot \hat{\boldsymbol{\phi}} = 0$, necessary conditions for unit basis vectors.

1.7 Express the Cartesian unit vectors in terms of their spherical counterparts, i.e., establish the validity of eqs. 1.26b.

1.8 Calculate $d\mathbf{r}/dt$ in cylindrical coordinates.

1.9 Calculate $d^2\mathbf{r}/dt^2$ in both cylindrical and spherical polar coordinates.

1.10 Calculate the components of the gradient operator in cylindrical and spherical polar coordinates, i.e., establish the validity of eqs. 1.33 and 1.34.

1.11 Calculate the divergence of a vector point function in cylindrical and spherical polar coordinates; i.e., establish the validity of eqs. 1.35b and 1.35c.

1.12 A curve in the x-y plane is defined by the function $y = f(x)$. The radius of curvature of the function at the point x is defined as $\rho = \left(\dfrac{ds}{d\theta}\right)$ where ds is an element of length of the curve and θ is the angle made by the tangent to the curve with the x-axis. Show that

$$\rho = \left| \frac{\left[1 + \left(\frac{df}{dx}\right)^2\right]^{3/2}}{\left(\frac{d^2f}{dx^2}\right)} \right|.$$

Show further that if the instantaneous velocity and acceleration of a particle moving in a plane are $\mathbf{v}$ and $\mathbf{a}$, $|\mathbf{v} \times \mathbf{a}| = v^3\rho^{-1}$.

1.13 By direct computation establish the following vector calculus identities:

(a) div curl $\mathbf{f} = 0$;

(b) div grad $g = \left(\dfrac{\partial^2}{\partial x^2} + \dfrac{\partial^2}{\partial y^2} + \dfrac{\partial^2}{\partial z^2}\right)g$;

(c) div $(\mathbf{A} \times \mathbf{B}) = \mathbf{B} \cdot$ curl $\mathbf{A} - \mathbf{A} \cdot$ curl $\mathbf{B}$.

1.14 Show that curl $\mathbf{f}(r) \equiv 0$ where $r = |\mathbf{r}|$.

1.15 Show that div $(\mathbf{r}/r^3) \equiv 0$ except at the point $\mathbf{r} = 0$.

1.16 Calculate curl $\mathbf{r}$ and div $\mathbf{r}$.

1.17 If $\mathbf{A}$ is a constant vector, show that grad $(\mathbf{r} \cdot \mathbf{A}) = \mathbf{A}$.

1.18 A charged particle moving in a vector field $\mathbf{B}$ experiences a force $\mathbf{f} = q\mathbf{v} \times \mathbf{B}$. Show that the kinetic energy of the particle is a constant of the motion.

1.19 Determine whether the following forces are conservative, and, if so, calculate the associated potential energy.

(a) $f_x = \alpha yz$, $f_y = \alpha xz$, $f_z = \alpha xy$;

(b) $f_x = f_y = f_z = \dfrac{\beta xyz}{x^2 + y^2 + z^2}$.

1.20 Calculate the angular momentum of a system of two interacting particles about the center of mass. Show under what conditions this angular momentum is a constant of the motion. If the particles interact with the force given in eq. 6.1 of Chapter 6 (the Lorentz force), is the angular momentum of the two particles conserved?

2 | Coulomb's Force Law;
The Electrostatic Field and Potential
of Point Charges in Vacuo

Before embarking on a detailed discussion of electrostatics, it would be well to contrast this subject with analytical mechanics. In developing the subject of mechanics, Newton succeeded in formulating a theory in which it was possible to discuss the motion of any system in terms of the forces acting on and within the system; however, nowhere in Newtonian mechanics is any mention made of the sources and precise agencies of these forces. It is worthwhile to ponder the elegance and power of a physical theory which is able to treat such motion without reference to the specific nature of the forces inducing this motion. All problems of motion (and of rest) are soluble at least in principle within the Newtonian framework; there are certain kinds of forces with very specific properties that allow a very detailed description of a large class of physical problems. The universal gravitational force which acts between objects possessing that attribute physicists call *mass* is an example of a kind of force whose consequences can be explored in great detail in a myriad of physical situations. It becomes useful to carry out such a detailed discussion because mass is such a general attribute of physical systems; it becomes convenient to do this because the gravitational force law takes on such a very simple form. The so-called *electrostatic* force is another example of this kind of force. In both of these cases, a detailed study of the behavior of objects moving under the action of the forces allows not only a discussion of how the objects do move under the action of these forces but also how the forces themselves are modified by the change in such kinematical quantities as position, velocity, etc. of the objects experiencing the forces.

The existence of the electrostatic force was discovered centuries ago, and the research of natural philosophers carried on over many centuries lead to the establishment of what is now known as Coulomb's law. The entire subject of electrostatics is based upon this one force law. Its

24

consequences will be explored in great detail, using the logical methods of mathematics and such physical concepts as energy, work, momentum, etc. developed in the general theory of analytical mechanics.

Coulomb's law is based upon physical observation and is not logically derivable from any other concept, unless one wishes to view it as a logical consequence of the Maxwell–Lorentz theory of electromagnetism—a tenable point of view but not historically sound and not appropriate for an introduction to the subject of electrostatics. It is well to note that the physical experiments performed to explore the properties of the electrostatic force were carried out with ponderable macroscopic objects in normal environments. On the other hand, Coulomb's law as it is to be stated here refers to an idealized experiment—that is, an experiment carried out with two point objects possessing the property of electric charge and residing at rest in a vacuum.

2.1 Coulomb's Force Law

Many objects possess the attribute of electric charge. It is not possible, however, to isolate the concept of charge from the forces which charged particles exert upon one another.[1] The analytic law of force between two *point* charges *at rest* in *vacuo* is attributed to Coulomb who, with others,

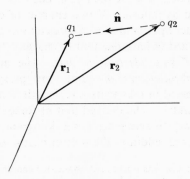

Fig. 2.1 Charges q_1 and q_2 are located at positions $\mathbf{r}_1$ and $\mathbf{r}_2$ respectively. The vector $\hat{\mathbf{n}}$ is a unit vector pointing from $\mathbf{r}_2$ to $\mathbf{r}_1$: $\hat{\mathbf{n}} = 1/(|\mathbf{r}_2 - \mathbf{r}_1|)(\mathbf{r}_1 - \mathbf{r}_2)$.

[1] In more advanced texts, it is sometimes remarked that the charge of a particle is a measure of the strength of the interaction of a photon (a quantum of electromagnetic radiation) and the particle. Such a definition is equivalent to the one used above, and though it is a more fruitful definition in the quantum mechanics of electromagnetism, it tells us nothing of the nature of charge.

noted that the force between two such charges is central (i.e., depends in magnitude only upon the scalar distance between the particles and is directed along the line joining the two particles), varying inversely as the square of the distance between the particles.   It was also noted that this interaction force could be attractive or repulsive, a fact suggesting that charge unlike mass was an algebraic rather than an arithmetic quantity. These experimental observations are summarized in one analytic expression known as Coulomb's law of force[2] (see Fig. 2.1):

$$\mathbf{f}_{12} = -\mathbf{f}_{21} = K \frac{q_1 q_2}{|\mathbf{r}_1 - \mathbf{r}_2|^2} \hat{\mathbf{n}}. \tag{2.1}$$

In eq. 2.1, $\mathbf{f}_{12}$ is the force that the particle with charge q_2 exerts on the charge q_1; the symbol $\hat{\mathbf{n}}$ represents a vector of unit magnitude pointing from q_2 to q_1.   The symbol K is a constant factor whose value depends upon the system of units chosen.   Since the charge is not a mechanical concept, it is obvious that the numerical value assigned to a given charge is quite arbitrary.   It is, of course, possible to ascertain that one charge has, say, ten times the magnitude of another by measuring the forces that these two charges exert on a third charge and then employing eq. 2.1 to determine the ratio of the two charges.   In the so-called *Gaussian* system of units, all mechanical quantities are measured in cgs units (i.e., length in centimeters, mass in grams, time in seconds), and the multiplicative constant is chosen to have the magnitude of 1.   The Gaussian unit of charge is defined as follows.   If two charges of equal magnitude are placed one centimeter apart and exert a force on one another of one dyne, the charges are defined to have one unit of charge.   Such a charge unit is sometimes called an esu or *electrostatic unit*.   The units to be used in this text are the so-called *rationalized mks* units.   In this system all mechanical quantities are expressed in mks units (i.e., length in meters, mass in kilograms, time in seconds).   The derived unit of force is the newton, which is the force necessary to accelerate a one kilogram mass one meter per second squared, and in addition the unit of charge is so chosen that the

[2] Although Coulomb's law was postulated about two centuries ago to correlate the behavior of macroscopic charged objects, it is interesting to note that this law has been subject to intensive scrutiny over the last fifty years and has been shown to be valid in the realm of atoms and atomic nuclei where the distances involved range between 10^{-10} and 10^{-15} meters.   In fact, it is in this extreme submicroscopic realm that the law has been tested with greatest precision.   One of the most precise tests of the validity of the Coulomb force law is in the determination of the electronic energy levels in atomic hydrogen.   These so-called *Lamb shift* measurements test Coulomb's law down to 2×10^{-15} meters.   The scattering of high energy electrons from protons gives an even more precise test of the agreement of experiment with theory; this experiment substantiates the Coulomb law down to 0.6×10^{-15} meters.

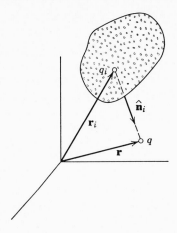

Fig. 2.2   A cluster of charges $q_1 \ldots q_i \ldots q_N$ is located in the neighborhood of charge q.   A characteristic member of the charge cluster q_i is located at $\mathbf{r}_i$; the charge q is located at $\mathbf{r}$.   The vector $\hat{\mathbf{n}}_i$ is a unit vector pointing from $\mathbf{r}_i$ to $\mathbf{r}$: $\hat{\mathbf{n}}_i = 1/(|\mathbf{r} - \mathbf{r}_i|)$ $(\mathbf{r} - \mathbf{r}_i)$.

constant K takes on the value $1/4\pi\epsilon_0 = 10^{-7}c^2$, with c the velocity of light in vacuum.   In this system the unit of charge is called the coulomb.[3]

It is possible to generalize eq. 2.1 and write the force $\mathbf{f}$ experienced by a charge q in an environment of charges $q_1, q_2, \ldots, q_N$ (see Fig. 2.2):

$$\mathbf{f} = \mathbf{f}_1 + \mathbf{f}_2 + \cdots + \mathbf{f}_N = \left(\frac{1}{4\pi\epsilon_0}\right) q \sum_{j=1}^{N} \frac{q_j}{|\mathbf{r} - \mathbf{r}_j|^2} \hat{\mathbf{n}}_j. \qquad (2.2)$$

In eq. 2.2, $\mathbf{f}_j$ is the force exerted by q_j on q.   For a *fixed ensemble* of charges $q_1 \ldots q_N$, $\mathbf{f}$ depends on the position of the charge q and has the properties of a vector point function; that is, a vector $\mathbf{f}$ can be associated with every point in the space populated by the charges q; $q_1, q_2, \ldots, q_N$. When this association is made, a so-called *force field* results.

[3] It is quite apparent that Coulomb's force law has a somewhat more complicated appearance in rationalized mks units than it does in Gaussian units.   It will be seen in later chapters, however, that rationalized mks units afford a simplification in the so-called *field equations*.   Although engineers and many physicists have adopted the rationalized mks system, much of the current physics literature and almost all the classic physics texts are written in other, usually Gaussian, units.   It is important to realize that no specific choice of units yields more physical information than any other choice.   Certain sets of units are more appropriate to certain problems than others.   However, the "suitability" of a given set of units is a matter of taste; being so, standards of taste in units change sometimes quite rapidly and irrationally.   The choice of rationalized mks units merely reflects the standards of the time in which this text is written.

2.2   The Electrostatic Field

The magnitude of all the vectors in the above force field depends upon the magnitude of the charge q. Examination of eq. 2.2 shows, however, that this relationship is linear in q, and therefore the vector field $\mathbf{E(r)}$ defined by eq. 2.3 is independent of the charge q and depends only on the fixed charges $q_1, q_2, \ldots, q_N$.

$$\mathbf{E(r)} \equiv \frac{\mathbf{f}}{q} = \left(\frac{1}{4\pi\epsilon_0}\right) \sum_{j=1}^{N} \frac{q_j}{|\mathbf{r} - \mathbf{r}_j|^2} \,\hat{\mathbf{n}}_j. \tag{2.3}$$

The vector field $\mathbf{E(r)}$ is called the *electrostatic field* or, more loosely, the *electric field*. Equation (2.3) provides the so-called *operational* definition of the E-field; that is, *the E-field at a point* $\mathbf{r}$ *is the force on a charge placed at* $\mathbf{r}$ *divided by the magnitude of the charge.* Measurements of the electrostatic field reduce ultimately to the measurement of a force on a charged particle usually referred to as a "test" charge.

Implicit in the definition of the electrostatic field produced by an ensemble of fixed charges is the assumption that this field is the vector sum of the fields produced by the individual charges making up the charge ensemble. This is sometimes referred to as the *principle of superposition*. The validity of this assumption is established by the fact that $\mathbf{E}$ is the force per unit charge on a test charge; since from the study of classical mechanics, a force field may be represented by a vector point function, then it follows

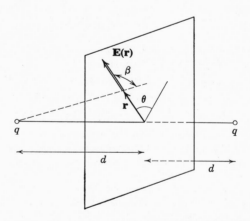

Fig. 2.3   Two equal charges q are separated by a distance $2d$. The E-field is calculated at a point on the plane which is the perpendicular bisector of the line joining the charges. The vector $\mathbf{r}$ is a position vector in the plane; the origin of coordinates is taken as the point of intersection between the plane and the line joining the two charges.

that **E** also may be represented in this manner. Since the **E**-fields produced by the individual charges are vector point functions, it follows that the total **E**-field is the vector sum of the individual **E**-fields.

Although the **E**-field produced by an arbitrary charge distribution may be calculated directly from its definition, eq. 2.3, this is a laborious task in all but the simplest cases because of the nature of vector addition. Those cases in which the **E**-field may be simply calculated usually possess some kind of geometrical symmetry which simplifies the calculation. Several of these cases are considered below.

EXAMPLE 2.1   Calculate the **E**-field produced by two equal charges q separated by a distance $2d$.   Restrict consideration to a plane which bisects the line connecting the charges and is perpendicular to it (see Fig. 2.3).

The component of **E** in the $\hat{r}$-direction from each charge is

$$\left(\frac{1}{4\pi\epsilon_0}\right) \frac{q}{(r^2 + d^2)} \cos\beta \quad \text{where} \quad \cos\beta = \frac{r}{\sqrt{r^2 + d^2}}.$$

The component of **E** perpendicular to the $\hat{r}$-direction vanishes since the contributions from the charges are equal in magnitude but opposite in sign.   Consequently the symmetry inherent in this problem yields

$$\mathbf{E(r)} = E(r)\hat{r} \quad \text{where} \quad E(r) = \left(\frac{1}{4\pi\epsilon_0}\right) \frac{2qr}{(r^2 + d^2)^{3/2}}.$$

EXAMPLE 2.2   Two charges, q_1 and q_2, are separated by a distance d. Discuss the locus of points for which $\mathbf{E} = 0$.

Since the field at any point is equal to the vector sum of the fields produced by q_1 and q_2 separately, it is evident that the points for which $\mathbf{E} = 0$ must lie on the line joining the two charges.   If q_1 and q_2 have the same sign, there exists one (and only one) point for which $\mathbf{E} = 0$ lying between the charges; if q_1 and q_2 have opposite signs, there exists one (and only one) point lying on the line connecting the two charges but a distance greater than d from the larger of the two charges.

In the general case in which the geometric symmetry requisite for ease in calculation is absent, it is desirable to have an alternative way of calculating the **E**-field.

2.3   The Electrostatic Potential

The alternative procedure referred to in Section 2.2 for calculating the **E**-field is provided through the so-called *electrostatic potential function* $\varphi(\mathbf{r})$ defined as follows.   Suppose a charge q is located somewhere in

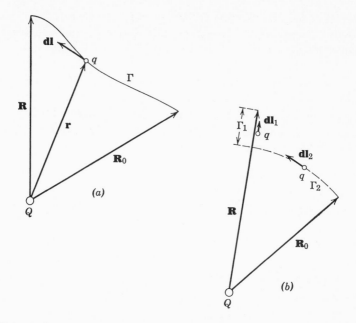

Fig. 2.4(a) A charge q is moved from $\mathbf{R}_0$ to $\mathbf{R}$ along a path Γ. The origin of co-ordinates is taken at the position of the charge Q. An arbitrary point on the path Γ is designated by $\mathbf{r}$; $\mathbf{dl}$ is a vector element of the path Γ. (b) the path Γ in (a) is replaced by the composite path $\Gamma_1 + \Gamma_2$. Γ_2 is an arc of a circle of radius R_0; Γ_1 is a segment of length $(R - R_0)$ of the radius of the circular arc. On Γ_1 the position vector of q is parallel to the element of path $\mathbf{dl}$; on Γ_2 the position vector of q is perpendicular to the element of path $\mathbf{dl}$.

space a distance $\mathbf{R}_0$ from another fixed charge Q. The charge q is then moved to a point a distance $\mathbf{R}$ from Q along a path Γ (see Fig. 2.4a). In order to move the charge q, an amount of work must be done on the charge since it exists in a force field. In order to calculate the work, it will be assumed that the relative velocity of q and Q at all points on Γ is negligibly small so that Coulomb's law of force may be used.

$$W_\Gamma(\mathbf{R}_0 \to \mathbf{R}) \equiv \int_\Gamma \mathbf{f}_{\text{applied}} \cdot \mathbf{dl} = - \left(\frac{1}{4\pi\epsilon_0}\right) qQ \int_\Gamma \frac{\mathbf{r} \cdot \mathbf{dl}}{r^3}. \qquad (2.4)$$

In eq. 2.4 the substitution $\mathbf{f}_{\text{applied}} = - \mathbf{f}_{\text{coulomb}}$ has been made since q is moved with essentially zero velocity. Now the Coulombic force field is *conservative*, and consequently the work done in moving q from $\mathbf{R}_0$ to $\mathbf{R}$ is independent of the path connecting $\mathbf{R}_0$ with $\mathbf{R}$.[4] The path Γ may then

---

[4] In classical mechanics, it is shown that the necessary and sufficient conditions that the work done in moving an object in a force field $\mathbf{f(r)}$ be dependent only upon the

be replaced by the composite path $\Gamma_1 + \Gamma_2$ defined in Fig. 2.4b. Since $\hat{\mathbf{r}}$ is parallel to **dl** for all points on Γ_1, and since $\hat{\mathbf{r}}$ is perpendicular to **dl** for all points on Γ_2,

$$W(\mathbf{R}_0 \to \mathbf{R}) = - \left(\frac{1}{4\pi\epsilon_0}\right) qQ \int_{\Gamma_1} \frac{dr}{r^2} = \left(\frac{1}{4\pi\epsilon_0}\right) qQ \left\{\frac{1}{R} - \frac{1}{R_0}\right\}. \quad (2.5)$$

The quantity $\varphi(\mathbf{R}_0, \mathbf{R})$ resulting from dividing $W(\mathbf{R}_0 \to \mathbf{R})$ by q, the charge that was moved, is called the *electrostatic potential difference* between **R** and $\mathbf{R}_0$ produced by the stationary charge Q.

$$\varphi(\mathbf{R}_0, \mathbf{R}) = \left(\frac{1}{4\pi\epsilon_0}\right) Q \left\{\frac{1}{R} - \frac{1}{R_0}\right\}. \quad (2.6)$$

If R_0 is allowed to become infinitely large, the resulting expression is the electrostatic potential difference between a point a distance R from Q and an arbitrary point at infinity. This potential difference $\varphi(\mathbf{R}) = \varphi(\infty, \mathbf{R})$, is called the *electrostatic potential* at the point **R** due to the charge Q. [Note that the electrostatic potential at an infinite distance from Q is implicitly set equal to zero in the above definition; i.e., $\varphi(\infty, \infty) = 0$.]

If the charge Q is a distance $\mathbf{r}_0$ from the origin of coordinates and the point where the potential function is to be evaluated a distance $\mathbf{r}$, then $\varphi(\mathbf{R})$ may be written

$$\varphi(\mathbf{r}) = \left(\frac{1}{4\pi\epsilon_0}\right) \frac{Q}{|\mathbf{r} - \mathbf{r}_0|}, \qquad \mathbf{R} \equiv \mathbf{r} - \mathbf{r}_0. \quad (2.7)$$

Equation 2.7 may be generalized to the potential produced by the charge distribution of Fig. 2.2 as

$$\varphi(\mathbf{r}) = \left(\frac{1}{4\pi\epsilon_0}\right) \sum_{j=1}^{N} \frac{q_j}{|\mathbf{r}_j - \mathbf{r}|}. \quad (2.8)$$

The electrostatic potential is a scalar quantity. Thus the sum on the right-hand side of eq. 2.8 is simpler to perform than the sum on the right-hand side of eq. 2.3, being algebraic instead of vectorial. The scalar field φ and the **E**-field may now be related by noting that for a general charge distribution

$$\frac{W}{q}(\infty \to \mathbf{r}) = \varphi(\mathbf{r}) = - \int \mathbf{E} \cdot \mathbf{dl}. \quad (2.9)$$

---

initial and final positions of the object are: (1) $\partial \mathbf{f}/\partial t = 0$ (2) curl $\mathbf{f} = 0$ where in Cartesian coordinates curl $f_z \equiv \partial f_y/\partial z - \partial f_z/\partial y$, etc. The Coulombic force satisfies both of these conditions which may be verified by direct calculation. See Chapter 1 for further discussion of this point.

In eq. 2.9 it is understood that the integral is to be performed from some arbitrary point at infinity to the point **r** along any arbitrary path. This integral relationship between φ and **E** is convenient whenever **E** is known and φ is to be determined. However, since it is usually φ that is directly calculable and not **E**, a method must be evolved to express **E** in terms of φ. This is accomplished as follows. In Cartesian coordinates

$$\mathbf{E} \cdot \mathbf{dl} = E_x \, dx + E_y \, dy + E_z \, dz, \quad (\mathbf{dl} \equiv \hat{\mathbf{x}} \, dx + \hat{\mathbf{y}} \, dy + \hat{\mathbf{z}} \, dz). \quad (2.10)$$

In addition, from the fundamental theorem of the calculus

$$\varphi(\mathbf{r}) = \int d\varphi(\mathbf{r}). \quad (2.11)$$

Since φ is a function of the three independent variables (x, y, z), the differential $d\varphi$ may be expressed in terms of the differentials dx, dy, dz and the partial derivatives of the potential function.

$$d\varphi(\mathbf{r}) = \frac{\partial \varphi}{\partial x} \, dx + \frac{\partial \varphi}{\partial y} \, dy + \frac{\partial \varphi}{\partial z} \, dz. \quad (2.12)$$

Combining the results of equations 2.9–2.12 produces a relationship between Cartesian components of **E** and the partial space derivatives of φ.

$$E_x = -\frac{\partial \varphi}{\partial x}, \quad E_y = -\frac{\partial \varphi}{\partial y}, \quad E_z = -\frac{\partial \varphi}{\partial z}. \quad (2.13)$$

The three partial space derivatives may be considered as the three Cartesian components of a vector grad φ.[5] Equation 2.13 may then be written

$$\mathbf{E} \equiv - \, \text{grad} \, \varphi = - \left\{ \hat{\mathbf{x}} \frac{\partial}{\partial x} + \hat{\mathbf{y}} \frac{\partial}{\partial y} + \hat{\mathbf{z}} \frac{\partial}{\partial z} \right\} \varphi. \quad (2.14)$$

Equation 2.14 constitutes the relationship between **E** and φ, which allows the calculation of **E** once φ is known.

The relationship between **E** and φ expressed in eq. 2.14 suggests the following geometrical interpretation. The expression $\varphi(x, y, z) = a$ (where a is a constant) is the equation for a surface in three dimensions. Such a surface is called an *equipotential surface*. One equipotential

---

[5] The symbol grad is to be read "gradient"; it is sometimes written as grad $\varphi = \nabla \varphi$. In cylindrical coordinates the gradient operator is

$$\text{grad} = \hat{\rho} \frac{\partial}{\partial \rho} + \hat{\phi} \frac{1}{\rho} \frac{\partial}{\partial \phi} + \hat{\mathbf{z}} \frac{\partial}{\partial z};$$

in spherical polar coordinates

$$\text{grad} = \hat{\mathbf{r}} \frac{\partial}{\partial r} + \hat{\theta} \frac{1}{r} \frac{\partial}{\partial \theta} + \hat{\phi} \frac{1}{r \sin \theta} \frac{\partial}{\partial \phi}.$$

See Chapter 1 for further discussion.

surface passes through every point in space in which a charge distribution is imbedded. It can be shown that the gradient of any scalar point function $g(x, y, z)$ evaluated at the point (x^0, y^0, z^0) is parallel at that point to the normal of the surface defined by $g(x, y, z) = g(x^0, y^0, z^0)$. This means that $\mathbf{E}(x, y, z)$ is always perpendicular to the equipotential surface passing through the point (x, y, z). Now imagine the following operation: $\mathbf{E}$ is evaluated at a *neighboring* point (x', y', z') chosen such that the vector $(x' - x)\hat{\mathbf{x}} + (y' - y)\hat{\mathbf{y}} + (z' - z)\hat{\mathbf{z}}$ is parallel to $\mathbf{E}(x, y, z)$; then $\mathbf{E}(x', y', z')$ will be perpendicular to the equipotential surface passing through (x', y', z'). Subsequently $\mathbf{E}$ is evaluated at a neighboring point (x'', y'', z'') chosen such that the vector $(x'' - x')\hat{\mathbf{x}} + (y'' - y')\hat{\mathbf{y}} + (z'' - z')\hat{\mathbf{z}}$ is parallel to $\mathbf{E}(x', y', z')$; $\mathbf{E}(x'', y'', z'')$ will be perpendicular to the equipotential surface passing through (x'', y'', z''). If this operation is continued indefinitely, the points chosen by the above prescription will lie on a curve. This curve will have the property that it is everywhere perpendicular to equipotential surfaces; in addition, the tangent to this curve at a given point on the line is directed parallel to the E-field at that point. Such a line is called a *field line* (see Figs. 2.5 and 2.6).

These geometrical concepts are sometimes used to construct a measure of the "strength" of the E-field at a point. This is carried out as follows. Space can be considered to be densely filled with equipotential surfaces

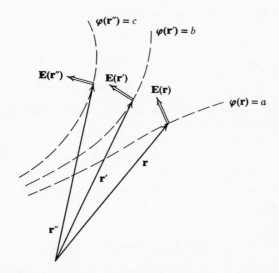

Fig. 2.5 **r**, **r**′ and **r**″ are points on the equipotential surfaces $\varphi = a$, $\varphi = b$, and $\varphi = c$, respectively. $\mathbf{E}(\mathbf{r})$ is perpendicular to the surface $\varphi = a$; similarly $\mathbf{E}(\mathbf{r}')$ and $\mathbf{E}(\mathbf{r}'')$ are perpendicular to the surfaces $\varphi = b$ and $\varphi = c$.

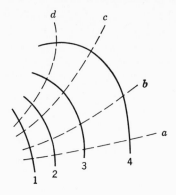

Fig. 2.6   Lines 1–4 are field lines intersecting the equipotential surfaces $\varphi = a$, $\varphi = b$, $\varphi = c$, and $\varphi = d$.   The field is larger in the neighborhood of equipotential surface d where the field lines tend to converge.

and field lines.   The "density of field lines" at a point is chosen to be proportional to the strength of the E-field at that point.   The density of field lines is defined as the number of field lines passing perpendicular through an infinitesimal area dA containing the point (x, y, z) of the equipotential surface divided by the area dA.

Since **E** can be expressed as the negative gradient of a scalar point function $\varphi(\mathbf{r})$, it follows immediately that

$$\text{curl } \mathbf{E} = 0.$$

This can be established by direct evaluation, that is,

$$\text{curl } \mathbf{E} = -\text{ curl grad } \varphi(\mathbf{r}) = 0.$$

The only requirement on $\varphi(\mathbf{r})$ is that the cross derivatives of φ satisfy relationships of the form

$$\frac{\partial^2}{\partial x \, \partial y} \varphi = \frac{\partial^2}{\partial y \, \partial x} \varphi.$$

This relation is satisfied by all physically realizable electrostatic potential functions.

2.4   Potential and Field of a Dipole

An interesting and useful example of the application of the above formalism is the calculation of the E-field produced by two charges equal in magnitude but opposite in sign (see Fig. 2.7).   Since the problem has rotational symmetry about the line joining the two charges, the calculation may be confined to a plane without any loss in generality. Defining r_+ and r_- as the distances from the positive and negative charges, respectively, to the field point, a direct application of eq. 2.7 yields

$$\varphi(r,\,\theta) = \left(\frac{1}{4\pi\epsilon_0}\right)q\left\{\frac{1}{r_+} - \frac{1}{r_-}\right\} \tag{2.15}$$

If attention is concentrated on the region in space for which $r > a$, the r_+ and r_- may be expanded by the binomial theorem, keeping only the first few terms in (a/r) as an adequate approximation.

$$\frac{1}{r_+} \simeq \frac{1}{r}\left(1 + \frac{a}{r}\cos\theta\right) \tag{2.16a}$$

$$\frac{1}{r_-} \simeq \frac{1}{r}\left(1 - \frac{a}{r}\cos\theta\right). \tag{2.16b}$$

Therefore

$$\varphi(r,\,\theta) \simeq \left(\frac{1}{4\pi\epsilon_0}\right)\frac{2qa\cos\theta}{r^2}, \quad r > a.$$

The *electric dipole moment* of this simple charge distribution is defined as

$$\mathbf{p} \equiv 2qa\hat{\mathbf{p}} \tag{2.17}$$

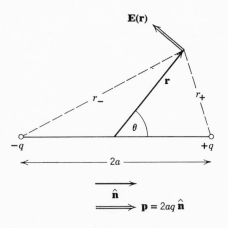

Fig. 2.7   Two equal but opposite charges are separated by a distance $2a$. The origin of coordinates is taken to be midway between the two charges. The position vector of the field point $\mathbf{r}$ is specified by the polar variables $(r,\,\theta)$. r_+ and r_- are the distances of the field point to the positive and negative charges respectively. The (E1) moment of the charge distribution is given by the vector $\mathbf{p}$ whose magnitude is $2aq$ and which points from $-q$ to $+q$.

where $\hat{\mathbf{p}}$ is a unit vector pointing from the negative to the positive charge.

$$\varphi(r, \theta) \simeq \left(\frac{1}{4\pi\epsilon_0}\right) \frac{\mathbf{p} \cdot \hat{\mathbf{r}}}{r^3}. \tag{2.18}$$

Equation 2.18 is the electric dipole component of the potential produced by the charge distribution. It becomes a more adequate representation of the actual potential the further the field point lies from the charges, that is, the smaller the ratio a/r.[6] The electric dipole component of the electrostatic field is calculated from eq. 2.18 using eq. 2.14.

$$\mathbf{E}(r, \theta) \simeq \left(\frac{1}{4\pi\epsilon_0}\right)\{2(\mathbf{p} \cdot \hat{\mathbf{r}})\hat{\mathbf{r}} + |\mathbf{p} \times \hat{\mathbf{r}}|\hat{\boldsymbol{\theta}}\} \frac{1}{r^3} \tag{2.19}$$

or equivalently

$$\mathbf{E}(\mathbf{r}) \simeq -\left(\frac{1}{4\pi\epsilon_0}\right)\left\{\frac{\mathbf{p}}{r^3} - \frac{3(\mathbf{p} \cdot \mathbf{r})\mathbf{r}}{r^5}\right\}.$$

Note that the magnitude of the electric dipole contribution to the E-field falls off as $1/r^3$, whereas the E-field of a point charge falls off as $1/r^2$.

2.5   Equivalent Dipole of an Arbitrary Charge Distribution

Since the electric dipole contributions to the potential and field are only adequate representations of the field and potential of a dipole at a large distance from the dipole, it suggests that eqs. 2.18 and 2.19 may have applicability to more general charge distributions. To see this explicitly, consider the general charge distribution sketched in Fig. 2.8. The potential produced by this charge distribution is given by eq. 2.8. If the origin of the coordinate system is located within the distribution, and if the magnitude of the position vector of the field point $\mathbf{r}$ is much larger than the largest dimension of the charge distribution, then the denominator in eq. 2.8 may be expanded for each contributing charge; that is,

$$\frac{1}{|\mathbf{r} - \mathbf{r}_i|} \simeq \frac{1}{r}\left(1 + \frac{\mathbf{r} \cdot \mathbf{r}_i}{r^2}\right). \tag{2.19a}$$

Consequently the electrostatic potential a large distance from the charge distribution is approximately

$$\varphi(\mathbf{r}) \simeq \left(\frac{1}{4\pi\epsilon_0}\right) \frac{1}{r} \sum_{i=1}^{N} q_i + \left(\frac{1}{4\pi\epsilon_0}\right) \frac{\mathbf{r}}{r^3} \cdot \sum_{i=1}^{N} q_i \mathbf{r}_i. \tag{2.20}$$

---

[6] A charge distribution consisting of two charges equal in magnitude but opposite in sign is sometimes called an *electric dipole*. Strictly, such an electric dipole produces a potential more complex than that given by eq. 2.18. Equation 2.18 merely represents an approximate expression for $\varphi(\mathbf{r})$ a long way from such a distribution.

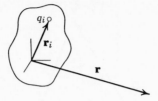

Fig. 2.8   A charge cluster is located with the origin of the coordinate system within the cluster. $\mathbf{r}$ is the position vector of the field point; $\mathbf{r}_i$ is the position vector of a typical charge in the cluster.

The following definitions are now made:

$$\sum_{i=1}^{N} q_i = q_{\text{total}} = \text{total charge or } \textit{monopole moment} \quad (2.21a)$$
$$\text{(E0) of the charge cluster;}$$

$$\sum_{i=1}^{N} q_i \mathbf{r}_i = \mathbf{p} = \textit{dipole moment} \text{ (E1) of the charge cluster.} \quad (2.21b)$$

It is straightforward to show that eq. 2.21 agrees with the special case of eq. 2.17.   Consequently

$$\varphi(\mathbf{r}) \simeq \left(\frac{1}{4\pi\epsilon_0}\right)\frac{q_{\text{total}}}{r} + \left(\frac{1}{4\pi\epsilon_0}\right)\frac{\mathbf{p}\cdot\mathbf{r}}{r^3}. \quad (2.22)$$

The two terms in eq. 2.22 may be called the *monopole* and *dipole* contributions to the electrostatic potential produced by an arbitrary charge distribution.   Although the monopole moment or total charge is uniquely defined by eq. 2.21a, the dipole moment has an inherent ambiguity since $\mathbf{p}$, in general, depends on the location of the origin of coordinates.   If, however, the charge distribution is neutral, i.e., $q_{\text{total}} = 0$, then $\mathbf{p}$ defined by eq. 2.21b is independent of the location of the origin of coordinates. This may be seen as follows: translate the origin of coordinates by an amount $\boldsymbol{\rho}$; charge q_i is then a distance $\mathbf{r}_i - \boldsymbol{\rho}$ from the new origin.   The new dipole moment $\mathbf{p}'$ is simply

$$\mathbf{p}' = \sum_{i=1}^{N} q_i(\mathbf{r}_i - \boldsymbol{\rho}) = \sum_{i=1}^{N} q_i\mathbf{r}_i - \boldsymbol{\rho}\sum_{i=1}^{N} q_i$$
$$\mathbf{p}' = \mathbf{p} - \boldsymbol{\rho}q_{\text{total}} \qquad \mathbf{p}' = \mathbf{p} \text{ if } q_{\text{total}} = 0.$$

The (E1) moment of a charge distribution is invariant with respect to a translation of the origin of coordinates if and only if the (E0) moment or total charge of the distribution vanishes.   Equation 2.22 is essentially the

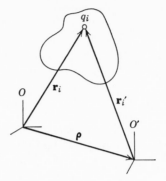

Fig. 2.9   The origin of coordinates O has been moved to a new position designated by O'.   The translation vector of this change in position is $\boldsymbol{\rho}$. $\mathbf{r}_i$ is the position vector of the charge $\mathbf{q}_i$ with respect to O; $\mathbf{r}_i' = \mathbf{r}_i - \boldsymbol{\rho}$.   The dipole moment of the charge cluster is invariant with respect to the translation of O to O' if and only if the total charge of the cluster is zero.

first two terms in the expansion of $\varphi(\mathbf{r})$ in terms of largest linear dimension of the charge cluster divided by r.   The neglected terms contain the higher electrostatic multipole contributions to the potential.

2.6   Equivalent Quadrupole of an Arbitrary Charge Distribution

The next term in the approximation is proportional to $1/r^3$ and is called the *electric quadrupole* or (E2) contribution to the potential.   To obtain the quadrupole contribution to $\varphi(\mathbf{r})$, the denominator in eq. 2.8

$$\frac{1}{|\mathbf{r} - \mathbf{r}_i|} \simeq \frac{1}{r} \frac{1}{\sqrt{1 + \left(\dfrac{r_i}{r}\right)^2 - 2\left(\dfrac{r_i}{r}\right) \cos \theta_i}}$$

where θ_i is the angle between $\mathbf{r}$ and $\mathbf{r}_i$,

is expanded in a power series in the small quantity

$$\alpha \equiv \left(\frac{r_i}{r}\right)^2 - 2\left(\frac{r_i}{r}\right) \cos \theta_i, \quad r \gg r_i.$$

The power series to be employed is $(n = -\tfrac{1}{2})$:

$$(1 + \alpha)^n = 1 + \frac{n\alpha}{1!} + \frac{n(n-1)\alpha^2}{2!} + \frac{n(n-1)(n-2)\alpha^3}{3!} + \cdots, \, \alpha < 1.$$

Keeping terms in this series up to and including $(r_i/r)^2$, the electrostatic potential at $\mathbf{r}$ is approximately

$$\varphi(\mathbf{r}) \simeq \left(\frac{1}{4\pi\epsilon_0}\right) \sum_{i=1}^{N} \frac{q_i}{r}$$
$$\left\{ 1 + \left(\frac{r_i}{r}\right) \cos\theta_i + \left(\frac{r_i}{r}\right)^2 \left(\frac{3\cos^2\theta_i - 1}{2}\right) + \cdots \right\}. \qquad (2.23)$$

The first two terms in eq. 2.23, $\varphi_0(\mathbf{r})$ and $\varphi_1(\mathbf{r})$, have already been considered and are, respectively, the (E0) and (E1) contributions to $\varphi(\mathbf{r})$. The term $\varphi_2(\mathbf{r})$ is the quadrupole contribution

$$\varphi_2(\mathbf{r}) = \left(\frac{1}{4\pi\epsilon_0}\right) \frac{1}{2r^3} \sum_{i=1}^{N} q_i r_i^2 (3\cos^2\theta_i - 1). \qquad (2.24)$$

It should be noted that $\varphi_2(\mathbf{r})$ depends on the *second moments* of the charges about the origin weighted by the indicated angular factor.

It should be remembered that the (E0) contribution to the potential can be characterized by a scalar, the (E0) moment or total charge; on the other hand, it is necessary to characterize the (E1) contribution by a set of three numbers, the vector (E1) moment. It is necessary to specify five numbers to characterize the (E2) contribution to the potential. These may be obtained by examining eq. 2.24, the definition of the quadrupole contribution to φ, which can be alternatively written as

$$\varphi_2(\mathbf{r}) = \left(\frac{1}{4\pi\epsilon_0}\right) \frac{1}{2r^5} \sum_{i=1}^{N} q_i \{3(\mathbf{r} \cdot \mathbf{r}_i)^2 - r^2 r_i^2\}. \qquad (2.25)$$

If the terms in the sum are expanded into Cartesian components, the resultant expression has the following property: each term in the expansion contains the product of two Cartesian components of $\mathbf{r}$ multiplied by a coefficient which depends only on the properties of the charge distribution and not on the field point. These coefficients may be arranged in an array as follows:

	x	y	z
x	$\sum_i q_i(3x_i^2 - r_i^2)$	$\sum_i 3q_i x_i y_i$	$\sum_i 3q_i x_i z_i$
y	$\sum_i 3q_i y_i x_i$	$\sum_i q_i(3y_i^2 - r_i^2)$	$\sum_i 3q_i y_i z_i$
z	$\sum_i 3q_i z_i x_i$	$\sum_i 3q_i z_i y_i$	$\sum_i q_i(3z_i^2 - r_i^2)$

The above table is to be interpreted in the following manner. The entry appearing in the x-row and the x-column is the coefficient of x^2 in the sum of eq. 2.25; the entry appearing in the x-row and the y-column is the coefficient of xy, etc. The entries in the above square array are said to form the elements of a 3×3 *matrix*. These entries are the *second moments* of the charge distribution or, alternatively, the elements of the *quadrupole matrix*.

It is evident on inspection of this matrix that it is symmetric (i.e., the x-y entry is equal to the y-x entry.)[7]   Consequently instead of nine second moments there are apparently only six.   In addition, not all of these six second moments are linearly independent of each other.   There is a linear relationship among the diagonal elements of the quadrupole matrix which is satisfied by all charge distributions; the sum of the principal diagonal elements (these are defined as Q_{jj}) vanishes identically; that is,

$$\sum_i q_i(3x_i^2 - r_i^2) + \sum_i q_i(3y_i^2 - r_i^2) + \sum_i q_i(3z_i^2 - r_i^2)$$
$$= \sum_i 3q_i(x_i^2 + y_i^2 + z_i^2 - r_i^2) \equiv 0.$$

This relationship reduces the number of linearly independent second moments to five.

The sum of the principal diagonal elements of a matrix is called the *trace* or *spur* of the matrix.   The quadrupole matrix has been shown to be a 3×3 symmetric matrix with zero trace.   Now it is always possible to choose an orientation of the coordinate axes which up to this point has been unspecified so that the nondiagonal elements vanish identically. This possibility of *diagonalization* of the quadrupole matrix is a property possessed by real symmetric matrices in general.[8]   With a suitable choice

[7] This has been assured by arbitrarily writing a term such as $(\alpha + \beta)^2$ as $(\alpha + \beta)^2 = \alpha^2 + \beta^2 + \alpha\beta + \beta\alpha$ in the expansion of eq. 2.25.   It is convenient to do this because symmetric matrices have certain very useful and interesting properties, one of which is the possibility of writing them in diagonal form.   In the case of a 3×3 matrix under discussion above, this means that the matrix can always be rewritten in the form:

$$Q_{ij} = \lambda_i \delta_{ij}, \quad i, j = 1, 2, 3,$$

where δ_{ij} is the so-called "Kronecker delta symbol" which takes on the following values

$$\delta_{ij} = \begin{cases} 0 & \text{if } i \neq j \\ 1 & \text{if } i = j \end{cases}$$

[8] It is beyond the scope of this discussion to verify this property of real symmetric matrices.   The reader is referred to any book on matrix algebra for further discussion; see, for example, Margenau and Murphy; *Mathematics of Physics and Chemistry*, Sections 10.15–10.17.

of the orientation of the coordinate axes, the quadrupole matrix becomes the very simply square array:

$$\begin{pmatrix} Q_{xx} & 0 & 0 \\ 0 & Q_{yy} & 0 \\ 0 & 0 & Q_{zz} \end{pmatrix}$$

where, for example,

$$Q_{zz} \equiv \sum_i q_i(3z_i'^2 - r_i'^2)$$

where $z_i' = z$ component of $\mathbf{r}_i$ defined with respect to the specially chosen coordinate axes which diagonalize the quadrupole matrix.

It is quite evident that the trace of the quadrupole matrix remains zero upon diagonalization. Consequently in diagonal form the quadrupole matrix has two linearly independent elements. At first glance it seems that three of the elements of the quadrupole matrix have been lost in the diagonalization. This is only apparently so since it is necessary to specify three numbers to fix the orientation of a set of coordinate axes. These three numbers could be, for example, the direction cosines of the coordinate axes with respect to a set of axes arbitrarily fixed in the charge cluster. Five numbers therefore remain in the problem: two in the quadrupole matrix in diagonal form and three in the specification of the coordinate axes with respect to which the diagonalized quadrupole matrix is defined.

If the charge distribution has rotational symmetry about some axis, then an orientation of the axes in which, for example, the z-axis is parallel to the symmetry axis will diagonalize the (E2) matrix. Because of the rotational symmetry of the charge distribution about the z-direction, it follows that $Q_{xx} = Q_{yy}$ and consequently if Q_{zz} is defined by the relation $Q_{zz} = Q$ it follows that

$$Q_{xx} = -\tfrac{1}{2}Q$$
$$Q_{yy} = -\tfrac{1}{2}Q$$

For such a system one number suffices to specify the (E2) properties of the system. This single number Q is usually referred to as the *quadrupole moment* and is the number which appears in tables of quadrupole moments of molecules, atomic nuclei, etc.[9] It has the dimensions of (charge × length²) and can be either positive or negative. For example, a uniformly

---

[9] Actually these systems must be treated by the methods of quantum mechanics. The quantum mechanical definition of the quadrupole matrix has the above classical analogue, however. It is the quantum mechanical analogue of Q_{zz} which appears in the tables of physical constants. For a more complete discussion, the reader is referred to Townes and Schawlow, *Microwave Spectroscopy*, pp. 133–138.

charged *prolate* ellipsoid has a *positive* Q, whereas an *oblate* ellipsoid uniformly charged has a *negative* Q.

As an example of a simple charge distribution which has an (E2) moment, consider the charge distribution illustrated in Fig. 2.10a. The elements of the quadrupole matrix can be written down by inspection:

$$\begin{pmatrix} 0 & 12qa^2 & 0 \\ 12qa^2 & 0 & 0 \\ 0 & 0 & 0 \end{pmatrix}$$

If the coordinate axes are rotated through 45° about the z-axis, the quadrupole matrix is thereby diagonalized (see Fig. 2.10b). The (E2) matrix has the diagonal form:

$$\begin{pmatrix} -12qa^2 & 0 & 0 \\ 0 & 12qa^2 & 0 \\ 0 & 0 & 0 \end{pmatrix}$$

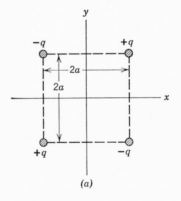

(a)

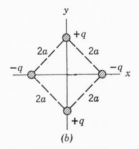

(b)

Fig. 2.10(a)   Four charges are located on the corners of a square as indicated. The (E2) matrix calculated with respect to the coordinate system indicated is nondiagonal. (b) The charge distribution of (a) is rigidly rotated through 45°. With the orientation of the charge distribution and the coordinate axes, the (E2) matrix is diagonal.

Since the charge distribution does not have rotational symmetry, the (E2) matrix does not have the simple form exhibited by rotationally symmetric distributions. However, since the distribution is two-dimensional, one number, namely, $12qa^2$, serves to represent the quadrupole properties of the distribution.

The student who has studied mechanics will notice that the above discussion parallels that of the second moments of the mass distribution of a system. These second moments also form the elements of a 3×3 matrix, the so-called *inertia matrix*. The off-diagonal elements of the inertia matrix are the *products of inertia*, the diagonal elements the *moments of inertia*. The inertia matrix is a real symmetric matrix and can be diagonalized by orienting the coordinate axes in a special manner. This diagonalization causes the products of inertia to vanish; the resultant diagonal elements of the matrix are called the *principal moments of inertia* of the mass distribution. Since the moments of inertia are arbitrarily defined to be positive, there is no linear relation among them and the inertia matrix has nonvanishing trace.[10]

2.7 Macroscopic Fields of Charged Objects Constructed From Microscopic Charges; Macroscopic Charge Densities

In the previous analysis, general expressions have been developed for the electrostatic field and potential produced by an ensemble of point charges. Even though the difficulty of calculating the force on a charge in the neighborhood of a fixed ensemble of point charges is reduced by the introduction of the electrostatic potential function φ, it is quite evident that the sum over the potentials produced by the individual charges indicated in eq. 2.8 will be exceedingly difficult if N is very large. The size that N might assume in practice is indicated by the relative size of the electric charge of the electron, the *unit charge* from which all charge distributions are composed and the unit of charge in the mks system, $e = 1.602 \times 10^{-19}$ coulombs. (The electron has a negative charge by definition; macroscopic bodies charged positively may simply be considered as system with a deficiency of electrons.) There is still another aspect of the problem which must be taken into consideration when one attempts to treat charged bodies from the microscopic point of view; the electrons which form a cloud of negatively charged particles around the positively charged nucleus of an atom are moving quite rapidly (0.01–0.1 times the velocity of light in vacuum). In order to reconcile the success of the

[10] For a discussion of the inertia matrix, see Landau and Lifshitz, *Mechanics*, pp. 98–101.

electrostatic theory of charged macroscopic objects and the microscopic nature of the structure of the macroscopic objects, one is forced to construct a model which adequately represents the field a finite distance from the macroscopic object.   This is done in the following way.

Consider the time dependent force field $\mathbf{f}(\mathbf{r}, t)$ acting on a stationary charge q produced by a charged macroscopic object. This field will fluctuate rapidly in position and time.   However, it is important to realize that the rapid fluctuation in position will occur over distances of the order of several angstroms (1 Å $= 10^{-10}$ meters) and the rapid fluctuations will have a period of about 10^{-15}–10^{-16} seconds.   Consequently it is useful to define the *macroscopic* electrostatic field produced by the object as a space average over many atomic diameters and a time average over many atomic periods of $\mathbf{f}(\mathbf{r}, t)/q$.   Such an averaging process will produce a time-independent or static electric field if the macroscopic object and charge q are held fixed.   As a hypothesis, it is assumed that this is the field measured by a macroscopic instrument.   In a similar fashion it is possible to define the macroscopic electrostatic potential function. Henceforth when the symbols $\mathbf{E}$ and φ appear, it will be understood that they refer to these macroscopic quantities unless it is specifically stated otherwise.   At this point the student should be warned about application of macroscopic theory to a specifically microscopic situation.

Still another quantity is useful in the discussion of the fields produced by a macroscopic charged object.   Consider the case in which there are

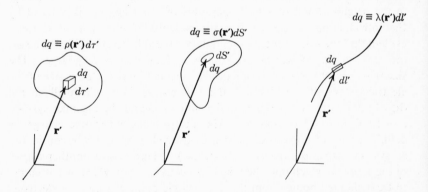

Fig. 2.11   A charge q is distributed throughout the volume τ.   A typical volume element of τ, $d\tau'$, is located at a distance $\mathbf{r}'$ from the origin of coordinates.   The field point is designated by the position vector $\mathbf{r}$.   In a similar fashion, a charge is distributed over a surface S; dS' is a typical element of the surface located at $\mathbf{r}'$.   A charge is distributed over a line of length l; dl' is a typical element of the line located at $\mathbf{r}'$.

many charges distributed throughout a volume τ; in addition, consider that it is possible to subdivide the volume τ into many subvolumes $\Delta\tau_i$ in such a way that there are many atomic charges contained within every subvolume. If the total charge contained within each subvolume $\Delta\tau_i$ is $\Delta q_i(t)$, a charge density averaged over many atomic periods is defined as

$$\bar{\rho}(\mathbf{r}_i) \equiv \frac{\Delta q_i}{\Delta\tau_i}$$

where Δq_i is defined as the time average of $\Delta q_i(t)$ and $\mathbf{r}_i$ is some arbitrary point in $\Delta\tau_i$. It is now assumed that one can assign to every point in space a volume density of charge defined by eq. 2.26:

$$\lim_{\Delta\tau_i \to 0} \bar{\rho}(\mathbf{r}_i) = \lim_{\Delta\tau_i \to 0} \frac{\Delta q_i}{\Delta\tau_i} \equiv \rho(\mathbf{r}), \tag{2.26}$$

in which $\mathbf{r}$ is the point to which $\Delta\tau_i$ has been shrunk. The actual limiting process only makes sense physically down to volumes of the order of several hundreds of atomic volumes. However, it will be assumed that the limiting process of eq. 2.26 makes sense in our macroscopic theory if we redefine $\rho(\mathbf{r})$ as the average charge density in a volume of the order of several hundred atomic volumes surrounding the point $\mathbf{r}$. The function $\rho(\mathbf{r})$, the *macroscopic* volume density of charge, will then be treated mathematically as a scalar point function. Once again, it is assumed that this introduces negligible error into the theory *as long as measuring devices are macroscopic in nature.*

In an entirely analogous fashion the macroscopic surface density of charge, $\sigma(\mathbf{r})$, defined everywhere on a surface carrying a macroscopic charge and the macroscopic line density of charge, $\lambda(\mathbf{r})$, defined everywhere on a line carrying a macroscopic charge may be introduced. Unless otherwise stated, the symbols $\rho(\mathbf{r})$, $\sigma(\mathbf{r})$, and $\lambda(\mathbf{r})$ will be used for the above-mentioned macroscopic charge densities.

The electrostatic potential produced by the volume distribution of charge indicated in Fig. 2.11 is

$$\varphi(\mathbf{r}) = \left(\frac{1}{4\pi\epsilon_0}\right) \int_\tau \frac{\rho(\mathbf{r}') \, d\tau'}{|\mathbf{r} - \mathbf{r}'|}.$$

In an analogous fashion the potentials produced by a charge distributed over a surface S and a line l are, respectively,

$$\left(\frac{1}{4\pi\epsilon_0}\right) \int_S \frac{\sigma(\mathbf{r}') \, dS'}{|\mathbf{r} - \mathbf{r}'|}, \qquad \left(\frac{1}{4\pi\epsilon_0}\right) \int_l \frac{\lambda(\mathbf{r}') \, dl'}{|\mathbf{r} - \mathbf{r}'|}.$$

Many of the electrostatic problems discussed in the following sections will concern themselves with distributed charges, that is, charge ensembles for which ρ, σ, and λ are defined.

It is sometimes convenient to ascribe to a point charge a volume charge density.   It is quite obvious that the function representing the volume density associated with a point particle has some very peculiar mathematical properties.   If the point charge is located at $\mathbf{r}_0$, then the function must vanish for all $\mathbf{r} \neq \mathbf{r}_0$, and must also be infinite for $\mathbf{r} = \mathbf{r}_0$ since the integral of this function over all space equals the charge of the point particle. The function which has the correct properties is given the symbol $q\delta(\mathbf{r} - \mathbf{r}_0)$ where $\delta(\mathbf{r} - \mathbf{r}_0)$ is the so-called "Dirac delta function" and q is the charge of the particle:

$$\delta(\mathbf{r} - \mathbf{r}_0) = \begin{cases} 0 & \text{if } \mathbf{r} \neq \mathbf{r}_0 \\ \infty & \text{if } \mathbf{r} = \mathbf{r}_0 \end{cases} \tag{2.27}$$

$$\int_{\text{all space}} \delta(\mathbf{r} - \mathbf{r}_0)\, d\tau = 1. \tag{2.28}$$

The delta function is really not a function at all in a mathematical sense. However, it can be handled quite rigorously in the mathematical theory of *distributions*.   In addition to the properties ascribed to it in eqs. 2.27 and 2.28, it is at least necessary to give a value to integrals of the following kind:

$$\int_\tau g(\mathbf{r})\, \delta(\mathbf{r} - \mathbf{r}_0)\, d\tau.$$

If $g(\mathbf{r})$ is an ordinary function with normal behavior at the point $\mathbf{r} = \mathbf{r}_o$, then the above integral takes on the value

$$\int_\tau g(\mathbf{r})\, \delta(\mathbf{r} - \mathbf{r}_0)\, d\tau = \begin{cases} g(\mathbf{r}_0) & \text{if } \mathbf{r}_0 \text{ lies in } \tau \\ 0 & \text{otherwise.} \end{cases} \tag{2.29}$$

No further attempt will be made here to discuss the mathematical properties of the delta function.   Suffice it to say that it can be used as a convenient artifice to convert a sum over a set of point charges into an integral over a volume containing a charge density.   For example, in terms of the δ function eq. 2.8 may be rewritten

$$\varphi(\mathbf{r}) = \left(\frac{1}{4\pi\epsilon_0}\right) \int \frac{d\tau'\, \rho(\mathbf{r}')}{|\mathbf{r}' - \mathbf{r}|} \tag{2.30}$$

where

$$\rho(\mathbf{r}') = \sum_{i=1}^{N} q_i\, \delta(\mathbf{r}' - \mathbf{r}_i),$$

as can be demonstrated by a direct application of eqs. 2.28 and 2.29.

PROBLEMS

2.1   Three charges of equal magnitude q are located at the vertices of an equilateral triangle of side length s.   Calculate the force on one of the charges due to the other two charges.

2.2   A fourth charge of magnitude Q is placed at the midpoint of one side of the triangle of problem 1.   Calculate the force on Q.

2.3   (a) A proton with 10 Mev (million electron volts) suffers a "head-on" collision with the nucleus of a lead atom.   What is the distance of closest approach; what is the mutual repulsive force at this separation?

(b) If a 10 Mev proton is incident on a lead nucleus with angular momentum $1\hbar$ ($\hbar = 1/2\pi \times$ Planck's constant), what is the distance of closest approach?   What physical argument can be presented to explain the qualitative difference of the answer in parts (a) and (b)?

2.4   Demonstrate by direct computation that the E-field produced by a point charge is conservative, i.e., show that curl $\mathbf{f} = 0$.

2.5   Using the result that the E-field produced by a point charge is conservative, show that the E-field produced by an ensemble of N charges is conservative.

2.6   A charge q is distributed uniformly along a circular loop of radius R. Calculate the E-field at a point on the axis of the loop.

2.7   Calculate the electrostatic potential at a point on the axis of the circular loop of Problem 2.6.   Calculate the E-field on this axis from the potential and compare with the direct evaluation carried out in Problem 2.6.

2.8   An infinitely long straight wire carries a charge of uniform linear density λ (coulombs/meter).   Calculate the E-field at a distance h from the wire.

2.9   Calculate the E-field at the center of a hemispherical shell of radius R carrying a total charge Q uniformly distributed over the shell.

2.10 Calculate the E-field at any point on the axis of rotational symmetry of the charge distribution of Problem 2.9.   Also calculate φ at any point on this axis and calculate $\mathbf{E}$ on the axis directly from φ.

2.11 Evaluate directly div $\dfrac{\hat{\mathbf{r}}}{|\mathbf{r} - \mathbf{r}'|^2}$.

2.12 A charge q is uniformly distributed over a spherical shell of radius R. (a) Calculate the E-field at a point within the volume enclosed by the shell; (b) calculate the E-field at a point outside the shell.

2.13 The charges in the distribution of Problem 2.1 are held in place by external forces.   Describe what happens when the forces are removed. Calculate the final velocity attained by the charges, assuming each charge has a mass m.

2.14 Calculate the amount of work necessary to place a charge Q at the center of a circle of radius R around which a charge q is uniformly distributed.

2.15 (a) Calculate the work necessary to move a charge q from one point within a volume enclosed by a spherical shell of radius R carrying a charge Q to another point within the same volume.

(b) Calculate the work necessary to move the charge from a point within the volume enclosed by the shell to a point outside the shell.

2.16 A charge q_1 is placed a distance s from a charge $-q_2(q_1 > q_2)$.   Show that the locus of points for which $\varphi = 0$ is a sphere of radius $R = [q_2/(q_1 - q_2)]s$ whose center is located on the line joining the two charges at a distance $d = R^2/(s + R)$ from q_2.

2.17 Verify eq. 2.19 by evaluating directly the negative gradient of the dipole potential.

2.18 (a) Show that the torque **N** on a dipole in a uniform applied field is **p × E**.
(b) If the field is nonuniform, show that an additional term **r × (p · ∇)E** must be added to the torque.

2.19 Compute the dipole moment of a spherical shell carrying a charge density $\sigma = \sigma_0 \cos \theta$, where θ is an angle measured from any axis passing through the center of the sphere.

2.20 Derive the conditions under which the elements of the quadrupole matrix of a charge distribution are independent of the location of the origin of the coordinate system.

2.21 Calculate the elements of the quadrupole matrix of the charge distribution of the accompanying figure:

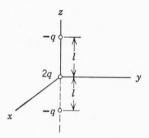

Derive an expression for the electrostatic potential at a distance r from the origin, where r is large compared to l.

2.22 A charge ring of radius R lies in the x-y plane. It carries a linear charge density given by the expression $\lambda = \lambda_1 \sin \phi + \lambda_2 \sin 2\phi$. Calculate the (E0) and (E1) moments of this distribution and the elements of the (E2) matrix.

2.23 The centers of two dipoles of moments $\mathbf{p}_1$ and $\mathbf{p}_2$ are separated by a distance d. If $d \gg$ extension of either dipole, calculate the torque that $\mathbf{p}_2$ exerts on $\mathbf{p}_1$. What force does $\mathbf{p}_2$ exert on $\mathbf{p}_1$?

2.24 Discuss the relative orientation of $\mathbf{p}_1$, $\mathbf{p}_2$ and $\mathbf{d}$, the vector distance from $\mathbf{p}_1$ to $\mathbf{p}_2$, which leads to a condition of stable equilibrium. Is there more than one position of stable equilibrium? If the orientation of one of the dipoles is changed by a small angle δ from the condition of stable equilibrium and the force maintaining the orientation of this dipole is removed, show that the dipole oscillates and calculate the frequency of the oscillation.

3 | Gauss's Law;
Electrostatics Involving Conductors

3.1   Gauss's Law

In Chapter 2 a suitable formulation was developed whereby the force on a charged particle at rest could be determined once the positions and magnitudes of all the charges in vacuum were known.   The formulation involves the introduction of two fruitful concepts—the electrostatic field and the electrostatic potential function—but is ultimately based on the empirically derivable Coulomb force law.   As has been discussed in Chapter 1, a primary goal of the study of electricity and magnetism is the reformulation of the empirical laws in the form of partial differential equations.   It is possible to recast Coulomb's law in the form of a partial differential equation involving the electrostatic field (or potential function) and the charge density ρ.   As an intermediate step an integral relationship involving the E-field and the source of the field (namely, charges) will be developed.

Consider a point charge q in vacuum, fixed for convenience at the origin of coordinates.   The E-field at a point $\mathbf{r}$ is given by eq. 2.3:

$$\mathbf{E}(\mathbf{r}) = \left(\frac{1}{4\pi\epsilon_0}\right) \frac{q}{r^2}\,\hat{\mathbf{r}}.$$

The magnitude of the E-field on a spherical surface of radius r centered at q is independent of position on the surface and is simply given by the scalar product of $\mathbf{E}(\mathbf{r})$ with unit vector $\hat{\mathbf{r}}$:

$$E(\mathbf{r}) = \left(\frac{1}{4\pi\epsilon_0}\right) \frac{q}{r^2}. \tag{3.1}$$

If both sides of eq. 3.1 are multiplied by the area of this spherical surface, $4\pi r^2$, the quantity Φ which results is called the *electrostatic flux* through the spherical surface; Φ is independent of the radius of the surface:

$$\Phi = \left(\frac{1}{4\pi\epsilon_0}\right) 4\pi q. \tag{3.2}$$

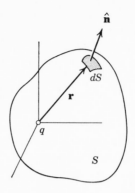

Fig. 3.1   A point charge q is located at the origin of coordinates, and a closed surface S contains the charge within its interior.   **r** is the position vector to an element of the surface dS.   **n̂** is that unit normal to dS pointing outward from the volume enclosed by S.

That Φ depends only on the charge located at the center of the spherical surface is, of course, a consequence of the *inverse square* nature of the Coulomb force.

The electrostatic flux has been defined above only in the case of a charge placed at the center of a spherical surface; it will be useful to adopt a more general definition of Φ.   For this purpose, consider an arbitrary *closed* surface S surrounding a point charge q located at the origin of coordinates (see Fig. 3.1).   The electrostatic flux Φ through this surface may be defined in terms of the flux $d\Phi$ threading through an arbitrary element of this surface.   For convenience, the element of a surface is considered a vector quantity and is defined as

$$\mathbf{dS} \equiv \mathbf{\hat{n}} \, dS. \tag{3.3}$$

In eq. 3.3, **n̂** is that normal to the surface element dS which points *outward* from the region enclosed by the surface S.   The electrostatic flux, $d\Phi$, through the vector surface element dS is defined in general as

$$d\Phi = \mathbf{E(r)} \cdot \mathbf{\hat{n}} \, dS. \tag{3.4}$$

The total flux through S is the sum of the individual $d\Phi$'s threading through all the vector surface elements of which S is composed.[1]

$$\Phi \equiv \int d\Phi = \oiint \mathbf{E(r)} \cdot \mathbf{\hat{n}} \, dS. \tag{3.5}$$

[1] The symbol $\oiint \cdots dS$ will stand for an integral over a closed surface; the symbol $\iint \cdots dS$, on the other hand, will represent an integral over an open surface S.

Since the source of the **E**-field is a fixed point charge q, the flux through **dS** may be written explicitly in terms of the charge q and the distance **r** of the surface element from the charge:

$$d\Phi = \left(\frac{1}{4\pi\epsilon_0}\right) q \frac{dS}{r^2} (\hat{\mathbf{r}} \cdot \hat{\mathbf{n}}) = \left(\frac{1}{4\pi\epsilon_0}\right) q \frac{dS}{r^2} \cos \theta. \qquad (3.6)$$

However, $dS \cos \theta$ is the projection of dS on a spherical surface of radius r centered at q passing through the point **r**. An element of area of a spherical surface divided by the square of the radius of the sphere is called the element of *solid angle* subtended by the·area at the center of the sphere. This element of solid angle will be designated by the symbol $d\Omega$. Hence $d\Phi$ can be rewritten in terms of $d\Omega$ using eq. 3.6:

$$d\Phi = \left(\frac{1}{4\pi\epsilon_0}\right) q \, d\Omega. \qquad (3.7)$$

The total flux Φ threading through the closed surface S is the integral of eq. 3.6 over the surface S or, equivalently, the integral of eq. 3.7 over the solid angle subtended by the closed surface at a point within the volume enclosed by the surface. The latter quantity is 4π (steradians). Consequently it follows quite generally that

$$\Phi = \left(\frac{1}{4\pi\epsilon_0}\right) 4\pi q. \qquad (3.8)$$

Examination of eq. 3.8 shows that the flux through a closed surface is independent of the shape of the surface. (The result obtained previously in the case of a spherical surface, eq. 3.2, is a special case of eq. 3.8.) Using the general expression for the electrostatic flux given in eq. 3.5, it is possible to express the integral of the **E**-field over a closed surface S in terms of the charge producing the field:

$$\oiint \mathbf{E(r)} \cdot \hat{\mathbf{n}} \, dS = \left(\frac{1}{4\pi\epsilon_0}\right) 4\pi q. \qquad (3.9)$$

Equation 3.9 is the integral form of Gauss's law for a point charge q. This law may be generalized to the case of N point charges lying within a volume enclosed by the surface S, since the total field produced by the charges is the vector sum of the individual fields:

$$\oiint \mathbf{E(r)} \cdot \hat{\mathbf{n}} \, dS = \left(\frac{1}{4\pi\epsilon_0}\right) 4\pi \sum_{i=1}^{N} q_i. \qquad (3.10)$$

In the development of eq. 3.10, the only case considered was one in which all the charges were enclosed by the surface S. It will now be demonstrated that any charges lying outside of S give no contribution

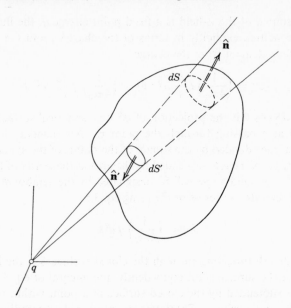

Fig. 3.2   A point charge q is located at the origin of coordinates which is, in turn, located outside a closed surface S.   A cone having infinitesimal opening angle with apex at q intersects the closed surface twice.   The surfaces of S contained within the cone are dS and dS' with outward normals $\hat{n}$ and $\hat{n}'$, respectively.   The infinitesimal solid angles subtended by dS and dS' at q are equal in magnitude but opposite in sign.

to the flux threading through S.   In Fig. 3.2 a point charge q is fixed outside a closed surface S.   A conical surface with an infinitesimal opening angle is constructed with its apex at the charge.   This conical surface encloses two elements of area of the surface S, namely, **ds** and **ds'**; the magnitudes of the elements of solid angle subtended by **ds** and **ds'** at q are equal.   This may be seen from the definition of the solid angle subtended by a surface element discussed above.   However, the outward normal to **ds** points away from q, whereas the outward normal of **ds'** points toward q.   Consequently the *sign* of the element of solid angle subtended at q by **ds** is positive, whereas the sign of the element of solid angle subtended at q by **ds'** is negative.   The total solid angle subtended at q by **ds** and **ds'** is zero.   Since all elements of S can be treated pairwise in the above fashion, it is evident that the solid angle subtended at q by the entire surface S is identically zero.   This constitutes the proof of the above contention that the charges lying outside a closed surface contribute nothing to the flux threading through the surface.

Gauss's law may be restated in terms of a partial differential equation.

The restatement of the law is carried out by means of the "divergence theorem" of the vector calculus. Suppose a vector point function $\mathbf{C}$ and its first derivatives are defined everywhere within a volume τ, and the function $\mathbf{C}$ is also defined everywhere on the surface S enclosing τ. The divergence theorem relates the derivatives of $\mathbf{C}$ in the region τ to the value of $\mathbf{C}$ on the surface S:[2]

$$\oiint \mathbf{C}(\mathbf{r}) \cdot \hat{\mathbf{n}} \, dS \equiv \int_\tau \operatorname{div} \mathbf{C} \, d\tau. \tag{3.11}$$

Consequently the flux of the E-field through a closed surface S is equal to the integral of the divergence of the E-field over the volume τ enclosed by S.

$$\oiint \mathbf{E} \cdot \hat{\mathbf{n}} \, dS = \Phi = \int_\tau \operatorname{div} \mathbf{E} \, d\tau. \tag{3.12}$$

It is now assumed (see discussion at the close of Chapter 2) that the charge residing within τ can be represented by a volume charge density ρ, i.e.,

$$\sum_{i=1}^{N} q_i \to \int_\tau \rho \, d\tau.$$

Comparison of eqs. 3.10 and 3.12 leads to the result that

$$\int_\tau \operatorname{div} \mathbf{E} \, d\tau = \frac{1}{\epsilon_0} \int_\tau \rho \, d\tau;$$

or equivalently

$$\operatorname{div} \mathbf{E}(\mathbf{r}) = \left(\frac{1}{4\pi\epsilon_0}\right) 4\pi \rho(\mathbf{r}). \tag{3.13}$$

Equation 3.13 is Gauss's law in differential form. Although little use will be made of this form of the law in the discussion of electrostatics, eq. 3.13 will play a fundamental role in the development of the Maxwell theory of electromagnetism.

[2] The symbol "div" is to be read "divergence." It is sometimes written $\nabla \cdot$ and is symbolic for the following operation:

$$\operatorname{div} \mathbf{C} = \left(\hat{\mathbf{x}} \frac{\partial}{\partial x} + \hat{\mathbf{y}} \frac{\partial}{\partial y} + \hat{\mathbf{z}} \frac{\partial}{\partial z}\right) \cdot \mathbf{C} = \left(\frac{\partial}{\partial x} C_x + \frac{\partial}{\partial y} C_y + \frac{\partial}{\partial z} C_z\right).$$

In spherical polar coordinates

$$\operatorname{div} \mathbf{C} = \frac{1}{r \sin \theta} \frac{\partial}{\partial \theta} (\sin \theta C_\theta) + \frac{1}{r \sin \theta} \frac{\partial C_\phi}{\partial \phi} + \frac{1}{r^2} \frac{\partial}{\partial r} (r^2 C_r);$$

in cylindrical coordinates

$$\operatorname{div} \mathbf{C} = \frac{1}{\rho} \frac{\partial}{\partial \rho} (\rho C_\rho) + \frac{1}{\rho} \frac{\partial}{\partial \phi} (C_\phi) + \frac{\partial C_z}{\partial z}.$$

For further discussion of this derivative operator, see Chapter 1.

3.2   Application of Gauss's Law to Distributed Charges

Gauss's law may be used to simplify the calculation of the E-field produced by a charge distribution when this distribution possesses a certain amount of geometrical symmetry. In addition, Gauss's law in integral form may be used to ascertain certain properties of the E-field produced by an arbitrary charge distribution even though the actual calculation of the field may be somewhat difficult because of the complicated nature of the source. The former use of Gauss's law will be illustrated first.

Consider a charge which has spherical symmetry distributed throughout a volume; i.e., $\rho(\mathbf{r}) = \rho(r)$. The magnitude of the E-field on the surface of a sphere centered at $r = 0$ is independent of position on the spherical surface because of the spherical symmetry of the charge distribution. For the same reason, the direction of the E-field on the surface is always normal to the spherical surface. Consequently the electrostatic flux through such a surface of radius r is

$$\Phi = 4\pi r^2 E(r).$$

Via Gauss's law, this flux is proportional to the charge $q(r)$ residing inside the spherical surface. Therefore

$$\mathbf{E}(\mathbf{r}) = \left(\frac{1}{4\pi\epsilon_0}\right)\frac{q(r)}{r^2}\,\hat{\mathbf{r}},$$

$$\text{(3.14)}$$

where
$$q(r) = 4\pi \int_0^r \rho(r')r'^2\,dr'.$$

Examination of eq. (3.14) shows that the E-field at a distance $\mathbf{r}$ from the center of a spherically symmetric charge distribution is the same as that produced by a point charge located at $\mathbf{r} = 0$, the magnitude of the charge being the total charge residing within a spherical surface of radius r centered at $\mathbf{r} = 0$. A corollary to the above statement may be stated as follows: the E-field at a point lying outside a spherically symmetric charge distribution is the same as that produced by a point charge located at the center of the distribution whose magnitude is the total charge of the distribution. Several illustrative examples appear below.

EXAMPLE 3.1   Calculate the E-field and φ function produced by a charge q distributed uniformly throughout a sphere of radius R.

The volume charge density of this distributed charge is $\rho = 3q/4\pi R^3$. The E-field at a point outside the charge distribution is

$$\mathbf{E}(\mathbf{r}) = \left(\frac{1}{4\pi\epsilon_0}\right)\frac{q}{r^2}\,\hat{\mathbf{r}}, \quad r \geqslant R.$$

The charge $q(r)$ residing within a sphere of radius $r(r \leqslant R)$ is $q(r) = q \cdot (r/R)^3$. Consequently the E-field at a point inside the charge distribution is

$$\mathbf{E(r)} = \left(\frac{1}{4\pi\epsilon_0}\right) \frac{q}{r^2} \left(\frac{r}{R}\right)^3 \hat{\mathbf{r}}, \quad r \leqslant R.$$

The φ function may be obtained by noting the general relationship between $\mathbf{E}$ and φ, namely, $\varphi(\mathbf{r}) = - \int \mathbf{E} \cdot \mathbf{dl}$, where the integral is to be evaluated along an arbitrary path extending from infinity to the field point $\mathbf{r}$. Since the charge distribution is spherically symmetric, it is convenient to choose the path of integration to be a straight line from infinity to $\mathbf{r}$, the path being antiparallel to the unit vector $\hat{\mathbf{r}}$. The integration is straightforward, yielding

$$\varphi(\mathbf{r}) = \frac{1}{4\pi\epsilon_0} \frac{q}{r}, \quad r \geqslant R;$$

$$\varphi(\mathbf{r}) = \frac{1}{4\pi\epsilon_0} \frac{q}{R} \left\{\frac{3}{2} - \frac{1}{2}\left(\frac{r}{R}\right)^2\right\}, \quad r \leqslant R.$$

EXAMPLE 3.2   Calculate the *potential energy* of a charge q distributed uniformly throughout a sphere of radius R.

The potential energy is conventionally defined as the work necessary to assemble the sphere from a charged cloud of infinite extent and negligible charge density. To calculate the work, it is presupposed that there already exists in space a sphere of radius $r(r < R)$ and charge density ρ. The work dW necessary to add a spherical sheet of thickness dr and density ρ to this sphere is

$$dW = - \frac{1}{4\pi\epsilon_0} \int_\infty^r \left(\frac{4\pi}{3} r^3 \rho\right)(4\pi r^2 \, dr\rho)\frac{dl}{l^2} = + \frac{3}{4\pi\epsilon_0} \left(\frac{4\pi\rho}{3}\right)^2 r^4 \, dr, \quad (3.15)$$

where $4\pi r^2 \, dr\rho$ = charge of the spherical shell. Since the electrostatic force is conservative, this work is independent of path; the spherical shell has been brought in as a point charge along a radius vector $-\hat{\mathbf{r}}$ (eq. 3.15 is the work necessary to do this), and the charge is then distributed uniformly over the surface of the sphere (the latter step takes no work, since charge is being moved perpendicular to the field produced by the sphere). To calculate the work (ΔW) necessary to increase the radius of the sphere to R by successively bringing in spherical shells of density ρ, eq. 3.15 is integrated from r to R; that is,

$$\Delta W = \int_r^R dW = \frac{1}{4\pi\epsilon_0} \frac{3}{5} \left(\frac{4\pi\rho}{3}\right)^2 (R^5 - r^5).$$

Finally, to calculate the work W to assemble the entire sphere, it is necessary to let $r \to 0$ in the expression for ΔW; that is,

$$W = \lim_{r \to 0} \Delta W = \frac{1}{4\pi\epsilon_0} \frac{3}{5} \frac{q}{R}.$$

It is also possible to use Gauss's law effectively for cylindrical symmetry. Consider a charge distributed throughout an infinitely long cylinder in such a way that $\rho(\mathbf{r})$ depends only on the distance from the axis of the cylinder. The electric field on a cylindrical surface of radius r coaxial with the cylinder is independent of position on the cylindrical surface. Application of Gauss's law to this cylindrical surface yields

$$E(r) = \frac{1}{\epsilon_0 r} \int_0^r \rho(r')r' \, dr'.$$

If $\rho(r) = 0$ for $r \geqslant R$, then

$$E(r) = \frac{1}{2\pi\epsilon_0} \frac{\tilde{q}}{r}, \quad r \geqslant R; \quad \text{where} \quad \tilde{\rho} \equiv 2\pi \int_0^R \rho(r)r \, dr, \quad (3.16)$$

the charge per unit length of the cylinder. It should be noted that outside this charge distribution, $E(r)$ is proportional to $1/r$. The electrostatic potential is calculated via its definition in terms of E and is given by

$$\varphi(r) = -\frac{1}{2\pi\epsilon_0} \tilde{q} \log r + \text{constant}. \quad (3.17)$$

The constant term in eq. 3.17 cannot be determined by arbitrarily setting $\lim_{r \to \infty} \varphi(r) = 0$, since then the constant would take on an infinite value; this procedure would evidently be unsatisfactory as it would produce a potential function which is infinite at every point a finite distance from the cylinder. The potential difference, $\Delta\varphi(\mathbf{r})$, between a point outside the cylinder and the surface of the cylinder is, however, finite.

$$\Delta\varphi(r) = \frac{1}{2\pi\epsilon_0} \tilde{q} \log \left(\frac{R}{r}\right). \quad (3.17a)$$

If one examines the operational manner in which the potential function was introduced in Chapter 2, it will be noticed that implicit in the arbitrary assignment, $\lim_{r \to \infty} \varphi(r) = 0$, is the condition that all charge be confined to a finite volume. The case of an infinitely long cylinder violates this implicit condition. The definition of the potential difference is not restricted to charge distributions of finite extent, since the potential difference between two points is defined operationally for any and all charge distributions. The potential function for this problem must therefore remain undefined.

The problem is, of course, an artificial one since all charged cylinders in reality are finite in length. The potential difference of eq. 3.17a is a very good approximation in the actual physical problem of a long but finite cylinder whose length is much greater than the radius of its cross section.

3.3 Electrostatics Involving Conductors

All matter is constructed from microscopic entities which possess electric charge; there are, however, only certain materials for which a significant number of these microscopic entities are free to move macroscopic distances within the material under the application of electrostatic fields. Since the phrase *electric current* is conventionally assigned to macroscopic flow of charged particles, these free microscopic charges in a material may be termed *current carriers*. For solids the current carriers are electrons; the positive ions are only free to oscillate about fixed equilibrium positions. For ionized gases and, for example, solutions of inorganic salts and water, both positive and negative ions as well as electrons can carry on translational motion of a macroscopic scale. Whether or not a given material will possess a significant density of current carriers under specified physical conditions of temperature, pressure, etc. is a question considered in the general area of the structure of matter. For the present discussion such materials exist under suitable physical conditions, and will be called *conductors*.

Under the conditions of electrostatics, for example no macroscopic motion of charge, it is evident that the **E**-field inside a conductor is everywhere zero. It should be emphasized that the **E**-field referred to here is the macroscopic field. If the **E**-field did not vanish, the current carriers would experience a net force and macroscopic motion of charge within the conductor would ensue. By virtue of the vanishing of the **E**-field, the interior of a conductor is at a constant potential. The above remarks are summarized in eq. 3.18:

$$\left.\begin{array}{l} \mathbf{E}(\mathbf{r}) = 0 \\ \varphi(\mathbf{r}) = \text{constant} \end{array}\right\} \text{ inside a conductor.} \tag{3.18}$$

Furthermore if a conductor possesses an electric charge, the charge must reside solely on the surface of the conductor. This may be deduced from a direct application of the differential form of Gauss's law. Since $\mathbf{E} = 0$ everywhere within a conductor, div $\mathbf{E} = 0$ there also; from eq. 3.13 it follows that $\rho(\mathbf{r}) = 0$.

If a conductor contains a cavity (i.e., an interior region completely surrounded by conducting media), the total charge residing on the surface

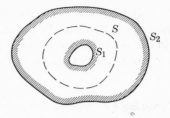

Fig. 3.3   A cavity exists within a conductor. The conductor has outer surface S_2 and inner surface S_1. An arbitrary closed surface S is constructed solely within the conductor. The total charge on S_1 is zero. There may be charge on the surface S_2.

of the conductor contiguous to the cavity is zero independent of the location of charges on the exterior surface of the conductor. Consider a closed surface drawn entirely within the conductor, as illustrated in Fig. 3.3. Since **E** is zero everywhere on this surface, it follows that the total charge residing on the interior surface of the conductor and within the cavity is zero. If the cavity itself contains no fixed charged particles, then the total charge residing on the interior surface of the conductor vanishes. It does not immediately follow by the above argument that $\sigma_{\text{interior}} = 0$; this point will be discussed subsequently.

Although the **E**-field in the immediate neighborhood of a conducting medium may be a complicated function of position, certain features of the field may be garnered from an application of Gauss's law. Consider a field point immediately exterior to a conducting surface, as illustrated in Fig. 3.4. A right circular cylinder containing the field point in its interior is constructed with base areas parallel to the conducting surface. (The base areas ΔS are small enough so that the area of the conductor contained within the cylinder is well approximated by an element of a plane.)

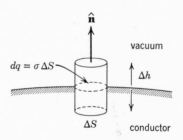

Fig. 3.4   A right circular cylinder of height Δh and base area ΔS is constructed with a field point adjacent to a conductor within its interior. The electrostatic flux Φ through the cylinder walls yields the result that $(\mathbf{E}_{\text{vac}} \cdot \hat{\mathbf{n}}) = 1/(4\pi\epsilon_0)\, 4\pi\sigma$.

The total flux through the surface of this cylinder, termed a "Gaussian pillbox", is given by

$$\Phi = (\mathbf{E}_{vac} \cdot \hat{n} - \mathbf{E}_{cond} \cdot \hat{n}) \Delta S \quad + \text{contribution from the cylinder walls.}$$

If the height of the cylinder is allowed to approach zero, keeping the field point always within the cylinder, the contribution to the flux from the cylinder walls will vanish since the area of the walls approaches zero. In addition, $\mathbf{E}_{cond} = 0$. Consequently

$$\lim_{\Delta h \to 0} \Phi = \mathbf{E}_{vac} \cdot \hat{n} \Delta S.$$

The total charge contained within the pillbox is

$$\Delta q = \sigma \Delta S.$$

Application of Gauss's law to the pillbox yields

$$\mathbf{E}_{vac} \cdot \hat{n} = \left(\frac{1}{4\pi\epsilon_0}\right) 4\pi\sigma. \tag{3.19}$$

Equation 3.19 yields information only about the normal component of $\mathbf{E}$ immediately exterior to a conducting surface. The component of $\mathbf{E}$ parallel to the tangent plane of the conductor at the field point may be evaluated as follows. A test charge q is moved in a rectangular path, as illustrated in Fig. 3.5. The work done in moving the test charge around the closed path is zero. This may be seen in several alternative and equivalent ways based upon the conservative nature of the Coulomb force field. If the altitude of the rectangle in Fig. 3.5 is allowed to approach zero, then the vanishing of the work done on the test charge on one complete transit of the rectangular circuit yields

$$\int_{\text{side 1}} \mathbf{E} \cdot d\mathbf{l} + \int_{\text{side 2}} \mathbf{E} \cdot d\mathbf{l} = 0. \tag{3.20}$$

vacuum

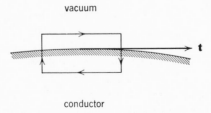

conductor

Fig. 3.5 A charge q is moved in a rectangular path, with part of the path in vacuum and part in conductor. The work done in traversing the path is zero. $\mathbf{t}$ is a vector parallel to the long side of the rectangle and tangent to the interface at the field point.

Since side 2 of the circuit is within a conductor, the work done along side 2 alone vanishes since $\mathbf{E}$ vanishes everywhere on side 2. If the length of side 1 is made small enough, then $\mathbf{E}$ will be everywhere constant on side 1 and side 1 will also be tangent to the conductor. Consequently

$$\mathbf{E}_{vac} \cdot \mathbf{t} = 0 \tag{3.21}$$

where $\mathbf{t}$ is any vector tangent to the conducting surface at the field point.

Equations 3.19 and 3.21 yield the result that the E-field immediately outside a conducting surface is normal to the surface; that is,

$$\mathbf{E} = \left(\frac{1}{4\pi\epsilon_0}\right) 4\pi\sigma\hat{\mathbf{n}}. \tag{3.22}$$

In terms of the electrostatic potential at the conducting surface

$$\frac{\partial\varphi}{\partial n} = -\left(\frac{1}{4\pi\epsilon_0}\right) 4\pi\sigma \tag{3.23}$$

where $\partial/\partial n$ means the derivative of φ evaluated with respect to a coordinate axis perpendicular to the conducting surface.

It is now possible to consider what happens when charges are placed in the neighborhood of a conductor. Consider two separate physical situations: (1) the conductor is isolated, that is, there is no physical connection with any other object which can transfer charge to or from it; (2) the conductor is maintained at a constant potential, φ_0.

An isolated conductor residing in vacuum with no charge residing on it or in its neighborhood will be at some potential which can be arbitrarily chosen to be zero. As a charge q is slowly brought from infinity and placed at a finite distance from the conductor an electrostatic field $\mathbf{E}$ will be produced at the surface of the conductor by the charge q. According to eq. 3.22 a surface charge density σ will be induced on the surface of the conductor. However, since the conductor is isolated, the total charge induced on the conductor vanishes; that is,

$$\oiint_{\Sigma} \sigma \, ds = q_{induced} = 0,$$

where Σ is the surface of the conductor. If the charge q is positive, it will attract some of the conduction electrons in the conductor, producing a net excess of electrons on that part of the conducting surface which is close to the charge q and thereby leaving a deficiency of electrons on that part of Σ furthest from q. After equilibrium is reached, there will be a static induced surface charge density on Σ. The electrostatic potential of the conductor will change as the charge q is brought into place, however; the charge q and the induced surface charge density produce a potential in the conductor which is different from zero.

A surface charge density will also be induced on the conducting surface when the conductor is kept at a fixed potential as a charge q is placed in its neighborhood. However, unlike the case of an isolated conductor, the net induced charge on the conductor kept at a fixed potential will be non-zero.

In illustration of the above remarks, it is instructive to consider several physical situations with spherical symmetry to avoid mathematical complications.

EXAMPLE 3.3   Consider first an isolated spherical conducting shell of inner radius a and outer radius b containing a charge q at its center (see Fig. 3.6). The charge density σ_a induced on the inner spherical surface of radius a may be calculated by a direct application of Gauss's law and eq. 3.22. According to Gauss's law, the E-field at the inner surface is due solely to the charge q. The magnitude of $\mathbf{E}$ at the inner surface is therefore

$$E_a = \left(\frac{1}{4\pi\epsilon_0}\right)\frac{q}{a^2}$$

and the surface charge density induced via eq. 3.22 is

$$\sigma_a = -\frac{1}{4\pi}\frac{q}{a^2}.$$

The minus sign appears because $\hat{n}$ in eq. 3.22 is the unit normal pointing outward from Σ_a; $\hat{n}$ is therefore antiparallel to $\mathbf{E}$ at Σ_a. The total charge induced on this spherical surface is

$$q_a = \oiint_{\Sigma_a} \sigma_a \, ds = -\frac{1}{4\pi}\frac{q}{a^2}\oiint_{\Sigma_a} ds = -\frac{1}{4\pi}\frac{q}{a^2}(4\pi a^2),$$

$$q_a = -q.$$

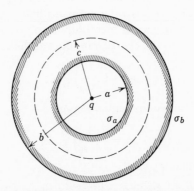

Fig. 3.6   A point charge q is located at the center of a spherical conducting shell of inner radius a and outer radius b. A spherical surface of radius c resides within the conducting shell ($b > c > a$). A surface charge density is induced on each surface of the shell as indicated.

This result can be obtained in another way.   Imagine a spherical surface of radius $c(b > c > a)$ drawn as in Fig. 3.6.   On this spherical surface **E** vanishes identically since it resides totally within the conducting region. Since **E** vanishes on this surface, so does the electrostatic flux.   From Gauss's law, therefore, the total charge residing within this surface must vanish.   The only charges within this surface are the charge q and the charge q_a induced on Σ_a.   Consequently $q_a = -q$.   Since the conducting shell is isolated, the total charge induced on the outer spherical surface of radius b must be equal but opposite in sign to q_a.   Therefore,

$$q_b = -q_a = -(-q) = q.$$

Because of the spherical symmetry inherent in the problem, σ_b may be calculated by dividing q_b by the area of a spherical surface of radius b:

$$\sigma_b = \frac{1}{4\pi b^2}\, q.$$

The electrostatic potential φ of the conductor may be calculated as follows. φ is produced by three charges $(q, q_a,$ and $q_b)$.   The potential at an arbitrary point within and on the conductor can be represented as

$$\varphi = \varphi_q + \varphi_a + \varphi_b$$

in an obvious notation.   The electrostatic potential φ evaluated at a point immediately outside the conductor is identical with φ of the conductor. φ immediately outside the conductor may also be thought of as being produced by three charges $(q, q_a,$ and $q_b)$.   Since q_a and q_b are spherically symmetric charge distributions, for the calculation of φ at a point immediately outside the shell they may be considered as point charges located at the center.   Since $q_a = -q_b$, the net contribution of q_a and q_b to the potential at the outer surface is identically zero. φ at the outer surface is therefore due solely to the charge q residing at the center and is

$$\varphi = \left(\frac{1}{4\pi\epsilon_0}\right)\frac{q}{b}.$$

Since a conductor is an equipotential region,

$$\varphi = \left(\frac{1}{4\pi\epsilon_0}\right)\frac{q}{b}$$

throughout the conducting shell.

EXAMPLE 3.4   If the conducting shell of Example 3.3 is not isolated but maintained at a potential φ_0, the analysis is altered somewhat.   The charge residing on the inner surface is still $q_a = -q$, the argument leading to q_a being independent of whether the conductor is isolated or not.

However, the charge residing on the outer surface must be calculated by requiring that the outer surface be an equipotential with $\varphi = \varphi_0$. On Σ_b, $\varphi(= \varphi_0)$ can be thought of as due to the three charges q, $q_a = -q$, and q_b. Employing Gauss's law and the arguments of spherical symmetry,

$$\varphi_0 = \left(\frac{1}{4\pi\epsilon_0}\right)\left\{\frac{q}{b} + \frac{q_a}{b} + \frac{q_b}{b}\right\} = \left(\frac{1}{4\pi\epsilon_0}\right)\frac{q_b}{b}.$$

Therefore

$$q_b = (4\pi\epsilon_0)b\varphi_0$$

and

$$\sigma_b = (4\pi\epsilon_0)\frac{\varphi_0}{4\pi b}.$$

If the conducting shell is grounded ($\varphi_0 = 0$), then the induced charge resides solely on the inner surface of the shell since $\sigma_b = 0$.

For more general cases of charges in the neighborhood of conductors, more powerful analytical methods must be employed. These methods will be developed in a later section of this chapter.

At this point it is interesting to consider the properties of $\mathbf{E}$ and φ in a region τ_0 completely enclosed by a conductor. If no charges reside in τ_0, it has already been remarked that the total charge residing on the surface Σ_0 bounding τ_0 vanishes independent of the position of charges exterior to the conductor. It is possible to say much more. Assume that no charges reside in τ_0 and consider a closed surface Σ all points of which are contained within τ_0 (see Fig. 3.7). According to Gauss's law, the flux of $\mathbf{E}$ through Σ vanishes. It does not immediately follow that $\mathbf{E}$ vanishes on Σ. However, the flux of $\mathbf{E}$ through Σ will vanish no

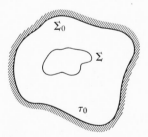

Fig. 3.7 τ_0 is a region completely enclosed by a conductor. Σ_0 is the surface of the conductor, and Σ is an arbitrary closed surface residing within τ_0. The flux of $\mathbf{E}$ through Σ vanishes; since Σ is arbitrary, $\mathbf{E}$ vanishes on Σ and τ_0 is an equipotential region.

matter what arbitrary changes in the shape of Σ are introduced as long as all points on Σ reside within τ_0. Since the flux of **E** vanishes on any and every surface Σ residing entirely within τ_0, it then follows that **E** itself must vanish in τ_0. Therefore τ_0 is a region of constant φ. Since φ is contiguous to the enveloping conductor (τ_0 is a cavity in the conductor), φ in τ_0 is the same as that of the conductor surrounding it. If the conductor is isolated, the value of φ depends upon the positions and magnitudes of the charges outside the conductor. However, a charge placed in the cavity experiences no force due to the charges residing outside the conductor, since **E** within the cavity due to the exterior charges vanishes. A cavity in an isolated conductor is said to be *dynamically screened* from the charges residing outside the conductor.

A similar situation obtains if the surrounding conductor is kept at a fixed electrostatic potential φ_0. A cavity in such a conductor is an equipotential region, the value of φ in the cavity being φ_0—the potential maintained on the conductor independent of the magnitudes and positions of charges residing outside the conductor. The cavity is also *screened* in this case from the influence of such charges.

The above electrostatic property of a cavity within a conductor, that is, the vanishing of **E** within the cavity, was derived from Gauss's law. The reader may wonder why a similar argument cannot be applied to the region τ_1 outside the conductor. It is possible to draw a closed surface Σ_1 all points of which lie within τ_1 for which the electrostatic flux Φ vanishes; it is only necessary that τ_1 does not contain charge within it (see Fig. 3.8). It is further possible to distort Σ_1 in a variety of ways and still insure the vanishing of the electrostatic flux through the distorted Σ_1. However, it does *not* follow that **E** vanishes on Σ_1 and therefore everywhere in τ_1 because it is not possible to distort Σ_1 *arbitrarily* and

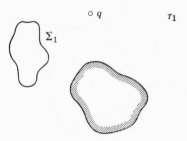

Fig. 3.8 τ_1 is the region outside a conductor. Σ_1 is a closed surface, all points of which reside in τ_1. Although the flux through Σ_1 vanishes if it does not enclose any charge, it is not possible to make arbitrary distortions in Σ_1 without enveloping charge.

maintain the vanishing of the flux through it. There are many distortions of Σ_1 which will cause charge to be enveloped within it and therefore for which Φ does not vanish. Since it is not possible to distort Σ_1 arbitrarily within τ_1 and maintain $\Phi = 0$, it follows that **E** is not zero at every point outside the conductor.

3.4   *Poisson's Equation and the Uniqueness Theorem*

Many special methods of solving certain electrostatic problems and several general theorems of electrostatics may be developed by investigating the properties of the partial differential equation satisfied by the electrostatic potential function.   Up to this point the partial differential equations considered have involved the E-fields, the so-called differential form of Gauss's law:

$$\text{div } \mathbf{E} = \left(\frac{1}{4\pi\epsilon_0}\right) 4\pi\rho \tag{3.13}$$

and the equation expressing the conservative nature of the E-field, namely, curl $\mathbf{E} = 0$.   Equation 3.13 is easily transformed into an equation involving the electrostatic potential function since $-\text{grad } \varphi = \mathbf{E}$.   With this substitution, Gauss's differential law becomes

$$\text{grad div } \varphi = -\left(\frac{1}{4\pi\epsilon_0}\right) 4\pi\rho. \tag{3.24}$$

The differential operator (div grad) may be evaluated in Cartesian coordinates, using the definitions of the individual operators div and grad. The result is

$$\left(\frac{\partial^2}{\partial x^2} + \frac{\partial^2}{\partial y^2} + \frac{\partial^2}{\partial z^2}\right)\varphi = -\left(\frac{1}{4\pi\epsilon_0}\right) 4\pi\rho. \tag{3.25}$$

This linear second-order derivative operator is given the symbol ∇^2 and is called the Laplacian operator.[3]   Equation 3.25 is sometimes called Poisson's equation; the homogeneous form of this equation (i.e., for $\rho = 0$ everywhere) is called Laplace's equation.

[3] The Laplacian operator in spherical polar coordinates is

$$\frac{1}{r^2}\frac{\partial}{\partial r}\left(r^2 \frac{\partial}{\partial r}\right) + \frac{1}{r^2 \sin \theta}\frac{\partial}{\partial \theta}\left(\sin \theta \frac{\partial}{\partial \theta}\right) + \frac{1}{r^2 \sin \theta}\frac{\partial^2}{\partial \phi^2};$$

in cylindrical coordinates

$$\frac{1}{\rho}\frac{\partial}{\partial \rho}\left(\rho \frac{\partial}{\partial \rho}\right) + \frac{1}{\rho^2}\frac{\partial^2}{\partial \phi^2} + \frac{\partial^2}{\partial z^2}.$$

The special methods and general theorems referred to previously are based on the uniqueness of the solutions to eq. 3.25. To investigate the mathematical properties of the solutions to eq. 3.25, recourse must be made to a set of very important identities of the vector calculus called Green's identities. The starting point for these identities is Gauss's theorem, namely,

$$\oiint \mathbf{C} \cdot \hat{\mathbf{n}} \, dS \equiv \int \text{div } \mathbf{C} \, d\tau.$$

Suppose the vector point function $\mathbf{C}$ can be written as the product of a scalar point function ψ and a vector point function $\mathbf{G}$, that is,

$$\mathbf{C}(\mathbf{r}) = \psi(\mathbf{r})\mathbf{G}(\mathbf{r}). \tag{3.26}$$

Straightforward calculation yields

$$\text{div } \mathbf{C} = \psi \text{ div } \mathbf{G} + \text{grad } \psi \cdot \mathbf{G}. \tag{3.27}$$

Consequently, noting eqs. 3.26 and 3.27, Gauss's theorem becomes

$$\oiint \psi \mathbf{G} \cdot \hat{\mathbf{n}} \, dS = \int \psi \text{ div } \mathbf{G} \, d\tau + \int \text{grad } \psi \cdot \mathbf{G} \, d\tau. \tag{3.28}$$

It is further supposed that the vector point function $\mathbf{G}$ represents a conservative field and consequently that $\mathbf{G}$ may be written as the gradient of a scalar point function ϕ; that is, $\mathbf{G} = \text{grad } \phi$. Noting that $\text{grad } \phi \cdot \hat{\mathbf{n}} = (\partial/\partial n)\phi$ and that $\text{div grad } \phi = \nabla^2\phi$, eq. 3.28 takes the form

$$\oiint \psi\left(\frac{\partial}{\partial n} \phi\right) dS = \int \psi \, \nabla^2\phi \, d\tau + \int \text{grad } \psi \cdot \text{grad } \phi \, d\tau. \tag{3.29}$$

If the symbols ψ and ϕ are interchanged and the resulting equation is subtracted from eq. 3.29, eq. 3.30 results:

$$\oiint \left\{\psi \frac{\partial}{\partial n} \phi - \phi \frac{\partial}{\partial n} \psi\right\} dS = \int \{\psi \, \nabla^2\phi - \phi \, \nabla^2\psi\} \, d\tau. \tag{3.30}$$

Equations 3.29 and 3.30 are the first and second identities of Green.

Equation 3.29 shall be used to examine the so-called *uniqueness* of the solutions to Laplace's equation. A special case of the uniqueness theorem shall be treated here to avoid complications that might obscure the important aspects of the theorem. It is possible to develop the theorem for the most general electrostatic problem. Assume that all charges present in space reside on the surfaces of conductors. Further there exists two scalar point functions $\varphi_1(\mathbf{r})$ and $\varphi_2(\mathbf{r})$ which satisfy Laplace's equation; in addition, $\varphi_1(\mathbf{r}) = \varphi_2(\mathbf{r})$ on the conducting surfaces. The uniqueness theorem states that $\varphi_1(\mathbf{r}) = \varphi_2(\mathbf{r})$ everywhere. To demonstrate this, define $\Phi(\mathbf{r}) \equiv \varphi_1(\mathbf{r}) - \varphi_2(\mathbf{r})$ and substitute $\Phi(\mathbf{r})$ for both ϕ and ψ in Green's theorem of eq. 3.29. Since $\varphi_1(\mathbf{r})$ and $\varphi_2(\mathbf{r})$ are solutions of Laplace's equation, $\Phi(\mathbf{r})$ is also a solution; and eq. 3.29 becomes

$$\oiint \Phi \frac{\partial}{\partial n} \Phi \, dS = \int (\text{grad } \Phi)^2 \, d\tau. \tag{3.31}$$

(Note that the ∇^2 operator is a "linear" operator: if L is any linear operator and f_1 and f_2 are two solutions of the equation $Lf = 0$, then $af_1 + bf_2 = f_3$ is also a solution of $Lf = 0$.)   The closed surface S on the left-hand side of eq. 3.31 shall be made up of the conducting surfaces upon which the charges reside and a large spherical surface of radius R surrounding the entire charge distribution.   Since $\varphi_1(\mathbf{r}) = \varphi_2(\mathbf{r})$ on the conducting surfaces, the contribution to the integral on the left-hand side of eq. 3.31 vanishes. In addition, if $R \to \infty$, Φ vanishes *at least* as fast as $1/R$ on this surface and $(\partial/\partial n)\Phi$ *at least* as fast as $1/R^2$.   Since dS increases as R^2 only, the integrand vanishes on this spherical surface as $R \to \infty$.   As a consequence

$$\int (\text{grad } \Phi)^2 \, d\tau = 0. \tag{3.32}$$

However, $(\text{grad } \Phi)^2 \geqslant 0$ everywhere, and therefore the only way eq. 3.32 can be satisfied is for

$$\text{grad } \Phi = 0 \text{ everywhere in } V. \tag{3.33}$$

Equation 3.33 tells us that $\Phi(\mathbf{r})$ is a constant.   Since the value of $\Phi(\mathbf{r})$ is known on conducting surfaces where $\Phi(\mathbf{r}) = 0$, $\Phi(\mathbf{r})$ must vanish everywhere; that is,

$$\varphi_1(\mathbf{r}) = \varphi_2(\mathbf{r}) \text{ everywhere in } V$$

and on the surfaces bounding V.   This is the substance of the uniqueness theorem.

If the value of the electrostatic potential is not known on *any* of the conducting surfaces but only information concerning the charge residing on these surfaces is given, then there are many possible electrostatic potential functions which are solutions to the physical problem.   These solutions differ from one another by at most an arbitrary constant.   If, on the other hand, the value of the potential function is known on *at least one* conducting surface, then there exists only one electrostatic potential function which is a solution to the physical problem.

3.5   The Method of Images

The uniqueness theorem forms the basis for a very powerful method of solving certain electrostatic problems involving fixed charges and conductors.   Consider the problem of finding the electrostatic field everywhere in space produced by a point charge q fixed at a distance a from a semi-infinite slab of conducting material at the potential $\varphi = 0$, i.e., grounded (see Fig. 3.9). Suppose one imagines a hemispherical surface of infinite radius which together with the face of the conducting slab forms a closed surface surrounding the charge q. The potential is everywhere zero on this closed surface. We now search for a distribution of fixed charges in vacuo which is composed of the charge q and other charges outside of this closed surface and which satisfies the condition that $\varphi = 0$ on the closed surface. According to the uniqueness theorem, the potential everywhere *within* the closed surface produced by this charge distribution will be the same as that produced by the charge q and the conducting slab (of course, the potential produced *outside* the closed surface by this distribution will *not* be identical to that produced by q and the conducting slab). Unfortunately, the uniqueness theorem says nothing about the existence of this distribution nor, if it exists, how to find the correct distribution. In this particular problem, however, it is quite easy to see that the required distribution is an electric dipole of dipole moment $2qa$ (see Fig. 3.9). The negatively charged member of the dipole is called the *image* of the charge q. The potential in the region to the right of the conducting slab is given by eq. 2.15. In the slab itself $\varphi = 0$, and the potential given by the charge q and its image is incorrect in this region.

The charge induced on the conducting slab by the charge q may be calculated in the following manner. At a point on the surface of the conductor at a distance r from the point formed by the intersection of the dipole axis and the slab, the electrostatic field is, by direct calculation using the methods of Section 2.1,

$$\mathbf{E} = -\frac{1}{4\pi\epsilon_0} \frac{2qa}{(r^2 + a^2)^{3/2}} \hat{\mathbf{n}} \tag{3.34}$$

where $\hat{\mathbf{n}}$ is a unit vector normal to the conducting slab pointing outward from the slab. The surface density of charge is determined from the value of the E-field, using eq. 3.27:

$$\sigma = -\frac{1}{4\pi} 2qa \frac{1}{(r^2 + a^2)^{3/2}}. \tag{3.35}$$

The total charge induced on the slab is simply the integral of σ over the conducting slab:

$$q_{\text{induced}} = 2\pi \int_0^\infty r\, dr\sigma = -qa \int_0^\infty \frac{r\, dr}{(r^2 + a^2)^{3/2}}$$

$$q_{\text{induced}} = -q.$$

The method of images can be applied to many cases consisting of fixed charges in the neighborhood of conductors. The most tractable of these

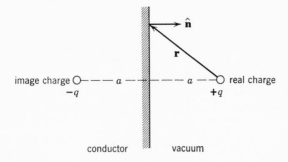

Fig. 3.9   A point charge q is located a distance from a semi-infinite conducting slab. The electrostatic flux Φ through the surface Σ defined by the face of the conducting slab and a hemispherical surface of infinite radius is zero.   The image of the charge and the charge itself form a dipole of moment $p = 2aq$.   The **E**-field in vacuum is given correctly by this dipole.   The **E**-field in the conducting slab is zero.

problems are, for example, a point charge in the vicinity of a conducting right angle slab, a point charge in the vicinity of a conducting sphere, and a line charge in the neighborhood of a conducting cylinder.   The magnitudes and positions of the appropriate image charges are illustrated in Fig. 3.10.   The method of solution to these image problems is left as an exercise for the reader.

The method of solution of Laplace's equation through the introduction of an equivalent set of image charges is convenient when it is possible to specify the image charges in an intuitively obvious manner.   There also exist other special methods which can be developed to handle certain classes of potential problems.[4]   However, it is possible to develop methods to solve the most general electrostatic problems; these general methods are particularly useful and simple if the physical situation under consideration has a certain amount of symmetry in some coordinate system.

A very simple example which does not illustrate the salient features of the method but which does illustrate the simplifying features introduced by geometrical symmetry is an inherently one-dimensional problem in which the potential difference between two parallel conducting planes is specified (see Fig. 3.11).   In the region between the plates, Laplace's equation is

$$\frac{d^2}{dx^2}\,\varphi(x) = 0$$

[4] See, for example, J. D. Jackson, *Classical Electrodynamics*, Chapter 2, John Wiley & Sons, 1962; Panofsky and Phillips, *Classical Electricity and Magnetism*, Chapters 3 and 4, Addison-Wesley, 1962.

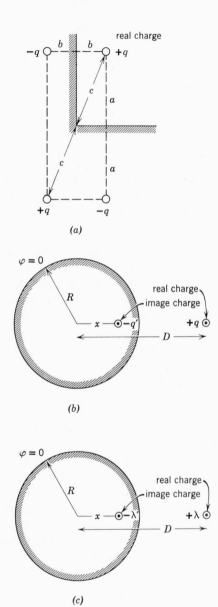

(a)

(b)

(c)

with the accompanying boundary condition: $\varphi(b) - \varphi(a) = \Delta\varphi$. The solution to the differential equation is

$$\varphi(x) = \alpha x + \beta$$

where the constant α is determined from the specified boundary condition

$$\alpha = \frac{\Delta\varphi}{b - a}.$$

The constant β may be determined if the potential on one of the conductors is specified.

3.6   Solution of Laplace's Equation in Two Dimensions

The general method of solving Laplace's equation in two dimensions is illustrative of a method which can be extended easily to three dimensions. It is convenient to work in plane-polar coordinates, although the method may be applied equally well in Cartesian coordinates. In plane polar coordinates, Laplace's equation assumes the form

$$\left[\frac{1}{\rho}\frac{\partial}{\partial\rho}\left(\rho\frac{\partial}{\partial\rho}\right) + \frac{1}{\rho^2}\frac{\partial^2}{\partial\theta^2}\right]\varphi(\rho, \theta) = 0. \tag{3.36}$$

There is a particular class of solutions to this equation in which $\varphi(\rho, \theta)$ is written as a product function of the form

$$\varphi(\rho, \theta) = R(\rho)\Theta(\theta). \tag{3.37}$$

Fig. 3.10(*a*)   A charge $+q$ is placed in the vicinity of a grounded (i.e., $\varphi = 0$) right angle conducting wedge. The image charges and the charge itself give the correct electrostatic potential function in the region not occupied by the conductor. (*b*) A charge $+q$ is placed in the vicinity of a grounded spherical conductor. The image of the charge $+q$ is q' where $q' = -(R/D)q$. As in the case of the optical analogue, the object distance (D) and the image distance (x) as measured from the center of the sphere obey the relationship $xD = R^2$. If the sphere is not grounded but is maintained at a potential φ_0, an additional image charge of magnitude $(4\pi\epsilon_0)R\varphi_0$ must be added at the center of the sphere; this will insure that the surface of the sphere is an equipotential surface with $\varphi = \varphi_0$. (*c*) A line charge with linear charge density λ is placed parallel to the axis of a conducting cylinder of radius R. If the cylinder is grounded, the image of the line charge is another line charge of linear charge density $-\lambda$. As in the case of the optical analogue, the object distance (D) and the image distance (x) as measured from the axis of the cylinder obey the relationship $xD = R^2$. If the cylinder is maintained at a potential φ_0, no additional image charge need be added because of the arbitrary constant in the expression for the potential function for a problem with cylindrical symmetry (see eqs. 3.17 and 3.17a).

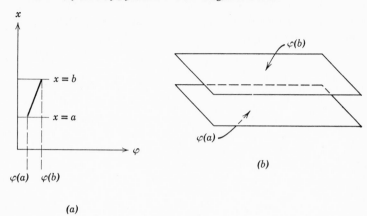

(a)

(b)

Fig. 3.11   Two conducting plates defined to be the planes $x = a$ and $x = b$ have a potential difference $\Delta\varphi$ between them.

General solutions to Laplace's equation in plane polar coordinates may be written as linear superpositions of the product solutions of eq. 3.37. When the product form of φ is substituted into eq. 3.36, Laplace's equation becomes after some manipulation

$$\frac{1}{R}\,\rho\,\frac{d}{d\rho}\left(\rho\,\frac{d}{d\rho}\,R\right) = -\frac{1}{\Theta}\,\frac{d^2\Theta}{d^2\theta}. \tag{3.38}$$

Since the left-hand side of eq. 3.38 is a function of ρ only and the right-hand side a function of θ, it follows that the functions must be constant functions since ρ and θ are independent variables.   This constant function shall be designated by α^2 which is called the *separation constant*:

$$\frac{d^2\Theta}{d\theta^2} + \alpha^2\Theta = 0 \tag{3.39a}$$

$$\rho\,\frac{d}{d\rho}\left(\rho\,\frac{d}{d\rho}\,R\right) - \alpha^2 R = 0. \tag{3.39b}$$

The solutions to eq. 3.39b are

$$\left.\begin{array}{c}\sin\alpha\theta\\\cos\alpha\theta\end{array}\right\} \qquad \alpha^2 > 0$$

$$\left.\begin{array}{c}\exp\left(-|\alpha|\theta\right)\\\exp\left(+|\alpha|\theta\right)\end{array}\right\} \qquad \alpha^2 < 0.$$

Since the potential function must be a single-valued function of θ (in particular, $\varphi(\rho, 0) = \varphi(\rho, 2\pi))$, it follows that the exponential solutions must be rejected, and therefore $\alpha^2 > 0$. Since the trigonometric solutions are periodic with periods $2n\pi$ (where n is an integer), the single-valuedness condition requires that $\alpha = n$. The value $n = 0$ must also be included since $\Theta = $ constant is a solution to eq. 3.39a. Returning to the solution of eq. 3.39b, it can be verified by direct substitution that two linearly independent forms of the function $R(\rho)$ are ρ^{-n} and ρ^{+n}. However, when $n = 0$, these two solutions are coincident, namely, a constant; the other linearly independent solution for $n = 0$ is $\ln \rho$. Table 3.1 lists the functional forms for R and Θ out of which the general form of φ may be constructed.

Table 3.1

n	$\Theta(\theta)$	$R(\rho)$
0	constant	constant $\ln \rho$
$\pm 1, \pm 2, \pm 3$	$\sin n\theta$ $\cos n\theta$	ρ^n

The general solution to Laplace's equation in plane polar coordinates is written as

$$\varphi(\rho, \theta) = \varphi_0 + \varphi_1 \ln \left(\frac{\rho}{a}\right) + \sum_{n=1}^{\infty} \left(\frac{\rho}{a}\right)^n (b_n \sin n\theta + c_n \cos n\theta)$$

$$+ \sum_{m=1}^{\infty} \left(\frac{a}{\rho}\right)^m (d_m \sin m\theta + f_m \cos m\theta) \quad (3.40)$$

where the constant coefficients b_n, c_n, d_m, f_m are to be determined by the physical boundary conditions. (The constant a having the dimensions of length has been arbitrarily inserted into eq. 3.40 in order that φ_0, φ_1, and the constant coefficients have the same dimensions as the electrostatic potential.)

EXAMPLE 3.5 Consider a long circular conducting cylindrical shell of radius R which is at a potential φ and carries a charge per unit length $\tilde{q}$. (This problem has already been solved by elementary methods previously in this chapter. However, it is instructive to apply the general methods developed above to this simple situation.) Since the conductor has rotational symmetry, it is evident that $\varphi(\rho, \theta)$ will be independent of θ.

Consequently the constant coefficients in the sums in eq. 3.40 must be identically zero; that is,

$$\varphi(\rho, \theta) = \varphi_0 + \varphi_1 \ln \left(\frac{\rho}{a}\right).$$

Furthermore at $\rho = R$, the potential must be that of the conductor, namely, φ. For a point outside the shell ($\rho > R$), eq. 3.27 may be employed to relate φ_1 to the charge per unit length $\tilde{q}$; that is,

$$\frac{\partial \varphi}{\partial \rho}\bigg)_{\rho = R} = -\left(\frac{1}{4\pi\epsilon_0}\right) 4\pi\sigma \quad \text{where} \quad \sigma \equiv \frac{\tilde{q}}{2\pi R}$$

Consequently

$$\varphi(\rho, \theta) = \varphi_0 + \frac{\tilde{q}}{2\pi\epsilon_0} \ln \left(\frac{R}{\rho}\right)$$

in agreement with eq. 3.17a.

EXAMPLE 3.6   Consider next the case of a long conducting cylindrical shell of radius a placed in an originally uniform E-field which is perpendicular to the axis of the cylinder (see Fig. 3.12). The potential has the

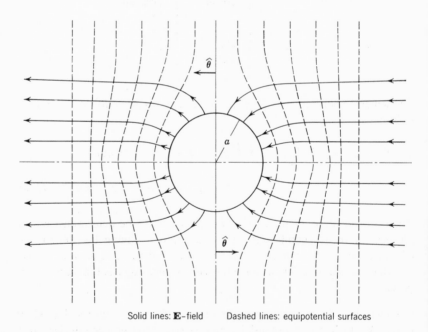

Solid lines: **E**-field   Dashed lines: equipotential surfaces

Fig. 3.12   A long conducting cylindrical shell of circular cross section is oriented in a region of originally uniform E-field ($\mathbf{E}_0$) such that $\mathbf{E}_0$ is perpendicular to the cylinder axis. A line parallel to $\mathbf{E}_0$ passing through the cylinder axis is the axis from which θ is measured. The field pattern is symmetric about this axis. The field lines and equipotential curves are indicated.

general form exhibited in eq. 3.40; the constant coefficients may be evaluated as follows. The physical problem has reflectional symmetry about the applied field direction; this implies that

$$E_\theta\left(\rho, \frac{\pi}{2}\right) = -E_\theta\left(\rho, -\frac{\pi}{2}\right)$$

since

$$\hat{\theta} \text{ at } \frac{\pi}{2} = -\hat{\theta} \text{ at } -\frac{\pi}{2}.$$

However,

$$E_\theta = \sum_{n=1}^{\infty} \frac{n}{\rho} \left(\frac{\rho}{a}\right)^n (b_n \cos n\theta - c_n \sin n\theta)$$

$$+ \sum_{m=1}^{\infty} \frac{m}{\rho} \left(\frac{a}{\rho}\right)^m (d_m \cos m\theta - f_m \sin m\theta). \quad (3.41)$$

Since $\cos n\theta$ is an even function of θ, this implies that b_n and d_n are identically zero for all n. Consequently

$$\varphi(\rho, \theta) = \varphi_0 + \varphi_1 \ln\left(\frac{\rho}{a}\right) + \sum_{n=1}^{\infty} \left(\frac{\rho}{a}\right)^n c_n \cos n\theta$$

$$+ \sum_{m=1}^{\infty} \left(\frac{a}{\rho}\right)^m f_m \cos m\theta.$$

The c- and f-coefficients are evaluated as follows: at a long distance from the cylinder, φ must yield a good approximation to the applied field; that is,

$$\lim_{\rho \to \infty} \varphi(\rho, \theta) = \text{constant} + \rho E_0 \cos \theta. \quad (3.42)$$

Consequently

$$c_n = \begin{cases} aE_0 & \text{for } n = 1 \\ 0 & \text{for } n > 1. \end{cases}$$

If the cylinder is at potential φ_0 and is uncharged, then $\varphi_1 \equiv 0$ and the constant in eq. 3.42 is simply φ_0. Finally, at the surface of the cylinder ($\rho = a$), the potential must be independent of θ; consequently

$$f_m = \begin{cases} -aE_0 & \text{for } m = 1 \\ 0 & \text{for } m > 1. \end{cases}$$

The solution to the problem is complete, namely;

$$\varphi(\rho, \theta) = \varphi_0 + aE_0 \cos \theta\left(1 - \frac{a}{\rho}\right). \quad (3.43)$$

The resultant **E**-field is displayed in Fig. 3.12 and has the value

$$E_\rho = -\frac{\partial\varphi}{\partial\rho} = \frac{a^2}{\rho^2} E_0 \cos \theta \quad (3.44)$$

$$E_\theta = -\frac{1}{\rho}\frac{\partial\varphi}{\partial\theta} = \left(\frac{a}{\rho}\right)\left(1 - \frac{a}{\rho}\right) E_0 \sin \theta.$$

3.7 Solution of Laplace's Equation in Three Dimensions

Very general methods can be developed to obtain the solutions to Laplace's equation in three dimensions.   The usefulness of a given method depends on the kind of boundary conditions that are given, that is, the behavior of φ on surfaces of a particular geometrical shape.[5]   In this section, a particular method will be developed which is suitable for problems in which spherical polar coordinates are appropriate.

Laplace's equation in spherical polar coordinates takes the form

$$\frac{1}{r^2}\frac{\partial}{\partial r}\left(r^2\frac{\partial}{\partial r}\varphi\right) + \frac{1}{r^2\sin\theta}\frac{\partial}{\partial\theta}\left(\sin\theta\frac{\partial\varphi}{\partial\theta}\right) + \frac{1}{r^2\sin^2\theta}\frac{\partial^2\varphi}{\partial\phi^2} = 0. \quad (3.45)$$

This can be handled in a manner analogous to that employed in plane polar coordinates, namely, a product solution is assumed of the form

$$\varphi(r,\,\theta,\,\phi) = \frac{R(r)}{r}\,\Theta(\theta)\Phi(\phi). \quad (3.46)$$

Substituting this form into eq. 3.45 yields the result

$$r^2\sin^2\theta\left[\frac{1}{R}\frac{d^2R}{dr^2} + \frac{1}{r^2\sin\theta\Theta}\frac{d}{d\theta}\left(\sin\theta\frac{d\Theta}{d\theta}\right)\right] + \frac{1}{\Phi}\frac{d^2\Phi}{d\phi^2} = 0, \quad (3.47)$$

after multiplication by the factor $r^2\sin^2\theta(R\Theta\Phi)^{-1}$.   Since the last term in eq. 3.47 depends only on ϕ and the other terms do not depend upon ϕ, it is obvious that the last term must be a constant which shall be called $-m^2$; that is,

$$\frac{1}{\Phi}\frac{d^2\Phi}{d\phi^2} = -m^2. \quad (3.48)$$

The solutions to eq. 3.48 are

$$\begin{array}{ll}\begin{array}{l}\sin m\phi\\\cos m\phi\end{array} \quad \text{or} \quad \left.\begin{array}{l}\exp(+im\phi)\\\exp(-im\phi)\end{array}\right\} & \text{for } m^2 > 0\\[2mm]\exp(+m\phi),\quad \exp(-m\phi) & \text{for } m^2 < 0.\end{array}$$

The solutions for $m^2 < 0$ are not acceptable since φ must be periodic in the azimuthal angle ϕ with period 2π.   This periodicity condition applied to the solutions for $m^2 > 0$ leads to the result that m must be an integer.   Using eq. 3.48 and dividing eq. 3.47 by $\sin^2\theta$ yields eq. 3.49:

$$\frac{1}{R}r^2\frac{d^2R}{dr^2} + \frac{1}{\Theta}\frac{1}{\sin\theta}\frac{d}{d\theta}\left(\sin\theta\frac{d\Theta}{d\theta}\right) - \frac{m^2}{\sin^2\theta} = 0. \quad (3.49)$$

Since the first term on the left-hand side of eq. 3.49 is a function of r only and the remaining terms of θ, it follows that the first term is a constant

[5] These methods are developed in great detail in Chapters 2 and 3 of *Classical Electrodynamics* by J. D. Jackson, John Wiley & Sons, 1962.

which shall be written as $l(l + 1)$. Consequently the equations satisfied by Θ and R separately are

$$\frac{1}{\sin \theta} \frac{d}{d\theta} \left(\sin \theta \frac{d\Theta}{d\theta} \right) + \left[l(l + 1) - \frac{m^2}{\sin^2 \theta} \right] \Theta = 0, \qquad (3.50)$$

$$\frac{d^2R}{dr^2} - \frac{l(l + 1)}{r^2} R = 0. \qquad (3.51)$$

The general solution to eq. 3.51 is

$$R(r) = ar^{l+1} + br^{-l} \qquad (3.52)$$

where the constants a and b are to be determined and where l is a constant which can be evaluated by investigating the solutions to eq. 3.50.

To handle the differential equation satisfied by Θ, namely, eq. 3.50, it is convenient to define a new variable x by the relation $\cos \theta = x$ and to set $\Theta(\cos \theta) = P(x)$. The resulting equation satisfied by P is

$$\frac{d}{dx} \left[(1 - x^2) \frac{dP}{dx} \right] + \left[l(l + 1) - \frac{m^2}{1 - x^2} \right] P = 0. \qquad (3.53)$$

The case of $m = 0$ will be examined first. Since $P(x)$ is one factor in the potential function, it is evident that $P(x)$ must be finite, single-valued, and continuous on the interval $-1 \leqslant x \leqslant 1$ (the range of θ is 0 to π radians). Investigation [6] of eq. 3.51 shows that the only solutions of this type that can be obtained are for values of l given by $l = 0, 1, 2, \ldots$ (i.e., a positive integer including zero). These acceptable solutions are polynomials in x and are called Legendre polynomials of order l. These polynomials are given the symbol $P_l(x)$ and are arbitrarily normalized to have the value $+1$ at $x = +1$. Listed below are the Legendre polynomials of low order:

$$P_0(x) = 1$$
$$P_1(x) = x$$
$$P_2(x) = 1/2(3x^2 - 1)$$
$$P_3(x) = 1/2(5x^3 - 3x)$$
$$\vdots$$

For three-dimensional potential problems with rotational or azimuthal symmetry, i.e., $\partial \varphi / \partial \phi = 0$, the solution to Laplace's equation can be written, noting eqs. 3.46 and 3.52,

$$\varphi(r, \theta) = \sum_{l=0}^{\infty} [a_l r^l + b_l r^{-(l+1)}] P_l(\cos \theta). \qquad (3.54)$$

---

[6] See, for example, J. D. Jackson, *Classical Electrodynamics*, John Wiley & Sons, 1962, pp. 56–57 with footnote.

As mentioned previously, the constants a_l, b_l are to be determined by the physical boundary conditions: eq. 3.54 may be interpreted as the expansion of a function of r, θ in terms of power series in r and r^{-1} and the Legendre polynomials.

EXAMPLE 3.7   Consider as the first application of eq. 3.54 an uncharged isolated conducting sphere of radius R placed in a uniform E-field (see Fig. 3.13).   This problem has rotational symmetry about a line parallel to the field direction passing through the center of the sphere.   Taking this line as the polar or z-axis, the potential at a large distance from the sphere is given in eq. 3.42, i.e.,

$$\lim_{r \to \infty} \varphi(r, \theta) = \text{constant} + rE_0 \cos \theta. \tag{3.42'}$$

Taking the limit of the right-hand side of eq. 3.54 for large r yields

$$\lim_{r \to \infty} \varphi(r, \theta) = \sum_{l=0}^{\infty} a_l r^l P_l(\cos \theta).$$

Consequently

$$\begin{cases} a_0 = \text{constant in eq. 3.42'} \\ a_1 = E_0 \\ a_l = 0 \text{ for } l > 1. \end{cases}$$

At $r = R$, the surface of the sphere, the potential must be independent of θ.   Consequently

$$b_l = 0 \text{ for } l > 1$$

and

$$RE_0 + b_1 \cdot 1/R^2 = 0$$
$$\text{or} \quad b_1 = -R_0^3 E_0.$$

In addition, if the sphere is at the potential φ_0, then

$$a_0 + (1/R)b_0 = \varphi_0.$$

This completes the determination of the constants and the potential is expressed as

$$\varphi(r, \theta) = \varphi_0 + RE_0 \left[\frac{r}{R} - \frac{R^2}{r^2} \right] \cos \theta, \quad r \geqslant R. \tag{3.55}$$

The E-field determined from eq. 3.55 is sketched (in Fig. 3.13):

$$E_r = -\frac{\partial}{\partial r} \varphi = -E_0 \left[1 + 2\frac{R^3}{r^3} \right] \cos \theta, \tag{3.56a}$$

$$E_\theta = -\frac{1}{r} \frac{\partial}{\partial \theta} \varphi = E_0 \left(1 - \frac{R^3}{r^3} \right) \sin \theta. \tag{3.56b}$$

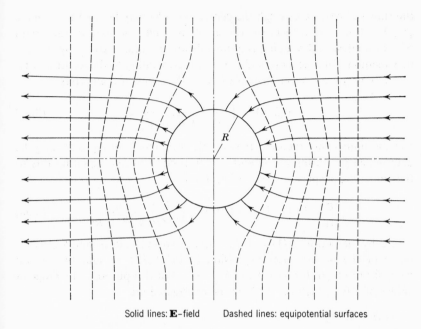

Solid lines: **E**-field   Dashed lines: equipotential surfaces

Fig. 3.13   A conducting sphere of radius R is placed in an originally uniform field $\mathbf{E}_0$. The field lines and the equipotential surfaces are as indicated.

The surface charge density induced on the sphere is determined from eqs. 3.56 by the relation

$$\frac{\partial}{\partial r}\,\varphi = -\left(\frac{1}{4\pi\epsilon_0}\right)4\pi\sigma \quad \text{at } r = R,$$

since the r-direction is normal to the sphere

or $$\sigma = (4\pi\epsilon_0)\frac{3}{4\pi}\,E_0\cos\theta.$$

The total induced charge is obtained by integrating this value of σ over the surface of the sphere yielding $q_{\text{induced}} = 0$.

EXAMPLE 3.8   As another example of the solution to Laplace's equation in three dimensions, it is instructive to indicate how eq. 3.54 may be employed along with the uniqueness property of the solution of Laplace's equation to handle a physical situation which, at first glance, is somewhat complicated. For this purpose, consider a uniformly charged circular ring of total charge q and radius R (see Fig. 3.14). Since the potential is rotationally symmetric about the line perpendicular to the plane of the ring and passing through the center, eq. 3.54 may be used to evaluate $\varphi(r, \theta)$. For convenience, the center of the ring is located at the origin of coordinates. Although it is quite difficult to evaluate $\varphi(r, \theta)$ by elementary methods for a general field point, it is elementary to demonstrate that φ at a point on the axis a distance h from the plane of the loop is

$$\varphi(h, 0) = \left(\frac{1}{4\pi\epsilon_0}\right) \frac{q}{\sqrt{h^2 + R^2}}. \tag{3.57}$$

Via the uniqueness theorem the constants a_l and b_l in eq. 3.54 may be determined by setting $r = h$ and $\theta = 0$ in eq. 3.54 and equating this to the value of φ displayed in eq. 3.57; that is,

$$\sum_{l=0}^{\infty} [a_l h^l + b_l h^{-(l+1)}]P_l(1) = \left(\frac{1}{4\pi\epsilon_0}\right) \frac{q}{\sqrt{h^2 + R^2}} \tag{3.58}$$

where by definition $P_l(1) = 1$ for all l. To evaluate a_l and b_l, use is made of the power series expansion of $(h^2 + R^2)^{-1/2}$ and the known behavior of $\varphi(h, 0)$ for $h \to 0$ and $h \to \infty$. For this purpose, the range of values of h for which eq. 3.58 will be considered are

(1) $h > R$
(2) $0 \leqslant h \leqslant R.$

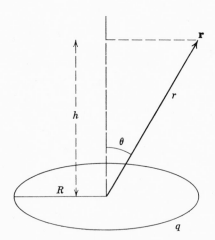

Fig. 3.14   A charge q is uniformly distributed around a circular ring of radius R. The axis of the ring is taken to be the polar axis of a spherical coordinate system. The potential may be evaluated on the axis by elementary methods, and the potential evaluated off the axis by employing the uniqueness theorem in conjunction with the expansion of φ in spherical harmonics.

For region 1, the expansion of eq. 3.59a is employed,

$$\frac{1}{\sqrt{h^2 + R^2}} = \frac{1}{h}\left(1 + \frac{R^2}{h^2}\right)^{-1/2}$$

$$= \frac{1}{h}\left\{1 + n\frac{R^2}{h^2} + \frac{n(n-1)}{2!}\frac{R^4}{h^4}\right.$$

$$\left. + \frac{n(n-1)(n-2)}{3!}\frac{R^6}{h^6} + \cdots\right\} \quad (3.59a)$$

with $n = -1/2$,

along with the boundary condition

$$\lim_{h \to \infty} \varphi(h, 0) = 0.$$

Consequently in region 1 $(r > R)$

$$\begin{cases} a_l \equiv 0 \quad \text{for all } l \\ b_l = \left(\frac{1}{4\pi\epsilon_0}\right)qR^l \dfrac{n(n-1)\cdots\left(n - \dfrac{l}{2} + 1\right)}{\dfrac{l}{2}!} \quad \text{if } l \text{ is even} \\ b_l = 0 \quad \text{if } l \text{ is odd.} \end{cases}$$

For region 2 the factor $(h^2 + R^2)^{-1/2}$ must be expanded in powers of $(h/R)(<1)$:

$$\frac{1}{\sqrt{h^2 + R^2}} = \frac{1}{R}\left(1 + \frac{h^2}{R^2}\right)^{-1/2}$$

$$= \frac{1}{R}\left\{1 + n\left(\frac{h}{R}\right)^2 + \frac{n(n-1)}{2!}\left(\frac{h}{R}\right)^4 + \cdots\right\} \quad (3.59b)$$

with $n = -1/2$, with application of the boundary condition

$$\lim_{h \to 0} \varphi(h, 0) = \text{finite number.}$$

Therefore in region 2 $(r < R)$

$$\begin{cases} b_l \equiv 0 \quad \text{for all } l \\ a_l = \left(\frac{1}{4\pi\epsilon_0}\right)qR^{-(l+1)} \dfrac{n(n-1)\cdots\left(n - \dfrac{l}{2} + 1\right)}{\dfrac{l}{2}!} \quad \text{if } l \text{ is even} \\ a_l = 0 \quad \text{if } l \text{ is odd.} \end{cases}$$

These values of a_l, b_l can be substituted into eq. 3.59 to obtain a complete expression for $\varphi(r, \theta)$ valid at all angles θ.

To handle those cases in which rotational symmetry about some direction is absent, the solutions to eq. 3.50 must be examined for the case

$m^2 \neq 0$. As has already been remarked, m must be an integer (positive or negative) in order that $\Phi(\phi)$ be periodic in the azimuth angle with period 2π. In addition, the condition that $P(x)$ be finite on the interval $-1 \leqslant x \leqslant 1$ requires that l be an integer and that the range of m is given by $-l \leqslant m \leqslant +l$. The solutions to eq. 3.50 which have the necessary properties are the so-called *associated Legendre functions* $P_l^m(x)$. These functions may be derived from the Legendre functions introduced in the case of rotational symmetry by the relationships

$$P_l^m(x) = (-1)^m (1 - x^2)^{m/2} \frac{d^m}{dx^m} P_l(x), \quad m > 0 \tag{3.60a}$$

$$P_l^m(x) = P_l(x), \quad m = 0 \tag{3.60b}$$

$$P_l^m(x) = (-1)^m \frac{(l + m)!}{(l - m)!} P_l^{-m}(x), \quad m < 0. \tag{3.60c}$$

It is convenient to express that part of the potential function which depends upon the angles (θ, ϕ) in terms of so-called *spherical harmonics* $Y_{lm}(\theta, \phi)$ which are constructed from the solutions to the azimuthal equation, eq. 3.51, $\exp(\pm im\phi)$ and the polar equation, eq. 3.50, $P_l^m(x)$. The spherical harmonics are defined to be

$$Y_{lm}(\theta, \phi) = \sqrt{\frac{2l + 1}{4\pi} \frac{(l - m)!}{(l + m)!}} P_l^m(\cos \theta) \exp(im\phi) \tag{3.61}$$

with the phase of the spherical harmonics defined to be

$$Y_{lm}^*(\theta, \phi) = (-1)^m Y_{l-m}(\theta, \phi) \tag{3.62}$$

where * represents the complex conjugation operation. The spherical harmonics form a complete orthonormal set of functions on the surface of the unit sphere; that is,

completeness

$$\sum_{l=0}^{\infty} \sum_{m=-l}^{+l} Y_{lm}^*(\theta', \phi') Y_{lm}(\theta, \phi) = \delta(\phi - \phi') \, \delta(\cos \theta - \cos \theta'); \tag{3.63a}$$

orthonormality

$$\int_0^{2\pi} d\phi \int_0^{\pi} \sin \theta \, d\theta \, Y_{l'm'}^*(\theta, \phi) Y_{lm}(\theta, \phi) = \delta_{ll'} \delta_{mm'}. \tag{3.63b}$$

It is beyond the intention of this text to discuss the spherical harmonics in any detail. It suffices to remark that *any* function of θ and ϕ which satisfies the continuity and periodicity conditions mentioned above can be expanded in a series involving the spherical harmonics.   In particular, the potential function may be written

$$\varphi(r, \theta, \phi) = \sum_{l=0}^{\infty} \sum_{m=-l}^{l} (A_{lm}r^l + B_{lm}r^{-(l+1)}) Y_{lm}(\theta, \phi). \qquad (3.64)$$

Equation 3.64 is the generalization of eq. 3.54 to encompass the case in which the potential function depends on the azimuth angle ϕ.

For a more complete discussion of method of solution of Laplace's equations and examples of the application of eq. 3.64, the reader is referred to more advanced texts.

PROBLEMS

3.1   The Thomson model of the hydrogen atom, which was in vogue before the Bohr model was introduced, consisted in an electron of charge $-e$ and mass m moving inside a charge $+e$ uniformly distributed throughout a sphere of radius R.   Show that the motion of the electron in this model would be simple harmonic and calculate the frequency of this motion.

3.2   Calculate the charge distribution which would produce a potential given by the expression $\varphi = (1/4\pi\epsilon_0)q \, \alpha \exp(-\alpha r)$.

3.3   Calculate the charge distribution which would produce a potential given by the expression $\varphi = (1/4\pi\epsilon_0)(q/r) \exp(-\alpha r)$.   Note that this potential has a singularity at $r = 0$ in contrast to the potential in Problem 3.2. What effect does this singularity have upon the charge distribution?

3.4   A charge q is uniformly distributed over the surface of a conducting spherical shell of radius R.   What is the electrostatic potential at the center of the shell?   How much work is necessary to add an additional charge q to the shell?   What change does this effect on the potential at the center of the shell?

3.5   A conducting sphere of radius r_1 is placed inside a conducting spherical shell of inner radius r_2 and outer radius r_3.   A charge q is placed on the sphere and the shell is grounded (i.e., $\varphi = 0$).   Calculate E in the regions: $r_1 < r < r_2$; $r > r_3$.

3.6   Two conducting discs are separated by a distance d and carry equal but opposite charges.   (This is a parallel plate capacitor.)   If the linear dimensions of the discs are very large compared with their separation, the E-field between the discs far from the edges will be uniform.   Invoking the conservative nature of the E-field, show that the field near the edge of the discs cannot be uniform and that the field lines at the edges bow outward, i.e., a "fringing" field.

3.7   A plane *nonconducting* surface carries a uniform surface charge density. Calculate the E-field in the immediate neighborhood of the surface. Contrast this with the case of a plane *conducting* surface carrying a uniform surface charge density, and qualitatively discuss the reason for the difference between the two cases.

3.8   An electric dipole of moment **p** is placed at the center of a conducting spherical shell of radius *R*. Calculate the charge distribution induced on the *interior* surface of the shell (assume $R \gg$ linear dimensions of the dipole). What is the charge distribution induced on the *outer* surface of the shell?

3.9   A system consists in an isolated conductor carrying a charge q_1 and a grounded conductor carrying a charge q_2. Show that the electrostatic potential is determined uniquely everywhere. Is it possible to specify the charges residing on a system of conductors and the potentials of these conductors independently? Explain.

3.10   Two parallel wires have equal but opposite uniform line densities of charge. If λ is the line charge density of the positive wire, calculate the electrostatic potential at a point a distance r_+ from the positive wire and r_- from the negative wire.

3.11   A hemispherical surface is drawn around a dipole **p** with the center of the surface at the center of the dipole. If the radius of the surface $\gg$ extent of the dipole, calculate the flux of the E-vector through the surface. Express the result in terms of the orientation angle between the bounding circle of the hemisphere and the dipole.

3.12   Verify the magnitude and position of the image charge indicated in Fig. 3.10 for a point charge in the neighborhood of a conducting sphere. What additional image charge is needed if the sphere is maintained at a potential $\varphi_0 \neq 0$?

3.13   A point charge q is placed midway between two plane grounded conducting slabs separated by a distance *d*. Discuss the location and magnitude of the image charges.

3.14   A long conducting cylindrical shell of radius *a* is placed in a uniform E-field which is perpendicular to the axis of the cylinder. Using the results of Problem 3.6, calculate the charge density induced on the surface of the shell.

3.15   (*a*) Calculate integrals of the type $\int_{-1}^{1} [P_l(x)]^2 \, dx$ for $l = 0, 1, 2,$ and 3.
       Attempt to generalize this result for arbitrary *l*.

       (*b*) Calculate integrals of the type $\int_{-1}^{1} P_l(x)P_{l'}(x) \, dx$ for $l, l' = 0, 1, 2, 3$.
       Attempt to generalize this result for arbitrary *l, l'*.

3.16   From the expressions for $P_l(x)$ and the definition of $P_l^m(x)$ given in the text, calculate explicit expressions for $P_l^m(x)$ for $l = 0, 1, 2, 3$ and all appropriate values of *m*.

3.17   Consider a conducting sphere of radius *a* composed of two hemispheres separated by a small insulating ring. The hemispheres are kept at potentials $\pm \varphi_0$.   Calculate the electrostatic potential both inside and outside the sphere using the method of Section 3.7.

3.18 Calculate the electrostatic potential produced by a charged circular disc of radius a carrying a charge Q uniformly distributed over its surface using the method of Section 3.7.

3.19 The electrostatic potential at the surface of a nonconducting sphere of radius a is given by $\varphi = \varphi_0 \cos \theta$.   Find the potential both inside and outside the sphere.

4 | *The Electrostatic Energy of a Charged System*

The discussion of electrostatic phenomena carried out in Chapters 2 and 3 was based upon Coulomb's force law. The concept of the electrostatic field has been developed in these chapters primarily to formulate the force problem in a manner more subject to a concise mathematical treatment. In this chapter the interaction energy of a system of charged particles will be introduced, and it will be shown that the energy of the system can be expressed solely in terms of the fields produced by the charges. The formulation of the energy of the charged system when generalized to explicitly time-dependent electric fields will form a useful basis for the discussion of the propagation of energy via electromagnetic waves.

4.1 Charge Distribution in an External Field

Before embarking on a discussion of the general problem mentioned above, the work necessary to position a charge distribution in the electrostatic field produced by a fixed ensemble of charges will be calculated. This work is written as

$$W = \sum_{j=1}^{N} q_j \varphi(\mathbf{r}_j) \qquad (4.1)$$

where $\varphi(\mathbf{r}_j)$ is the electrostatic potential produced by the charges exterior to the charge distribution being positioned, or, more succinctly, the external potential. (It should be noted that eq. 4.1 does not define the energy necessary to *assemble* the charge distribution, since the interaction among the charges in the distribution is not considered.) In arriving at W, it is assumed that the charge distribution is assembled at an infinite distance from the charged ensemble producing φ; the assembled distribution is then positioned a finite distance from the source of φ, keeping the charges in the distribution fixed with respect to each other. If the structure of the charge distribution and the external potential φ are sufficiently simple,

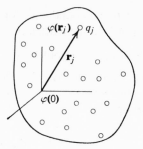

Fig. 4.1 A charge distribution is located in an external potential. The external potential at the *j*th charge, $\varphi(\mathbf{r}_j)$ may be conveniently expanded about its value at the origin if φ is slowly varying throughout the distribution. The interaction energy of the charge distribution with the external potential is given in terms of the (E0) and (E1) moments of the distribution in eq. 4.5. The next term in the expansion is given in eq. 4.10 for a rotationally symmetric charge distribution.

then W may be calculated in a straightforward manner from the defining equation. This simplicity is rarely achieved in practice, however, and a method alternative to the direct evaluation of W must be employed. Ordinarily an approximate expression for W is sufficient, and the method of approximating W that follows closely parallels the discussion of Sections 2.5 and 2.6 in which the multipole moments of a charge distribution were introduced.

Consider a set of coordinate axes constructed with its origin somewhere inside the charge distribution (see Fig. 4.1). The potential representing the applied field may be expanded in a Taylor's series about its value at the origin; the first few terms in the expansion are

$$\begin{aligned}
\varphi(\mathbf{r}_j) = \varphi_0 &+ (x_j\varphi_x^\circ + y_j\varphi_y^\circ + z_j\varphi_z^\circ) \\
&+ \tfrac{1}{2}\{x_j^2\varphi_{xx}^\circ + x_jy_j\varphi_{xy}^\circ + x_jz_j\varphi_{xz}^\circ \\
&+ y_jx_j\varphi_{yx}^\circ + y_j^2\varphi_{yy}^\circ + y_jz_j\varphi_{yz}^\circ \\
&+ z_jx_j\varphi_{zx}^\circ + z_jy_j\varphi_{zy}^\circ + z_j^2\varphi_{zz}^\circ\} + \cdots,
\end{aligned} \qquad (4.2)$$

where, for example,

$$\varphi_x^\circ \equiv \left\{\frac{\partial}{\partial x_j}\varphi(\mathbf{r}_j)\right\}_{\mathbf{r}_j = 0}$$

and

$$\varphi_{xy}^\circ \equiv \varphi_{yx}^\circ = \left[\frac{\partial^2}{\partial x_j\,\partial y_j}\varphi(\mathbf{r}_j)\right]_{\mathbf{r}_j = 0}$$

The derivatives of φ appearing in eq. 4.2 are all evaluated at the origin and are constants independent of the suffix *j* denoting a particular charge in the distribution. If the terms containing, for example, φ°_{xy}, etc., are momentarily neglected, eq. 4.2 can be written in more compact form as

$$\varphi(\mathbf{r}_j) = \varphi_0 + \mathbf{r}_j \cdot \text{grad } \varphi_0 + \cdots. \tag{4.3}$$

However, grad $\varphi_0 = -\mathbf{E}_0$, where $\mathbf{E}_0$ is the external electrostatic field evaluated at the origin, and with this observation eq. 4.3 can be substituted into eq. 4.1, yielding

$$W \approx \sum_{j=1}^{N} q_j\{\varphi_0 - \mathbf{r}_j \cdot \mathbf{E}_0 + \cdots\} = W_0 + W_1 + \cdots. \tag{4.4}$$

The energy of the charge distribution in an external field characterized by the values φ_0 and $\mathbf{E}_0$ at the origin is, in the above approximation,

$$W \approx \varphi_0 \sum_{j=1}^{N} q_j - \mathbf{E}_0 \cdot \sum_{j=1}^{N} q_j\mathbf{r}_j + \cdots. \tag{4.5}$$

Using the definitions of the (E0) and (E1) moments introduced in Section 2.5, the interaction energy can be written approximately:

$$W = W_0 + W_1 + \cdots, \quad \text{where } W_0 = q_{\text{total}}\varphi_0$$
$$\text{and} \quad W_1 = -\mathbf{p} \cdot \mathbf{E}_0. \tag{4.6}$$

It should be reiterated that W does not contain terms which represent the interaction of the constituent charges of the distribution with themselves.

In a later discussion the behavior of a dipole (i.e., a charge distribution, all of whose multipole moments vanish except the (E1) moment) in an applied field will be considered in some detail (see Chapter 5). The energy of such a dipole is simply

$$W_1 = -\mathbf{p} \cdot \mathbf{E}_0.$$

This energy depends on the relative orientation of $\mathbf{p}$ and $\mathbf{E}_0$ and is sometimes called an orientation energy. If α is the angle between $\mathbf{p}$ and $\mathbf{E}_0$, then

$$W_1(\alpha) = -pE_0 \cos \alpha.$$

The derivative of W_1 with respect to the orientation angle is the magnitude of the generalized force associated with α or simply the magnitude of the torque $\mathbf{M}$ acting on the dipole:

$$\frac{\partial W_1}{\partial \alpha} = |\mathbf{M}| = pE_0 \sin \alpha = |\mathbf{p} \times \mathbf{E}_0|$$

The direction of the torque $\mathbf{M}$ is perpendicular to the plane formed by $\mathbf{p}$ and $\mathbf{E}_0$; in addition, since $W_1(\alpha)$ is a minimum for $\alpha = 0$, the torque due to $\mathbf{E}_0$ will tend to decrease α if $\alpha > 0$. Consequently

$$\mathbf{M} = \mathbf{p} \times \mathbf{E}_0. \tag{4.7}$$

Since the first two terms of W contain the (E0) and (E1) moments of the distribution explicitly, it is evident that the next terms in the expansion should be expressible in terms of the elements of the (E2) matrix. Consider the terms explicitly written in eq. 4.2 but which have so far been neglected. When these terms are substituted into the equation for W, their contribution (W_2) is

$$W_2 = \tfrac{1}{6} \sum_{j=1}^{N} 3q_j\{x_j^2\varphi_{xx}^{\circ} + x_jy_j\varphi_{xy}^{\circ} + x_jz_j\varphi_{xz}^{\circ}$$
$$+ y_jx_j\varphi_{yx}^{\circ} + y_j^2\varphi_{yy}^{\circ} + y_jz_j\varphi_{yz}^{\circ}$$
$$+ z_jx_j\varphi_{zx}^{\circ} + z_jy_j\varphi_{zy}^{\circ} + z_j^2\varphi_{zz}^{\circ}\}. \qquad (4.8)$$

It should be noted that terms appearing in eq. 4.8 such as

$$\sum_{j=1}^{N} 3q_jx_jy_j, \qquad \sum_{j=1}^{N} 3q_jy_jz_j\ldots,$$

are the off-diagonal elements of the quadrupole matrix for the charge distribution. If the orientation of the coordinate axes, so far unspecified, is chosen so that the quadrupole matrix is diagonal, W_2 of eq. 4.8 simplifies to

$$W_2 = \tfrac{1}{6} \sum_{j=1}^{N} 3q_j\{x_j^2\varphi_{xx}^{\circ} + y_j^2\varphi_{yy}^{\circ} + z_j^2\varphi_{zz}^{\circ}\}. \qquad (4.9)$$

A further simplification of the expression for W_2 may be effected by the following artifice. It is asserted that the term

$$\tfrac{1}{3}r_j^2(\varphi_{xx}^{\circ} + \varphi_{yy}^{\circ} + \varphi_{zz}^{\circ})$$

may be subtracted from the bracket in the summand on the right-hand side of eq. 4.9 without changing its value. This assertion is based on the observation that

$$\varphi_{xx}^{\circ} + \varphi_{yy}^{\circ} + \varphi_{zz}^{\circ} = (\nabla^2\varphi)_{r_j=0} = \nabla^2\varphi_0.$$

As has been shown in Chapter 3 (see eq. 3.25) $\nabla^2\varphi$ vanishes at all points where the charge producing $\varphi(\mathbf{r})$ does not reside. Since the origin of coordinates is *inside* the charge distribution under consideration and since the source of φ is *outside* the distribution, it follows that $\nabla^2\varphi_0 = 0$. Consequently, carrying out the above subtraction,

$$W_2 = \tfrac{1}{6} \sum_{j=1}^{N} \{q_j(3x_j^2 - r_j^2)\varphi_{xx}^{\circ} + q_j(3y_j^2 - r_j^2)\varphi_{yy}^{\circ} + q_j(3z_j^2 - r_j^2)\varphi_{zz}^{\circ}\}.$$

In terms of the elements of the diagonalized (E2) matrix, W_2 may be expressed as

$$W_2 = \tfrac{1}{6}\{Q_{xx}\varphi_{xx}^{\circ} + Q_{yy}\varphi_{yy}^{\circ} + Q_{zz}\varphi_{zz}^{\circ}\}$$

with the restriction that $Q_{xx} + Q_{yy} + Q_{zz} = 0$ (see eq. 2.26). For a charge distribution with rotational symmetry about the z-axis the following definitions may be made: $Q_{zz} = Q$, $Q_{xx} = -1/2Q$, $Q_{yy} = -1/2Q$, and therefore

$$W_2 = \tfrac{1}{6}Q\{\varphi_{zz}^\circ - \tfrac{1}{2}(\varphi_{xx}^\circ + \varphi_{yy}^\circ)\}.$$

Once again use may be made of the fact that $\nabla^2\varphi_0 = 0$, yielding

$$W_2 = \tfrac{1}{6}Q\{(\varphi_{zz}^\circ + \tfrac{1}{2}\varphi_{zz}^\circ) - \tfrac{1}{2}(\varphi_{xx}^\circ + \varphi_{yy}^\circ + \varphi_{zz}^\circ)\}$$

and

$$W_2 = \tfrac{1}{4}Q\varphi_{zz}^\circ = -\tfrac{1}{4}Q\left(\frac{\partial}{\partial z}E_z\right)_0. \tag{4.10}$$

To an excellent approximation the energy of a rotational symmetric charge distribution in an external field may be written as

$$W = q_{\text{total}}\varphi_0 - \mathbf{p}\cdot\mathbf{E}_0 + \tfrac{1}{4}Q\varphi_{zz}^\circ + \cdots. \tag{4.11}$$

The remaining terms in this expansion are negligible if the potential does not vary too rapidly over the extent of the charge distribution. If the (E0) and (E1) moments do not vanish, the first two terms in eq. 4.11 usually suffice in situations of practical interest. However, many systems of physical interest are neutral and do not have a dipole moment; for these systems W_2 given by eq. 4.11 is the leading contribution to the interaction energy. Note that W_2 depends only on the variation of external field along the symmetry axis of the charge distribution.

If the charges producing the external field are far from the charge distribution under consideration, then the external potential may be expressed in terms of a multipole expansion (see Sections 2.5 and 2.6). Such an approximate expression for φ_0 and $\mathbf{E}_0$ is consistent with the approximation for W already made in terms of the multipole moments of the charge distribution. For clarity, the charge distribution producing the field is labeled (*b*) and the charge distribution which has been brought into position (*a*); see Fig. 4.2. A coordinate system is constructed within charge distribution (*b*), and a vector from the origin of (*b*) to that of (*a*) is called $\mathbf{r}$. According to eqs. 2.18, 2.19, and 2.22,

$$\varphi_0 \approx \left(\frac{1}{4\pi\epsilon_0}\right)\left(\frac{q_{b,\text{ total}}}{r} + \frac{\mathbf{p}_b\cdot\mathbf{r}}{r^3} + \cdots\right),$$

$$\mathbf{E}_0 \approx \left(\frac{1}{4\pi\epsilon_0}\right)\left(\frac{q_{b,\text{ total}}}{r^3}\mathbf{r} - \left[\frac{\mathbf{p}_b}{r^3} - \frac{3(\mathbf{p}_b\cdot\mathbf{r})\mathbf{r}}{r^5}\right] + \cdots\right).$$

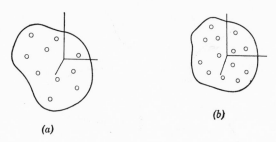

Fig. 4.2   Two nonoverlapping charge distributions interact via their fields. The potential at each produced by the other distribution may be expanded in terms of the multipole moments.

These expressions can be substituted into eq. 4.11 to obtain an approximate expression for W.   This can be written in an obvious notation as

$$W = \sum_{j,\,k} W_{jk} \qquad j, k = 0, 1, 2, 3, \ldots$$

where, for example,

$$W_{00} = \left(\frac{1}{4\pi\epsilon_0}\right) \frac{q_{a,\,\text{total}}\, q_{b,\,\text{total}}}{r} \qquad \text{(monopole–monopole interaction)}$$

$$W_{11} = \left(\frac{1}{4\pi\epsilon_0}\right) \left[\frac{\mathbf{p}_a \cdot \mathbf{p}_b}{r^3} - \frac{3(\mathbf{p}_a \cdot \mathbf{r})(\mathbf{p}_b \cdot \mathbf{r})}{r^5}\right] \qquad \text{(dipole–dipole interaction)}$$

$$(4.12)$$

The dipole–dipole interaction is of particular interest in its physical applications.   This interaction is sometimes called a *tensor interaction*; it depends on the relative orientation of three vectors $\mathbf{p}_a$, $\mathbf{p}_b$, and $\mathbf{r}$.

4.2   Energy Associated with a Charge Distribution

It is important to realize that the W considered in Section 4.1 is only the work necessary to position a charge distribution in a fixed external field. Consider a somewhat more general problem, namely, the evaluation of the work necessary to assemble a system of N particles from an initial configuration in which all the charges are infinitely separated.   Here none of the charges are considered external to the distribution.

Suppose a system of N charged particles (labeled q_1, $q_2, \ldots, q_N$) all of which are initially separated by an infinite distance is slowly brought together to the configuration illustrated in Fig. 4.3.   It will be assumed that the charges reside in vacuum.   Since the charged particles exert

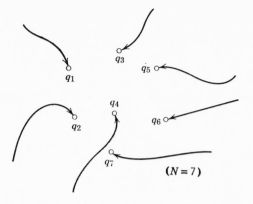

$(N = 7)$

Fig. 4.3   A charge distribution consisting of N-charges is assembled. The work required to accomplish this is equated to the electrostatic energy of the distribution.

forces on one another, it is evident that a certain amount of work must be done in assembling this charge distribution.   This work is equated to the *electrostatic energy* U of the charge distribution.   Electrostatic energy plays the same role in electrostatics as the potential energy of a mechanical system plays in Newtonian mechanics, since these two energies are introduced into the subjects in entirely analogous fashions.   Since the electrostatic force acting on each charged particle is conservative, the electrostatic energy of the final configuration is independent of the mode by which the configuration is assembled.   The energy will be calculated in the following simple manner, which is subject to an obvious generalization.

As the initial step charge q_1 is brought into its final position within the configuration without any work, since the remaining charges are still residing an infinite distance from q_1.   Charge q_2 is then brought into place; the amount of work, W_2, expended in positioning q_2 is

$$W_2 = q_2\varphi_{12} \tag{4.13}$$

where $\varphi_{12} = \left(\dfrac{1}{4\pi\epsilon_0}\right)\dfrac{q_1}{|\mathbf{r}_1 - \mathbf{r}_2|},$ the electrostatic potential

at $\mathbf{r}_2$ due to the charge q_1 located at $\mathbf{r}_1$.   Charge q_3 is subsequently positioned at the expenditure of an amount of work W_3:

$$W_3 = q_3(\varphi_{13} + \varphi_{23})$$

where $\varphi_{j3} = \left(\dfrac{1}{4\pi\epsilon_0}\right)\dfrac{q_j}{|\mathbf{r}_j - \mathbf{r}_3|},$ $j = 1, 2.$

If the charge distribution consists of only three particles, then the total work done in assembling the distribution U is simply

$$U = \left(\frac{1}{4\pi\epsilon_0}\right)\left\{\frac{q_1 q_2}{|\mathbf{r}_1 - \mathbf{r}_2|} + \frac{q_1 q_3}{|\mathbf{r}_1 - \mathbf{r}_3|} + \frac{q_2 q_3}{|\mathbf{r}_2 - \mathbf{r}_3|}\right\}. \tag{4.14}$$

Equation 4.14 can be written in a somewhat more complex but ultimately more useful form by noting, for example, that

$$\left(\frac{1}{4\pi\epsilon_0}\right)\frac{q_1 q_2}{|\mathbf{r}_1 - \mathbf{r}_2|} \equiv \frac{1}{2}\left\{q_1\left[\frac{1}{4\pi\epsilon_0}\frac{q_2}{|\mathbf{r}_2 - \mathbf{r}_1|}\right] + q_2\left[\frac{1}{4\pi\epsilon_0}\frac{q_1}{|\mathbf{r}_1 - \mathbf{r}_2|}\right]\right\}$$
$$= \frac{1}{2}\{q_1\varphi_{21} + q_2\varphi_{12}\}. \tag{4.15}$$

Noting eq. 4.15, eq. 4.14 can be rewritten as

$$U = \frac{1}{2}(q_1\varphi_{21} + q_2\varphi_{12} + q_1\varphi_{31} + q_3\varphi_{13} + q_2\varphi_{32} + q_3\varphi_{33}). \tag{4.16}$$

The generalization of eq. 4.16 to a system of N particles is

$$U = \frac{1}{2}\sum_{i=1}^{N}\sum_{j=1}^{N} q_i\varphi_{ji}, \quad (i \neq j). \tag{4.17}$$

The quantity inside the double summation is the electrostatic potential at the ith charge produced by the jth charge multiplied by the value of the ith charge.

It might have been tempting to write down eq. 4.17 immediately, without carrying out the indicated steps in the logical development leading to eq. 4.17. However, any intuitive argument which leads from the definition of the *electrostatic potential* to the *electrostatic potential energy* is more than likely to ignore the factor $\frac{1}{2}$ which stands outside the summation signs in eq. 4.17. This factor is a consequence of the fact that the potential energy associated with any two charges is a property of both charges but is not a property which can be assigned to each charge separately.

If some of the charges of an ensemble can be described by distributed charges, then eq. 4.17 can be modified to include these charges:

$$U = \frac{1}{2}\sum_{i \neq j}^{N}\sum_{j=1}^{N} q_i\varphi_{ji} + \frac{1}{2}\int \rho\varphi \, d\tau + \frac{1}{2}\int \sigma\varphi \, ds. \tag{4.18}$$

However, it will now be assumed that all the charges in the ensemble can be described by a volume density of charge $\rho(\mathbf{r})$ associated with every point in space (see the comments at the end of Chapter 2). The electrostatic energy of such a distribution is simply

$$U = \frac{1}{2}\int_{\tau} \rho(\mathbf{r})\varphi(\mathbf{r}) \, d\tau \tag{4.19}$$

where $\varphi(\mathbf{r})$ is the electrostatic potential at $\mathbf{r}$ produced by the charge distribution and τ is the volume containing all the charge. To demonstrate that it is possible to transform the integrand of eq. 4.19 so that it depends only on the electrostatic field, it is noted that $\rho(\mathbf{r})$ may be replaced in eq. 4.19 by ϵ_0 div $\mathbf{E}$, using Gauss's law in differential form; for example,

$$U = (4\pi\epsilon_0) \frac{1}{8\pi} \int_\tau (\text{div } \mathbf{E}) \varphi \, d\tau. \tag{4.20}$$

The expression for U in eq. 4.20 contains both φ and $\mathbf{E}$; as has been remarked previously, either φ or $\mathbf{E}$ may be considered a redundant attribute of the charge distribution since they are related directly via $\mathbf{E} = -\text{grad } \varphi$. For the present discussion, it is φ that will be considered redundant and removed from eq. 4.20. Use is made of the following identity from the vector calculus.

$$\text{div } (\varphi\mathbf{E}) = \varphi \text{ div } \mathbf{E} + \mathbf{E} \cdot \text{grad } \varphi. \tag{4.21}$$

The identity of eq. 4.21 is a mathematical one, that is, it does not depend upon the physical significance of φ and $\mathbf{E}$. Here $\mathbf{E} = -\text{grad } \varphi$, and consequently

$$\varphi \text{ div } \mathbf{E} = \text{div } (\varphi\mathbf{E}) + E^2, \text{ where } E^2 \equiv \mathbf{E} \cdot \mathbf{E}.$$

If this expression for φ div $\mathbf{E}$ is substituted into eq. 4.20, the electrostatic energy has the form displayed in eq. 4.22:

$$U = (4\pi\epsilon_0) \frac{1}{8\pi} \left\{ \int_\tau \text{div } (\varphi\mathbf{E}) \, d\tau + \int_\tau E^2 \, d\tau \right\}. \tag{4.22}$$

The first integral on the left-hand side of eq. 4.22 may be transformed into an integral over the surface Σ enclosing the volume τ via the divergence theorem of the vector calculus; this yields

$$U = (4\pi\epsilon_0) \frac{1}{8\pi} \left\{ \oiint_\Sigma \varphi\mathbf{E} \cdot \hat{\mathbf{n}} \, ds + \int_\tau E^2 \, d\tau \right\}. \tag{4.23}$$

If the charge producing the field is confined to a finite volume, then φ (and $\mathbf{E}$) will vanish at infinity. Consequently the surface integral on the left-hand side of eq. 4.23 will vanish if Σ is allowed to increase to envelope all space. Therefore

$$U = (4\pi\epsilon_0) \frac{1}{8\pi} \int_{\text{all space}} E^2 \, d\tau \tag{4.24}$$

where the integral is to be taken over all space. At this point it should be remarked that although eqs. 4.19 and 4.24 look very dissimilar, their physical content is identical; one is a mathematical reformulation of the other.

Equations 4.18 and 4.24 are also valid when conducting media are present if U is equated to the "reversible work" done in assembling the charge distribution; that is, if one neglects in calculating U all energy expended in overcoming any Joule heat losses which develop due to the rearrangement of charge in the conducting media as the charge distribution is assembled.

The expression for U in eq. 4.24 can be reinterpreted in the following manner: define a scalar point function

$$u(\mathbf{r}) \equiv (4\pi\epsilon_0)\left[\frac{1}{8\pi} E^2(\mathbf{r})\right]. \tag{4.25}$$

The integral of $u(\mathbf{r})$ over all space is the electrostatic energy of the charges producing the E-field; that is,

$$\int_{\text{all space}} u(\mathbf{r})\, d\tau = U.$$

$u(\mathbf{r})$ is called the *energy density* of the electrostatic field; in this reinterpretation of eq. 4.24 an amount of energy $u(\mathbf{r})$ per unit volume is assigned to every volume element $d\tau$. The energy is said to "reside" in or to be "stored" in the field. This is in no sense required by the theory of electrostatics developed up to this point; in fact, it is an additional hypothesis. Although it is not necessary to introduce the energy density function at present, it will be a fruitful concept especially when the theory is extended to explicitly time-dependent problems.

The electrostatic energy and the electric fields produced by a uniformly charged sphere were calculated in Chapter 3. The electrostatic energy of such a sphere will now be calculated via eq. 4.24. The field inside the sphere has been shown to be

$$\mathbf{E}(\mathbf{r}) = \left(\frac{1}{4\pi\epsilon_0}\right) \frac{q}{r^2} \left(\frac{r}{R}\right)^3 \hat{\mathbf{r}}, \quad r \leqslant R.$$

The contribution, U_1, to the electrostatic energy from the interior region of the sphere is

$$U_1 = (4\pi\epsilon_0) \frac{1}{8\pi} \left(\frac{q}{4\pi\epsilon_0 R^3}\right)^2 \int_{r \leqslant R} r^2\, d\tau = \frac{1}{10}\left(\frac{1}{4\pi\epsilon_0}\right) \frac{q^2}{R}.$$

The electrostatic field in the region lying exterior to the sphere is

$$\mathbf{E}(\mathbf{r}) = \left(\frac{1}{4\pi\epsilon_0}\right) \frac{q}{r^2} \hat{\mathbf{r}}, \quad r \geqslant R$$

yielding a contribution to the electrostatic energy of

$$U_2 = \frac{1}{2} \left(\frac{1}{4\pi\epsilon_0} \right) \frac{q^2}{R}.$$

The total electrostatic energy of the sphere is

$$U = U_1 + U_2 = \left(\frac{1}{4\pi\epsilon_0} \right) \frac{3}{5} \frac{q^2}{R}$$

a result obtained in Chapter 3 by a different but related method. It should be noted that if the idea of the electrostatic energy density $u(\mathbf{r})$ is adopted, five times as much energy "resides" in the region exterior to the sphere (vacuum) as in the region occupied by the sphere itself.

There is at least one physical situation in which the two expressions for the electrostatic energy—eq. 4.17 where U is expressed in terms of charge and electrostatic potential, and eq. 4.24 where U is expressed only in terms of the E-field produced by the charges—yield apparently different results. Equation 4.17 applied to an isolated point charge yields $U = 0$, a result consistent with the idea that the electrostatic energy is an interaction energy. However, since $\mathbf{E}(\mathbf{r})$ for a point charge varies as $1/r^2$, eq. 4.24 yields $U = \infty$ for an isolated point charge. The reason for this latter result is quite clear: eq. 4.24 was derived assuming that all the charge in a distribution could be represented by a volume density of charge. If one adopts the operational definition of the electrostatic energy, one sees that eq. 4.24 yields in this physical situation the amount of work necessary to assemble a finite amount of charge in zero volume; this quantity is evidently infinite. Equations 4.17 and 4.24 only yield these divergent results for point charges; for all other charge distributions they yield the same value for U. It is therefore not strictly necessary (in classical electrostatics) to choose the correct expression between eqs. 4.17 and 4.24. This is due essentially to the fact that electrostatics, as developed in this text, is based on Coulomb's force law, and the physically significant concept is the force on a charged particle. Consequently both eqs. 4.17 and 4.24, when interpreted operationally, have equal logical validity. However, it is possible to formulate the subject of electrostatics such that the electrostatic energy and the fields produced by a system of charges are fundamental quantities and the force between charged particles is a derived concept. In this latter approach eq. 4.24 is taken to be the fundamental expression for the electrostatic energy. This approach is a more fruitful formulation of electrostatics for more advanced problems and in the realm of quantum phenomena, and here the electrostatic energy of an isolated point charge is necessarily infinite. This infinity is called the *self-energy* of the point particle; it is carried over into the realm of quantum phenomena where it plays a fundamental role. It need not be of further concern here, however, except to remark that in the calculation of the electrostatic energy of a charged system it is necessary to subtract from the result gleaned from eq. 4.24 the electrostatic self-energy of the constituent point particles.

EXAMPLE 4.2   Calculate the electrostatic energy of a system consisting of a point charge q located at the center of a spherical conducting shell of inner radius r_1 and outer radius r_2.

Using Gauss's law, the electrostatic field has the following values:

$$\mathbf{E(r)} = \left(\frac{1}{4\pi\epsilon_0}\right)\frac{q}{r^2}\hat{\mathbf{r}} \quad r < r_1 \text{ and } r > r_2$$
$$\mathbf{E(r)} = 0 \quad r_1 \leqslant r \leqslant r_2.$$

The electrostatic energy of this system is calculated using eq. 4.24 and subtracting out the self-energy of the charge q; that is,

$$U = (4\pi\epsilon_0)\frac{1}{8\pi}\left\{ \int_0^{r_1} \left(\frac{1}{4\pi\epsilon_0}\frac{q}{r^2}\right)^2 4\pi r^2\, dr + \int_{r_2}^{\infty} \left(\frac{1}{4\pi\epsilon_0}\frac{q}{r^2}\right)^2 4\pi r^2\, dr \right.$$
$$\left. - \int_0^{\infty} \left(\frac{1}{4\pi\epsilon_0}\frac{q}{r^2}\right)^2 4\pi r^2\, dr \right\}.$$
$$U = \frac{1}{4\pi\epsilon_0}\frac{1}{2}q^2\left(\frac{1}{r_2} - \frac{1}{r_1}\right).$$

The electrostatic energy U has the same properties as the mechanical energy of a system of uncharged particles. This is intuitively evident since U was equated to the reversible work necessary to assemble a charge distribution. To add more substance to the intuitive ideas concerning U, it will be instructive to prove the following theorem: charges residing on a system of fixed conductors will distribute themselves over the conducting surfaces such that the resulting electrostatic energy is a minimum. An equivalent theorem exists for a mechanical system. The proof of the electrostatic theorem proceeds in the following manner. Suppose N charged conductors are fixed in space along with an arbitrary number of fixed charges. The electrostatic field produced by this charged system obeys the following general relations: on the surface of the conductors

$$\oiint_i (\mathbf{E} \cdot \hat{\mathbf{n}})\, ds = \left(\frac{1}{4\pi\epsilon_0}\right)4\pi q_i \quad (i = 1, 2, \ldots, N); \tag{4.26}$$

in the region exterior to the conductors

$$\text{div } \mathbf{E} = \left(\frac{1}{4\pi\epsilon_0}\right)4\pi\rho. \tag{4.27}$$

In addition, the potential φ is constant on each conductor ($\varphi = \varphi_i$ on the ith conductor) and is related to the E-field everywhere via the relation

$$\mathbf{E} = -\operatorname{grad} \varphi. \tag{4.28}$$

Now let $\mathbf{E}'$ be another field which satisfies the general relations 4.26 and 4.27, but which corresponds to a distribution of charge on the conductors different from the actual one.   The electrostatic energies associated with these two fields are

$$U = (4\pi\epsilon_0) \frac{1}{8\pi} \int E^2 \, d\tau \tag{4.29a}$$

$$U' = (4\pi\epsilon_0) \frac{1}{8\pi} \int E'^2 \, d\tau. \tag{4.29b}$$

If we set

$$\mathbf{E}' = \mathbf{E} + \boldsymbol{\varepsilon},$$

the difference in electrostatic energy associated with the two fields is

$$U' - U = (4\pi\epsilon_0) \frac{1}{8\pi} \left\{ \int (\mathbf{E} + \boldsymbol{\varepsilon})^2 \, d\tau - \int E^2 \, d\tau \right\} \tag{4.30a}$$

or

$$U' - U = (4\pi\epsilon_0) \frac{1}{8\pi} \left\{ \int \varepsilon^2 \, d\tau + 2 \int \boldsymbol{\varepsilon} \cdot \mathbf{E} \, d\tau \right\}. \tag{4.30b}$$

The integrals in eqs. 4.29 and 4.30 extend over all space.   However, the latter integral on the right-hand side of eq. 4.30b need only extend over the region exterior to the conductors (vacuum) since $\mathbf{E}$ vanishes everywhere within the conductor.   Since $\mathbf{E}$ is the field produced by the actual charge distribution, eq. 4.28 may be employed, yielding

$$U' - U = (4\pi\epsilon_0) \frac{1}{8\pi} \left\{ \int \varepsilon^2 \, d\tau - 2 \int' \operatorname{grad} \varphi \cdot \boldsymbol{\varepsilon} \, d\tau \right\} \tag{4.31}$$

where $\int' \cdots$ stands for an integral over vacuum only.   However, the vector calculus identity of eq. 4.21 allows the integrand of the second integral on the right-hand side of eq. 4.31 to be written as

$$\boldsymbol{\varepsilon} \cdot \operatorname{grad} \varphi = \operatorname{div}(\varphi\boldsymbol{\varepsilon}) - \varphi \operatorname{div} \boldsymbol{\varepsilon}.$$

Consequently

$$U' - U = (4\pi\epsilon_0) \frac{1}{8\pi} \left\{ \int \varepsilon^2 \, d\tau + 2 \int' \varphi \operatorname{div} \boldsymbol{\varepsilon} \, d\tau - 2 \int' \operatorname{div}(\varphi\boldsymbol{\varepsilon}) \, d\tau \right\}. \tag{4.32}$$

Since both $\mathbf{E}$ and $\mathbf{E}'$ satisfy eq. 4.27 in the region exterior to the conductors, it follows from eq. 4.27 that

$$\text{div } \boldsymbol{\varepsilon} = 0$$

in the vacuum; consequently the second integral on the right-hand side of eq. 4.32 vanishes. The last integral on the right-hand side of eq. 4.32 may be transformed, using the divergence theorem as follows:

$$\int' \text{div } (\varphi\boldsymbol{\varepsilon}) \, d\tau = \oiint_S \varphi\boldsymbol{\varepsilon} \cdot \hat{\mathbf{n}} \, dS - \sum_{i=1}^N \oiint_{S_i} \varphi\boldsymbol{\varepsilon} \cdot \hat{\mathbf{n}} \, dS \qquad (4.33)$$

since the region exterior to the conductors must be considered a volume enclosed by a large surface (S) at infinity plus the surfaces (S_i) of all the conductors. If all the charge resides in a finite volume, then φ (the actual potential function) vanishes in the integrand of the first integral on the right-hand side of eq. 4.33. The second integral on the right-hand side of eq. 4.33 is handled as follows: since φ is constant on each conductor,

$$\sum_{i=1}^N \oiint_{S_i} \varphi\boldsymbol{\varepsilon} \cdot \hat{\mathbf{n}} \, dS = \sum_{i=1}^N \varphi_i \oiint_{S_i} \boldsymbol{\varepsilon} \cdot \hat{\mathbf{n}} \, dS.$$

However, both $\mathbf{E}$ and $\mathbf{E}'$ were assumed to satisfy eq. 4.26; consequently

$$\oiint_{S_i} \boldsymbol{\varepsilon} \cdot \hat{\mathbf{n}} \, dS = 0.$$

It has been demonstrated therefore that

$$U' - U = (4\pi\epsilon_0) \frac{1}{8\pi} \int \varepsilon^2 \, d\tau. \qquad (4.34)$$

The right-hand side of eq. 4.23 is, of necessity, a positive quantity; consequently the required theorem is proved, namely,

$$U' \geqslant U. \qquad (4.35)$$

4.3 Capacitance

In order to place a charge q on an originally uncharged conductor, a certain amount of work must be performed. This can be seen in a variety of ways. A charged conductor produces an electric field which, according to eq. 4.24, means that the charged conductor possesses a finite amount of electrostatic energy. Or, as a charge q is placed in the neighborhood of an isolated uncharged conductor, certain image charges are induced in the conductor; an amount of work must therefore be expended to move the charge in the force field produced by its images. The amount of work expended will be proportional to q^2 since the magnitude of each of the image charges is proportional to q. Consequently the electrostatic potential of the charged conductor, that is, the work per unit charge φ necessary to place the charge on the conductor, is proportional to q.

$$q = C\varphi \qquad (4.36)$$

where $C =$ coefficient of self-capacitance of the conductor. The value of C depends only upon the shape and size of the conductor.

Suppose another conductor of charge q' is placed in the neighborhood of the conductor of charge q. An image charge distribution proportional to q' will be induced in the first conductor, and consequently the potential of the first conductor will be increased by an amount proportional to q'. If the first conductor is labeled i and the second conductor labeled j, then

$$\varphi_i = p_{ii}q_i + p_{ij}q_j \qquad (4.37a)$$

where $q_i = q, q_j = q', p_{ii} = 1/C$, and $p_{ij} =$ mutual coefficient of potential between the two conductors.

A similar expression holds for the jth conductor, namely,

$$\varphi_j = p_{jj}q_j + p_{ji}q_i. \qquad (4.37b)$$

Equations 4.37a and 4.37b can be solved for the charges on each conductor in terms of the potential on both conductors, yielding

$$q_i = \frac{p_{jj}\varphi_i}{\det p_{ij}} + \frac{-p_{ij}\varphi_j}{\det p_{ij}} \qquad (4.38a)$$

$$q_j = \frac{p_{ii}\varphi_j}{\det p_{ij}} + \frac{-p_{ji}\varphi_i}{\det p_{ij}} \qquad (4.38b)$$

where

$$\det p_{ij} = \begin{vmatrix} p_{ii} & p_{ij} \\ p_{ji} & p_{jj} \end{vmatrix} = p_{ii}p_{jj} - p_{ij}p_{ji}.$$

It is useful to adopt a shorthand notation for the constants of eqs. 4.38; that is,

$$q_i = C_{ii}\varphi_i + C_{ij}\varphi_j. \qquad (4.39a)$$

$$q_j = C_{jj}\varphi_j + C_{ji}\varphi_i. \qquad (4.39b)$$

where $C_{ii} =$ coefficient of self-capacitance and
$\quad\quad C_{ij} =$ coefficient of mutual capacitance.

Equation 4.39 can be generalized in an elementary manner to a system of N charged conductors:

$$q_i = \sum_{j=1}^{N} C_{ij}\varphi_j. \tag{4.40}$$

The development of eq. 4.40 has been carried out using arguments based on the method of images. Equation 4.40 could have been derived in a somewhat more elegant manner by considering the properties of Laplace's equation. These two methods are equivalent since the validity of the method of images rests on the properties of Laplace's equation. The salient property of Laplace's equation which could be used to arrive at the result summarized in eq. 4.40 is its "linearity"; that is, if φ_1 and φ_2 are two possible solutions to Laplace's equation, $\nabla^2\varphi = 0$, then $a\varphi_1 + b\varphi_2$ is also a solution, where a and b are two arbitrary constants. A system for which eq. 4.40 is valid is characterized as being a *linear* system.

In a similar manner eqs. 4.37 can be generalized to a system of N charged conductors:[1]

$$\varphi_i = \sum_{j=1}^{N} p_{ij}q_j. \tag{4.41}$$

The electrostatic energy of a system of N charged conductors can be written in terms of the coefficients of capacitance using eqs. 4.17 and 4.40:

$$U \equiv \tfrac{1}{2} \sum_{i=1}^{N} q_i\varphi_i = \tfrac{1}{2} \sum_{i=1}^{N} \sum_{j=1}^{N} C_{ij}\varphi_i\varphi_j. \tag{4.42}$$

[1] Equations 4.40 and 4.41 can be written in matrix notation. The N^2 numbers C_{ij} can be considered the elements of an $N \times N$ matrix C where, for example, C_{rs} is the r-s element of the matrix C. In a similar fashion the numbers p_{ij} can be considered the elements of a square matrix p. The N values φ_i and the N values q_i can be treated as elements of a column matrix φ and q respectively. In matrix notation

$$q = C\varphi \tag{4.40a}$$

and $$\varphi = pq. \tag{4.41a}$$

The result of eq. 4.41a can be substituted directly into eq. 4.40a and vice versa, yielding

$$q = Cpq \quad \text{and} \quad \varphi = pC\varphi.$$

The only way the above can be true is if

$$Cp = pC = 1,$$

where 1 is the so-called identity matrix. The matrix p is said to be the inverse of C and vice versa; that is,

$$CC^{-1} = 1 = pp^{-1}, \quad \text{where } p \equiv C^{-1} \text{ and } C \equiv p^{-1}.$$

As is shown in eqs. 4.46, the matrices C and p are symmetric matrices; that is, $C_{ij} = C_{ji}$ and $p_{ij} = p_{ji}$.

An equivalent expression involving the coefficients of potential may be obtained using eqs. 4.17 and 4.41:

$$U = \tfrac{1}{2} \sum_{i=1}^{N} q_i \varphi_i = \tfrac{1}{2} \sum_{i=1}^{N} \sum_{j=1}^{N} p_{ij} q_i q_j. \tag{4.43}$$

It is straightforward to demonstrate that $C_{ij} = C_{ji}$ and equivalently $p_{ij} = p_{ji}$. Consider a system composed of two conductors i and j. Suppose that conductor j is kept uncharged and that charge q_i is placed on conductor i. The amount of work necessary to do this is

$$W_1 = \tfrac{1}{2} p_{ii} q_i^2. \tag{4.44}$$

Charge is subsequently added to conductor j, keeping the charge on conductor i unchanged until conductor j reaches a potential $\varphi < \varphi_j$ and charge $q < q_j$; an additional increment of charge dq is then added to the jth conductor. The work necessary to accomplish this latter step is

$$dW_2 = \varphi \, dq = p_{jj} q \, dq + p_{ji} q_i \, dq.$$

The total work required to add charge q_j to the jth conductor is the integral of dW_2, keeping q_i fixed.

$$W_2 = \tfrac{1}{2} p_{jj} q_j^2 + p_{ji} q_i q_j. \tag{4.45}$$

The total work necessary to charge the conductors in this fashion is $W_1 + W_2$ or

$$W = \tfrac{1}{2} p_{ii} q_i^2 + \tfrac{1}{2} p_{jj} q_j^2 + p_{ji} q_i q_j. \tag{4.46}$$

This work must be equal to the electrostatic energy of the two conductors even though the conductors have been charged in a very particular manner; this is due to the conservative nature of the Coulomb force. The expression for the electrostatic energy may be gleaned from eq. 4.43. In order that $U = W$ (i.e., eqs. 4.43 and 4.46 satisfied simultaneously), the following equality must hold:

$$\tfrac{1}{2}(p_{ij} + p_{ji}) = p_{ji},$$

or equivalently

$$p_{ij} = p_{ji}, \tag{4.47a}$$

that is, the coefficients of potential are symmetric in their indices. A similar result holds for the coefficients of capacitance; that is

$$C_{ij} = C_{ji}. \tag{4.47b}$$

The symmetry of the coefficients of potential and capacitance is easy to establish using purely mathematical methods which are, of course, equivalent to the physical method given above. Consider eq. 4.43 which serves to define the p_{ij}:

$$U = \tfrac{1}{2} \sum_{i=1}^{N} \sum_{j=1}^{N} p_{ij} q_i q_j.$$

Since both i and j are summation indices, they may be interchanged without affecting the value of the sum; that is,

$$U = \tfrac{1}{2} \sum_{j=1}^{N} \sum_{i=1}^{N} p_{ji} q_j q_i.$$

If the summations of the latter expression are interchanged, eq. 4.43a is obtained:

$$U = \tfrac{1}{2} \sum_{i=1}^{N} \sum_{j=1}^{N} p_{ji} q_j q_i. \qquad (4.43a)$$

Since the charges on the conductors i and j are independent of each other, comparison of eqs. 4.43 and 4.43a yields the desired result immediately:

$$p_{ij} = p_{ji}.$$

EXAMPLE 4.2   The above concepts involving the coefficients of capacitance and potential will now be applied to spherical condensers. Consider two concentric spherical shells of radius a and b $(a < b)$. The inner shell carries a charge $+q$; the outer shell a charge of $-q$. The electric field between the shells has a radial component only and is only a function of the radial coordinate r; that is,

$$\mathbf{E}(r) = -\frac{d}{dr} \varphi(r)\hat{\mathbf{r}}. \qquad (4.48)$$

The electrostatic field may be calculated by a direct application of Gauss's law applied to another concentric spherical surface of radius r, $a \leqslant r \leqslant b$:

$$\oiint \mathbf{E} \cdot \hat{\mathbf{n}} \, dS = 4\pi r^2 E(r) = \left(\frac{1}{4\pi\epsilon_0}\right) 4\pi q. \qquad (4.49)$$

Applying eqs. 4.48 and 4.49, the potential difference between the spherical shells is

$$\varphi_b - \varphi_a = \left(\frac{1}{4\pi\epsilon_0}\right) q \int_a^b \frac{dr}{r^2} = \left(\frac{1}{4\pi\epsilon_0}\right) q \left(\frac{a-b}{ab}\right)$$

or

$$\varphi_b = \frac{q}{4\pi\epsilon_0} \left(\frac{a-b}{ab}\right) + \varphi_a. \qquad (4.50)$$

The coefficient of self-capacitance of the shells considered as a conducting system is simply

$$(4\pi\epsilon_0) \left(\frac{ab}{b-a}\right). \qquad (4.51)$$

This coefficient for a conducting sphere can be gleaned by letting $b \to \infty$, with the result: $(4\pi\epsilon_0)a$. Equation 4.50 can be employed to calculate the capacitance of what is sometimes referred to as a *parallel plate* capacitor. The radii of the inner and outer spherical shells are allowed to approach infinity, keeping the difference between the radii a constant equal to d—the separation of the plates (see Fig. 4.4). If b is allowed to approach some large value L, the capacitance of the system becomes

$$C \approx (4\pi\epsilon_0) \frac{L(L - d)}{d} \approx (4\pi\epsilon_0) \frac{4\pi L^2}{4\pi d}.$$

However, $4\pi L^2$ is simply the area A of the outer sphere; consequently

$$C \approx (4\pi\epsilon_0) \frac{A}{4\pi d}. \tag{4.52}$$

As $L \to \infty$, A and C also approach infinity. However, eq. 4.52 is an excellent approximation to the capacitance of a parallel plate capacitor of finite A if *edge effects* are ignored, that is, for a system in which $L \gg d$.

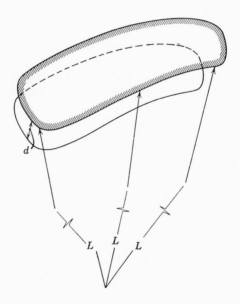

Fig. 4.4   The surfaces sketched are segments of concentric spherical conducting shells of extremely large radius. The distance between the shells is d. The radius of the outer shell is L. If d is small compared to the smallest linear dimension of either segment, the capacitance of these conductors approximates that of an idealized parallel plate capacitor given in eq. 4.52.

PROBLEMS

4.1 By direct methods, calculate the amount of work necessary to assemble a distribution consisting of two charges $(q, -q)$ a distance d apart in an applied field $\mathbf{E}$ which is uniform over the distance between the charges.

4.2 Calculate the torque on a dipole consisting of the charge distribution described in Problem 4.1 by evaluating the forces on the component charges. Show that the result is identical with eq. 4.7. Calculate the work done in rotating the dipole through a finite angle with an applied torque.

4.3 The first nonvanishing multipole moments of two rotationally symmetric charge distributions are quadrupole moments. Calculate the quadrupole–quadrupole interaction energy of these charge distributions.

4.4 The only multipole moment possessed by each of two charge distributions is a dipole moment. Find the relative orientation of the two distributions which produces a minimum in the interaction energy.

4.5 Calculate the electrostatic energy of a system of equal charges q placed at the corners of a cube of side length s.

4.6 Show by a very careful argument that $\oiint_{\Sigma} \varphi \mathbf{E} \cdot \hat{\mathbf{n}} \, ds \to 0$ if φ and $\mathbf{E}$ are produced by a charge distribution contained within a volume V, every point of which is very far from every point on the closed surface Σ containing V within its interior.

4.7 A dipole of moment $\mathbf{p}$ is at the center of a mathematical sphere of radius R. Calculate the electrostatic energy residing outside the sphere. If the dipole consists in two charges $(q, -q)$ separated by a distance d $(\ll R)$, calculate the amount of energy residing within the spherical surface.

4.8 Calculate the electrostatic energy per unit length of a long conducting wire of circular cross section of radius R carrying a charge λ per unit length. For the calculation of this quantity, is an infinitely long wire a good approximation to a long but finite wire?

4.9 Find the capacitance per unit length of a capacitor consisting of a pair of long coaxial cylinders having inner and outer radii r_1 and r_2.

4.10 Calculate the capacitance per unit length of a long conducting cylinder of radius r oriented parallel to an infinite conducting plane and a distance d from the plane.

5 | *Electrostatics of Dielectric Media*

5.1 Macroscopic Theory of Dielectrics

The discussion of Chapters 2–4 concerned itself with electrostatic phenomena involving charged particles fixed in vacuo or residing on conductors. However, there exists a large bulk of matter which cannot be considered conducting; that is, under specified conditions of temperature and pressure, the number of current carriers per unit volume in this material is negligible. In this chapter, a macroscopic theory involving such materials—nonconductors or dielectrics—will be developed, and many of the concepts previously developed for vacuum and conductors will be re-examined for applicability to nonconductors.

To aid in the development of a macroscopic theory of dielectric media, a greatly simplified microscopic view will be adopted. When no external E-field is present, a typical atom or molecule of a dielectric material will have the center of charge of its negatively charged constituents (electrons) coincident with the center of charge of its positively charged constituents (nuclei). The center of charge of a charge distribution of total charge q and N-charged constituents is defined as

$$\bar{\mathbf{r}} \equiv \frac{1}{q} \sum_{i=1}^{N} q_i \mathbf{r}_i.$$

Such an atom or molecule is neutral and has no electric dipole moment. (There exist molecules which possess a permanent electric dipole moment; however, such molecules shall not be considered in this discussion.) If a molecule is placed in an electrostatic field, the cloud of electrons will experience a force equal and opposite to that experienced by the positively charged nuclei. Consequently, the center of charge of the electrons will be displaced relative to the center of charge of the nuclei, and a net electric dipole or (E1) moment will be induced. When the applied E-field is removed, the (E1) moment will vanish, but not instantaneously. In general, the applied E-field did work in creating the (E1) moment; the molecule in which the dipole is induced will lose its excess energy to its surroundings. The dielectric sample of which the molecule is a constituent will thus experience an increase in temperature. The magnitude of the

106

separation of the centers of positive and negative charge induced will depend on the strength of the applied E-field and the internal molecular forces which tend to resist the effect of the applied E-field. It is supposed that the E-field is weak enough so that the internal molecular forces are still able to bind the electrons to the neighborhood of the nuclei; if such a condition does not obtain, the electrons will be liberated, and the dielectric will exhibit some of the properties of a conductor. When the E-field is strong enough to liberate originally bound electrons, dielectric breakdown is said to ensue.

The induction of a dipole moment in the molecules of a dielectric under the action of an applied E-field will affect the electrostatic energy of a system of charged particles, conductors, and nonconductors. It will be shown that as far as electrostatics is concerned, the dielectrics may be replaced by equivalent charge distributions fixed on conductors and in vacuo. Consider the energy of orientation of a dipole of moment $p = 2qd$ placed in an E-field. Such a dipole will experience a torque in an E-field, but will experience no net force if the E-field is slowly varying such that it may be considered uniform over the extension of the dipole. According to eq. 4.3 the electrostatic potential at such a dipole is

$$\varphi(\mathbf{r}_j) = \varphi_0 - \mathbf{r}_j \cdot \mathbf{E} + \cdots \tag{5.1}$$

where $\mathbf{E}$ has been assumed to be slowly varying over the extent of the molecule, and to a good approximation $\mathbf{E}_0 = \mathbf{E}$. Substituting this value of the potential into eq. 4.4, the interaction energy becomes:

$$U_{\text{int}} = \varphi_0 \sum_{j=1}^{N} q_j - \mathbf{E} \cdot \sum_{j=1}^{N} q_j \mathbf{r}_j + \cdots. \tag{5.2}$$

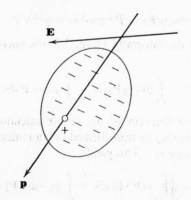

Fig. 5.1 The electric field at a given atom (or molecule) schematically represented induces a dipole moment **p**. The interaction energy between the field and the induced dipole is simply $-\mathbf{p} \cdot \mathbf{E}$.

Since the molecule is electrically neutral, the first term on the right-hand side of eq. 5.2 vanishes; in addition, the sum in the second term is simply the (E1) moment of the molecule. Consequently the interaction energy may be written as

$$U_{\text{int}} = -\mathbf{p} \cdot \mathbf{E}. \tag{5.3}$$

The macroscopic theory of dielectrics is based on the following hypothesis. A dielectric in an applied **E**-field may be considered equivalent to a volume distribution of induced dipoles; to every point in the dielectric is assigned a vector point function **P** equal to the dipole moment per unit volume in the neighborhood of that point. The energy of the dielectric in the applied field is then

$$U = -\int_\tau \mathbf{P} \cdot \mathbf{E} \, d\tau, \quad \text{where} \quad \mathbf{P} \equiv \frac{d\mathbf{p}}{d\tau}. \tag{5.4}$$

It should be remembered that eq. 5.4 gives only that contribution to the energy of the system due to the orientation of the submicroscopic dipoles in the material; eq. 5.4 does *not* contain the amount of work necessary to polarize the dielectric. The introduction of a dielectric into space does not destroy the conservative nature of the force field, and consequently **E** in eq. 5.4 may be replaced by $-\text{grad }\varphi$;

$$U = \int_\tau \mathbf{P} \cdot \text{grad } \varphi \, d\tau. \tag{5.5}$$

Once again, use is made of the identity of the vector calculus, which converts the divergence of the product of a vector and scalar point function into an expression involving derivatives of the scalar and vector functions separately, namely

$$\text{div}(\varphi \mathbf{P}) = \mathbf{P} \cdot \text{grad } \varphi + \varphi \, \text{div } \mathbf{P}. \tag{5.6}$$

Applying eq. 5.6 to the integrand of eq. 5.5, the energy of the dielectric may be expressed as

$$U = \int_\tau \text{div}(\varphi \mathbf{P}) \, d\tau - \int_\tau \varphi \, \text{div } \mathbf{P} \, d\tau.$$

Using the divergence theorem of the vector calculus, the first integral on the right-hand side may be transformed into an integral over the surface Σ, bounding the volume τ. This yields

$$U = \oiint_\Sigma \varphi(\mathbf{P} \cdot \hat{\mathbf{n}}) \, dS + \int_\tau \varphi(-\text{div } \mathbf{P}) \, d\tau. \tag{5.7}$$

Suppose one searches for a charge distribution residing in vacuum in the field **E**, which would contribute the same amount to the energy of the system as the above dielectric with its induced dipole moments. If σ_P and ρ_P are the surface and volume densities of this charge distribution, then σ_P and ρ_P must satisfy the following relation:

$$U = \oiint_\Sigma \varphi \sigma_P \, dS + \int_\tau \varphi \rho_P \, d\tau. \qquad (5.8)$$

Inspection of eqs. 5.7 and 5.8 yields

$$\sigma_P = \mathbf{P} \cdot \hat{\mathbf{n}} \quad \text{and} \quad \rho_P = -\operatorname{div} \mathbf{P}. \qquad (5.9)$$

The substance of eqs. 5.9 may be stated as follows. The electrostatic energy of a system of charges with charge densities σ_P and ρ_P residing in vacuum in an applied field $\mathbf{E}$ is the same as that of a dielectric with dipole moment per unit volume $\mathbf{P}$ placed in the same field if $\sigma_P = \mathbf{P} \cdot \hat{\mathbf{n}}$ and $\rho_P = -\operatorname{div} \mathbf{P}$ everywhere. Of course, in proving the above theorem it has not been shown that no other distribution of charge will produce the same interaction energy. It is possible to show that σ_P and ρ_P produce the same fields as the polarized dielectric, although this demonstration will not be carried out here.[1]

5.2 Gauss's Law for Dielectrics

The effect of the presence of dielectric material on Gauss's law may be seen as follows. Suppose there exists in a volume τ enclosed by a surface Σ an amount of charge q. Suppose further that the region τ contains only vacuum and/or conductors. Gauss's law then states that

$$\oiint_\Sigma (\mathbf{E} \cdot \hat{\mathbf{n}}) \, dS = \left(\frac{1}{4\pi\epsilon_0}\right) 4\pi q. \qquad (5.10)$$

If dielectric material is present in τ, the effect of the dielectric may be simulated by a charge q_P residing in vacuum, where

$$q_P \equiv \int_{\tau'} (-\operatorname{div} \mathbf{P}) \, d\tau + \oiint_{\Sigma'} \mathbf{P} \cdot \hat{\mathbf{n}} \, dS,$$

where $\begin{pmatrix} \tau' \\ \Sigma' \end{pmatrix} = \begin{pmatrix} \text{volume occupied by} \\ \text{surface bounding} \end{pmatrix}$ the dielectric.

---

[1] See Sect. 4.3 of *Classical Electrodynamics*, J. D. Jackson, John Wiley & Sons, New York, 1962.

Making the substitution $q = q_{\text{real}} + q_P$ in eq. 5.10 and converting the left-hand side of eq. 5.10 by use of the divergence theorem to an integral over τ, Gauss's law becomes:

$$\epsilon_0 \int_\tau \text{div } \mathbf{E} \, d\tau = q_{\text{real}} + \int_{\tau'} (-\text{div } \mathbf{P}) \, d\tau + \oiint_{\Sigma'} (\mathbf{P} \cdot \hat{\mathbf{n}}) \, dS. \quad (5.11)$$

The second integral on the right-hand side of eq. 5.13 may be combined with the integral on the left-hand side if it is noted that

$$\int_{\tau'} (-\text{div } \mathbf{P}) \, d\tau = \int_\tau (-\text{div } \mathbf{P}) \, d\tau - \int_{\tau_0} (-\text{div } \mathbf{P}) \, d\tau, \quad (5.12)$$

where τ_0 is that portion of τ *not* occupied by dielectric.

It is tempting to set the integral over the region τ_0 in eq. 5.12 equal to zero, since $\mathbf{P}$ is everywhere zero except in dielectrics; however, div $\mathbf{P}$ is zero everywhere in τ_0 *except* on the surface Σ' (i.e., dielectric surface) where it may be infinite. Substituting eq. 5.12 into eq. 5.11 yields, after some rearrangement of terms,

$$\int_\tau \text{div } \mathbf{D} \, d\tau = q_{\text{real}} + \int_{\tau_0} \text{div } \mathbf{P} \, d\tau + \oiint_{\Sigma'} \mathbf{P} \cdot \hat{\mathbf{n}} \, dS, \quad (5.13)$$

where

$$\mathbf{D} \equiv \epsilon_0 \mathbf{E} + \mathbf{P}. \quad (5.14)$$

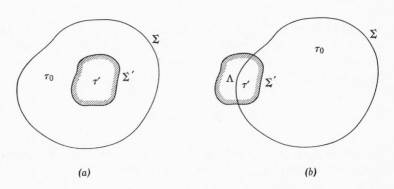

(a)   (b)

Fig. 5.2(*a*) A sample of dielectric material occupies the volume τ' and has a surface area designated by Σ'. A mathematical closed surface Σ is drawn surrounding τ. The volume enclosed between the surfaces Σ and Σ' is empty and is designated by τ_0. (*b*) A sample of dielectric material occupies a given volume. A closed mathematical surface is drawn which passes through the dielectric. That part of the mathematical surface which lies outside of the dielectric is designated by Σ whereas that lying within the material is given the symbol Λ. The volume and surface of the dielectric which lie within the mathematical surface are designated by the symbols τ' and Σ' respectively. Once again, τ_0 is the empty region contained between the surfaces Σ and Σ'.

It shall now be shown that the two integrals on the right-hand side of eq. 5.13 cancel one another identically. For this demonstration it will be assumed at first that the surface Σ enclosing τ does not intersect the dielectric surface Σ' (see Fig. 5.2a). The first integral on the right-hand side of eq. 5.13 may be transformed into a surface integral by use of the divergence theorem. There are two surfaces bounding τ_0, namely, Σ and Σ'. In addition, the interface between τ' and τ_0 (namely, Σ') is to be considered positive for τ' and consequently negative for τ_0. Therefore the integral over τ_0 transforms into

$$\int_{\tau_0} \operatorname{div} \mathbf{P} \, d\tau = \oiint_{\Sigma} \mathbf{P} \cdot \hat{\mathbf{n}} \, dS - \oiint_{\Sigma'} \mathbf{P} \cdot \hat{\mathbf{n}} \, dS. \qquad (5.15)$$

However, since $\mathbf{P}$ vanishes everywhere in vacuum and in particular on the surface Σ,

$$\oiint_{\Sigma} (\mathbf{P} \cdot \hat{\mathbf{n}}) \, dS = 0.$$

Consequently

$$\int_{\tau_0} \operatorname{div} \mathbf{P} \, d\tau = - \oiint_{\Sigma'} (\mathbf{P} \cdot \hat{\mathbf{n}}) \, dS$$

which upon substitution into eq. 5.13 cancels the second integral on the right-hand side identically. Therefore, providing Σ does not intersect a dielectric surface,

$$\int_{\tau} \operatorname{div} \mathbf{D} \, d\tau = q_{\text{real}}, \qquad (5.16)$$

or equivalently

$$\oiint_{\Sigma} (\mathbf{D} \cdot \hat{\mathbf{n}}) \, dS = q_{\text{real}}.$$

The form of Gauss's law for dielectrics has not as yet been developed for the most general case because of the provision mentioned above that Σ not intersect a dielectric surface. This provision may now be removed as follows. Redefine $\left(\dfrac{\Sigma'}{\tau'} \right)$ as the $\left(\dfrac{\text{surface}}{\text{volume}} \right)$ of dielectric contained within Σ and define Λ as that part of Σ which lies within the dielectric, i.e., $\Sigma = \Sigma' + \Lambda$ (see Fig. 5.2b). With this redefinition, eq. 5.13 is still valid; that is,

$$\int_{\tau} \operatorname{div} \mathbf{D} \, d\tau = q_{\text{real}} + \int_{\tau_0} \operatorname{div} \mathbf{P} \, d\tau + \iint_{\Sigma'} \mathbf{P} \cdot \hat{\mathbf{n}} \, dS.$$

Equation 5.15 must be modified, however, since the outer bounding surface of τ_0 is no longer Σ:

$$\int_{\tau_0} \text{div } \mathbf{P} \, d\tau = \oiint_\Sigma \mathbf{P} \cdot \hat{\mathbf{n}} \, dS - \iint_\Lambda \mathbf{P} \cdot \hat{\mathbf{n}} \, dS - \iint_{\Sigma'} \mathbf{P} \cdot \hat{\mathbf{n}} \, dS. \quad (5.17)$$

However, the sum of the first two integrals on the right-hand side of eq. 5.17 vanishes, since this sum represents the flux of $\mathbf{P}$ through that portion of Σ lying totally outside of the dielectric. Consequently, even in the case that Σ cuts through the dielectric,

$$\int_{\tau_0} \text{div } \mathbf{P} \, d\tau = - \iint_{\Sigma'} \mathbf{P} \cdot \hat{\mathbf{n}} \, dS$$

and consequently eq. 5.16 follows once again.

Gauss's law for dielectric media has been developed for the most general case. Assuming that all the real charge can be represented by a volume charge density ρ_{real}, the differential form of Gauss's law may be written as

$$\text{div } \mathbf{D} = \rho_{\text{real}}, \quad (5.18)$$

or equivalently

$$\text{div } (\epsilon_0 \mathbf{E} + \mathbf{P}) = \rho_{\text{real}}.$$

The vector field $\mathbf{D}$ is called the *displacement* field. This name is not very illuminating; a name more expressive of physical content is *electrostatic induction* field. Since only the volume density of real charge enters into the differential equation involving $\mathbf{D}$, the $\mathbf{D}$-field is sometimes said to have only real charge as its source, whereas $\mathbf{P}$ as well as real charge contributes to the $\mathbf{E}$-field in macroscopic theory.

5.3 Continuity Relations for the D-Field

The behavior of the $\mathbf{D}$-field at an interface separating two media may be garnered by a direct application of eq. 5.16. The development here will be similar to that carried out in the investigation of the behavior of the $\mathbf{E}$-field at the surface of a conductor (see Chapter 3). Consider a field point on the interface separating media 1 and 2 (see Fig. 5.3). A Gaussian pillbox is constructed with the field point in its interior. The flux of the $\mathbf{D}$-field through the walls of the pillbox is

$$\psi = (\mathbf{D}_2 \cdot \hat{\mathbf{n}} - \mathbf{D}_1 \cdot \hat{\mathbf{n}}) \, \Delta S + \text{contribution from the cylinder walls.}$$

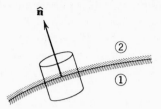

Fig. 5.3   A Gaussian cylinder or *pillbox* is constructed with one base area within region 1 filled with dielectric material of permittivity ϵ_1 and the other base area within region 2 filled with dielectric material of permittivity ϵ_2. $\hat{n}$ is a normal to the interface.   Gauss's Law applied to this cylinder yields the result: $(D_2 - D_1) \cdot \hat{n} = \sigma_{real}$ where σ_{real} is the real surface charge density residing on the interface.

If the height of the pillbox is shrunk to zero, then the contribution to ψ from the cylinder walls will vanish; consequently

$$\lim_{\Delta h \to 0} \psi = (D_2 \cdot \hat{n} - D_1 \cdot \hat{n}) \Delta S.$$

The total real charge contained within the pillbox is

$$\Delta q_{real} = \sigma_{real} \Delta S.$$

Application of Gauss's law to the pillbox yields

$$(D_2 \cdot \hat{n} - D_1 \cdot \hat{n}) = \sigma_{real}. \tag{5.19}$$

In other words, the normal component of the **D**-field suffers a discontinuity across an interface equal to the surface charge density residing on the interface.   The behavior of the tangential component of the **D** at an interface may be garnered from an argument similar to that employed in Chapter 3 in the investigation of the behavior of the tangential component of the **E**-field at the surface of a conductor.   A test charge q is moved in a rectangular path enclosing a portion of the interface between regions 1 and 2 (see Fig. 5.4).   The work done in moving the charge

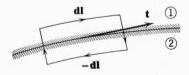

Fig. 5.4   A charge q is moved in a closed rectangular path as illustrated with part of the path in region 1 and region 2.   The work done in traversing this rectangular path is zero.   Consequently $E_1 \cdot t = E_2 \cdot t$ where t is any vector tangential to the interface between the two dielectrics at the field point.

around the closed path is zero.   This follows directly from the assumption that even in the presence of dielectric material, $\mathbf{E} = -\operatorname{grad} \varphi$ (see discussion immediately preceding eq. 5.5).   If the altitude of the rectangle in Fig. 5.4 is allowed to approach zero, then the vanishing of the work done on the test charge on one complete transit of the rectangular circuit yields

$$\int_{\text{side 1}} \mathbf{E} \cdot d\mathbf{l} + \int_{\text{side 2}} \mathbf{E} \cdot d\mathbf{l} = 0. \tag{5.20}$$

If the lengths of sides 1 and 2 are made small enough, then $\mathbf{E}$ will take on a constant value on each side; in addition, $d\mathbf{l}$ for side 1 is equal and opposite to $d\mathbf{l}$ for side 2.   Consequently eq. 5.20 becomes

$$(\mathbf{E}_2 - \mathbf{E}_1) \cdot \mathbf{t} = 0, \tag{5.21}$$

where $\mathbf{t}$ is any vector tangent to the interface at the field point.   The tangential component of the $\mathbf{E}$-field is continuous across the interface. The behavior of the tangential component of the $\mathbf{D}$-field depends upon the relationship between $\mathbf{E}$ and $\mathbf{D}$, which will now be discussed.

For most materials the induced polarization is proportional to the $\mathbf{E}$-field.   Such dielectrics are said to behave *linearly* under the application of electrostatic forces.   In addition, if such materials are isotropic, $\mathbf{P}$ may be written

$$\mathbf{P} = (4\pi\epsilon_0)\chi\mathbf{E} \tag{5.22}$$

where χ is a constant for a given material (it may depend upon temperature, pressure, etc.) and is called the *electric susceptibility* of the material. Since $\mathbf{D} = \epsilon_0\mathbf{E} + \mathbf{P}$ for linear materials,

$$\mathbf{D} = \epsilon\mathbf{E} \tag{5.23}$$

where $\epsilon = \epsilon_0(1 + 4\pi\chi)$ is the *electric permittivity* of the material.   For linear dielectrics the continuity of the tangential component of the $\mathbf{E}$-field across an interface may be expressed in terms of the discontinuity of the $\mathbf{D}$-field across such an interface:

$$\left(\frac{1}{\epsilon_2}\mathbf{D}_2 - \frac{1}{\epsilon_1}\mathbf{D}_1\right) \cdot \mathbf{t} = 0.$$

In turn, if no real charge resides on the interface, the continuity of the normal component of the $\mathbf{D}$-field across the interface can be expressed in terms of the discontinuity of the normal component of the $\mathbf{E}$-field across the interface:

$$(\epsilon_2\mathbf{E}_2 - \epsilon_1\mathbf{E}_1) \cdot \hat{\mathbf{n}} = 0.$$

The value of ϵ (or χ) for a given material cannot be determined from the macroscopic theory of dielectrics, but can be gleaned either from experiment or from a microscopic theory of the behavior of a dielectric in an applied **E**-field.

It is possible to consider the behavior of *nonisotropic linear* materials in an applied electrostatic field. Such nonisotropic materials could, for example, be crystalline in nature. For such materials *any* component of **P** may depend linearly on *every* component of **E**; that is, in place of eq. 5.22, eq. 5.24 must be substituted.

$$P_j = (4\pi\epsilon_0) \sum_{i=1}^{3} \chi_{ji}E_i, \quad j = 1, 2, 3, \tag{5.24}$$

where the set of nine numbers χ_{ji} are constants for a given material. This set of numbers can be thought of as the elements of a 3×3 susceptibility matrix. It is straightforward to show that the susceptibility matrix is symmetric, i.e., $\chi_{ji} = \chi_{ij}$. The demonstration proceeds as follows. The interaction energy per unit volume, u_{int} can be written down via eqs. 5.4 and 5.24 as

$$u_{\text{int}} = -\sum_{i=1}^{3}\sum_{j=1}^{3} \chi_{ji}E_jE_i = -\sum_{j=1}^{3} P_jE_j. \tag{5.25}$$

However, since the indices (i, j) are summed, they can be interchanged without changing the value of the sum on the right-hand side of eq. 5.25. Therefore

$$u_{\text{int}} = -\sum_{i=1}^{3}\sum_{j=1}^{3} \chi_{ij}E_jE_i \tag{5.26}$$

where the order of summation has also been interchanged. It follows immediately that $\chi_{ij} = \chi_{ji}$ since the Cartesian components of **E** are independent of each other.

5.4   The Energy of a System of Conductors and Dielectrics

The work done in charging a system of conductors residing in vacuum was calculated in Chapter 4. In that discussion all nonreversible physical processes such as Joule heating of the conductors were ignored—the resulting work, the *reversible work*, was then equated to the electrostatic energy U_e of the system. The physical situation in which charges are placed on conductors residing in space, part of which is filled with dielectric material, will be examined. Once again, only those physical processes will be considered to ensue which are reversible and the reversible work done in charging the conductors calculated.

The case of one conductor is treated for notational simplicity only. A careful perusal of the following discussion will indicate that it can be generalized quite easily to the case of an arbitrary number of conductors. The conductor is assumed to possess already a charge q and to be at a potential (constant throughout the conductor) of φ, and the amount of work necessary to add an additional amount of charge δq is calculated. This work is simply

$$\delta W = \varphi \, \delta q. \tag{5.27}$$

However, from Gauss's law it is known that an increase of charge on the conducting surface will cause the **D**-field to change on the conducting surface by an amount $\delta \mathbf{D}$ given by direct application of eq. 5.16

$$\oiint_{\Sigma} \delta \mathbf{D} \cdot \mathbf{n} \, dS = \delta q$$

where Σ is a closed surface surrounding the conductor and arbitrarily close to the conducting surface (see Fig. 5.5). Substituting into eq. 5.27 and remembering that φ is constant on Σ, it is found that

$$\delta W = \oiint_{\Sigma} \varphi \, \delta \mathbf{D} \cdot \hat{\mathbf{n}} \, dS. \tag{5.28}$$

Since $\delta \mathbf{D}$ suffers an abrupt discontinuity as one passes across the conducting surface, it is convenient to convert the integral over Σ in eq. 5.28 into an integral over the volume lying outside the conductor. This is done as follows: eq. 5.28 can be replaced by

$$\delta W = \oiint_{\Sigma} \varphi \, \delta \mathbf{D} \cdot \hat{\mathbf{n}} \, dS + \oiint_{\Sigma'} \varphi \, \delta \mathbf{D} \cdot \hat{\mathbf{n}} \, dS \tag{5.29}$$

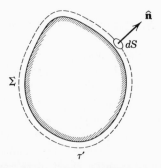

Fig. 5.5 A closed surface Σ is drawn immediately outside and surrounding a conductor at a potential φ. An element of Σ is designated by $dS \cdot \hat{\mathbf{n}}$ is the normal to dS pointing into the region τ' lying outside the conductor.

where Σ' is a closed surface at infinity; on Σ' both φ and $\delta\mathbf{D}$ vanish rapidly enough to insure the vanishing of the integral over Σ', since the conductor is assumed to be finite in extent. The right-hand side of eq. 5.29 can be converted into an integral over the volume τ' outside the conductor by use of the divergence theorem, since the surface $\Sigma_0 \equiv \Sigma + \Sigma'$ in the surface enveloping the volume τ':

$$\delta W = -\int_{\tau'} \text{div} \, (\varphi \, \delta\mathbf{D}) \, d\tau. \tag{5.30}$$

The minus sign appears in eq. 5.30 because $\hat{\mathbf{n}}$ is a unit vector pointing *into* the volume τ'. The integrand in eq. 5.30 can be expanded by use of a vector calculus identity (see eq. 5.6 for another application of this identity):

$$\text{div} \, (\varphi \, \delta\mathbf{D}) = \delta\mathbf{D} \cdot \text{grad} \, \varphi + \varphi \, \text{div} \, \delta\mathbf{D}.$$

Since the integrand is to be evaluated outside of the conductor where the charge density vanishes, the second term in the above identity may be neglected (taking cognizance of the differential form of Gauss's law—eq. 5.18):

$$\delta W = -\int_{\tau'} \delta\mathbf{D} \cdot \text{grad} \, \varphi \, d\tau. \tag{5.31}$$

However, the presence of dielectrics does not alter the conservative nature of the E-field, and grad φ may be replaced by $-\mathbf{E}$ in the integrand of eq. 5.31.   Consequently the amount of work necessary to add a charge δq to a conductor keeping the conductor at constant potential is

$$\delta W = \int_{\tau'} (\mathbf{E} \cdot \delta\mathbf{D}) \, d\tau. \tag{5.32}$$

The total work done in placing a finite charge on a conductor can be obtained from eq. 5.32 by integration.   However, to carry out this integral a functional relation must be given for $\mathbf{D}$ in terms of $\mathbf{E}$.   In the particularly simple and useful case of a homogeneous linear dielectric in which $\mathbf{D} = \epsilon\mathbf{E}$, eq. 5.32 can be integrated immediately, yielding

$$W = \tfrac{1}{2} \int_{\tau'} \epsilon E^2 \, d\tau, \tag{5.33}$$

or

$$W = \tfrac{1}{2} \int_{\tau'} (\mathbf{E} \cdot \mathbf{D}) \, d\tau.$$

The physical situation considered previously in which $\epsilon = \epsilon_0$ everywhere is obviously a special case of eq. 5.33.   For convenience, W is equated with the electrostatic energy of the system, U_e.

The following question now arises.   Suppose a system of N-charged conductors resides in vacuum; the space between the conductors is subsequently filled with material of permittivity ϵ.   What happens to the electrostatic energy of the system?   The question as it stands is unanswerable, for the manner in which the dielectric material is added plays an important role in determining the change in U_e.   To demonstrate this the following two cases will be considered: (1) the charges q_i on the conductors are held fixed (i.e., the conductors are isolated); (2) the potentials φ_i on the conductors are maintained (i.e., the conductors remain connected to the charging batteries).   Let $\mathbf{E}_0$ be the value of the E-field *before* the addition of the dielectric.   When the dielectric is added keeping the q_i fixed (case 1), then the application of Gauss's law to the conducting surfaces S_i yields

$$q_i = \oiint_{S_i} \epsilon \mathbf{E} \cdot \hat{\mathbf{n}} \, dS \quad \text{(after the addition of the dielectric)} \tag{5.34}$$

$$q_i = \oiint_{S_i} \epsilon_0 \mathbf{E}_0 \cdot \hat{\mathbf{n}} \, dS \quad \text{(before the addition of the dielectric).}$$

It does not immediately follow from eq. 5.34 that $\epsilon \mathbf{E} = \epsilon_0 \mathbf{E}_0$; eq. 5.34 merely states that $\epsilon \mathbf{E}$ and $\epsilon_0 \mathbf{E}_0$ satisfy the same boundary conditions (i.e., the same conditions on the conducting surfaces which are the surfaces that bound the region in which the conductors are imbedded).   However, in the region between the conductors, $\epsilon \mathbf{E}$ and $\epsilon_0 \mathbf{E}_0$ satisfy the same differential equation since all the charge is assumed to be held fixed:

$$\text{div} \, (\epsilon_0 \mathbf{E}_0) = \text{div} \, (\epsilon \mathbf{E}) = \rho. \tag{5.35}$$

Since $\epsilon \mathbf{E}$ and $\epsilon_0 \mathbf{E}_0$ satisfy the same boundary conditions and the same differential equation, they are identical:

$$\epsilon \mathbf{E} = \epsilon_0 \mathbf{E}_0 \quad \text{(for case 1).} \tag{5.36}$$

The general conclusion may be stated as follows.   If the permittivity of a region is allowed to change but all charges are held fixed during the change, the D-field is everywhere unaltered.   The energy in the field *before* the introduction of the dielectric is given by

$$U_0 = \frac{\epsilon_0}{2} \int E_0^2 \, d\tau.$$

The energy in the field *after* the introduction of the dielectric is given by

$$U = \tfrac{1}{2} \int \mathbf{E} \cdot \mathbf{D} \, d\tau \quad \begin{array}{l} \text{with } \mathbf{D} = \epsilon \mathbf{E} \text{ (by definition)} \\ \text{and } \mathbf{D} = \epsilon_0 \mathbf{E}_0 \text{ (from eq. 5.36).} \end{array} \tag{5.37}$$

Consequently

$$U = (\epsilon_0/\epsilon)U_0. \tag{5.38}$$

The energy of the field is *reduced* by the factor (ϵ_0/ϵ) upon introduction of the dielectric. To recapitulate, if the charges on the conductors are kept fixed, introduction of a linear homogeneous dielectric of permittivity ϵ between the conductors reduces the energy of the system. Since the energy of the system of conductors can be expressed in terms of the coefficients of capacitance and potential (see eqs. 4.42 and 4.43), it is evident that the coefficients of capacitance are increased by the factor (ϵ/ϵ_0) upon introduction of the dielectric, whereas the coefficients of potential are decreased by this ratio.

If the dielectric is added keeping the potentials φ_i on all the conductors fixed (case 2), then the electrostatic potential everywhere is unchanged by the addition of the dielectric material. Since the **E**-field is defined uniquely in terms of φ (i.e., $\mathbf{E} = -\operatorname{grad} \varphi$), it follows that the **E**-field is unchanged by the addition of the dielectric:

$$\mathbf{E}_0 = \mathbf{E} \quad \text{(case 2)}. \tag{5.39}$$

Consequently the energy of the system with the dielectrics present is

$$U = \tfrac{1}{2} \int \mathbf{E} \cdot \mathbf{D} \, d\tau \quad \begin{matrix} \text{with } \mathbf{D} = \epsilon\mathbf{E} \text{ (by definition)} \\ \text{and } \mathbf{D} = \epsilon\mathbf{E}_0 \text{ (from eq. 5.39).} \end{matrix}$$

Therefore U is *increased* by the factor (ϵ/ϵ_0); that is,

$$U = (\epsilon/\epsilon_0)U_0 \tag{5.40}$$

when the dielectric is added keeping the potential on the conductors fixed. Once again, the coefficients of capacitance are increased by the factor (ϵ/ϵ_0), and the coefficients of potential decreased by the factor (ϵ_0/ϵ) just as in case 1. This is not too surprising since these coefficients should *not* depend on the charges or on potentials of the various conductors in the system. It is evident that the increase in energy when the dielectric is added as in case 2 is provided by the batteries, which keep the conductors at a constant potential.

5.5 Body Forces in Electrostatics

In general, the matter occupying a volume element $d\tau$ experiences a force when an **E**- or **D**-field is present. For the calculation of this force, the matter in the volume element $d\tau$ will be assumed moving with the velocity **u**. The velocity **u** will be chosen small enough so that the considerations of electrostatics can be applied. If **f** is the force per unit volume acting on the matter in the volume element $d\tau$, then over-all conservation of energy requires that

$$\frac{dU_e}{dt} + \int \mathbf{f} \cdot \mathbf{u} \, d\tau = 0, \tag{5.41}$$

where dU_e/dt is the increase of the electrostatic energy of the system per unit time and $\int \mathbf{f} \cdot \mathbf{u} \, d\tau$ is the rate at which mechanical forces do work on the system. The electrostatic energy U_e is known uniquely when ρ, the charge density, and ϵ, the electric permittivity, are known. Consequently changes in time of U_e must be accompanied by changes in ρ and/or ϵ. Once again, it will be instructive to consider two special cases. (1) $\partial U_e/\partial \epsilon = 0$; i.e., the charge density ρ is varied but the electric permittivity remains constant. (2) $\partial U_e/\partial \rho = 0$; i.e., the electric permittivity is allowed to vary but the charges are fixed. In either case the change in the electrostatic energy is given simply by

$$U_2 - U_1 = \tfrac{1}{2} \int (\mathbf{E}_2 \cdot \mathbf{D}_2 - \mathbf{E}_1 \cdot \mathbf{D}_1) \, d\tau.$$

When ϵ is kept constant, the definition of the electric permittivity yields the result everywhere that $D_2/E_2 = D_1/E_1$, from which it follows that

$$U_2 - U_1 = \tfrac{1}{2} \int (\mathbf{E}_1 + \mathbf{E}_2) \cdot (\mathbf{D}_2 - \mathbf{D}_1) \, d\tau.$$

If the change in ϵ is infinitesimal, then to first order in the change

$$\mathbf{E}_1 = \mathbf{E}_2 \quad \text{and} \quad \mathbf{D}_2 - \mathbf{D}_2 = \mathbf{\Delta D}, \qquad (5.42)$$

yielding
$$\Delta U = \int \mathbf{E} \cdot \mathbf{\Delta D} \, d\tau.$$

The integrand of eq. 5.42 can be transformed into an expression involving the electrostatic potential function φ and the charge density ρ. In essence, the process leading to the general expression for U_e of eq. 5.33 is reversed: $\mathbf{E}$ is replaced by $-\,\text{grad}\,\varphi$, and use is made of the vector calculus identity

$$-(\text{grad}\,\varphi) \cdot \mathbf{\Delta D} = -\text{div}\,(\varphi \, \mathbf{\Delta D}) + \varphi \, \text{div}\,(\mathbf{\Delta D}).$$

However, Gauss's law in differential form (eq. 5.18) states that

$$\text{div}\, \mathbf{D}_1 = \rho_1 \quad \text{and} \quad \text{div}\, \mathbf{D}_2 = \rho_2$$

or
$$\text{div}\, \mathbf{\Delta D} = \Delta\rho.$$

Consequently

$$\Delta U = \int \varphi \Delta\rho \, d\tau \qquad \text{for } \epsilon \text{ fixed}, \qquad (5.43)$$

or alternatively

$$\frac{dU_e}{dt} = \int \varphi \frac{\partial \rho}{\partial t} \, d\tau \quad \text{when} \quad \frac{\partial \epsilon}{\partial t} = 0 \quad \text{(case 1)}. \qquad (5.44)$$

Thomson's theorem developed previously for conductors in vacuum only may now be proven quite generally using eq. 5.43. If all the charge resides on the conducting surfaces S_i, then $\rho \Delta \tau$ in eq. 5.44 may be replaced by $\sigma \Delta S$:

$$\Delta U = \sum_i \oiint_{S_i} \varphi \Delta \sigma \, dS. \tag{5.45}$$

Since the potential is constant over the surface of a conductor ($\varphi = \varphi_i$ on S_i), eq. 5.45 takes the form

$$\Delta U = \sum_i \varphi_i \Delta \oiint_{S_i} \sigma \, dS. \tag{5.46}$$

However, the integral on the right-hand side of eq. 5.46 is simply the charge on the ith conductor.   If the total charge is kept constant, i.e.,

$$\Delta \oiint_{S_i} \sigma \, dS = 0$$

but σ is allowed to be redistributed over the conducting surfaces, then $\Delta U = 0$.   This therefore constitutes the proof of Thomson's theorem in the general case: the electrostatic energy of a system is an extremum with respect to small displacements of charge over the surface of conductors.

When the charge density within a volume $d\tau$ is kept fixed but the electric permittivity changes, a change in the electrostatic energy of the system results in general.   Suppose a system of conductors carrying charge is originally placed in vacuum.   The electrostatic field strength everywhere will be designated by $\mathbf{E}_0$.   If the space between the conductors is filled with dielectric of permittivity ϵ keeping the charges fixed, the electrostatic energy per unit volume becomes (see eq. 5.38)

$$dU = (\epsilon_0/\epsilon)(\tfrac{1}{2}\epsilon_0 E_0^2) \, d\tau.$$

The difference between the electrostatic energy per unit volume for a dielectric of permittivity ϵ_2 and another of ϵ_1 is simply

$$\frac{dU_2}{d\tau} - \frac{dU_1}{d\tau} = \left(\frac{\epsilon_0}{\epsilon_2} - \frac{\epsilon_0}{\epsilon_1} \right) \tfrac{1}{2}\epsilon_0 E_0^2 = \tfrac{1}{2}(\epsilon_2 E_2^2 - \epsilon_1 E_1^2).$$

If ϵ_1 and ϵ_2 are functions of position (as well as time) and everywhere differ from one another by an infinitesimal amount [i.e., $\epsilon_2 = \epsilon_1 + \Delta\epsilon$ and as a consequence $E_2 = E_1 + \Delta E$ ($\epsilon_0 E_0 = \epsilon E$); therefore $\Delta E = -(\Delta\epsilon/\epsilon)E$], then the resultant difference in the electrostatic energy U_e is simply

$$\Delta U = -\tfrac{1}{2} \int \Delta\epsilon E^2 \, d\tau$$

or equivalently

$$\frac{dU_e}{dt} = -\frac{1}{2} \int \frac{\partial \epsilon}{\partial t} E^2 \, d\tau \quad \text{for fixed } \rho \text{ (case 2).} \tag{5.47}$$

The most general case is obtained when both ρ and ϵ are allowed to vary with time. Combining the results summarized in eqs. 5.44 and 5.47, the time rate of change of U_e may be written

$$\frac{dU_e}{dt} = -\frac{1}{2} \int \frac{\partial \epsilon}{\partial t} E^2 \, d\tau + \int \varphi \frac{\partial \rho}{\partial t} \, d\tau. \tag{5.48}$$

The desired relationship between the force density $\mathbf{f}$ and rates of change of the permittivity and charge density is gleaned from inspection of eqs. 5.41 and 5.48:

$$\int \mathbf{f} \cdot \mathbf{u} \, d\tau = \frac{1}{2} \int \frac{\partial \epsilon}{\partial t} E^2 \, d\tau - \int \varphi \frac{\partial \rho}{\partial t} \, d\tau. \tag{5.49}$$

In order to infer the force density $\mathbf{f}$ from eq. 5.49, the integrands on the right-hand side of eq. 5.48 must be transformed into a scalar product between the velocity vector $\mathbf{u}$ and some other vector,

$$\frac{1}{2} \int \frac{\partial \epsilon}{\partial t} E^2 \, d\tau \rightarrow \int \mathbf{f}_\epsilon \cdot \mathbf{u} \, d\tau$$

$$-\int \varphi \frac{\partial \rho}{\partial t} \, d\tau \rightarrow \int \mathbf{f}_\rho \cdot \mathbf{u} \, d\tau$$

where $\mathbf{f}_\epsilon$ and $\mathbf{f}_\rho$ are the force densities due to time-varying permittivity and charge density, respectively. $\mathbf{f}_\rho$ may be evaluated by applying the concept of the conservation of charge to a volume τ; that is

$$\frac{dQ}{dt} + \oiint_S \rho \mathbf{u} \cdot \hat{\mathbf{n}} \, dS = 0$$

where dQ/dt is the rate of increase of charge in the volume τ and the integral is the rate at which charge is flowing out of the surface S surrounding τ ($\rho \mathbf{u}$ is the current density). Writing $Q = \int \rho \, d\tau$ and applying the divergence theorem of the vector calculus to the integral results in an expression for $\partial \rho / \partial t$ in terms of the velocity $\mathbf{u}$, namely

$$\frac{\partial \rho}{\partial t} + \text{div} (\rho \mathbf{u}) = 0.$$

Consequently the second integral on the right-hand side of eq. 5.49 becomes

$$-\int \varphi \frac{\partial \rho}{\partial t} \, d\tau = +\int \varphi \, \text{div} (\rho \mathbf{u}) \, d\tau. \tag{5.50}$$

Once again, use is made of the powerful identity of the vector calculus:

$$\text{div} \{\varphi (\rho \mathbf{u})\} = \varphi \, \text{div} (\rho \mathbf{u}) + \rho \mathbf{u} \cdot \text{grad} \, \varphi.$$

Noting the above identity, eq. 5.50 transforms to

$$-\int \varphi \frac{\partial \rho}{\partial t} \, d\tau = -\int \rho \, \text{grad} \, \varphi \cdot \mathbf{u} \, d\tau + \int \text{div} [\varphi(\rho \mathbf{u})] \, d\tau. \tag{5.51}$$

Assuming that the charge density at infinity goes to zero and/or $\mathbf{u}$ is zero across any surface at infinity, the second integral on the right-hand side of eq. 5.51 vanishes making use of the divergence theorem. Consequently the force density due to changing charge density is simply

$$\mathbf{f}_\rho = -\rho \, \text{grad} \, \varphi = \rho \mathbf{E}. \qquad (5.52)$$

To evaluate the force density due to a changing permittivity, the following assumption will be made: the change in the permittivity at a point $\mathbf{r}$ is due only to bulk flow of material past point $\mathbf{r}$ (i.e., changes in ϵ due to changes in mass density ρ_m unaccompanied by bulk flow of material will be neglected). This will remove from consideration the group of phenomena classified as electrostriction, which are a part of the electro-statics of compressible fluids. Under the above assumption, the change in permittivity of the material in an element $d\tau$ is due to a flow of material into (or out) of $d\tau$. This means that if a coordinate system is constructed at $\mathbf{r}$ in $d\tau$ moving with the velocity of the material flowing into (or out) of $d\tau$, the time rate of change of ϵ evaluated in this moving coordinate system will vanish. The time derivative of ϵ evaluated in this moving system will be designated by $d\epsilon/dt$; according to the restriction mentioned above;

$$\frac{d\epsilon}{dt} = 0. \qquad (5.53)$$

However, to evaluate the contribution to the force density, $\partial\epsilon/\partial t$ must be evaluated where this derivative is evaluated in the stationary system. The question now arises: what relation, if any, exists between the "flow derivative" $d\epsilon/dt$ and the "normal derivative" $\partial\epsilon/\partial t$. This relationship is easily obtained if it is remembered that ϵ is a function of $\mathbf{r}$ and t. Consequently

$$\frac{d\epsilon}{dt} = \frac{\partial\epsilon}{\partial t} + \sum_{i=1}^{3} \left(\frac{\partial\epsilon}{\partial r_i}\right) \frac{dr_i}{dt} \qquad (5.54a)$$

where $r_i = i$th Cartesian component of $\mathbf{r}$. Equation 5.54a can be written in a more convenient form as

$$\frac{d\epsilon}{dt} = \frac{\partial\epsilon}{\partial t} + \text{grad} \, \epsilon \cdot \mathbf{u} \qquad (5.54b)$$

where $\mathbf{u}$ is the velocity of the material flowing into (or out of) $d\tau$. It has already been remarked that the left-hand side of eq. 5.54b vanishes. Therefore it is seen that

$$\frac{\partial\epsilon}{\partial t} = -\mathbf{u} \cdot \text{grad} \, \epsilon,$$

from which it follows that the force density due to changes in permittivity (see eq. 5.46) is

$$\mathbf{f}_\epsilon = -\tfrac{1}{2}E^2 \operatorname{grad} \epsilon. \tag{5.55}$$

The total force density is the sum of the effects of changing ρ and ϵ, namely

$$\mathbf{f} = \mathbf{f}_\rho + \mathbf{f}_\epsilon = \rho\mathbf{E} - \tfrac{1}{2}E^2 \operatorname{grad} \epsilon. \tag{5.56}$$

The occurrence of the first term in eq. 5.56 for $\mathbf{f}$, namely, $\rho\mathbf{E}$, is almost self-evident, since the operational definition of $\mathbf{E}$ is simply the force per unit charge in vacuum.   However, it was necessary to carry out the above derivation of this term in order to make certain the effect of the permittivity ϵ.

In the mechanics of fluids the force density $\mathbf{f}$ is sometimes called a *body force*.   The relationship between the body force and the pressure in a fluid (in this case an incompressible fluid) may be determined as follows.   Consider an infinitesimal cylinder in the fluid with base areas dA, one face of the cylinder located at $\mathbf{r}_2$ and the other at $\mathbf{r}_1$ (see Fig. 5.6). Since the fluid is in equilibrium, the net force on the cylinder must vanish:

$$(\mathbf{f} \cdot \mathbf{dr})\, dA + p_2\, dA - p_1\, dA = 0$$

where $\mathbf{dr} = \mathbf{r}_2 - \mathbf{r}_1$ and p_2, p_1 are the *hydrostatic pressures* on the faces of the cylinder located at $\mathbf{r}_2$ and $\mathbf{r}_1$, respectively, due to the fluid itself. The difference in pressure between the two points separated by the distance $\mathbf{dr}$ is then simply

$$dp = -\mathbf{f} \cdot \mathbf{dr}.$$

Since in the case of electrostatics the body force $\mathbf{f}$ is conservative, the

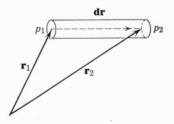

Fig. 5.6   A cylindrical tube of length $\mathbf{dr}$ is drawn in a fluid.   The base areas of the cylinder are located at $\mathbf{r}_1$ and $\mathbf{r}_2$.   The fluid pressures at the two bases are p_1 and p_2, respectively.

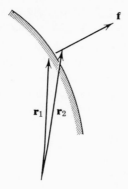

Fig. 5.7 r_1 and r_2 are two position vectors to points lying immediately inside and outside a conducting surface.   If a charge resides on the surface, there is a net force **f** outward from the conductor tending to enlarge the area of the conductor.

force density may be expressed in terms of the gradient of the pressure p (see arguments leading up to eq. 2.12):

$$\mathbf{f} = -\operatorname{grad} p.$$

The pressure difference between any two points in the electrostatic system may be written as

$$p_2 - p_1 = -\int_\Gamma (\rho \mathbf{E} - \tfrac{1}{2}E^2 \operatorname{grad} \epsilon) \cdot \mathbf{dr} \qquad (5.57)$$

where the integral is to be taken along *any* arbitrary path Γ connecting r_1 with r_2.

EXAMPLE 5.1   Equation 5.57 may be used to calculate the pressure difference between points immediately outside and immediately inside a conducting surface residing in vacuum (see Fig. 5.7).   For this case $\operatorname{grad} \epsilon \approx 0$, since the electric permittivity of most conductors is essentially ϵ_0.   The major contribution to the pressure difference comes from the term $\int \rho \mathbf{E} \cdot \mathbf{dr}$.   Since **E** inside a conductor vanishes and **E** outside has a component parallel to an outward normal if the surface charge density is positive and antiparallel if the surface charge density is negative, it is seen that the integral $\int \rho \mathbf{E} \cdot \mathbf{dr}$ is always positive (where r_1 is the point inside the conductor and r_2 the point outside).   Consequently

$$p_2 - p_1 < 0,$$

or the fields exert pressure on the surface of the conductor tending to enlarge the conducting surface and thereby decreasing the fields immediately outside the conductor. This is a phenomena analogous to the surface tension of a liquid drop in which the drop assumes a shape so as to minimize the surface energy of the droplet. A simple example will suffice to illustrate this analogy between a charged conductor and a water droplet. Consider the case of a conducting sphere of radius R and charge q residing in vacuum. The electrostatic energy of such a sphere may be determined from eq. 4.13:

$$U_e = \tfrac{1}{2}\epsilon_0 \int E^2 \, d\tau$$

where
$$\mathbf{E} = \left(\frac{1}{4\pi\epsilon_0}\right) \frac{q}{r^2} \hat{\mathbf{r}} \quad \text{for } r \geqslant R$$
$$= 0 \qquad\qquad \text{for } 0 \leqslant r \leqslant R$$

yielding
$$U_e = \left(\frac{1}{4\pi\epsilon_0}\right) \frac{1}{2} \frac{q^2}{R}.$$

Consequently if the sphere would be allowed to expand due to the outward pressure produced by the field generated by the sphere, it is seen that the electrostatic energy would be reduced.

EXAMPLE 5.2   Consider an uncharged dielectric slab partially filling up the space between the plates of a parallel plate capacitor (see Fig. 5.8). If the total charge on the conducting plates is held fixed, it has already been demonstrated that a lower energy of the capacitor would be reached if the slab were to move in to completely fill the space between the conducting plates (see eq. 5.38).

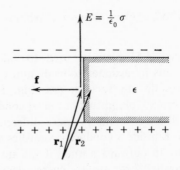

Fig. 5.8   The space between the plates of a parallel plate condenser is partially filled with a dielectric of permittivity ϵ. The field at the dielectric vacuum face is tangential to the face and is equal to $(1/4\pi\epsilon_0)4\pi\sigma$ where σ is the surface charge density on the positively charged plate at the dielectric vacuum interface. $\mathbf{r}_1$ and $\mathbf{r}_2$ are points lying respectively immediately outside and inside the slab. There is a net force on the slab tending to pull it into the capacitor.

An equivalent demonstration of this effect can be carried out by calculating the net pressure produced by the fields on the face of the dielectric slab. If the face of the slab is a long way from the ends of the capacitor, then the electric field at the face of the slab is parallel to the slab and has the value σ/ϵ_0, where σ is the surface charge density on the conductors in vacuum. The strength of the field is the same both immediately outside and immediately inside of the dielectric face, since the tangential component of E is continuous across an interface. Consequently

$$p_2 - p_1 = \frac{1}{2} \int \frac{\sigma^2}{\epsilon_0^2} \operatorname{grad} \epsilon \cdot \mathbf{dr} = \frac{\sigma^2}{2\epsilon_0^2} \int_\Gamma \operatorname{grad} \epsilon \cdot \mathbf{dr} \qquad (5.58)$$

where Γ is a path connecting points $(\mathbf{r}_1/\mathbf{r}_2)$ which are immediately outside and inside the face, respectively. Now $\operatorname{grad} \epsilon \cdot \mathbf{dx} = (d\epsilon/dx)\, dx$, and consequently

$$p_2 - p_1 = \frac{\sigma^2}{2\epsilon_0^2} (\epsilon - \epsilon_0) > 0.$$

There is a net pressure on the dielectric face tending to draw the slab into the capacitor and thereby reducing the electrostatic energy of the capacitor.

5.6   Electric Field Strengths Inside Dielectric Media

It has already been remarked that from the microscopic point of view, the E-field inside material (whether conducting or not) interpreted as the force field per unit charge is a violently fluctuating function of position and time. A microscopic probe of such a field would be, for example, a slowly moving electron with charge e. The force such an electron would experience would simply be given by

$$\mathbf{f}(\mathbf{r}, t) = e\mathbf{E}(\mathbf{r}, t). \qquad (5.59)$$

Of course, there is a hypothesis upon which eq. 5.59 is based that has not as yet been stated: namely, the force per unit charge on a slowly moving charged particle is the electric field strength irrespective of the fact that the force per unit charge may be an explicit function of time. The discussion of this hypothesis will subsequently be amplified when time-dependent problems are considered. It suffices here to remark that eq. 5.59 will define the method by which an instantaneous value of the E-field will be assigned.

However, the symbol E also appears, for example, in eq. 5.14:

$$\mathbf{D} = \epsilon_0 \mathbf{E} + \mathbf{P},$$

and it is abundantly clear that this **E** is not the **E** appearing in eq. 5.59; i.e., it is not the instantaneous electric field strength. It is, however, some time and volume average of the instantaneous field. The precise averaging process sensitively depends on what physical phenomena are being investigated. Two cases shall be considered here: (1) a charged particle moving through the material; (2) a molecule residing within the dielectric. In case (1) the averaging process consists in the following. In a time interval δT the particle will have traveled a distance $\delta \mathbf{l}$ along its trajectory. If the time interval δT is large compared to the period of motion of the electrons in their atomic orbits within the material and also large compared with the periods of the vibrational motion of the positive ions of the material, then it makes some sense to talk about a time average electric field seen by the moving particle. If the magnitude of $\delta \mathbf{l}$ is large compared to interatomic spacings, it makes additional sense to talk about a space average field. If both conditions are satisfied, it is evident that the moving charged particle can be visualized as moving in a macroscopic field **E** which is just a time and space average of the instantaneous microscopic field. This statement can be made more precise as follows. Suppose it is *assumed* that the instantaneous microscopic electric field $\mathbf{E}(\mathbf{r}, t)$ satisfies the differential Gauss's equation

$$\text{div } \mathbf{E}(\mathbf{r}, t) = \left(\frac{1}{4\pi\epsilon_0}\right) 4\pi\rho(\mathbf{r}, t). \tag{5.60}$$

Both sides of eq. 5.60 may be averaged over δT and $\delta \mathbf{l}$ explicitly as follows:

$$\int_{-\delta T/2}^{\delta T/2} d\theta \int_{\delta \mathbf{l}} \text{div } \mathbf{E}(\mathbf{r} + \mathbf{z}, t + \theta) \, \mathbf{dz}$$
$$= \left(\frac{1}{4\pi\epsilon_0}\right) 4\pi \int_{-\delta T/2}^{\delta T/2} d\theta \int_{\delta \mathbf{l}} \rho(\mathbf{r} + \mathbf{z}, t + \theta) \, \mathbf{dz} \tag{5.61}$$

where $\mathbf{r} + \mathbf{z}$ is a point on the trajectory of the particle and $\mathbf{dz}$ is an element of the trajectory.

More succinctly, the averaging operation can be expressed as

$$\langle \text{div } \mathbf{E}(\mathbf{r}, t) \rangle_{\delta T, \, \delta \mathbf{l}} = \left(\frac{1}{4\pi\epsilon_0}\right) 4\pi \langle \rho(\mathbf{r}, t) \rangle_{\delta T, \, \delta \mathbf{l}}. \tag{5.62}$$

Since the divergence operation is with respect to the space variable **r** and not with respect to the integration variables in the averaging process, the order of differentiation (in the divergence operation) and of integration (in the averaging operation) may be interchanged; in other words

$$\langle \text{div } \mathbf{E}(\mathbf{r}, t) \rangle_{\delta T, \, \delta \mathbf{l}} = \text{div } \langle \mathbf{E}(\mathbf{r}, t) \rangle_{\delta T, \, \delta \mathbf{l}}. \tag{5.63}$$

Consequently

$$\text{div } \langle \mathbf{E}(\mathbf{r}, t) \rangle_{\delta T, \, \delta \mathbf{l}} = \left(\frac{1}{4\pi\epsilon_0}\right) 4\pi \langle \rho(\mathbf{r}, t) \rangle_{\delta T, \, \delta \mathbf{l}}. \tag{5.64}$$

The content of eq. 5.64 is simply: the moving charged particle experiences an average field and charge density which satisfy Gauss's law. It therefore is reasonable to define macroscopic $\mathbf{E}$ and ρ as the space and time average of their instantaneous values if one is examining the motion of a charged particle through a medium.

The situation is somewhat different if one attempts to define a macroscopic $\mathbf{E}$-field seen by a constituent molecule of a polarized medium (case 2). Assume that a very large sample of the dielectric is placed in a uniform electric field and that the dielectric is linear and isotropic. Now imagine a small spherical surface constructed within the material. The volume of the sphere is chosen so that it is (a) small compared to the entire sample of the material, and (b) large enough so that it contains a number of molecules sufficient to carry out an averaging process to be discussed subsequently. The surface of the sphere may be considered to possess a surface charge density $(\mathbf{P} \cdot \hat{\mathbf{n}})$. This surface charge density is macroscopic and arises from the induced dipole moment of the molecules residing outside the spherical surface. The contribution of these polarization charges to the field at the center of the sphere is written down by the methods of Chapter 2 (see Fig. 5.9):

$$\mathbf{E}_P = \left(\frac{1}{4\pi\epsilon_0}\right) \oiint_{\substack{\text{spherical} \\ \text{surface}}} \hat{\mathbf{r}}\,\frac{\mathbf{P} \cdot \hat{\mathbf{n}}}{r^2}\,dS \qquad (5.65)$$

where $\qquad\qquad \hat{\mathbf{r}} = -\hat{\mathbf{n}}.$

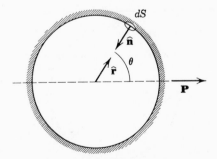

Fig. 5.9 A spherical surface is imagined constructed in a dielectric material in which there is a dipole moment per unit volume $\mathbf{P}$. The contribution to the field at the center of sphere due to all the material lying outside the sphere is $(1/4\pi\epsilon_0)(4\pi/3\ \mathbf{P})$. In the diagram, dS is an element of the spherical surface; $\hat{\mathbf{n}}$ is a unit normal at dS pointing toward the center of the sphere.

Only the component to $\mathbf{E}$ from each surface element parallel to $\mathbf{P}$ contributes to $\mathbf{E}_P$; i.e., $\hat{\mathbf{r}}$ in eq. 5.65 can be replaced by

$$\hat{\mathbf{r}} \rightarrow \frac{\mathbf{P}}{P} \cos \theta.$$

In addition, $\mathbf{P} \cdot \hat{\mathbf{n}} = P \cos \theta$.   Consequently

$$\mathbf{E}_P = \left(\frac{1}{4\pi\epsilon_0}\right) 2\pi\mathbf{P} \int_0^\pi \cos^3 \theta \, d\theta = \left(\frac{1}{4\pi\epsilon_0}\right)\left(\frac{4\pi\mathbf{P}}{3}\right). \tag{5.66}$$

The contribution to the E-field at the center of the sphere due to the molecules within the sphere will now be calculated.   For this purpose, consider the contribution to the potential at the center of the sphere ($\mathbf{r} = 0$) of the jth molecule within the sphere.   Via eq. 2.18 this is (see Fig. 5.10)

$$\varphi_j(0) = -\left(\frac{1}{4\pi\epsilon_0}\right) \frac{\mathbf{p}_j \cdot \mathbf{r}_j}{r_j^3}.$$

The contribution of the jth molecule to the electric field at the center of the sphere is

$$\mathbf{E}_j(0) = -\mathrm{grad}_j \, \varphi_j(0) = \left(\frac{1}{4\pi\epsilon_0}\right)\left\{\frac{\mathbf{p}_j}{r_j^3} - \frac{3(\mathbf{p}_j \cdot \mathbf{r}_j)}{r_j^5} \mathbf{r}_j\right\}.$$

The field at the center of the sphere due to all the molecules within the sphere is simply

$$\mathbf{E}_s = \left(\frac{1}{4\pi\epsilon_0}\right) \sum_{j=1}^N \left\{\frac{\mathbf{p}_j}{r_j^3} - \frac{3(\mathbf{p}_j \cdot \mathbf{r}_j)}{r_j^5} \mathbf{r}_j\right\}.$$

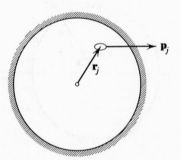

Fig. 5.10   The jth molecule inside the spherical surface discussed in Fig. 5.9 is located at $\mathbf{r}_j$ and has a dipole moment $\mathbf{p}_j$.   If there are many such molecules in the sphere and the material is homogeneous and isotropic, the contribution of all the molecules within the sphere to the field vanishes.

If the material is homogeneous and isotropic, then the induced dipole moment of each of the molecules is the same, namely, $\mathbf{p}$; consequently

$$\mathbf{E}_s = \left(\frac{1}{4\pi\epsilon_0}\right)\left\{\mathbf{p}\sum_{j=1}^{N}\frac{1}{r_j^3} - \sum_{j=1}^{N}(\mathbf{p}\cdot\mathbf{r}_j)\frac{\mathbf{r}_j}{r_j^5}\right\}.$$

It will be sufficient to consider one component of $\mathbf{E}_s$:

$$(\mathbf{E}_s)_x = \left(\frac{1}{4\pi\epsilon_0}\right)\left\{p_x\sum_{j=1}^{N}\frac{1}{r_j^3} - p_x\sum_{j=1}^{N}\frac{x_j^2}{r_j^5} - p_y\sum_{j=1}^{N}\frac{y_jx_j}{r_j^5} - p_z\sum_{j=1}^{N}\frac{z_jx_j}{r_j^5}\right\}. \quad (5.67)$$

If the material is isotropic, then for each molecule with a given set of coordinates (x, y, z) there will be another with the set $(x, -y, -z)$. The fraction of the molecules within the sphere unpaired in this manner will become smaller the larger the number of molecules within the sphere. In the limit of a very large number of molecules the relatively few unpaired ones can be ignored and

$$\sum_{j=1}^{N}\frac{y_jx_j}{r_j^5} = 0 = \sum_{j=1}^{N}\frac{z_jx_j}{r_j^5}. \quad (5.68)$$

In addition, for a large number of molecules of an isotropic material

$$\sum_{j=1}^{N}\frac{x_j^2}{r_j^5} = \sum_{j=1}^{N}\frac{y_j^2}{r_j^5} = \sum_{j=1}^{N}\frac{z_j^2}{r_j^5} = \frac{1}{3}\sum_{j=1}^{N}\frac{1}{r_j^3}. \quad (5.69)$$

Substituting the results of eqs. 5.68 and 5.69 into eq. 5.67, it is seen that $\mathbf{E}_s$ vanishes:

$$\mathbf{E}_s = 0.$$

Consequently the effective macroscopic field at a molecule within the dielectric is

$$\mathbf{E}_{\text{eff}} = \mathbf{E} + \left(\frac{1}{4\pi\epsilon_0}\right)\frac{4\pi\mathbf{P}}{3} \quad (5.70)$$

where $\mathbf{E}$ is the field causing $\mathbf{P}$.

PROBLEMS

5.1 A long dielectric cylinder whose cross section is an equilateral triangle of side length s is uniformly polarized with $\mathbf{P}$ perpendicular to the cylinder axis and to one of the cylinder faces. Find the equivalent charge distribution in vacuum which produces the same E-field everywhere.

5.2   An infinite slab of a linear homogeneous dielectric possesses a uniform polarization field **P**. Imagine that a small thin cylinder whose axis is parallel to **P** is excised from the slab without distorting the **P**-field elsewhere in the slab. Calculate **E** within the cylindrical cavity. Repeat the above calculation for a flat cylinder whose axis is parallel to the **P**-field.

5.3   A dielectric cylinder of length L and circular cross section of radius R is uniformly polarized with **P** parallel to the cylinder axis. Calculate the **E**-field at some arbitrary point on the cylinder axis.

5.4   A sphere of radius R is composed of a linear homogeneous dielectric material which is uniformly polarized. Calculate the **E**-field outside the sphere and show that it is that of a dipole. What is the equivalent dipole moment of the sphere?

5.5   Two slabs of linear dielectric material of permittivity ϵ_1 and ϵ_2 have a common planar interface. If the **E**-field in region 1 at the interface makes an angle θ with respect to the normal to the interface, what is the direction of the **E**-field in region 2 at the interface?

5.6   Calculate the electric field inside and outside a dielectric sphere of radius R and permittivity ϵ which has a point charge q located at its center.

5.7   A plane slab of dielectric material has a thickness t and permittivity ϵ. A real charge is uniformly distributed over one surface of the plane slab. If the surface density associated with this charge is σ, calculate: (a) **E** on both sides of the slab, (b) **E** within the slab, (c) the real charge density that is equivalent to the dielectric slab.

5.8   Calculate the electrostatic energy of system of charges imbedded in a crystalline dielectric which behaves linearly but nonisotropically in an **E**-field in terms of the fields **E** and **D**. Compare the result to that of eq. 5.33, which is valid for a linear but isotropic material.

5.9   The plates of a parallel plate capacitor are connected to a battery which maintains a constant potential difference $\Delta\varphi$ between the plates. The capacitance of the capacitor is C when the medium separating the plates is vacuum. The region between the plates is filled with a linear dielectric material of permittivity ϵ. How much work must be done in order to accomplish this? Repeat the calculation assuming the battery is disconnected but the plates of the capacitor charged before the dielectric is introduced.

5.10   A point charge q resides in vacuum a distance d from a planar semi-infinite slab of dielectric material of permittivity ϵ. Develop a "method of images" to find **E** both inside and outside the slab. Discuss the magnitude and location of the image charges.

5.11   Find the differential equation satisfied by the electrostatic potential φ in a homogeneous isotropic dielectric material of permittivity ϵ.

5.12   Using the equation developed for φ in problem 5.11 and the methods developed in Chapter 3 to solve such an equation, calculate the **E**- and **D**-field inside and outside a dielectric sphere of radius R and permittivity ϵ placed in an originally uniform **E**-field, E_0.

5.13 A parallel plate capacitor whose plates are separated by a distance d is filled with a dielectric material whose permittivity increases linearly from ϵ_1 and ϵ_2 from one plate to the other. Calculate the capacitance of this capacitor.

5.14 A parallel plate capacitor whose plates are separated by a distance d is placed vertically with one edge immersed in a dish of liquid of mass density ρ_0 and permittivity ϵ. If the plates of the capacitor are maintained at a potential difference $\Delta\varphi$, calculate the height h to which the liquid will rise within the capacitor.

6 | *Magnetostatics in Vacuum*

So far only those physical situations involving charged particles at rest have been examined. Although some situations have arisen in which moving charges were involved, the effect of this motion was neglected in the force law assumed to obtain among the charges. Stated in another way, the physical problems considered have been those to which Coulomb's force law was applicable. Attention now will be focused on a series of phenomena in which the effect of the motion of charges upon the force law cannot be neglected. However, the motion will be assumed to be approximately uniform, and the velocities of the charges involved will be assumed to be small. The phenomena will be termed *magnetostatic* phenomena.

In a certain sense, this is an unfortunate name for this class of phenomena. First, the basic characteristic of the phenomena is charge in motion—a characteristic far from static. Second, the name itself immediately suggests phenomena involving what are commonly called *magnets*. Actually, the physical description of phenomena associated with magnets is extremely complex. Historically, however, phenomena involving magnets have been studied much more extensively than the simple physical phenomena upon which this discussion of magnetostatics will be based. This is very easy to understand since magnetic material such as lodestone was readily obtainable, and it was a relatively simple matter to perform experiments with lodestone. It is, however, difficult to construct a theory of magnetostatics based upon the results of these experiments without introducing exceedingly artificial concepts and unadulterated physical fictions such as the *magnetic pole*, the magneto-static equivalent of the electrostatic charge, the electric monopole. It was only after many years of experimentation that physicists began to realize that the simple understanding of magnetostatic phenomena lay in the relatively difficult experiments involving moving charges and not in the relatively simple experiments involving magnets. (The ease with which an experiment can be performed does not guarantee the usefulness of the results of the experiment.) The modern viewpoint of magnetostatics will be considered here, and the discussion will be based on an experimentally verifiable force law involving charges in uniform motion. This force

134

law will play the same role in magnetostatics as Coulomb's law in electrostatics.

6.1 The Force Law for Slowly Moving Charges

Consider two charges q_1 and q_2 moving with uniform velocities $\mathbf{v}_1$ and $\mathbf{v}_2$, respectively; the instantaneous position of each of the charges is $\mathbf{r}_1$ and $\mathbf{r}_2$ (see Fig. 6.1). Experimentally it has been shown that there exists a force on each of the charges which depends on the velocity of both of the charges. This force shall be called the *magnetostatic* or Lorentz force. The force on charge 1 due to charge 2 is given by the expression

$$\mathbf{f}_{12} = K \frac{q_1 q_2}{|\mathbf{r}_1 - \mathbf{r}_2|^2} \mathbf{v}_1 \times (\mathbf{v}_2 \times \hat{\mathbf{n}}) \tag{6.1}$$

where

$$\hat{\mathbf{n}} \equiv \frac{\mathbf{r}_1 - \mathbf{r}_2}{|\mathbf{r}_1 - \mathbf{r}_2|}$$

and K is a constant depending on the choice of units. This force law holds only for charges moving "slowly," with negligible acceleration. It is difficult at this point in the discussion to indicate how slowly the charges must be moving and in what sense the acceleration must be negligible in order that the force law apply. It will suffice to say that the magnitudes of both $\mathbf{v}_1$ and $\mathbf{v}_2$ must be small compared to the velocity of light in vacuum; this will be justified in later chapters. In the later

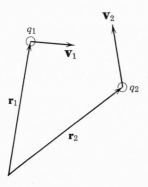

Fig. 6.1 Two charges q_1 and q_2 are instantaneously at the position $\mathbf{r}_1$ and $\mathbf{r}_2$, respectively. The charges are moving with velocity $\mathbf{v}_1$ and $\mathbf{v}_2$, the magnitudes of which are small compared to the velocity of electromagnetic waves in vacuum. The acceleration of both charges is also small. A force exists between these charges in addition to the Coulomb force. This Lorentz force is given by eq. 6.1.

discussion it will also be shown that accelerated charges lose (or gain) energy so that the accelerations must be small enough so that the energy lost (or gained) by the charges can be neglected.

The Lorentz force law upon which magnetostatics is based has a comparatively complex analytical structure; it depends upon the magnitudes and relative orientations of *three* vectors ($\mathbf{v}_1$, $\mathbf{v}_2$, and $\mathbf{r}_1 - \mathbf{r}_2$). (This is to be compared with Coulomb's law which depends only upon the magnitude and orientation of *one* vector $\mathbf{r}_1 - \mathbf{r}_2$.) In addition to its rather complex analytical structure, the Lorentz force law has the peculiar property that $\mathbf{f}_{12}$ is not parallel to $\hat{\mathbf{n}}$. As a consequence

$$\mathbf{f}_{12} + \mathbf{f}_{21} \neq 0.$$

This can be seen as follows: the force on charge 2 due to charge 1 can be obtained from eq. 6.1 by simply interchanging the symbols 1 and 2, and remembering that in this interchange, $\hat{\mathbf{n}}$ must be replaced by $-\hat{\mathbf{n}}$.

$$\mathbf{f}_{21} = -K \frac{q_1 q_2}{|\mathbf{r}_1 - \mathbf{r}_2|^2} \mathbf{v}_2 \times (\mathbf{v}_1 \times \hat{\mathbf{n}}). \tag{6.2}$$

By noting the vector analysis identity

$$\mathbf{a} \times (\mathbf{b} \times \mathbf{c}) = (\mathbf{a} \cdot \mathbf{c})\mathbf{b} - (\mathbf{a} \cdot \mathbf{b})\mathbf{c},$$

it is easy to establish that

$$\mathbf{f}_{12} + \mathbf{f}_{21} = K \frac{q_1 q_2}{|\mathbf{r}_1 - \mathbf{r}_2|^2} \hat{\mathbf{n}} \times (\mathbf{v}_2 \times \mathbf{v}_1). \tag{6.3}$$

Only in the special cases that $\mathbf{v}_2$ is parallel to $\mathbf{v}_1$ or that $\hat{\mathbf{n}}$ is perpendicular to the plane defined by the vectors $\mathbf{v}_1$ and $\mathbf{v}_2$ does the right-hand side of eq. 6.3 vanish. As a consequence, Newton's third law of motion cannot be directly applied to magnetostatic phenomena. This curious feature of the magnetostatic force will be discussed later in some detail in section 10.8. (The electrostatic force law, on the other hand, is of the type envisioned by Newton in his third law.)

6.2   The Magnetostatic Induction Field

Just as in electrostatics, the force law can be used to define an appropriate field which may be looked upon operationally in this case as the medium by which the moving charges exert forces upon one another. The so-called *magnetostatic induction field* **B** at the positions $\mathbf{r}_1$ and $\mathbf{r}_2$ of charges

1 and 2 can be defined in terms of the forces $\mathbf{f}_1$ and $\mathbf{f}_2$ on these charges via eq. 6.4:

$$\mathbf{f}_1(\mathbf{r}_1) = K_a q_1 \mathbf{v}_1 \times \mathbf{B}(\mathbf{r}_1)$$
$$\mathbf{f}_2(\mathbf{r}_2) = K_a q_2 \mathbf{v}_2 \times \mathbf{B}(\mathbf{r}_2) \tag{6.4}$$

where

$$\mathbf{B}(\mathbf{r}_1) = K_b q_2 \frac{(\mathbf{r}_2 - \mathbf{r}_1) \times \mathbf{v}_2}{|\mathbf{r}_2 - \mathbf{r}_1|^3}$$
$$\mathbf{B}(\mathbf{r}_2) = K_b q_1 \frac{(\mathbf{r}_1 - \mathbf{r}_2) \times \mathbf{v}_1}{|\mathbf{r}_2 - \mathbf{r}_1|^3} \tag{6.5}$$

and $K = K_a K_b$. (The constants K_a and K_b depend on the units chosen.)

The force on a charge q having the instantaneous position $\mathbf{r}$ and velocity $\mathbf{v}$ due to an ensemble of charges $q_1 \ldots q_N$ with instantaneous positions $\mathbf{r}_1 \ldots \mathbf{r}_N$ and velocities $\mathbf{v}_1 \ldots \mathbf{v}_N$ is given by an obvious generalization of eq. 6.1:

$$\mathbf{f}(\mathbf{r}) = K q \mathbf{v} \times \sum_{i=1}^{N} q_i \frac{(\mathbf{v}_i \times \hat{\mathbf{n}}_i)}{|\mathbf{r}_i - \mathbf{r}|^2}, \tag{6.6}$$

where

$$\hat{\mathbf{n}}_i \equiv \frac{\mathbf{r} - \mathbf{r}_i}{|\mathbf{r} - \mathbf{r}_i|}.$$

The **B**-field at the charge q is simply

$$\mathbf{B}(\mathbf{r}) = K_b \sum_{i=1} q_i \frac{\mathbf{v}_i \times \hat{\mathbf{n}}_i}{|\mathbf{r}_i - \mathbf{r}|^2}. \tag{6.7}$$

Equations 6.6 and 6.7 can be written in integral form by noting that the charge density at $\mathbf{r}'$ associated with point charges $q_1 \ldots q_N$ located at $\mathbf{r}_1 \ldots \mathbf{r}_N$, respectively, is

$$\rho(\mathbf{r}') \equiv \sum_{i=1}^{N} q_i \, \delta(\mathbf{r}_i - \mathbf{r}'). \tag{6.8}$$

It is straightforward to verify that eqs. 6.6a and 6.7a are equivalent to eqs. 6.6 and 6.7

$$\mathbf{f}(\mathbf{r}) = K q \mathbf{v} \times \int d\tau' \, \frac{\mathbf{v}' \times \hat{\mathbf{n}}}{|\mathbf{r}' - \mathbf{r}|^2} \, \rho(\mathbf{r}') \tag{6.6a}$$

and

$$\mathbf{B}(\mathbf{r}) = K_b \int d\tau' \, \frac{\mathbf{v}' \times \hat{\mathbf{n}}}{|\mathbf{r}' - \mathbf{r}|^2} \, \rho(\mathbf{r}') \tag{6.7a}$$

where

$$\hat{\mathbf{n}} = \frac{\mathbf{r} - \mathbf{r}'}{|\mathbf{r} - \mathbf{r}'|}.$$

6.3   *Magnetostatic Units*

A specific choice will now be made for the constant K, which appears in the force law, and the constant K_b, which appears in the definition of the magnetostatic induction field. It should be noted that both the force and field equations contain the electric charge of the particles experiencing the force and producing the field. Since the ultimate goal for this study of electric and magnetic phenomena is a unified theory encompassing all such phenomena, it would be wise to choose the same units for electric charge in magnetostatics as in electrostatics. In Gaussian units (cgs units for dynamical quantities such as force, length, time and unit value of the multiplicative constant in Coulomb's force law), the K in the magnetostatic force law must have the dimensions of the inverse of the square of velocity:

$$K = \frac{1}{c^2} \tag{6.9}$$

where c has the dimensions of centimeters per second. It turns out that the experimental value of c is 3×10^{10} cm/sec, the velocity of light in vacuum. It is worthwhile to note two things about c: (i) it cannot be determined from the previous discussion since no connection between electric and magnetic phenomena has as yet been demonstrated in this text; (ii) the numerical value of c is no mere coincidence but is based on a connection between electric and magnetic phenomena that must be explored in later chapters.

Further, in Gaussian units the constants K_a and K_b both have the dimensions of reciprocal velocity and both are chosen to have the value c^{-1}. Both these assignments are completely arbitrary; the former allows **B** to have the same units as **E**, whereas the latter simply injects some symmetry into the force and field laws which read in Gaussian units:

$$\mathbf{f}(\mathbf{r}) = q\,\frac{\mathbf{v}}{c} \times \mathbf{B}(\mathbf{r}) \tag{6.6g}$$

$$\mathbf{B}(\mathbf{r}) = \int d\tau' \, \frac{\left(\dfrac{\mathbf{v}'}{c}\right) \times \hat{\mathbf{n}}}{|\mathbf{r} - \mathbf{r}'|^2} \, \rho(\mathbf{r}'). \tag{6.7g}$$

The units in which the present discussion of magnetostatics will be carried out are the rationalized mks units. In this system the constant K is expressed as

$$K = (1/4\pi)\mu_0 \tag{6.10}$$

and has the value of 10^{-7} mks units which are given the special name of henries/meter. This value of K is determined from experiment; the dimensions of the force are newtons, that of the velocities meters/second, and that of the charges coulombs. In these units the constant K_b is also chosen to be $(1/4\pi)\mu_0$ so that the force and field equations in rationalized mks units read

$$\mathbf{f}(\mathbf{r}) = q\mathbf{v} \times \mathbf{B}(\mathbf{r}) \tag{6.6b}$$

$$\mathbf{B}(\mathbf{r}) = \left(\frac{\mu_0}{4\pi}\right) \int d\tau' \, \frac{\mathbf{v}' \times \hat{\mathbf{n}}}{|\mathbf{r} - \mathbf{r}'|^2} \, \rho(\mathbf{r}'). \tag{6.7b}$$

There are several other systems of units which have occasional use in the literature; the student is referred to the Appendix for a further discussion of units.

6.4   Steady-State Currents

In the expressions for $\mathbf{f}(\mathbf{r})$ and $\mathbf{B}(\mathbf{r})$ there appears the quantity

$$\mathbf{j}(\mathbf{r}') = \rho(\mathbf{r}')\mathbf{v}'. \tag{6.11}$$

This quantity $\mathbf{j}$ is commonly called the *current density*; it has the dimensions of charge per unit area per unit time (i.e., coulombs per square meter per second). The current density (a vector point function) is related to the current (a scalar) in the following manner. Consider a surface element $\mathbf{ds}$ centered at the point $\mathbf{r}$; the current at this surface element is defined by

$$dI \equiv \mathbf{j} \cdot \mathbf{ds} = \rho(\mathbf{r})\mathbf{v} \cdot \mathbf{ds}. \tag{6.12}$$

If $\mathbf{ds}$ is an element of a finite surface S, the current flowing through the surface is given by the integral of dI over the entire surface:

$$I \equiv \iint_S dI = \iint_S \mathbf{j} \cdot \mathbf{ds}. \tag{6.13}$$

The definition of the current I expressed in eq. 6.13 is precise but suffers from being extremely formal. The question now arises whether I defined in this manner is the same as the intuitive notion of an electric current. To examine this, consider Fig. 6.2. The cylinder sketched within a current carrier is chosen in the following manner: the size of the cylinder is small enough so that the charge density ρ and the velocity of charges within the cylinder are essentially constant. Under these conditions the total charge Δq within the cylinder is simply the charge density ρ times the cylindrical volume ($\Delta s \, \Delta l \cos \theta$). In the time interval Δt, defined by $\Delta l = v \, \Delta t$, where v is the magnitude of the velocity of the charges in the volume, an amount of charge Δq will have flowed out of the cylindrical

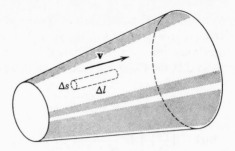

Fig. 6.2   A small cylinder of base area Δs and length Δl is imagined inside a current-carrying conductor.   The sides of the cylinder are parallel to the direction of charge flow **v**.

volume through the surface Δs.   The rate at which charge flows out of the volume through the surface Δs (i.e., the electric current within the cylinder) is given by

$$\Delta I \equiv \frac{\Delta q}{\Delta t} = \rho v \, \Delta s \cos \theta,$$

or equivalently,

$$\Delta I = \rho \mathbf{v} \cdot \hat{\mathbf{n}} \, \Delta s. \tag{6.14}$$

If Δs is infinitesimally small, which it must be if the arguments leading to eq. 6.14 are to apply in the general case, then eqs. 6.14 and 6.12 are identical.

If the above arguments are to hold in the general case, Δt and Δq must also be infinitesimally small.   This condition leads to the alternative and less formal definition of the electric current as

$$I = dq/dt. \tag{6.15}$$

There exists a very simple relationship involving the changes in space and time of the current density **j** and the charge density ρ.   This relationship is called the *continuity relation* and is a direct consequence of the hypothesis of charge conservation.   To establish the continuity relation, consider a volume τ enclosed by a surface Σ (see Fig. 6.3).   If the amount of charge residing in τ changes in time, it must be caused by charges flowing into (or out of) τ through the surface Σ since there is no creation or annihilation of charge within τ.   The rate at which the amount of charge is changing within τ is given by eq. 6.16:

$$\frac{dQ}{dt} = \frac{d}{dt} \int_{\tau} d\tau \rho(\mathbf{r}, t), \quad (> 0 \text{ if charge increases}). \tag{6.16}$$

This must be equal to the rate at which charge flows into τ through the surface Σ, which is simply

$$-\oiint_\Sigma \mathbf{j} \cdot \hat{\mathbf{n}} \, ds, \quad (> 0 \text{ if charge flows into } \tau). \qquad (6.17)$$

The equality is expressed as

$$\frac{d}{dt} \int_\tau \rho(\mathbf{r}, t) \, d\tau + \oiint_\Sigma \mathbf{j} \cdot \hat{\mathbf{n}} \, ds = 0. \qquad (6.18)$$

Equation 6.18 is the analytic statement of the conservation of electric charge. Since τ is not changing in time, the time differentiation in the first term of eq. 6.18 can be brought inside the integral sign; here it must be interpreted as a partial time derivative since ρ depends, in general, upon $\mathbf{r}$ as well as t. In addition, the integral over Σ in the second term can be converted into an integral over τ by use of the divergence theorem of the vector calculus, yielding

$$\int_\tau d\tau \left\{ \frac{\partial}{\partial t} \rho(\mathbf{r}, t) + \text{div } \mathbf{j}(\mathbf{r}, t) \right\} = 0. \qquad (6.19)$$

Since eq. 6.19 holds for arbitrary τ, the integrand must vanish. The vanishing of the integrand in eq. 6.19 is the differential form of the charge conservation law or the desired continuity relation, namely,

$$\frac{\partial}{\partial t} \rho(\mathbf{r}, t) + \text{div } \mathbf{j}(\mathbf{r}, t) = 0. \qquad (6.20)$$

In a nonstatic ($\mathbf{j} \neq 0$) but steady-state $[(\partial/\partial t)\rho = 0]$ situation, it immediately follows that div $\mathbf{j} = 0$ everywhere.

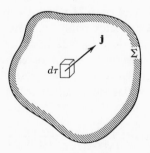

Fig. 6.3 A closed surface Σ surrounds a volume τ. Application of the law of conservation of charge to τ leads to a differential relationship involving the charge density ρ and the current density $\mathbf{j}$ at every point within Σ. This "continuity relation" is given in eq. 6.20.

6.5   The Vector Potential

It is convenient at this point to define the *vector potential* **A** which plays a role in magnetostatics similar to that played by the *scalar potential* φ in electrostatics.   It can be introduced simply as follows.   Consider the following expression defining a vector point function:

$$\mathbf{A}(\mathbf{r}) \equiv \left(\frac{\mu_0}{4\pi}\right) \int d\tau' \, \frac{\mathbf{j}(\mathbf{r}')}{|\mathbf{r} - \mathbf{r}'|}. \tag{6.21}$$

The assertion is now made that curl **A** = **B**.   This assertion is easy to verify by computing directly the curl of both sides of eq. 6.21

$$\text{curl } \mathbf{A} = \left(\frac{\mu_0}{4\pi}\right) \int d\tau' \, \text{curl} \left\{ \mathbf{j}(\mathbf{r}') \cdot \frac{1}{|\mathbf{r} - \mathbf{r}'|} \right\}.$$

It should be remembered that the derivative operators in the curl are with respect to **r** and *not* **r**′ (the variable of integration on the right-hand side of eq. 6.21).   Since **j** is a function of **r**′ and not of **r**, it is a constant vector as far as the curl operation is concerned and therefore

$$\text{curl} \left\{ \mathbf{j}(\mathbf{r}') \, \frac{1}{|\mathbf{r} - \mathbf{r}'|} \right\} = \mathbf{j}(\mathbf{r}') \times \text{grad } \frac{1}{|\mathbf{r} - \mathbf{r}'|} = \mathbf{j}(\mathbf{r}') \times \frac{\hat{\mathbf{n}}}{|\mathbf{r} - \mathbf{r}'|^2}.$$

Making use of this result, it follows directly that

$$\text{curl } \mathbf{A}(\mathbf{r}) = \left(\frac{\mu_0}{4\pi}\right) \int d\tau' \, \frac{\mathbf{j}(\mathbf{r}') \times \hat{\mathbf{n}}}{|\mathbf{r} - \mathbf{r}'|^2}$$

or

$$\text{curl } \mathbf{A} = \mathbf{B}. \tag{6.22}$$

Equation 6.22 is the equation connecting the vector potential **A** and the magnetostatic induction field **B**.   It is necessary to remark at this point that the prescription for **A** of eq. 6.21 which yields the correct expression for **B** is not unique.   Any vector point function whose curl is zero may be added to the right-hand side of eq. 6.22, and the value of **B** thus obtained would be unchanged.   The prescription of eq. 6.21 is a very natural one, however, since it bears a certain formal resemblance to the definition in electrostatics of the scalar potential in terms of the charge density $\rho(\mathbf{r})$, namely

$$\varphi(\mathbf{r}) = \left(\frac{1}{4\pi\epsilon_0}\right) \int d\tau' \, \frac{\rho(\mathbf{r}')}{|\mathbf{r} - \mathbf{r}'|}. \tag{6.23}$$

A comparison of eqs. 6.21 and 6.23 yields the observation that **j** plays a role in magnetostatics similar to ρ in electrostatics.   Of course, eq. 6.21 is really a set of three equations since **A** is a vectorial quantity.   It is quite obvious that the integral in eq. 6.21 for **A** is much simpler to perform in general than the integral for **B** in eq. 6.7*b* because of the relative simplicity of the integrand. The same situation holds in electrostatics in which **E** is given by

$$\mathbf{E}(\mathbf{r}) = \left(\frac{1}{4\pi\epsilon_0}\right) \int d\tau' \, \rho(\mathbf{r}') \frac{\hat{\mathbf{n}}}{|\mathbf{r} - \mathbf{r}'|^2} \tag{6.24}$$

the integral on the right-hand side of eq. 6.23 for φ being simpler to perform than that on the right-hand side of eq. 6.24. Although **A** plays a role in magnetostatics analogous to φ in electrostatics, it should be noted that **A** has not been given any simple operational definition. **A** has been introduced at this point as a convenient auxiliary vector field which can be used to simplify the calculation of many magnetostatic problems. We shall postpone until later any attempt to arrive at a more physical description of the **A**-field.

EXAMPLE 6.1 The **B**-field and the vector potential **A** may be calculated in a straightforward manner from their defining equations. In many cases the integrals appearing in these equations may be performed by elementary methods. As a simple example consider **A** and **B** at the center of a spherical conducting shell of inner radius a and outer radius b carrying a current density **j** which is uniform and always tangent to circles of constant latitude (see Fig. 6.4). From eq. 6.21 it is noted that

$$\mathbf{A}(0) = \left(\frac{\mu_0}{4\pi}\right) \int_V d\tau' \, \frac{\mathbf{j}(\mathbf{r}')}{r'}$$

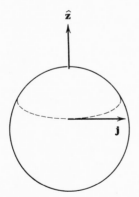

Fig. 6.4 A spherical shell is conducting a current. The current density **j** is everywhere tangent to circles of constant latitude. The unit vector $\hat{\mathbf{z}}$ is the polar axis of the sphere.

where V = volume of the shell and the origin of coordinates is located at the center of the sphere, i.e., the field point. Since the magnitude of $\mathbf{j}$ is uniform throughout V, it is obvious from the geometrical symmetry inherent in the problem that $\mathbf{A}(0) = 0$. On the other hand, $\mathbf{B}(0)$ does not vanish. Examining the expression for $\mathbf{B}(0)$,

$$\mathbf{B}(0) = \left(\frac{\mu_0}{4\pi}\right) \int_V d\tau' \, \frac{\mathbf{j(r')} \times \hat{\mathbf{n}}}{r'^2}$$

it is obvious, once again from symmetry considerations, that only that component of $\mathbf{j} \times \hat{\mathbf{n}}$ which is parallel to the polar axis of the sphere contributes to $\mathbf{B}(0)$. As a consequence

$$\mathbf{B}(0) = \left(\frac{\mu_0}{4\pi}\right) j \int_V d\tau' \, \frac{\sin \theta}{r'^2} \, \hat{\mathbf{z}}.$$

Noting that $d\tau' = \sin \theta \, d\theta \, d\phi r'^2 \, dr'$, the volume integral can be performed immediately:

$$\mathbf{B}(0) = \left(\frac{\mu_0}{4\pi}\right) j\hat{\mathbf{z}} \int_a^b dr' \int_0^\pi \sin^2 \theta \, d\theta \int_0^{2\pi} d\phi = \left(\frac{\mu_0}{4\pi}\right) \pi^2 (b - a) j\hat{\mathbf{z}}$$

On the other hand, the shell is conducting a total current i given by the expression

$$i = \frac{\pi}{2} j(b^2 - a^2),$$

and as a consequence

$$\mathbf{B}(0) = \left(\frac{\mu_0}{4\pi}\right) \frac{2\pi i}{b + a} \, \hat{\mathbf{z}}.$$

In the limit that $b \to a$ but i remains fixed (an infinitely thin shell conducting a finite current), this yields

$$\mathbf{B}(0) = \left(\frac{\mu_0}{4\pi}\right) \frac{\pi i}{a} \, \hat{\mathbf{z}}.$$

6.6   Magnetic Effects Associated with Closed Current-Carrying Loops: the Biot–Savart Law

There are situations in which the expressions for $\mathbf{f}$, $\mathbf{B}$, and $\mathbf{A}$ discussed so far can be written in somewhat more convenient form. The situations referred to are extremely common and are those in which the charges participating in the motion are confined to regions in space whose cross section is negligibly small. An example of this is charge in motion within

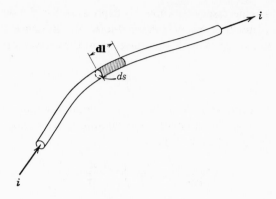

Fig. 6.5 Current is flowing in a filamentary conductor. The current density is everywhere parallel to the conductor. For an elemental vector length of the filament **dl**, $\rho \mathbf{v}\, d\tau = v\, ds\, \mathbf{dl} = i\, \mathbf{dl}$, where $d\tau$ is an elemental volume of the conductor and ds is a cross-sectional area perpendicular to **dl**.

a filamentary conductor or thin wire. Consider a current flowing in a filamentary conductor exhibited in Fig. 6.5. In this case, the flow of charge is always parallel to the filament; as a consequence, for an elementary length **dl** of the filamentary conductor

$$\rho \mathbf{v}\, d\tau = \rho v\, ds\, \mathbf{dl} = i\, \mathbf{dl}$$

where i is the current flowing in the filament. Since ρ is everywhere zero except within the filamentary conductors, the integrals over all space in the equations for **f**, **B**, and **A** now may be interpreted as integrals around the contours of the filamentary conductors. These contours are always closed since there can be no sources or sinks of electric charge. Consequently we may write

$$\mathbf{A(r)} = \left(\frac{\mu_0}{4\pi}\right) \sum_j i_j \oint_j \frac{\mathbf{dl'}}{|\mathbf{r} - \mathbf{r'}|} \qquad (6.21a)$$

$$\mathbf{B(r)} = \left(\frac{\mu_0}{4\pi}\right) \sum_j i_j \oint_j \frac{\mathbf{dl'} \times \hat{\mathbf{n}}}{|\mathbf{r} - \mathbf{r'}|^2} \qquad (6.7c)$$

where the sum over j is over all the filamentary current carriers. Naturally the electric current within each filament is constant over the filament and is therefore not a function of the variable of integration.

In a similar fashion the force on a charge q moving with velocity **v** in the environment of current carrying loops reads

$$\mathbf{f(r)} = \left(\frac{\mu_0}{4\pi}\right) q\mathbf{v} \times \left\{ \sum_j i_j \oint_j \frac{\mathbf{dl'} \times \hat{\mathbf{n}}}{|\mathbf{r} - \mathbf{r'}|^2} \right\}. \qquad (6.6c)$$

Sometimes it is necessary to know an expression for the net force on a filamentary conductor specified by k due to the presence of other filamentary conductors. For this purpose, $q\mathbf{v}$ in the above is replaced by

$$q\mathbf{v} \rightarrow i_k \oint_k \mathbf{dl}.$$

The resulting expression is not a vector point function but simply a vector since it refers to a conductor spanning a macroscopic portion of space. The resultant expression is

$$\mathbf{f} = \left(\frac{\mu_0}{4\pi}\right) \sum_{j \neq k} i_k i_j \oint_j \oint_k \frac{\mathbf{dl} \times (\mathbf{dl'} \times \hat{\mathbf{n}})}{|\mathbf{r} - \mathbf{r'}|^2}. \tag{6.6d}$$

This expression is symmetric in the variables referring to the conductors k and j. A bit of reflection reveals that this must indeed be so. This expression is sometimes called the Biot–Savart law and is normally taken as the fundamental force law in magnetostatics. However, the Biot–Savart law has the distinct disadvantage that it yields an expression for the force on a macroscopic conductor and does not immediately yield a desirable microscopic law for a vector force field. The Biot–Savart law has been developed from the force law which is assumed to hold between two arbitrarily moving point charges.

EXAMPLE 6.2. A particularly simple example of the application of the equations for the **B**- and **A**-fields of a current loop occurs when the field point is located on the axis of a circular loop (see Fig. 6.6). If the origin of coordinates is located at the center of the loop, it is obvious, just as in Example 6.1, that $\mathbf{A}(\mathbf{r})$ vanishes everywhere on the axis. In a similar fashion, only that component of **B** parallel to the axis need be considered, the component perpendicular to $\hat{\mathbf{z}}$ vanishing identically. Consequently

$$\mathbf{B}(\mathbf{r}) = \left(\frac{\mu_0}{4\pi}\right) i\hat{\mathbf{z}} \oint \frac{\mathbf{dl'} \times \hat{\mathbf{n}} \cdot \hat{\mathbf{z}}}{|\mathbf{r} - \mathbf{r'}|^2},$$

$$= \left(\frac{\mu_0}{4\pi}\right) i\hat{\mathbf{z}} \int_0^{2\pi} a \, d\phi \, \frac{1}{h^2 + a^2} \frac{a}{\sqrt{h^2 + a^2}}$$

where $|\mathbf{dl'}| = a \, d\phi$, $|\mathbf{r'}| = a$, and $|\mathbf{r}| = h$.

Consequently

$$\mathbf{B}(\mathbf{r}) = \left(\frac{\mu_0}{4\pi}\right) \frac{2\pi i a^2}{(h^2 + a^2)^{3/2}} \hat{\mathbf{z}}.$$

EXAMPLE 6.3 The result of the previous example may be used to calculate **A** and **B** on the axis of a tightly wound solenoid. Once again it is evident that $\mathbf{A} = 0$ on the axis; it is also evident that **B** is parallel to the axis

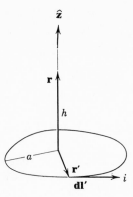

Fig. 6.6   The **B** and **A** fields are evaluated at a point on the axis of a circular loop. $\hat{z}$ is a unit vector parallel to the axis and is defined in the right-handed sense.

of the solenoid and if the solenoid is infinitely long, **B** is uniform along the axis.   This approximates the physical situation of a long solenoid with the field point well within the solenoid, the edge effects being ignored. It is assumed that the "pitch" of the solenoid is zero.   (The case in which the turns of the solenoid make an angle different from $90°$ with respect to the axis is left as an exercise.)   If n is the number of turns per unit length of the solenoid, then the contribution to **B** from an elemental length dh of the solenoid is

$$\mathbf{dB} = \left(\frac{\mu_0}{4\pi}\right) 2\pi nia^2 \frac{dh}{(h^2 + a^2)^{3/2}} \hat{z}.$$

The above expression may be integrated over dh from $-\infty$ to $+\infty$ with the result

$$\mathbf{B} = \left(\frac{\mu_0}{4\pi}\right) 4\pi ni\hat{z}.$$

6.7   Gauss's Magnetic Law

The possibility of deriving **B** from a vector potential **A** through the relation curl $\mathbf{A} = \mathbf{B}$ is equivalent to a very important property of the **B**-field, namely, its vanishing divergence.   It is a very elementary exercise to show that

$$\text{div } \mathbf{B} = 0.$$

This relationship follows immediately, taking cognizance of the vector calculus identity

$$\text{div curl } \mathbf{g} = 0$$

where $\mathbf{g}$ = any vector point function with defined second derivatives. In particular, if the vector point function is chosen to be $\mathbf{A}$, it is seen that div $\mathbf{B}$ = 0.   This is sometimes referred to as the differential form of Gauss's magnetic law.   The integral form may be obtained by integrating div $\mathbf{B}$ over a finite volume τ and converting the volume integral into an integral over the surface Σ bounding τ via the divergence theorem

$$\oiint_{\Sigma} \mathbf{B} \cdot \hat{\mathbf{n}} \, dS = 0.$$

If the concept of *magnetic field lines* is introduced in a manner analogous to that employed in Chapter 2 for electric field lines, it is a consequence of Gauss's magnetic law that every magnetic field line must intersect any closed surface an even number of times to insure the vanishing of the flux of $\mathbf{B}$ through the surface.   Since this statement must hold for any closed surface, it follows that all magnetic field lines form closed curves.

6.8   Multipole Expansion of the Field Produced by an Arbitrary Distribution of Current Carriers

In Chapter 2 was demonstrated the possibility of approximating the electrostatic field a large distance from an arbitrary charge distribution and expressing the field in terms of the characteristic multipole moments of the charge distribution.   It will now be demonstrated that a similar approximation may be developed for the magnetostatic field evaluated at a large distance from an arbitrary distribution of current carriers. The methods of calculation are precisely the same as in the electrostatic case.   Consider a finite volume V containing all the current-carrying conductors (see Fig. 6.7).   The current density $\mathbf{j}$ will be assumed to vanish

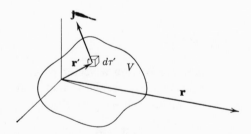

Fig. 6.7   All the conductors carrying current are contained in the volume V.   To every point in V is ascribed a current density $\mathbf{j}$. $\mathbf{r}'$ is a vector to an elemental volume element $d\tau'$; $\mathbf{r}$ is the field point.   The origin of coordinates is located within V.   The magnitude of $\mathbf{r}$ is greater than the largest linear dimension of V.

everywhere exterior to V. A coordinate system is erected with its origin somewhere within V and the vector potential $\mathbf{A}$ is evaluated at a point $\mathbf{r}$ exterior to V. It is assumed that $|\mathbf{r}|$ is much larger than the greatest linear dimension of V. In eq. 6.21 for $\mathbf{A}$, the factor $|\mathbf{r} - \mathbf{r}'|^{-1}$ appearing in the integrand is replaced by the first two terms in a power series expansion, keeping terms up to and including $(r'/r)^2$ (see eqs. 2.22a and 2.22b of Chapter 2). The resulting approximate expression for $\mathbf{A(r)}$ is

$$\mathbf{A(r)} = \left(\frac{\mu_0}{4\pi}\right) \int d\tau' \frac{\mathbf{j(r')}}{r} \left\{ 1 + \left(\frac{r'}{r}\right) \cos \vartheta + \left(\frac{r'}{r}\right)^2 \left(\frac{3 \cos^2 \vartheta - 1}{2}\right) + \cdots \right\}$$

$$(6.25)$$

where ϑ is the angle between $\mathbf{r}$ and $\mathbf{r}'$.

Equation 6.25 may be written as

$$\mathbf{A(r)} = \mathbf{A_0(r)} + \mathbf{A_1(r)} + \mathbf{A_2(r)} + \cdots. \tag{6.26}$$

The various terms in eq. 6.26 are, respectively, the (M0), (M1), and (M2) contributions to $\mathbf{A(r)}$, where (M0) = magnetic monopole, (M1) = magnetic dipole, (M2) = magnetic quadrupole. The (M0) contribution has the following interesting feature: note that

$$\mathbf{A_0(r)} = \left(\frac{\mu_0}{4\pi}\right) \frac{1}{r} \int_V d\tau' \mathbf{j(r')}. \tag{6.27}$$

However, since it has been stated that the integral on the right-hand side of eq. 6.27 is to be taken over the volume containing all the current carriers, the integral vanishes. The result may be stated simply as follows: the magnetostatic monopole contribution to the field produced by an arbitrary distribution of current carriers vanishes or equivalently that the (M0) moment of an arbitrary distribution of current carriers is identically zero. This implies that there is no magnetic equivalent to electric charge. We shall return to this observation at a later point in the discussion. The vanishing of $\mathbf{A_0(r)}$ can be seen in another way: suppose that all the moving charges contributing to $\mathbf{j}$ are carried in filamentary conductors. Under this condition the following replacement can be made:

$$\int d\tau' \mathbf{j(r')} \to \sum_{k=1}^{N} i_k \oint_k \mathbf{dl}.$$

Therefore

$$\mathbf{A_0(r)} = \left(\frac{\mu_0}{4\pi}\right) \frac{1}{r} \sum_{k=1}^{N} i_k \oint_k \mathbf{dl}.$$

However, $\oint \mathbf{dl}$ is identically zero for each current loop and consequently $\mathbf{A_0(r)} = 0$.

The (M1) contribution to the vector potential is therefore the leading contribution at large distances and is given by

$$\mathbf{A}_1(\mathbf{r}) = \left(\frac{\mu_0}{4\pi}\right) \frac{1}{r^3} \int_V d\tau'(\mathbf{r} \cdot \mathbf{r}')\mathbf{j}(\mathbf{r}'). \tag{6.28}$$

It would be convenient at this point to introduce the concept of the (M1) moment of the distribution of current carriers. However, it is not immediately evident from eq. 6.28 how to define the (M1) moment. The method used in the case of the (E1) moment is not immediately applicable, since the integrand of eq. 6.28 has an entirely different structure from that appearing in the definition of the (E1) moment.

A procedure that may be used is the following. Examine the integral

$$\mathbf{m} = \int d\tau'(\mathbf{r} \cdot \mathbf{r})\mathbf{j}(\mathbf{r}').$$

The projection of $\mathbf{m}$ along any direction $\hat{\mathbf{n}}$ is given by

$$(\mathbf{m} \cdot \hat{\mathbf{n}}) = \int d\tau'(\mathbf{r} \cdot \mathbf{r}')(\mathbf{j} \cdot \hat{\mathbf{n}}). \tag{6.29}$$

Equation 6.29 may be written in a more complex but ultimately more useful form as

$$(\mathbf{m} \cdot \hat{\mathbf{n}}) = (\mathbf{m} \cdot \hat{\mathbf{n}})_s + (\mathbf{m} \cdot \hat{\mathbf{n}})_a$$

with

$$(\mathbf{m} \cdot \hat{\mathbf{n}})_s \equiv \tfrac{1}{2} \int d\tau'\{(\mathbf{r} \cdot \mathbf{r}')(\mathbf{j} \cdot \hat{\mathbf{n}}) + (\mathbf{r}' \cdot \hat{\mathbf{n}})(\mathbf{j} \cdot \mathbf{r})\} \tag{6.29s}$$

and

$$(\mathbf{m} \cdot \hat{\mathbf{n}})_a \equiv \tfrac{1}{2} \int d\tau'\{(\mathbf{r} \cdot \mathbf{r}')(\mathbf{j} \cdot \hat{\mathbf{n}}) - (\mathbf{r}' \cdot \hat{\mathbf{n}})(\mathbf{j} \cdot \mathbf{r})\}. \tag{6.29a}$$

However, noting that $\mathrm{grad}'\,(\mathbf{t} \cdot \mathbf{r}') = \mathbf{t}$ for any constant (with respect to $\mathbf{r}'$) vector $\mathbf{t}$, and that $\mathrm{grad}'\,(fg) = f(\mathrm{grad}'\,g) + g(\mathrm{grad}'\,f)$ for any two scalar functions of $\mathbf{r}'$, eq. 6.29s may be written as

$$(\mathbf{m} \cdot \hat{\mathbf{n}})_s = \tfrac{1}{2} \int d\tau'\mathbf{j} \cdot \mathrm{grad}'\,\{(\hat{\mathbf{n}} \cdot \mathbf{r}')(\mathbf{r} \cdot \mathbf{r}')\}.$$

However

$$\mathbf{v} \cdot \mathrm{grad}\,s = \mathrm{div}\,(s\mathbf{v}) + s\,\mathrm{div}\,\mathbf{v}$$

where $(\mathbf{v}, s)$ are arbitrary vector and scalar point functions, respectively. Setting $\mathbf{j} = \mathbf{v}$ and $(\hat{\mathbf{n}} \cdot \mathbf{r}')(\mathbf{r} \cdot \mathbf{r}') = s$, we note that

$$\begin{aligned}(\mathbf{m} \cdot \hat{\mathbf{n}})_s = &\tfrac{1}{2} \int d\tau'(\hat{\mathbf{n}} \cdot \mathbf{r}')(\mathbf{r} \cdot \mathbf{r}')\,\mathrm{div}\,\mathbf{j} \\ &+ \tfrac{1}{2} \int d\tau'\,\mathrm{div}\,\{\mathbf{j}(\hat{\mathbf{n}} \cdot \mathbf{r}')(\mathbf{r} \cdot \mathbf{r}')\}.\end{aligned}$$

In the steady-state situation treated here, $\mathrm{div}\,\mathbf{j} = 0$, and the first integral vanishes identically. The integral over V in the second term may be converted into an integral over Σ bounding V by the divergence theorem. This yields

$$(\mathbf{m} \cdot \hat{\mathbf{n}})_s = \tfrac{1}{2} \oiint_\Sigma ds'(\hat{\mathbf{n}}' \cdot \mathbf{j})(\hat{\mathbf{n}} \cdot \mathbf{r}')(\mathbf{r} \cdot \mathbf{r}')$$

where $\hat{\mathbf{n}}' \equiv$ unit normal of ds'. However, $on \Sigma$ $(\hat{\mathbf{n}}' \cdot \mathbf{j}) = 0$, and therefore $(\mathbf{m} \cdot \hat{\mathbf{n}})_s = 0$. Finally it is noted that

$$(\mathbf{m} \cdot \hat{\mathbf{n}})_a = \hat{\mathbf{n}} \cdot \{\tfrac{1}{2} \int d\tau' \mathbf{r} \times (\mathbf{j} \times \mathbf{r}')\},$$

so that

$$\mathbf{m} = \tfrac{1}{2} \int d\tau' \mathbf{r} \times (\mathbf{j} \times \mathbf{r}')$$

since $\hat{\mathbf{n}}$ is an arbitrary unit vector. From this it follows that

$$\mathbf{A}_1(\mathbf{r}) = \left(\frac{\mu_0}{4\pi}\right) \frac{1}{2r^3} \mathbf{r} \times \int d\tau'(\mathbf{j} \times \mathbf{r}'). \tag{6.30}$$

The integral

$$\boldsymbol{\mu} \equiv \tfrac{1}{2} \int d\tau' \mathbf{r}' \times \mathbf{j} \tag{6.31}$$

is called the *magnetic dipole moment* of the distribution of current carriers. Therefore after much labor we have found that

$$A_1(\mathbf{r}) = \left(\frac{\mu_0}{4\pi}\right) \frac{\boldsymbol{\mu} \times \mathbf{r}}{r^3}. \tag{6.32}$$

It is interesting to note that $\boldsymbol{\mu}$ is independent of the location of the origin of the coordinate system. This follows immediately from the identical vanishing of the (M0) moment and is proved as follows. The origin of the coordinate system is shifted by a vector amount $\boldsymbol{\rho}$. The resulting (M1) moment $\boldsymbol{\mu}'$ is then

$$\boldsymbol{\mu}' = \tfrac{1}{2} \int d\tau'\{(\mathbf{r}' - \boldsymbol{\rho}) \times \mathbf{j}\}$$
$$= \tfrac{1}{2} \int d\tau'\{\mathbf{r}' \times \mathbf{j}\} - \tfrac{1}{2}\boldsymbol{\rho} \times \int d\tau'\mathbf{j},$$

or

$$\boldsymbol{\mu}' = \boldsymbol{\mu} - \tfrac{1}{2}\boldsymbol{\rho} \times \int d\tau'\mathbf{j} \tag{6.33}$$

since

$$\int d\tau'\mathbf{j} = 0,$$

we have the desired result

$$\boldsymbol{\mu}' = \boldsymbol{\mu}.$$

The argument leading from the form of $A_2(\mathbf{r})$ to the definition of the (M2) moment is sufficiently involved to warrant its omission from this discussion.

6.9 Dipole Moment of a Current Loop

Perhaps the simplest kind of magnetic dipole is a current-carrying loop. Remembering how one passes from a situation characterized by current

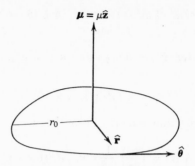

Fig. 6.8   The magnetic moment of a circular loop of radius r_0 carrying a current i is $\boldsymbol{\mu} = i(\pi r_0{}^2)\hat{\mathbf{z}}$. $\hat{\mathbf{z}}$ is the unit vector perpendicular to the plane of the loop and is defined in the right-handed sense.

densities $\mathbf{j}$ to filamentary conductors, we note that for a closed filamentary loop

$$\boldsymbol{\mu} = \tfrac{1}{2} \int d\tau (\mathbf{r} \times \mathbf{j}) = \tfrac{1}{2} i \oint \mathbf{r} \times \mathbf{dl}. \tag{6.34}$$

If the loop is a circle with radius r_0 (see Fig. 6.8) and the origin of coordinates is located at the center of the loop, then

$$\boldsymbol{\mu} = \tfrac{1}{2} i r_0^2 \oint (\hat{\mathbf{r}} \times \hat{\boldsymbol{\theta}}) \, d\theta$$

where $\hat{\mathbf{r}} = $ unit vector from center to the element of the loop $\mathbf{dl}$ given by

$$\mathbf{dl} = r_0 \hat{\boldsymbol{\theta}} \, d\theta.$$

Now $(\hat{\mathbf{r}} \times \hat{\boldsymbol{\theta}})$ is a unit vector $\hat{\mathbf{z}}$ perpendicular to the loop, and the integral over $d\theta$ yields 2π. Consequently

$$\boldsymbol{\mu} = i(\pi r_0^2)\hat{\mathbf{z}} = iA\hat{\mathbf{z}} \tag{6.35}$$

where $A = $ area of the loop. Actually this result holds for any shaped loop as long as the loop lies in a plane. This may be demonstrated as follows (see Fig. 6.9). The magnetic dipole moment of a planar current-carrying loop is

$$\boldsymbol{\mu} = \tfrac{1}{2} i \oint \mathbf{r} \times \mathbf{dl} = \tfrac{1}{2} i \hat{\mathbf{z}} \oint r \sin \vartheta (r \, d\phi) \tag{6.36}$$

where $|\mathbf{dl}| = r \, d\phi$, and ϑ is the angle between $\mathbf{r}$ and $\mathbf{dl}$. However, $r^2 \sin \vartheta \, d\phi$ is just twice the area dA of the triangle shaded in Fig. 6.7. Consequently

$$\boldsymbol{\mu} = i\hat{\mathbf{z}} \oiint dA. \tag{6.37}$$

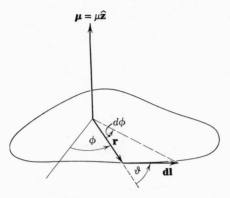

Fig. 6.9 A planar loop (not necessarily circular) of area A has a magnetic dipole moment $\boldsymbol{\mu} = iA\hat{\mathbf{z}}$.

The integral over dA yields the area of the loop, and thus for *any* planar loop

$$\boldsymbol{\mu} = iA\hat{\mathbf{z}}. \tag{6.38}$$

The vector potential $\mathbf{A}$ evaluated far from any planar loop ("far" defined by the statement that multipole contributions to $\mathbf{A}$ higher than dipole can be neglected) is given by eqs. 6.32 and 6.30:

$$\mathbf{A}(\mathbf{r}) \simeq \left(\frac{\mu_0}{4\pi}\right) \frac{iA}{r^2} (\hat{\mathbf{z}} \times \hat{\mathbf{r}}). \tag{6.39}$$

If cylindrical coordinates are adopted (see Fig. 6.10), then

$$\mathbf{A}(\mathbf{r}) \approx \left(\frac{\mu_0}{4\pi}\right) \frac{iA}{r^2} \sin\theta\,\hat{\boldsymbol{\phi}}. \tag{6.40}$$

The $\mathbf{B}$-field at $\mathbf{r}$ may be obtained by evaluating directly the curl of eq. 6.39:

$$\mathbf{B}(\mathbf{r}) = -\frac{\mu_0}{4\pi} \left[\left\{ \frac{\boldsymbol{\mu}}{r^3} - \frac{3(\boldsymbol{\mu}\cdot\mathbf{r})}{r^5}\mathbf{r} \right\} - \frac{8\pi}{3}\,\boldsymbol{\mu}\,\delta(\mathbf{r}) \right]. \tag{6.41}$$

A particle of charge q and mass m_0 moving with uniform speed in a circular orbit of radius r_0 produces a time-varying field at a given point in space. If the distance of the field point from the charge is always larger than the radius of the orbit, then the time average of the field is that produced by a magnetic dipole. The equivalent dipole moment of the charge may be calculated as follows. The amount of charge

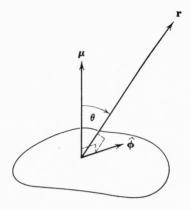

Fig. 6.10   The (M1) contribution to the vector potential produced by a planar loop is given in cylindrical coordinates as $A(r) = (\mu_0/4\pi)iA(\sin \theta/r^2)\hat{\phi}$. θ is the angle between the (M1) moment of the loop, and the vector to the field point as illustrated $\hat{\phi}$ is the unit normal to the plane defined by the vectors μ, r.

passing a given point on the circular orbit per second averaged over many periods of motion is simply the amount of charge passing a given point per revolution (q) divided by the time taken for one revolution $(2\pi r_0/v)$. The (M1) moment is

$$\mu = \frac{qv}{2\pi r_0}\, \pi r_0^2 \hat{z},$$

or

$$\mu = \frac{qvr_0}{2}\, \hat{z}.$$

However, the angular momentum l of the particle is by definition

$$l = r \times (m_0 v) = m_0 r_0 v \hat{z}.$$

It is therefore noted that the ratio of the (M1) moment and the angular momentum depends solely on the charge-to-mass ratio of the particle and not on its velocity or its particular orbit.

Specifically

$$\mu = \frac{q}{2m_0}\, l. \tag{6.42}$$

Since it has already been demonstrated that the (M1) moment of a given current distribution is independent of the location of the origin of co-ordinates, it follows that the equivalent (M1) moment of a system of charges with the same q/m_0 moving in circular orbits of arbitrary location, orientation, and size can be simply written as

$$\mathbf{\mu}_{(t)} = \frac{q}{2m_0} \mathbf{l}_{(t)}$$

where

$$\mathbf{l}_{(t)} = \sum_{i=1}^{N} \mathbf{\mu}_i$$

$$\mathbf{l}_{(t)} = \sum_{i=1}^{N} \mathbf{l}_i.$$

This result will be useful when we attempt to calculate the magnetic moment of a macroscopic specimen from considerations involving the motion of electrons in the constituent atoms of the material.

6.10   Formal Comparison Between Electrostatics and Magnetostatics and Gauss's Law

The similarities between electrostatics and magnetostatics have been mentioned as well as some of the differences. It is well to carry the comparison of these two physical subjects further at this point. Both $\mathbf{E}$ and $\mathbf{B}$ were defined in terms of forces: $\mathbf{E}$ in terms of the force on a stationary charge, $\mathbf{B}$ in terms of the force on a moving charge. Whereas $\mathbf{E}$ was defined via $q\mathbf{E} = \mathbf{f}$ and is consequently a vector point function since $\mathbf{f}$ is a vector point function, $\mathbf{B}$ was defined via $\mathbf{f} = q\mathbf{v} \times \mathbf{B}$ and consequently cannot possess the same mathematical properties as $\mathbf{E}$. Quantities such as $\mathbf{f}$, $\mathbf{r}$, and $\mathbf{v}$ (and therefore $\mathbf{E}$) are called *polar vectors*, whereas the cross product between two polar vectors is an *axial vector*. (The cross product between two axial vectors is itself an axial vector, whereas the cross product between an axial vector and a polar vector is a polar vector.) $\mathbf{B}$ at a point is therefore an axial vector. In the above it is assumed, of course, that q is a scalar.

The difference between an axial vector and a polar vector is contained in their transformation properties under a reflection and may be demonstrated as follows. Consider a polar vector whose Cartesian components are (x, y, z) in a specified coordinate system. If the coordinate axes are then reflected in the "mirror" formed by the x-y plane, the Cartesian components of the vector in the new (primed) coordinate system are given by the transformation relations: $x' = x, y' = y, z' = -z$. (See Fig. 6.11.) If the polar vector was parallel to the z-axis in the original system, the polar vector will be pointing in the negative z-direction in the reflected system. On the other hand, consider an axial vector defined by the cross product between

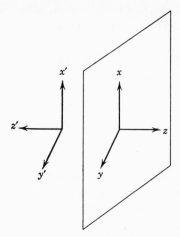

Fig. 6.11   The Cartesian axes (x, y, z) are "reflected" in the mirror of the (x, y) plane.   The new coordinate system is (x', y', z'); i.e., the image of (x, y, z) is simply $(x, y, -z)$.

a polar vector parallel to the x-axis and a polar vector parallel to the y-axis.   When the coordinate axes are reflected in the "mirror" formed by the x-y plane, the axial vector produced by the cross product of the vectors defined above will also point in the positive z-direction in the reflected system.[1]

This formal difference between **E** and **B** appears in the Gaussian laws for magnetostatics and electrostatics.   It should be remembered that Gauss's law in electrostatics in vacuum reads

integral form: $\displaystyle\oiint_\Sigma (\mathbf{E} \cdot \hat{\mathbf{n}})\, ds = \left(\frac{1}{4\pi\epsilon_0}\right) 4\pi q,$

differential form: $\displaystyle \operatorname{div} \mathbf{E} = \left(\frac{1}{4\pi\epsilon_0}\right) 4\pi\rho,$

whereas the equivalent law for magnetostatics is

integral form: $\displaystyle\oiint_\Sigma (\mathbf{B} \cdot \hat{\mathbf{n}})\, ds = 0,$

differential form: $\operatorname{div} \mathbf{B} = 0.$

The form of Gauss's magnetic law is not surprising once Gauss's law for electrostatics is known, since it has been shown that there is no magnetic

---

[1] The three *components* of an axial vector are actually the three linearly independent elements of a 3×3 antisymmetric matrix.   An antisymmetric matrix with elements K_{jk} is one in which $K_{jk} = -K_{kj}$; that is, the "transpose" of an antisymmetric matrix is the negative of the matrix itself.

equivalent to electric charge. It is interesting to note that if "magnetic charge" did exist, it would have an exceedingly peculiar property. Notice that the left-hand side of Gauss's magnetic law changes sign when a transformation is carried out from a right-handed to a left-handed set of coordinate axes. This means that the magnetic charge, if it did exist, would also have to change sign under such a transformation. A quantity which has all the properties of a scalar except that it has this peculiarity under reflections is called a *pseudoscalar*. To recapitulate, under a reflection

$$q'_{\text{electrostatic}} = q_{\text{electrostatic}}$$

$$q'_{\text{magnetostatic}} = -q_{\text{magnetostatic}}$$

If magnetic charge did exist, it would be the only quantity in classical physics which possessed this property. An observant reader will note the q_m could be chosen to be a scalar, from which it would follow that q_e would be a pseudoscalar. The more correct statement is therefore that if q_m exists, then either it *or* q_e must have the properties of a pseudoscalar.

The (E1) and (M1) moments are related in a similar fashion as **E** and **B**. The (E1) moment is by definition a polar vector:

$$\mathbf{p} \equiv \int d\tau \rho \mathbf{r}$$

whereas the (M1) moment is an axial vector:

$$\boldsymbol{\mu} \equiv \tfrac{1}{2} \int d\tau \mathbf{r} \times \mathbf{j}.$$

Another very interesting difference exists between the **E**- and **B**-fields—and also between the (E1) and (M1) moments. In addition to the behavior of physical quantities under a rigid rotation of the coordinate axes and the reflection of the coordinate axes in a plane, is their behavior under a *time inversion*. The time inversion operation consists in replacing t in all the equations by $-t$. Under a time inversion, position vectors remain unchanged, i.e., $(\mathbf{r} \to \mathbf{r})$. However, since the velocity vector **v** is defined as $d\mathbf{r}/dt$, all velocities are reversed, i.e., $(\mathbf{v} \to -\mathbf{v})$. Similarly the acceleration vector defined as $(d/dt)(d\mathbf{r}/dt)$ remains unchanged. It follows immediately from Newton's laws that forces acting on a system are invariant with respect to a time inversion, provided we assume that the inertial mass of all objects is invariant with respect to a time inversion. Since the **E**-field is defined as the force per unit charge, it follows immediately that **E** is invariant with respect to the time inversion operation—provided that the charge q does not change under a time inversion. To arrive at the invariance of **E** under time inversion it is not necessary to assume that both inertial mass and charge are invariant, but only that their ratio possesses this attribute.

The situation with respect to the **B**-field is somewhat different.   Examination of eq. 6.4 or any of the other equations which can be used as equivalent definitions of **B** shows that **B** changes sign under time inversion, using the same assumption as employed in examining the transformation properties of **E**—namely, the invariance of the charge-to-mass ratio of all physical particles.   To summarize, **E** transforms like a position vector, whereas **B** transforms like a velocity vector under the time inversion operation.   It immediately follows that the (E1) and (M1) moments transform like position and velocity vectors, respectively.

Although the properties of electrostatic and magnetostatic quantities under space rotation, reflection, and time inversion are of little more than academic interest in classical physics, transformation properties of such physical quantities play a very important role in the construction of modern physical theories.   Many contemporary attempts to understand the basic laws of physics draw heavily upon the properties of physical quantities under transformations of the type mentioned above.   Symmetry arguments currently seem to be an important ingredient of all physical theories.[2]

PROBLEMS

6.1   Calculate the force acting between two charged particles moving parallel to one another.   Repeat the calculation for particles moving perpendicular to one another.   Does $f_{12} = -f_{21}$ for each case?

6.2   According to the simple Bohr picture of the hydrogen atom, the atom in its ground state consists in an electron moving in a circular orbit of radius $r_0 = 0.5$ Å (1 Å $= 10^{-10}$ meters) about a point nucleus, the proton.   If the total energy of the atom in its ground state is -13.6 ev (1 electron volt $= 1.6 \times 10^{-19}$ joules), calculate the strength of the magnetic field at the proton due to the motion of the electron.

6.3   A particle of mass m and charge q is injected into a region of uniform magnetic field **B** with a velocity **v**.   Show that the path of the particle in the magnetic field is a helix.   Calculate the maximum strength of the magnetic field on the axis of this helical path produced by the charge itself.   Is the magnitude of this field significant compared to the applied field?

6.4   Develop an expression for the vector potential **A** corresponding to a uniform magnetic field **B**.

6.5   A spherical conducting shell of radius R carries a uniform surface current density **K** tangent to circles of constant latitude.   Calculate the vector potential **A** and the field **B** at some arbitrary point on the diameter of the sphere which passes through the poles.

[2] See, for example, C. N. Yang *Elementary Particles*, Princeton Univ. Press, Princeton, N.J., 1962.

6.6 Calculate the vector potential **A** and the field **B** at the center of a conducting square of side length s carrying a current I.

6.7 Calculate the vector potential **A** produced by two long straight wires separated by a distance d each carrying current I but in opposite directions.

6.8 Calculate the magnetic field on the axis of a solenoid of length L and radius r_0. Evaluate an approximate expression for **B** at a point on the axis a distance d from the center, assuming $d \ll L/2$. Keep terms in the approximate expression up to and including terms of magnitude $(d/L)^2$.

6.9 Calculate the force per unit length between two parallel straight wires separated by a distance d carrying currents I_1 and I_2.

6.10 A square conducting loop of side length s carries a current I in a uniform magnetic field **B**. If the plane of the loop makes an angle ϑ with respect to the field direction, calculate the force and torque on the loop. Repeat the calculation for a circular loop of radius R. Is it possible to generalize the result for a planar loop of arbitrary shape?

6.11 Calculate the work necessary to rotate a circular conducting loop of radius R carrying a current I through a finite angle α in a uniform magnetic field. From this result and the definition of the magnetic moment of a loop (eq. 6.35), write down an expression for the energy of orientation of the loop in a uniform field.

6.12 A charge q is uniformly distributed over the surface of a sphere of radius R. The sphere rotates with angular velocity ω about a diameter. Calculate the magnetic moment of the rotating sphere. Repeat the calculation assuming that the charge is distributed uniformly throughout the volume of the sphere.

6.13 Starting from the expression for the dipole contribution to the vector potential **A**, establish eq. 6.41 for the dipole contribution to the magnetic field **B**.

6.14 Two magnetic dipoles $\boldsymbol{\mu}_1$ and $\boldsymbol{\mu}_2$ of negligible size are placed a distance d apart. Calculate the interaction energy of the dipoles.

6.15 As mentioned in Section 6.11, both $\boldsymbol{\mu}$ and **B** are axial vectors which may be represented by antisymmetric matrices. Taking for both $\boldsymbol{\mu}$ and **B** the matrix

$$G_{jk} = \begin{pmatrix} 0 & G_z & -G_y \\ -G_z & 0 & G_x \\ G_y & -G_x & 0 \end{pmatrix}$$

show that the interaction energy of a dipole with a magnetic field is given by

$$U_{\text{int}} = \frac{1}{2} \sum_{\substack{k=1 \\ j=1}}^{3} \mu_{kj} B_{jk}.$$

$\sum_{j=1}^{3} \mu_{kj} B_{jl}$ is the (k, l) element of a 3×3 matrix, the sum of whose diagonal elements is twice U_{int}. What interpretation can be given to the off-diagonal elements of this matrix (i.e., $k \neq l$)?

7 | Ampère's Law;
An Alternative Discussion of
Magnetostatics

7.1 Ampère's Law

The discussion of magnetostatics in the previous chapter has led to a definition of the magnetic induction field $\mathbf{B}(\mathbf{r})$ based on the law of force between two charges moving with slow uniform motion. This definition has the analytic form

$$\mathbf{B}(\mathbf{r}) = \left(\frac{\mu_0}{4\pi}\right) \int d\tau \, \frac{\mathbf{j}(\mathbf{r}') \times \hat{\mathbf{n}}}{|\mathbf{r} - \mathbf{r}'|^2} \tag{7.1}$$

where

$$\hat{\mathbf{n}} \equiv \frac{\mathbf{r} - \mathbf{r}'}{|\mathbf{r} - \mathbf{r}'|}.$$

From this definition it was possible in Chapter 6 to deduce a partial differential equation satisfied by $\mathbf{B}(\mathbf{r})$. This equation, called Gauss's magnetic law, is

$$\operatorname{div} \mathbf{B}(\mathbf{r}) = 0. \tag{7.2}$$

In integral form Gauss's magnetic law involves the flux of the **B**-field through any closed surface Σ and states that this flux vanishes for any closed surface; that is,

$$\oiint_\Sigma \mathbf{B}(\mathbf{r}) \cdot \hat{\mathbf{n}} \, dS = 0. \tag{7.3}$$

Although the defining integral for $\mathbf{B}(\mathbf{r})$, eq. 7.1, contains the source of the field, namely, $\mathbf{j}$, Gauss's law does not involve the source explicitly. Therefore Gauss's law alone does not suffice to determine the properties of **B**. Another differential equation which is needed, together with Gauss's magnetic equation, will serve to define **B**. A priori, this additional equation will need to contain the source of the field. [The situation is

160

analogous to that in electrostatics, where two differential equations were introduced to specify **E**. One of the equations was homogeneous (curl **E** = 0), whereas the other contained the source of the E-field, namely, electric charge, (div **E** = $(1/4\pi\epsilon_0)4\pi\rho$).]

The second differential relationship involving **B** can be obtained in many ways. Paralleling the discussion in electrostatics, the desired relationship—the steady-state form of Ampère's law—is obtained from the defining integral for **B**. Ampère's law relates the curl of the induction field to its source, namely, current density. Taking the curl of both sides of eq. 7.1 yields

$$\text{curl } \mathbf{B}(\mathbf{r}) = \text{curl}\left\{\left(\frac{\mu_0}{4\pi}\right)\int d\tau \, \frac{\mathbf{j}(\mathbf{r}') \times \hat{\mathbf{n}}}{|\mathbf{r} - \mathbf{r}'|^2}\right\}. \tag{7.4}$$

Now the curl contains derivative operators with respect to the components of **r**; it may therefore be moved into the integral sign to operate on the integrand. The integrand itself contains functions of **r** as well as the current density **j**(**r**′), which is a constant vector as far as the curl operator is concerned. The problem therefore reduces to the calculation of

$$\text{curl } \{\mathbf{a} \times \mathbf{b}(\mathbf{r})\}$$

where **a** = constant vector and **b**(**r**) = vector function of **r**. This can be evaluated as follows: in Cartesian coordinates

$$\begin{aligned}\mathbf{a} \times \mathbf{b}(\mathbf{r}) = &[a_y b_z(\mathbf{r}) - a_z b_y(\mathbf{r})]\hat{\mathbf{x}} \\ &+ [a_z b_x(\mathbf{r}) - a_x b_z(\mathbf{r})]\hat{\mathbf{y}} \\ &+ [a_x b_y(\mathbf{r}) - a_y b_x(\mathbf{r})]\hat{\mathbf{z}}.\end{aligned}$$

The z-component of curl $\{\mathbf{a} \times \mathbf{b}(\mathbf{r})\}$ is

$$\text{curl}_z \{\mathbf{a} \times \mathbf{b}(\mathbf{r})\} = \left\{\frac{\partial}{\partial x}[\mathbf{a} \times \mathbf{b}(\mathbf{r})]_y - \frac{\partial}{\partial y}[\mathbf{a} \times \mathbf{b}(\mathbf{r})]_x\right\}$$

or

$$\text{curl}_z \{\mathbf{a} \times \mathbf{b}(\mathbf{r})\} = \left\{a_z \frac{\partial}{\partial x} b_x - a_x \frac{\partial}{\partial x} b_z - a_y \frac{\partial}{\partial y} b_z + a_z \frac{\partial}{\partial y} b_y\right\}.$$

For convenience, the term $[a_z(\partial/\partial z)b_z - a_z(\partial/\partial z)b_z = 0]$ is inserted on the right-hand side of the above, yielding

$$\begin{aligned}\text{curl}_z\{\mathbf{a} \times \mathbf{b}(\mathbf{r})\} = &a_z\left(\frac{\partial}{\partial x} b_x + \frac{\partial}{\partial y} b_y + \frac{\partial}{\partial z} b_z\right) \\ &- \left(a_x \frac{\partial}{\partial x} + a_y \frac{\partial}{\partial y} + a_z \frac{\partial}{\partial z}\right)b_z.\end{aligned}$$

This equation can be generalized to all the components of the curl $(\mathbf{a} \times \mathbf{b})$:

$$\text{curl}\,\{\mathbf{a} \times \mathbf{b(r)}\} = \mathbf{a}\,\text{div}\,\mathbf{b(r)} - (\mathbf{a} \cdot \nabla)\mathbf{b(r)} \tag{7.5}$$

where $(\mathbf{a} \cdot \nabla)$ is the operator

$$a_x \frac{\partial}{\partial x} + a_y \frac{\partial}{\partial y} + a_z \frac{\partial}{\partial z}.$$

Returning now to the calculation of curl $\mathbf{B(r)}$, the result of eq. 7.5 is used to transform eq. 7.4 into

$$\text{curl}\,\mathbf{B(r)} = \left(\frac{\mu_0}{4\pi}\right) \int d\tau \mathbf{j(r')}\,\text{div}\left\{\frac{\hat{\mathbf{n}}}{|\mathbf{r} - \mathbf{r'}|^2}\right\}$$
$$- \left(\frac{\mu_0}{4\pi}\right) \int d\tau (\mathbf{j(r')} \cdot \nabla)\left\{\frac{\hat{\mathbf{n}}}{|\mathbf{r} - \mathbf{r'}|^2}\right\}. \tag{7.6}$$

The first integral on the right-hand side of eq. 7.6 may be evaluated by employing information already discussed on the properties of inverse square fields of force: for example, the electrostatic field at a point $\mathbf{r}$ due to a charge q located at $\mathbf{r'}$ is given by

$$\mathbf{E(r)} = \left(\frac{1}{4\pi\epsilon_0}\right) q\,\frac{\hat{\mathbf{n}}}{|\mathbf{r} - \mathbf{r'}|^2}. \tag{7.7}$$

Therefore, $\hat{\mathbf{n}}/|\mathbf{r} - \mathbf{r'}|^2$ may be thought of as the electrostatic field produced by a point charge of magnitude $q = (4\pi\epsilon_0)$. It has also been shown, in general, that

$$\text{div}\,\mathbf{E(r)} = \left(\frac{1}{4\pi\epsilon_0}\right) 4\pi\rho(\mathbf{r}) \tag{7.8a}$$

with the charge density of a point charge expressed as

$$\rho(\mathbf{r}) = q\,\delta(\mathbf{r} - \mathbf{r'}). \tag{7.8b}$$

Comparison of eq. 7.7 with eqs. 7.8 reveals that

$$\text{div}\left\{\frac{\hat{\mathbf{n}}}{|\mathbf{r} - \mathbf{r'}|^2}\right\} = 4\pi\,\delta(\mathbf{r} - \mathbf{r'}). \tag{7.9}$$

Of course, Eq. 7.9 is a general result independent of the specific manner in which it has been obtained. Substitution of this result into eq. 7.6 yields

$$\text{curl}\,\mathbf{B(r)} = \left(\frac{\mu_0}{4\pi}\right) 4\pi\mathbf{j(r)} - \left(\frac{\mu_0}{4\pi}\right) \int d\tau (\mathbf{j(r')} \cdot \nabla)\left\{\frac{\hat{\mathbf{n}}}{|\mathbf{r} - \mathbf{r'}|^2}\right\}, \tag{7.10}$$

where use has been made of one of the defining properties of the δ function, namely,

$$\int d\tau f(\mathbf{r'})\,\delta(\mathbf{r} - \mathbf{r'}) = f(\mathbf{r})$$

discussed at the end of Chapter 2 and displayed in eq. 2.26.

The remaining integral on the right-hand side of eq. 7.10 can be shown to vanish as follows; note that

$$\frac{\partial}{\partial x}\left\{\frac{\hat{\mathbf{n}}}{|\mathbf{r} - \mathbf{r}'|^2}\right\} = -\frac{\partial}{\partial x'}\left\{\frac{\hat{\mathbf{n}}}{|\mathbf{r} - \mathbf{r}'|^2}\right\} \tag{7.11}$$

and similarly for the other components of the $\nabla \cdot$ operator. (Equation 7.11 can be obtained by a direct interchange of $\mathbf{r}$ and $\mathbf{r}'$.) The integral remaining in eq. 7.10 can be transformed using the result of eq. 7.11 to obtain

$$\int d\tau'[\mathbf{j}(\mathbf{r}') \cdot \nabla]\left\{\frac{\hat{\mathbf{n}}}{|\mathbf{r} - \mathbf{r}'|^2}\right\} = -\int d\tau'[\mathbf{j}(\mathbf{r}') \cdot \nabla']\left\{\frac{\hat{\mathbf{n}}}{|\mathbf{r} - \mathbf{r}'|^2}\right\}, \tag{7.12}$$

where the prime on the ∇ operator stands for differentiation with respect to the primed variables, the variables of integration. The resultant integral can then be integrated by parts. Consider one part of the integrand, the term $j_x(\mathbf{r}')(\partial/\partial x')\{\hat{\mathbf{n}}/|\mathbf{r} - \mathbf{r}'|^2\}$; the contribution of this term to the integral is

$$\int d\tau' j_x(\mathbf{r}') \frac{\partial}{\partial x'}\left\{\frac{\hat{\mathbf{n}}}{|\mathbf{r} - \mathbf{r}'|^2}\right\}.$$

The integral may be evaluated by integration by parts, yielding

$$\iint_S dS' j_x(\mathbf{r}') \frac{\hat{\mathbf{n}}}{|\mathbf{r} - \mathbf{r}'|^2} - \int d\tau'\left[\frac{\partial}{\partial x'} j_x(\mathbf{r}')\right] \frac{\hat{\mathbf{n}}}{|\mathbf{r} - \mathbf{r}'|^2}.$$

The surface S in the first integral is composed of two planes perpendicular to the x-direction located at $x' = \pm \infty$. Since the current distribution producing $\mathbf{B}$ is bounded, $j_x(\mathbf{r}')$ vanishes everywhere on S. Only the second term remains:

$$-\int d\tau\left[\frac{\partial}{\partial x'} j_x(\mathbf{r}')\right] \frac{\hat{\mathbf{n}}}{|\mathbf{r} - \mathbf{r}'|^2}.$$

If the entire integral of eq. 7.12 is treated in this manner, the following result is obtained:

$$\int d\tau[\mathbf{j}(\mathbf{r}') \cdot \nabla]\left\{\frac{\hat{\mathbf{n}}}{|\mathbf{r} - \mathbf{r}'|^2}\right\} = -\int d\tau[\text{div}' \,\mathbf{j}(\mathbf{r}')] \frac{\hat{\mathbf{n}}}{|\mathbf{r} - \mathbf{r}'|^2}. \tag{7.13}$$

Since uniform motion of charge is the source of the static $\mathbf{B}$-field, the continuity relation yields $\text{div}' \,\mathbf{j}(\mathbf{r}') = 0$ (see eq. 6.10), and consequently

$$\int d\tau'[\mathbf{j} \cdot \nabla]\left\{\frac{\hat{\mathbf{n}}}{|\mathbf{r} - \mathbf{r}'|^2}\right\} = 0.$$

Returning to eq. 7.10 in which the curl of $\mathbf{B}$ was evaluated, note that

$$\text{curl } \mathbf{B}(\mathbf{r}) = \left(\frac{\mu_0}{4\pi}\right) 4\pi \mathbf{j}(\mathbf{r}). \tag{7.14}$$

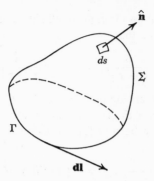

Fig. 7.1 Σ is an open surface capping the closed contour Γ. An element of the surface Σ is $\hat{\mathbf{n}}\, ds$, and an element of the contour Γ is $\mathbf{dl}$. The positive sense of $\hat{\mathbf{n}}$ is determined in the following manner: the fingers of the right hand point in the direction $\mathbf{dl}$, whereas the thumb of the right hand points in the direction $\hat{\mathbf{n}}$. The total current passing through Σ is I. Via Stokes's theorem, the line integral of $\mathbf{B}$ around Γ is equal to the flux of $\mathbf{B}$ through Σ.

This is Ampère's law in differential form for steady-state phenomena. The integral form of Ampère's law may be obtained by evaluating the flux of both sides of eq. 7.14 through an *open* surface Σ bounded by a contour Γ (see Fig. 7.1). This flux is given by the expression

$$\iint_{\Sigma} \hat{\mathbf{n}} \cdot \text{curl } \mathbf{B} \, dS = \left(\frac{\mu_0}{4\pi}\right) 4\pi \iint_{\Sigma} \hat{\mathbf{n}} \cdot \mathbf{j} \, dS. \tag{7.15}$$

The integral on the right-hand side of eq. 7.15 is the total current I passing through Σ; that is,

$$\iint_{\Sigma} \hat{\mathbf{n}} \cdot \mathbf{j} \, dS = I \quad \text{(by definition).} \tag{7.16}$$

The left-hand side may be transformed via Stokes's theorem to the line integral of $\mathbf{B}$ around the enclosing contour Γ; that is,

$$\iint_{\Sigma} \hat{\mathbf{n}} \cdot \text{curl } \mathbf{B} \, dS = \oint_{\Gamma} \mathbf{B} \cdot \mathbf{dl} \quad \text{(via Stokes's theorem).} \tag{7.17}$$

Combining the results of eqs. 7.16 and 7.17, the integral form of Ampère's law is obtained:

$$\oint_{\Gamma} \mathbf{B} \cdot \mathbf{dl} = \left(\frac{\mu_0}{4\pi}\right) 4\pi I. \tag{7.18}$$

7.2   The Magnetomotive Force

In electrostatics, the integral $\oint_{\Gamma} \mathbf{E} \cdot \mathbf{dl}$ could be given a precise operational meaning.   To recall the operational meaning of this contour integral it is noted that if a test charge q is placed at the point $\mathbf{r}$ holding fixed the charges that produce the E-field, $q\mathbf{E}(\mathbf{r})$ is the force $\mathbf{f}$ experienced by the test charge.   Further, the integral

$$\oint_{\Gamma} \mathbf{f} \cdot \mathbf{dl} = \oint_{\Gamma} q\mathbf{E} \cdot \mathbf{dl}$$

is the amount of work that the charges producing the field do on the test charge as it is moved slowly around the contour Γ.   This integral vanishes since the electrostatic field is conservative.   The work done on a test charge as it is moved around any closed contour Γ divided by the magnitude of the test charge is called the *electromotive force* or emf associated with Γ.   The conservative nature of the electrostatic field implies simply that the electromotive force associated with any closed loop vanishes.

By analogy the integral $\oint_{\Gamma} \mathbf{B} \cdot \mathbf{dl}$ is called the *magnetomotive force* or mmf associated with Γ.   In the absence of magnetic monopoles, however, no operational definition is possible for this quantity.   Ampère's law states that the mmf associated with any closed loop Γ is proportional to the total current threading through the loop (the constant of proportionality in rationalized mks units is μ_0; in Gaussian units it is 4π.)

It is worthwhile to examine this difference between the emf and the mmf more closely.   The vanishing of the emf associated with Γ in electrostatics is due to the conservative nature of the E-field, that is, curl $\mathbf{E} = 0$; stated alternatively, it is possible to define a potential function φ such that grad $\varphi = -\mathbf{E}$.   On the other hand, the nonvanishing, in general, of the mmf associated with Γ in magnetostatics implies that the B-field is nonconservative, that is, curl $\mathbf{B} \neq 0$; alternatively, it is not possible to define a single-valued magnetostatic potential function ψ related to $\mathbf{B}$ via the expression grad $\psi = -\mathbf{B}$.   Simply stated, the B-field cannot be derived from a scalar potential.

7.3   The Magnetic Scalar Potential

Even though it is not possible to derive the B-field from a scalar potential because the B-field is nonconservative, it is of some interest to examine the concept of a magnetic scalar potential ψ.   Since ψ will not have the

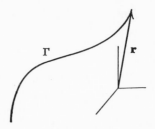

Fig. 7.2 Γ is a path leading from infinity to the point **r**. The line integral of **B** along Γ is defined as $-\psi(\mathbf{r})$, where ψ is the magnetic scalar potential.

operational definition assigned to the electrostatic potential φ, ψ will not play a fundamental role in the theory of steady-state phenomena. In addition, as will be shown immediately, $\psi(\mathbf{r})$ cannot be a single-valued function of **r**.

A magnetic scalar potential will be defined as follows. Assume that all the current carriers which produce the **B**-field are confined to a finite volume. $\psi(\mathbf{r})$ associated with the current carriers is defined by the following integral:

$$\psi(\mathbf{r}) \equiv -\int_\Gamma \mathbf{B} \cdot \mathbf{dl} \qquad (7.19)$$

where Γ is some path connecting a point an infinite distance from the source of **B** to the point **r** (see Fig. 7.2). The value of $\psi(\mathbf{r})$ depends on the path Γ that is chosen. This can be demonstrated as follows. Consider another path Γ' connecting the point at infinity with **r**, Γ' differing from Γ

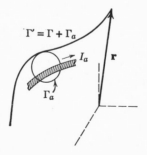

Fig. 7.3 Γ' is a path leading from infinity to the point **r**. It differs from Γ of Fig. 7.2 in that it contains a loop Γ_a through which a current I_a is threading. The magnetic scalar potential evaluated along Γ' differs from that evaluated along Γ by an amount $-(\mu_0/4\pi)4\pi I_a$.

in that it contains a *loop* Γ_a through which an amount of current I_a is threading. (See Fig. 7.3.) According to eq. 7.19, the magnetic scalar potential ψ' at **r** evaluated along the path Γ' is

$$\psi'(\mathbf{r}) = -\int_{\Gamma'} \mathbf{B} \cdot \mathbf{dl} = -\int_{\Gamma} \mathbf{B} \cdot \mathbf{dl} - \oint_{\Gamma_a} \mathbf{B} \cdot \mathbf{dl}. \tag{7.20}$$

The first term on the right-hand side of eq. 7.20 is just $\psi(\mathbf{r})$, whereas the second term can be evaluated using Ampère's law (eq. 7.18) with the result

$$\psi'(\mathbf{r}) = \psi(\mathbf{r}) - \left(\frac{\mu_0}{4\pi}\right) 4\pi I_a. \tag{7.21}$$

Equation 7.21 shows that the magnetic scalar potential is not a single-valued function of **r**. This is a manifestation of the nonconservative nature of the **B**-field; or, this is a manifestation of the fact that the mmf associated with a closed loop is, in general, nonzero. It is possible to define artificially an apparently single-valued magnetic scalar potential. The artifice consists in the following: (1) for an arbitrary distribution of current carriers confined to a finite volume, $\psi(\mathbf{r})$ is set equal to zero at all points an infinite distance from the current carriers; (2) $\psi(\mathbf{r})$ is evaluated using eq. 7.19, where the path of integration Γ is arbitrary except that it must not encircle any current carriers.

It would be useful to define such a magnetic scalar potential if "magnetic charges" existed. For, if so, $\psi(\mathbf{r})$ would have the obvious physical interpretation of the work per unit magnetic charge required to bring a magnetic charge from infinity and place it in the neighborhood of an ensemble of current carriers. There is, however, no physical evidence for the existence of magnetic charges, and consequently $\psi(\mathbf{r})$ has little, if any, utility. However, in those regions in which curl **B** = 0, it is sometimes useful to write $\mathbf{B} = -\operatorname{grad} \psi$, since then $\nabla^2 \psi = 0$ in this region and the techniques developed for solving Laplace's equation in Chapter 3 can be employed to obtain ψ and hence **B**. Then ψ has utility as a calculational device, although it has no physical significance. Several examples in which ψ is introduced for this purpose are given in Chapter 9.

7.4 *Behavior of* **B** *at an Interface*

The changes in **B** across an interface can be gleaned from direct application of Gauss's magnetic law and Ampère's law. The interface under consideration may be a physical interface or may be an arbitrarily constructed interface. Consider such an interface separating two regions with a field point on the interface (see Fig. 7.4). A small right circular cylinder containing the field point in its interior is constructed with base area parallel to the interface. The total flux of **B** through the surface of this cylinder is given by

$$\Phi_m = (\mathbf{B}_1 \cdot \hat{\mathbf{n}} - \mathbf{B}_2 \cdot \hat{\mathbf{n}})\,\Delta S + \text{contribution from the cylinder walls.}$$

($\hat{\mathbf{n}}$ is a unit vector pointing from region 2 to region 1 normal to the interface.) If the height of the cylinder is allowed to approach zero, keeping the field point always within the cylinder, the contribution to the flux from the cylinder walls will vanish since the area of the walls approaches zero. Consequently

$$\lim_{\Delta h \to 0}\ \Phi_m = (\mathbf{B}_1 - \mathbf{B}_2)\cdot\hat{\mathbf{n}}\,\Delta S.$$

However, since the flux of **B** through *any* closed surface vanishes, the normal component of **B** is continuous across any interface; that is,

$$\mathbf{B}_1 \cdot \hat{\mathbf{n}} = \mathbf{B}_2 \cdot \hat{\mathbf{n}}. \tag{7.22}$$

The behavior of the tangential component of **B** across an interface is gleaned from Ampère's law. Consider a small rectangular path having the field point in its interior (see Fig. 7.5). According to Ampère's law,

$$\oint_{\Gamma} \mathbf{B} \cdot \mathbf{dl} = 4\pi\left(\frac{\mu_0}{4\pi}\right)I.$$

If the altitude of the rectangular path Γ is allowed to approach zero, keeping the field point within the rectangle, then

$$\int_1 \mathbf{B} \cdot \mathbf{dl} + \int_2 \mathbf{B} \cdot \mathbf{dl} = 4\pi\left(\frac{\mu_0}{4\pi}\right)I.$$

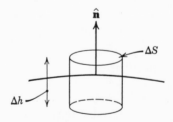

Fig. 7.4   A cylinder of height Δh and base area ΔS contains a point in its interior which lies on an interface separating two regions. The flux of **B** through this cylinder vanishes, leading to the continuity of the normal component of **B** across an interface.

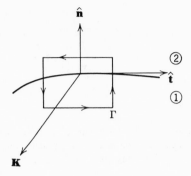

Fig. 7.5 A rectangular path Γ has a field point lying on an interface which lies within its interior. t is a unit vector tangent to the interface at the field point. **K** is the current density flowing along the interface. The behavior of the tangential component of **B** at such an interface is displayed in eq. 7.23.

If the length of the sides of the rectangle is small, **B** is essentially constant on each side. Defining $\hat{\mathbf{t}}$ as a unit vector tangent to the interface,

$$(\mathbf{B}_1 \cdot \hat{\mathbf{t}} - \mathbf{B}_2 \cdot \hat{\mathbf{t}}) \, \Delta l = 4\pi \left(\frac{\mu_0}{4\pi} \right) I.$$

Adopting the symbol **K** for the amount of current per unit length of surface flowing on the interface, I may be written

$$I = (\mathbf{K} \cdot \hat{\mathbf{s}}) \, \Delta l$$

where $\hat{\mathbf{s}}$ is a unit vector defined by $\hat{\mathbf{s}} = \hat{\mathbf{n}} \times \hat{\mathbf{t}}$, and consequently

$$(\mathbf{B}_1 \cdot \hat{\mathbf{t}} - \mathbf{B}_2 \cdot \hat{\mathbf{t}}) = 4\pi \left(\frac{\mu_0}{4\pi} \right) (\mathbf{K} \times \hat{\mathbf{n}}) \cdot \hat{\mathbf{t}}. \tag{7.23}$$

Equations 7.22 and 7.23 are the so-called *continuity conditions* satisfied by **B** at an interface.

7.5 *Application of Ampère's Law and the Boundary Conditions on* **B**

Several physical situations will now be considered in which Ampère's law and the boundary conditions on **B** will be used to determine **B**.

EXAMPLE 7.1 Consider an infinitely long straight wire of circular cross section with radius R carrying a uniform steady-state current I. (See Fig. 7.6.)

B is evaluated as follows. Consider a plane perpendicular to the wire

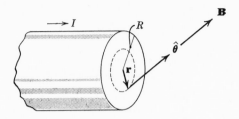

Fig. 7.6   A wire of cross-sectional area πR^2 carries a current I. $\hat{\theta}$ is a unit vector in a plane perpendicular to the axis of the wire. $\hat{\theta}$ is perpendicular to $\mathbf{r}$, the field point. $\mathbf{B}$ is everywhere parallel to $\hat{\theta}$. The magnitude of $\mathbf{B}$ is constant on a circle of radius r.

and locate the origin of coordinates at the center of the circular cross section of the wire in this plane. To evaluate the field at $\mathbf{r}$, construct a circular contour of radius r centered at the origin. If $r > R$, Ampère's law applied to the circular contour yields

$$\oint \mathbf{B} \cdot \mathbf{dl} = \left(\frac{\mu_0}{4\pi}\right) 4\pi I \qquad \text{with } \mathbf{dl} = \hat{\theta} r \, d\theta.$$

From symmetry considerations, however, it is evident that the magnitude of $\mathbf{B}$ is constant on the contour and, further, that $\mathbf{B}$ is tangential to the contour. Consequently

$$2\pi r B = \left(\frac{\mu_0}{4\pi}\right) 4\pi I,$$

or

$$\mathbf{B(r)} = \left(\frac{\mu_0}{4\pi}\right) \frac{2I}{r} \, \hat{\theta}, \quad r > R. \tag{7.24}$$

If $r < R$, Ampère's law reads

$$\oint \mathbf{B} \cdot \mathbf{dl} = \left(\frac{\mu_0}{4\pi}\right) 4\pi I \left(\frac{r}{R}\right)^2.$$

Symmetry considerations once again lead immediately to the result that

$$\mathbf{B(r)} = \left(\frac{\mu_0}{4\pi}\right) \frac{2I}{r} \left(\frac{r}{R}\right)^2 \hat{\theta}, \quad r < R. \tag{7.25}$$

Note that $\mathbf{B}$ is continuous across the interface between the wire and the vacuum which is consistent with eqs. 7.22 and 7.23.

EXAMPLE 7.2   Consider an infinitely long straight wire of circular cross section of radius R with a circular hole of radius a drilled concentrically through the wire. (See Fig. 7.7.) The wire carries a current with uniform density $\mathbf{j}$.

$\mathbf{B}$ may be evaluated, taking cognizance of the results of Example 7.1. For the region $r > R$, the result of eq. 7.24 still remains valid, namely,

$$\mathbf{B}(\mathbf{r}) = \left(\frac{\mu_0}{4\pi}\right) \frac{2I}{r} \hat{\boldsymbol{\theta}}, \quad r > R \qquad \text{with } I = \pi(R^2 - a^2)j.$$

For the region $R > r > a$, and the region $r < a$, the following method may be employed. The circular wire of radius R and with a hole of radius a may be thought of as two coaxial wires superimposed, each carrying a current with density

$$j = \frac{1}{\pi(R^2 - a^2)} I$$

but in opposite directions. This set of coaxial wires is completely equivalent to the single wire with a hole. In the region $R > r > a$, there are two contributions to $\mathbf{B}$: from the wire of larger cross section, eq. 7.25 must be employed with $I = j\pi R^2$

$$\mathbf{B}_1(\mathbf{r}) = \left(\frac{\mu_0}{4\pi}\right) \frac{2\pi j R^2}{r} \left(\frac{r}{R}\right)^2 \hat{\boldsymbol{\theta}};$$

from the wire of small cross section, eq. 7.24 must be employed with $I = j\pi a^2$

$$\mathbf{B}_2(\mathbf{r}) = -\left(\frac{\mu_0}{4\pi}\right) \frac{2\pi j a^2}{r} \hat{\boldsymbol{\theta}}.$$

The resultant field is

$$\mathbf{B}(\mathbf{r}) = \mathbf{B}_1(\mathbf{r}) + \mathbf{B}_2(\mathbf{r}) = \left(\frac{\mu_0}{4\pi}\right) \frac{2\pi j}{r} (r^2 - a^2)\hat{\boldsymbol{\theta}}, \quad R > r > a. \qquad (7.26)$$

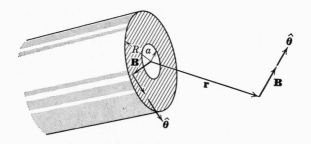

Fig. 7.7 A circular wire has a hole of radius a drilled coaxially. The $\mathbf{B}$-field inside the hole vanishes. In the wire and outside the wire the $\mathbf{B}$-field is in the $\hat{\boldsymbol{\theta}}$ direction, and its magnitude is constant on a circle of radius r.

For the region $r < a$, symmetry arguments applied to Ampère's law yield

$$\mathbf{B(r)} = 0, \quad r < a. \tag{7.27}$$

If the radius of the hole a is allowed to approach the radius R of the wire, keeping the total current fixed, then the physical situation of a cylindrical sheath of current is realized. The field in the region $r < R$ vanishes. Since the current density in the wire when $a < R$ is

$$j = \frac{1}{\pi(R^2 - a^2)} I,$$

the product $j(r^2 - a^2)$ at the surface of the wire remains finite when $a \to R$ and is simply $(1/\pi)I$. Consequently in the limit $a = R$, the field immediately outside the sheath as gleaned from eq. 7.26 is

$$\mathbf{B(r)} = \left(\frac{\mu_0}{4\pi}\right) \frac{2I}{R} \hat{\theta}, \quad r = R.$$

This means that the $\hat{\theta}$ or tangential component of **B** is discontinuous across the sheath since

$$\mathbf{B(r)} = 0, \quad r = R - \epsilon$$

$$\mathbf{B(r)} = \left(\frac{\mu_0}{4\pi}\right) \frac{2I}{R} \hat{\theta}, \quad r = R + \epsilon$$

where ϵ = arbitrarily small number. (Of course, the normal component of **B** is continuous and is identically zero.) This agrees with eq. 7.23, since **K** in this situation is nonzero and is given by $\mathbf{K} = (I/2\pi R)\hat{z}$. The method employed here becomes exceedingly useful when the circular hole is drilled off-center. This physical situation is left as an exercise.

PROBLEMS

7.1 A coaxial cable consists in a long thin wire of negligible cross section as the axis of a cylindrical conducting sheath of circular cross section of radius R. If the wire carries a current I and the sheath a current I in the opposite sense, calculate the magnetic field inside and outside the cable.

7.2 A conductor consists in a long straight wire of circular cross section of radius b with a cylindrical hole of circular cross section of radius a drilled with its axis parallel to but not coincident with the axis of the wire. If the center of the wire and the center of the hole are separated by a distance $d(a + d < b)$, and the wire carries a total current I of uniform density, calculate **B** at the center of the hole.

7.3 Using Ampére's law, show that the **B**-field inside an infinitely long solenoid is uniform.

7.4 Show that the **B**-field outside an infinitely long solenoid vanishes identically.

8 | *Magnetostatic Energy of a System of Current Carriers in Vacuum; Faraday's Law of Induction*

One of the main purposes of this chapter is to develop the concept of the energy associated with a system of conductors carrying steady-state currents. Since current-carrying loops exert forces and torques on each other, a finite amount of work must be expended in changing a given configuration of current carriers. An attempt will be made to develop methods to calculate the necessary work and to express the work solely in terms of the fields produced by the current carriers. If this attempt is successful, it will then be possible to ascribe energy to the magnetic field in the same manner that energy was associated with an electrostatic field in Chapter 4.

It is not possible, however, to follow the methods appropriate for electrostatics which were developed in Chapter 4. It will be instructive to review briefly the methods employed in the previous discussion of the energy residing in the electrostatic field and to point out why the discussion cannot be directly carried over into magnetostatics. It was shown in Chapter 4 that the energy associated with a system of N charged particles is (see eq. 4.5)

$$U_e = \tfrac{1}{2} \sum_{i=1}^{N} \sum_{j=1}^{N} q_i \varphi_{ji} \quad (i \neq j). \tag{8.1}$$

This equation was the starting point for the discussion which led to an expression for the electrostatic energy in terms of the fields themselves, namely, eq. 4.13:

$$U_e = (4\pi\epsilon_0) \frac{1}{8\pi} \int_\tau d\tau E^2 \quad \text{(vacuum).} \tag{8.2}$$

The goal for magnetostatics is to derive an expression involving the **B**-field similar to eq. 8.2. It will be possible to attain this goal, and the result will take the form

$$U_m = \left(\frac{4\pi}{\mu_0}\right) \frac{1}{8\pi} \int_\tau d\tau B^2. \tag{8.3}$$

173

However, there are two reasons why the logical development of the expression for the *magnetic energy*, U_m, in terms of the magnetic induction field must differ markedly from that used to calculate U_e.   The method employed for electrostatics depends on the existence of two well-defined physical quantities, namely, the electric charge (or monopole moment) q and the electrostatic potential φ.   In Chapters 6 and 7 it was shown that magnetic monopoles (magnetic charges) do not exist and further that it is not possible, in general, to define a magnetostatic potential which is a single-valued function of position.   Consequently a search must be made for a procedure to calculate U_m which differs from that used to calculate U_e.   (Of course, as has been previously indicated, logic could be cast aside and a magnetic monopole and a magnetostatic potential defined in such a way that the correct result is obtained.   This could be done by describing any current carrier as a sum of magnetic monopoles with the following properties: the monopole moment of the carrier should vanish, whereas the higher multipole moments should equal those of the current carrier itself.   In addition, the magnetostatic potential could be interpreted in the manner suggested in Chapter 7, such that the problem of its multi-valuedness never arises.   Such a procedure would lead to the correct result but would completely obscure the physics.   It would bury the physical essence of magnetostatic phenomena under a load of artificial, nonphysical constructs.)

Before actually proceeding to calculate U_m for a system of current carriers, an alternative procedure that could be followed will be indicated. The current carriers would all be placed an infinite distance apart so that they would experience no forces or torques due to their interaction.   Then, one by one, the current carriers would be brought into their final position and orientation, and the work necessary to do this could be calculated. At first sight this seems to be a very unambiguous and straightforward procedure.   However, there are two observations to be made: (1) each current-carrying loop or circuit contains a finite energy, that is, the loop would change its own shape if it were not for the mechanical stresses in the wires, etc., which hold it together (this is equivalent to the *self-energy* of the current carriers); (2) a certain amount of work would be necessary to keep the currents flowing in the loops as they were moved into their positions. The work referred to in (2) is not due to Joule heating losses in the loops, since in calculating U_m only the *reversible work* will be of interest; the work referred to is due to another physical effect not yet considered but which is fundamental in the discussion of magnetic effects.   This effect is based on an empirical law known as Faraday's law of induction, namely,

$$\mathcal{E} = -\frac{d}{dt} \iint_{\Sigma} \mathbf{B} \cdot \hat{\mathbf{n}} \, dS, \tag{8.4}$$

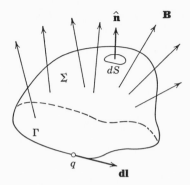

Fig. 8.1   A closed contour Γ is capped by a surface Σ. dS is an element of Σ; the direction of $\hat{n}$, the unit normal to dS, is defined in the right-hand sense relative to the contour Γ; $\mathbf{dl}$ is an element of the contour.   The work per unit charge necessary to move a charge q around Γ is the negative of the time rate of change of the flux of $\mathbf{B}$ through Σ.

where $\mathcal{E}$ = electromotive force or work per unit charge necessary to move a charge slowly around the contour Γ capped by the surface Σ (see Fig. 8.1). However, $\mathcal{E}$ is related to the electric field at the contour Γ by the expression

$$\mathcal{E} = \oint_{\Gamma} \mathbf{E} \cdot \mathbf{dl}$$

Consequently Faraday's law reads

$$\oint_{\Gamma} \mathbf{E} \cdot \mathbf{dl} = -\frac{d}{dt} \iint_{\Sigma} (\mathbf{B} \cdot \hat{n})\, dS = -\frac{d}{dt}\, \Phi_m \qquad (8.5)$$

where Φ_m = magnetic flux through Σ.   Equation 8.5 is an empirical law and cannot be derived from anything discussed previously.   It is the first physical law encountered which contains both $\mathbf{E}$ and $\mathbf{B}$.   It is also the first physical law encountered which explicitly contains time-dependent effects. Using Faraday's law, it is possible to take into consideration the two effects alluded to above, namely, the self-energy of the current loops and the reversible work necessary to keep the currents in the loops constant as the loops are moved into position.   (A detailed discussion of Faraday's law appears in Section 8.4.)

8.1   Self-Energy of a Current Loop

To calculate the self-energy $U_m^{(0)}$ of a loop, consider the magnetic flux Φ_m threading through a loop carrying a current i.   This may be written in terms of the magnetic induction field as

$$\Phi_m(i) = \iint_\Sigma \mathbf{B}(i) \cdot \hat{\mathbf{n}} \, dS \tag{8.6a}$$

or in terms of the vector potential as

$$\Phi_m(i) = \iint_\Sigma \text{curl } \mathbf{A}(i) \cdot \hat{\mathbf{n}} \, dS,$$

which becomes, via Stokes's theorem of the vector calculus

$$\Phi_m(i) = \oint_\Gamma \mathbf{A}(i) \cdot \mathbf{dl}. \tag{8.6b}$$

However, by definition

$$\mathbf{A}(\mathbf{r}) = \left(\frac{\mu_0}{4\pi}\right) \oint_\Gamma \frac{i \, \mathbf{dl'}}{|\mathbf{r} - \mathbf{r'}|}$$

and therefore

$$\Phi_m(i) = i\left\{\left(\frac{\mu_0}{4\pi}\right) \oint\oint \frac{\mathbf{dl} \cdot \mathbf{dl'}}{|\mathbf{r} - \mathbf{r'}|}\right\}. \tag{8.7}$$

The integral on the right-hand side of eq. 8.7 depends solely on the geometry of the loop. It is therefore a constant for a given loop. It is usually called the *coefficient of self-inductance* or simply the *inductance* of the loop and is given the symbol L; that is,

$$\Phi_m(i) = iL.$$

Faraday's law is now applied to calculate the self-energy of the loop. When the current in the loop is increased by an amount di, the change in the magnetic flux threading through Σ is simply

$$d\Phi_m = L \, di.$$

The rate at which energy is *added* to the circuit when the current is increased by an amount di is written

$$\begin{aligned}
\frac{dU_m^{(0)}}{dt} &= -i\mathcal{E} = i\frac{\partial}{\partial t}\Phi_m \\
\frac{dU_m^{(0)}}{dt} &= iL\frac{di}{dt}.
\end{aligned} \tag{8.8}$$

Consequently the self-energy of the loop defined as the total energy added to the loop when the current increases from zero to a final value i is

$$U_m^{(0)} = \int\left(\frac{dU_m^{(0)}}{dt}\right) dt = L\int_0^i i' \, di',$$

or

$$U_m^{(0)} = \tfrac{1}{2}Li^2. \tag{8.9}$$

Equation 8.9 can be written in terms of **A** and the current as follows:

$$U_m^{(0)} = \tfrac{1}{2} i(iL) = \tfrac{1}{2} i \oint_\Gamma \mathbf{A} \cdot \mathbf{dl}$$

or finally

$$U_m^{(0)} = \tfrac{1}{2} \oint_\Gamma i\mathbf{A} \cdot \mathbf{dl} = \tfrac{1}{2} \int_\tau d\tau \mathbf{j} \cdot \mathbf{A} \tag{8.10}$$

where the usual replacement $\oint_\Gamma i\, \mathbf{dl} \cdots \leftrightarrow \int_\tau d\tau \mathbf{j} \cdots$ has been made. The second expression for $U_m^{(0)}$ in terms of the current density is now analogous to the similar expression in electrostatics for the self-energy of a charge distribution, namely,

$$U_e^{(0)} = \tfrac{1}{2} \int_\tau d\tau \rho \varphi. \tag{8.11}$$

(As might have been expected, **j** and ρ play similar roles as do **A** and φ. Since $U_m^{(0)}$ is a scalar, it is plausible that the magnetic self-energy should take the form it does in eq. 8.10 involving the scalar product of **j** and **A**.)

8.2   Magnetic Energy of a System of Current Carriers

Equation 8.10 has only been derived for one loop, and the question still remains whether the *total* magnetic energy of a system of loops has the same form. The total magnetic energy is defined as

$$U_m = \sum_{k=1}^{N} [U_m^{(0)}]_k + \sum_{k \neq j}^{N} [U_{m\,\text{int}}]_{kj} \tag{8.12}$$

where $[U_{m\,\text{int}}]_{kj}$ = interaction energy between the k and j loops. U_m of eq. 8.12 will now be calculated by a modification of the procedure outlined previously. Consider a system of two current-carrying loops—the generalization to a system of N loops will be obvious. First place the two loops a and b in position and orientation with no current flowing in them. The current in loop a is then increased to its final value i_a, keeping the current in b at zero. The increase of current in loop a will have two effects: (1) an emf will be induced in loop a; (2) an emf will be induced in loop b. The consequence of effect (1) will be an amount of work expended—this will be the self-energy of loop a. The consequence of effect (2) will be that an amount of energy will have to be supplied to loop b to keep the current zero in b. The final step is to increase the current in b to its final value i_b. Once again, two effects must be considered: (3) the induction of

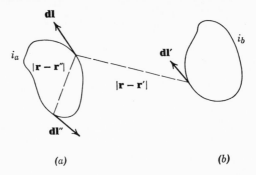

(a)   *(b)*

Fig. 8.2   Two loops *a* and *b* carry currents i_a and i_b, respectively.   The work done in establishing the currents in the loops is $W = \frac{1}{2}\{i_a^2 L_a + i_b^2 L_b + 2i_a i_b M_{ab}\}$.   **dl, dl″** are vector elements of loop *a*; **dl′** is a vector element of loop *b*.

an emf in coil *b* which results in a self-energy $U_b^{(0)}$ of loop *b*; (4) the induction of an emf in coil *a* which would change the current in coil *a* if energy were not supplied to coil *a* to maintain the current at its value i_a.

In order to analyze the above more closely, consider the most general situation in which current *i* is flowing in loop *a* and current *i′* in loop *b*. (See Fig. 8.2.)   The current in loop *a* is then incremented to $i + di$.   The resultant change in magnetic flux through both loops is

$$d\Phi = d\left[\iint_{\Sigma_a} (\mathbf{B} \cdot \hat{\mathbf{n}})\, dS + \iint_{\Sigma_b} (\mathbf{B} \cdot \hat{\mathbf{n}})\, dS \right].$$

Using curl $\mathbf{A} = \mathbf{B}$ and Stokes's theorem, the increment in flux can be written

$$d\Phi = d\left[\oint_a \mathbf{A} \cdot \mathbf{dl} + \oint_b \mathbf{A} \cdot \mathbf{dl} \right].$$

However, the vector potential at **r′** due to the current in loop *a* is

$$\mathbf{A(r')} = \left(\frac{\mu_0}{4\pi}\right) \oint_a i \frac{\mathbf{dl}}{|\mathbf{r} - \mathbf{r'}|}$$

and consequently

$$d\Phi = di\left[\left(\frac{\mu_0}{4\pi}\right) \oint_a \oint_a \frac{\mathbf{dl} \cdot \mathbf{dl''}}{|\mathbf{r} - \mathbf{r''}|} + \left(\frac{\mu_0}{4\pi}\right) \oint_b \oint_a \frac{\mathbf{dl} \cdot \mathbf{dl'}}{|\mathbf{r} - \mathbf{r'}|} \right]$$

or

$$d\Phi = di[L_a + M_{ab}] = d\Phi_a + d\Phi_b \tag{8.13}$$

where

$$M_{ab} \equiv \left(\frac{\mu_0}{4\pi}\right) \oint_b \oint_a \frac{\mathbf{dl} \cdot \mathbf{dl'}}{|\mathbf{r} - \mathbf{r'}|}$$

is the *coefficient of mutual inductance* between loops *a* and *b*.   (Note that $M_{ab} = M_{ba}$.)

If the current in loop a is changed at a rate di/dt, an emf will be induced in each loop:

$$\mathcal{E}_a = -\frac{d\Phi_a}{dt} = -L_a\left(\frac{di}{dt}\right); \qquad \mathcal{E}_b = -\frac{d\Phi_b}{dt} = -M_{ab}\left(\frac{di}{dt}\right).$$

The rate at which work must be done to increase the current in loop a by di when current i is flowing in loop a and i' in loop b is then

$$\frac{dW}{dt} = -(i\mathcal{E}_a + i'\mathcal{E}_b) = i\left(\frac{di}{dt}\right)l_a + i'\left(\frac{di}{dt}\right)M_{ab}. \qquad (8.14)$$

Integrating the above, that is, increasing i from zero to i_a and holding i' fixed, yields

$$W = \tfrac{1}{2}i_a^2 L_a + i'i_a M_{ab}. \qquad (8.15)$$

However, i' is fixed at zero in the first step in the physical process under consideration, and therefore the first contribution to the work is

$$W_1 = \tfrac{1}{2}i_a^2 L_a. \qquad (8.16)$$

To accomplish the last step (i.e., the current in b increased from zero to i_b holding the current in loop a at i_a) the steps leading to eq. 8.14 are repeated, interchanging the symbols a and b; in other words,

$$\frac{dW}{dt} = i\mathcal{E}_b + i'\mathcal{E}_a = i\left(\frac{di}{dt}\right)L_b + i'\left(\frac{di}{dt}\right)M_{ab}.$$

Increasing i from zero to i_b when i' is held fixed at i_a yields an amount of work

$$W_2 = \tfrac{1}{2}i_b^2 L_b + i_a i_b M_{ab}. \qquad (8.17)$$

The total amount of work done in this two-step process which is equated to the magnetic field energy is $W = W_1 + W_2 = U_m$:

$$U_m = \tfrac{1}{2}i_a^2 L_a + \tfrac{1}{2}i_b^2 L_b + \tfrac{1}{2}[i_a i_b M_{ab} + i_b i_a M_{ba}]. \qquad (8.18)$$

This can be generalized to N loops

$$U_m = \tfrac{1}{2}\sum_{j=1}^{N}\sum_{k=1}^{N} i_j i_k M_{jk} \qquad (8.19)$$

where $M_{jk} = L_j$ when $j = k$.

Another useful expression for U_m is obtained by noting that

$$U_m = \frac{1}{2}\sum_{j=1}^{N} i_j\left\{\sum_{k=1}^{N} i_k M_{jk}\right\} = \frac{1}{2}\sum_{j=1}^{N} i_j \sum_{k=1}^{N} i_k\left\{\frac{\mu_0}{4\pi}\oint_j\oint_k \frac{d\mathbf{l}_j \cdot d\mathbf{l}_k}{|\mathbf{r}_j - \mathbf{r}_k|}\right\}$$

or

$$U_m = \frac{1}{2}\sum_{j=1}^{N} i_j \oint_j\left\{\frac{\mu_0}{4\pi}\sum_{k=1}^{N} i_k \oint_k \frac{d\mathbf{l}_k}{|\mathbf{r}_j - \mathbf{r}_k|}\right\} \cdot d\mathbf{l}_j$$

where the expression in braces is the vector potential at a point on loop j due to current flowing in all the loops.   Therefore

$$U_m = \frac{1}{2} \sum_{j=1}^{N} \oint_j i_j \, \mathbf{dl}_j \cdot \mathbf{A} \Rightarrow \frac{1}{2} \int_\tau d\tau \mathbf{j} \cdot \mathbf{A}. \qquad (8.20)$$

Equation 8.20 may be handled analogously to the equation: $U_e = \frac{1}{2} \int_\tau d\tau \rho \varphi$,

which appeared in Chapter 4 for the electrostatic energy.   The procedure is as follows.   The current density $\mathbf{j}$ is removed from the integrand of eq. 8.20, employing the differential form of Ampère's law, namely,

$$\mathrm{curl}\, \mathbf{B} = \left(\frac{\mu_0}{4\pi}\right) 4\pi \mathbf{j}. \qquad (8.21)$$

The resultant expression for U_m will contain the **B**- and **A**-fields only, but no explicit reference to the sources of these fields.   It is therefore convenient to say that the energy U_m resides in the fields themselves.   This is not strictly necessary, but will be a convenient artifice in future discussions.

Of course, it is possible to remove either **B** or **A** from the expression for U_m by remembering that by definition curl $\mathbf{A} = \mathbf{B}$.   Substituting the results of eq. 8.21 into eq. 8.20, it is found that

$$U_m = \left(\frac{4\pi}{\mu_0}\right) \frac{1}{8\pi} \int d\tau \mathbf{A} \cdot \mathrm{curl}\, \mathbf{B}. \qquad (8.22)$$

An attempt is now made to use curl $\mathbf{A} = \mathbf{B}$ to remove the **A**-field from eq. 8.22 and to express U_m solely in terms of the **B**-field.   This is possible by use of the following identity from the vector calculus:

$$\mathrm{div}\, (\mathbf{A} \times \mathbf{B}) \equiv \mathbf{B} \cdot \mathrm{curl}\, \mathbf{A} - \mathbf{A} \cdot \mathrm{curl}\, \mathbf{B}. \qquad (8.23)$$

Equation 8.23 is valid for any vector point functions, and its validity does not depend on the physical significance of **A** and **B**.   Employing this identity, eq. 8.22 takes the form

$$U_m = \frac{1}{8\pi} \left(\frac{4\pi}{\mu_0}\right) \left\{ \int d\tau \mathbf{B} \cdot \mathrm{curl}\, \mathbf{A} - \int d\tau \, \mathrm{div}\, (\mathbf{A} \times \mathbf{B}) \right\}. \qquad (8.24)$$

In the first term on the right-hand side of eq. 8.24, curl **A** may be replaced by **B**, whereas the divergence theorem of the vector calculus may be employed in the second term in the usual manner, yielding

$$U_m = \left(\frac{4\pi}{\mu_0}\right) \frac{1}{8\pi} \left\{ \int d\tau B^2 - \oiint_\Sigma dS \hat{\mathbf{n}} \cdot (\mathbf{A} \times \mathbf{B}) \right\}. \qquad (8.25)$$

Since the volume of integration is of all space, all points on the closed surface Σ are infinitely distant from the current loops producing the fields.

Since magnetic charge is nonexistent, the **A**- and **B**-fields fall off at least as rapidly as those due to a magnetic dipole and vanish rapidly enough on the surface Σ to cause the integral over Σ to vanish. Consequently the magnetostatic energy may be written solely in terms of the induction field **B**; that is,

$$U_m = \left(\frac{4\pi}{\mu_0}\right)\frac{1}{8\pi}\int d\tau B^2. \tag{8.26}$$

Equation 8.26 is then a mathematical reformulation of eq. 8.20 for U_m; they both contain the same physical content.

EXAMPLE 8.1   As an application of eq. 8.26 consider two infinitely long straight wires with circular cross section each carrying a current I. Assume that the radii of the cross sections are a and b and that the current density is constant throughout each wire. (See Fig. 8.3.) Although the energy residing in the fields produced by each wire is divergent, the difference between the magnetostatic energies per unit length is finite. The magnitude of the **B**-field produced by such a wire of cross-sectional area πr_0^2 is

$$B(r) = \begin{cases} \left(\dfrac{\mu_0}{4\pi}\right)\dfrac{I}{2r}, & r > r_0 \\[2ex] \left(\dfrac{\mu_0}{4\pi}\right)\dfrac{I}{2r}\left(\dfrac{r}{r_0}\right)^2, & r < r_0. \end{cases} \tag{8.27}$$

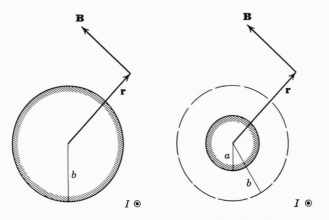

Fig. 8.3   Two infinitely long straight wires of circular cross sections πa^2 and πb^2 each carry a current I distributed uniformly over their circular cross sections. The magnetic energy per unit length of wire a is larger than that of wire b; this difference in energy comes solely from the region $b \geqslant r \geqslant a$.

Taking $b > a$, the contribution to the field energy per unit length $\tilde{U}$ of each wire in the region $r \geqslant b$ is the same for both wires since $B(r)$ is identical for both wires in this region. In addition, the contribution to $\tilde{U}$ of a circular wire of radius r_0 in the region $r_0 \geqslant r \geqslant 0$ is seen to be independent of the radius; this contribution is

$$\left(\frac{4\pi}{\mu_0}\right)\frac{1}{8\pi}\int_0^{r_0}\left[\left(\frac{\mu_0}{4\pi}\right)\frac{I}{2r}\left(\frac{r}{r_0}\right)^2\right]^2(2\pi r\,dr) = \left(\frac{\mu_0}{4\pi}\right)\frac{I^2}{32}. \tag{8.28}$$

Consequently the difference in $\tilde{U}$, namely, $\tilde{U}_a - \tilde{U}_b$, is due solely to the contribution to the field energy produced by the wire with radius a in the region $b \geqslant r \geqslant a$; this is

$$\tilde{U}_a - \tilde{U}_b = \left(\frac{4\pi}{\mu_0}\right)\frac{1}{8\pi}\int_a^b\left[\left(\frac{\mu_0}{4\pi}\right)\frac{I}{2r}\right]^2(2\pi r\,dr)$$

or
$$\tilde{U}_a - \tilde{U}_b = \left(\frac{\mu_0}{4\pi}\right)\frac{I^2}{16}\ln\frac{b}{a}. \tag{8.29}$$

8.3   Thomson's Theorem

It is possible to develop an "extremum principle" for U_m similar to Thomson's theorem for the equivalent electrostatic case. Consider two fields **B** and **B′** each of which satisfies Ampère's law; that is,

$$\oint_\Gamma \mathbf{B}\cdot\mathbf{dl} = \oint_\Gamma \mathbf{B}'\cdot\mathbf{dl} = \left(\frac{\mu_0}{4\pi}\right)4\pi i$$

for any closed path Γ, and curl **B** = curl **B′** = $\mu_0\mathbf{j}$ at any point in space. We suppose further that **j** is nonzero only in a finite region of space. In addition to satisfying the Ampèrian relation, **B** (but not **B′**) is the physical field; that is, it is derivable from a vector potential. The magnetostatic energy associated with **B** and **B′** are

$$U_m = \left(\frac{4\pi}{\mu_0}\right)\frac{1}{8\pi}\int d\tau B^2; \qquad U_m' = \left(\frac{4\pi}{\mu_0}\right)\frac{1}{8\pi}\int d\tau B'^2.$$

If **B′** is written in terms of **B** as **B′** = **B** + **β**, the difference in the magnetic energy associated with the fields is simply

$$U_m' - U_m = \left(\frac{4\pi}{\mu_0}\right)\left\{\frac{1}{8\pi}\int\beta^2\,d\tau + \frac{1}{4\pi}\int\boldsymbol{\beta}\cdot\mathbf{B}\,d\tau\right\}. \tag{8.30}$$

The first integral on the right-hand side of eq. 8.30 is *at least* equal to zero since the integrand is never negative anywhere, and therefore the equality of eq. 8.30 can be rewritten as the inequality of eq. 8.31:

$$U_m' - U_m \geqslant \frac{1}{\mu_0}\int\boldsymbol{\beta}\cdot\mathbf{B}\,d\tau. \tag{8.31}$$

It is now straightforward to show that the right-hand side of eq. 8.31 is zero. This may be accomplished as follows: since **B** is the physical field, it can be replaced by curl **A**; that is,

$$U'_m - U_m \geqslant \frac{1}{\mu_0} \int \boldsymbol{\beta} \cdot \text{curl } \mathbf{A} \, d\tau. \tag{8.32}$$

However, employing the vector calculus identity used in eq. 8.23 and the divergence theorem, eq. 8.32 may be rewritten as

$$U'_m - U_m \geqslant \frac{1}{\mu_0} \int \mathbf{A} \cdot \text{curl } \boldsymbol{\beta} \, d\tau - \frac{1}{\mu_0} \oiint_{\Sigma} dS \hat{\mathbf{n}} \cdot (\mathbf{A} \times \boldsymbol{\beta}). \tag{8.33}$$

Since $\boldsymbol{\beta}$ is the difference between **B** and **B'** and since **B** and **B'** both satisfy the differential form of Ampère's law, it follows that curl $\boldsymbol{\beta} = 0$. In addition, since **j** is nonzero only in a finite region of space, **A** and $\boldsymbol{\beta}$ both vanish on the surface Σ rapidly enough to cause the vanishing of the second integral on the right-hand side of eq. 8.33. Consequently we have the desired extremum principle

$$U'_m \geqslant U_m. \tag{8.34}$$

Any field other than the physical field which satisfies Ampère's law yields a magnetic energy at least as large as that associated with the physical field.

8.4   Faraday's Law

Faraday's law was introduced in the development of the concepts of the self-energy of a current-carrying loop and the interaction energy of a system of such loops. Faraday's law or the law of induction, an empirical law, was written in analytic form in eqs. 8.4 and 8.5, namely,

$$\oint_{\Gamma} \mathbf{E} \cdot d\mathbf{l} = -\frac{d}{dt} \iint_{\Sigma} (\mathbf{B} \cdot \hat{\mathbf{n}}) \, dS,$$

where Γ is any closed contour and Σ is any open surface capping the contour. The negative sign in Faraday's law is commonly referred to as *Lenz's rule*. If Γ is a conducting loop, the induced **E**-field at each point on the loop produced by a changing magnetic flux through the loop causes a current to flow in the conducting loop. However, it is important to realize that the contour Γ can be *any* closed curve and is not restricted to a conducting loop. In particular, Γ may be any closed mathematical curve chosen in an arbitrary manner. The **E**-field induced at a point on the arbitrary Γ and thus at an arbitrary point in space is nonconservative; the integral $\oint \mathbf{E} \cdot d\mathbf{l}$ does not vanish for **E**-fields produced by time-varying magnetic fields.   (This is in contrast to **E**-fields produced by static charges, i.e., electrostatic fields, which are conservative and for which $\oint \mathbf{E} \cdot \mathbf{dl}$ vanishes.)

The magnetic flux threading through a surface capping a closed contour may change in time in two distinct ways: (1) the **B**-field may be an explicit function of time; (2) the **B**-field may be static, but the contour Γ may itself be changing in time either through a rigid movement of Γ (translation and/or rotation) or through a distortion of Γ.   Case 1 does not represent anything unusual and merely allows for the following mathematical operation:

$$\frac{d}{dt} \iint_{\Sigma} \mathbf{B}(\mathbf{r}, t) \cdot \hat{\mathbf{n}} \, dS = \iint_{\Sigma} \left[\frac{\partial}{\partial t} \mathbf{B}(\mathbf{r}, t) \right] \cdot \hat{\mathbf{n}} \, dS.$$

To discuss case 2, it is useful to introduce several simple physical illustrations.   Consider first a *translation* of a closed loop through a region of nonuniform but static **B**-field (see Fig. 8.4).   To an observer at rest in the coordinate system in which the field is static, the magnetic flux threading the loop changes; the strength of the **B**-field at any given point on a surface capping the loop changes due to the translation of the loop through the nonuniform field.   Consequently an emf will be induced in the loop, causing a given amount of current to flow if the loop is conducting. However, to an observer at rest with respect to the loop, the relative motion

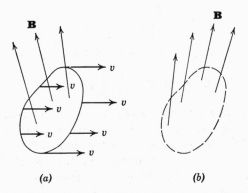

(a)   (b)

Fig. 8.4   A closed conducting loop is translated with velocity **v** through a region of static but nonuniform **B**.   The current induced in the coil is attributed by observer (a) fixed in the reference frame in which **B** is static to the Lorentz force, $\mathbf{f} = q\mathbf{v} \times \mathbf{B}$, acting on the current carriers in the conductor; observer (b) fixed with respect to the coil attributes the current to an induced **E**-field produced by a time-changing **B** acting on the current carriers, $\mathbf{f} = q\mathbf{E}$.

of the loop and the reference frame in which **B** is static is interpreted as a time-varying or nonstatic **B**-field threading through a surface capping the loop. The induced conduction current measured by the observer moving with the loop must be the same as the induced current measured by the observer in the reference frame in which **B** is static. The observer in the reference frame in which **B** is static will detect a force on one of the current carriers (electrons) in the conductor given by $\mathbf{f} = q\mathbf{v} \times \mathbf{B}$ where **v** is the translational velocity of the conducting loop with respect to this observer and **B** is the static field. (If **B** is uniform, this will result in no net flow of charge around the conducting loop.) The observer in the reference frame moving with the loop will also detect a force on one of the current carriers given here by $\mathbf{f} = q\mathbf{E}$ where **E** is the field induced by the time-varying **B** detected by this observer. (If **B** is uniform, this observer will detect a static **B**-field only and hence no induced **E**-field.) Since both observers must detect the same physical effect on the current carriers, it follows that

$$\mathbf{E} = \mathbf{v} \times \mathbf{B}. \tag{8.35}$$

The argument leading to eq. 8.35 is inherently *nonrelativistic*. Therefore it is only correct in the limit $v/c \ll 1$.

If a conducting loop is *rotated* in a static magnetic field, an emf will be induced in the loop. Once again, an observer in the coordinate system in which **B** is static notes a time-varying flux due to the physical rotation of the loop, whereas an observer stationary with respect to the loop experiences a time-varying flux interpreted to arise from a time-varying **B**-field. Example 8.2 considers a particularly simple case involving a rotating loop.

EXAMPLE 8.2   Consider a circular conducting loop of radius R rotating about a diameter with angular velocity $\boldsymbol{\omega}$ in a static uniform **B**-field. (See Fig. 8.5.) If $\hat{\mathbf{n}}$ is the normal to the plane of the coil, the magnetic flux through the coil is simply

$$\Phi = \pi R^2 \hat{\mathbf{n}} \cdot \mathbf{B}$$

or
$$\Phi = \pi R^2 B \cos(\omega t + \theta_0)$$

where θ_0 is the angle between $\hat{\mathbf{n}}$ and **B** at $t = 0$.

The emf induced in the coil is given by Faraday's law and is

$$\mathcal{E} = \pi \omega R^2 B \sin(\omega t + \theta_0)$$

where the sense of the emf is determined by Lenz's rule according to which an induced current should produce a flux through the coil whose algebraic sign is opposite to that associated with the change in the flux of the applied field.

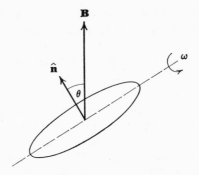

Fig. 8.5   A circular loop of radius R rotates about a diameter with angular velocity ω in a static **B**-field. $\hat{n}$ is a unit vector perpendicular to the plane of the coil. A current is induced in the loop by the time-varying magnetic flux threading the loop.

In Example 8.2 and the immediately preceding discussion, an emf was induced in a conducting coil by virtue of the motion of the coil through a static field.   To an observer at rest with respect to the coil, the emf can be attributed to an explicitly time-varying **B**-field.   There is another physical situation which can lead to an induced emf but to which the above discussion does not immediately apply.   Consider an area enclosed by a conducting loop that is changing due to a change in size and/or shape of the loop.   Here an emf is induced in the loop even though the static **B**-field may be uniform.   The analytic discussion of this situation will also lead to a precise formulation of the situation in which the loop translates and/or rotates without distortion.

Consider an arbitrarily shaped loop in a static **B**-field.   (See Fig. 8.6.) If an element **dl** of the loop is moving with instantaneous velocity **v**, the rate of increase of the area of the loop due to the motion of this element is **v** × **dl**, with a resultant rate of change of the magnetic flux through the loop given in eq. 8.36:

$$\frac{d\Phi}{dt} = \oint_\Gamma \mathbf{B} \cdot (\mathbf{v} \times \mathbf{dl}). \tag{8.36}$$

In particular, if **B** is uniform, it may be taken outside the integral, yielding

$$\frac{d\Phi}{dt} = \mathbf{B} \cdot \oint_\Gamma \mathbf{v} \times \mathbf{dl}, \quad \text{(uniform } \mathbf{B}\text{)}. \tag{8.37}$$

The integral in eq. 8.37 is the time rate of change of the area **a** enclosed by the loop Γ, and consequently

$$\frac{d\Phi}{dt} = \mathbf{B} \cdot \frac{d\mathbf{a}}{dt}, \quad \text{(uniform } \mathbf{B}\text{)}. \tag{8.38}$$

If **B** is uniform and the loop is translated (a situation alluded to in the previous discussion), then **v** may be removed from the integral in eq. 8.37, yielding

$$\frac{d\Phi}{dt} = (\mathbf{B} \times \mathbf{v}) \cdot \oint_\Gamma \mathbf{dl} = 0, \quad \text{since} \quad \oint_\Gamma \mathbf{dl} = 0. \tag{8.39}$$

To summarize, an emf is induced in a loop Γ, or **E** is induced at a point on Γ, if one or more of the following physical situations occur:

(1) **B** is an explicit function of time;
(2) **B** is static but nonuniform and Γ is rigidly translated;
(3) **B** is static and Γ is rigidly rotated;
(4) **B** is static and the area spanning Γ is changing in time due to a distortion of Γ itself.

These four physical situations and any arbitrary combination are envisaged in Faraday's law as sources of changing magnetic flux and thus of induced **E**-fields.

Faraday's law can be expressed in differential form as follows: the induced emf may be written in terms of the flux of the induced **E**-vector through the surface capping Γ via Stokes's theorem; that is,

$$\oint_\Gamma \mathbf{E} \cdot \mathbf{dl} = \iint_\Sigma \operatorname{curl} \mathbf{E} \cdot \hat{\mathbf{n}} \, dS = -\frac{d}{dt} \iint_\Sigma (\mathbf{B} \cdot \hat{\mathbf{n}}) \, dS.$$

This immediately yields a differential equation involving **E** and **B** if it is legitimate to carry out the following operation:

$$\frac{d}{dt} \iint_\Sigma (\mathbf{B} \cdot \hat{\mathbf{n}}) \, dS = \iint_\Sigma \left(\frac{\partial}{\partial t} \mathbf{B} \cdot \hat{\mathbf{n}} \right) dS. \tag{8.40}$$

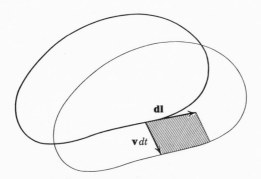

Fig. 8.6   A loop moves in an arbitrary fashion in a static **B**-field.   The motion may be considered as compounded of a translation, a rotation, and a distortion of the coil.   In a time dt an element of the coil **dl** sweeps out an area equal to $(\mathbf{v} \times \mathbf{dl}) \, dt$. The time rate of change in the magnetic flux threading the loop is given in eq. 8.36.

The interchange of integration over the variables in Σ and the differentiation with respect to time is legitimate if Γ is an arbitrary contour *fixed* in space. With this interpretation of Γ, the integrands of eq. 8.40 can be equated since the surface Σ is arbitrary. Consequently the differential form of Faraday's law is

$$\operatorname{curl} \mathbf{E} = - \frac{\partial}{\partial t} \mathbf{B}. \tag{8.41}$$

The fields $\mathbf{E}$ and $\mathbf{B}$ in eq. 8.41 must be measured in the *same* coordinate system, since the contour Γ must be fixed in passing from the integral form of Faraday's law to the differential form. In other words, the space derivatives of $\mathbf{E}$ are related to the time derivative of $\mathbf{B}$ at a point according to eq. 8.41 if measurements of these derivatives are made by the *same observer*.

PROBLEMS

8.1   Calculate the self-inductance per unit length of a long solenoid of cross-sectional area πR^2 and having N turns per unit length.

8.2   Two very long coaxial cylindrical shells of radius a and b $(a > b)$ carry current I but in opposite directions. Considering these shells to form a single closed electrical circuit, calculate the self-inductance per unit length of the circuit by direct methods.

8.3   Calculate the magnetic energy per unit length of the current-carrying system in Problem 8.2 in terms of the field produced by the system. Show that the self-inductance per unit length calculated from this value of the magnetic energy per unit length agrees with the direct calculation of this quantity in Problem 8.2.

8.4   A current carrier consists of a cylinder of radius R with a hole of radius R_0 drilled coaxially. The current density is uniform and corresponds to a total current I. Calculate the magnetic energy per unit length associated with the current carrying cylinder.

8.5   The planes of two circular loops each with radius a are parallel and are perpendicular to the line passing through the centers of the loops. The distance between the centers of the loops is d. Calculate the mutual inductance of these loops assuming $a/d \ll 1$ to lowest order in (a/d).

8.6   A long straight wire and a circular loop of radius R lie in a plane. The center of the loop is a distance $D(D > R)$ from the straight wire. Calculate the coefficient of mutual inductance of this system.

8.7   The long straight wire in Problem 8.6 carries a current I. The center of the circular loop is moved perpendicular to the wire with a speed v. Calculate the emf induced in the loop.

8.8   Repeat Problem 8.7, but assume that the center of the loop is fixed and its radius is increasing at the rate v. Calculate the emf induced in the loop.

8.9   Consider the system described in Problem 8.6. Suppose that current I_1 flows in the straight wire and that I_2 flows clockwise around the circular loop. Consider an identical geometric configuration with I_1 flowing in the straight wire in the same direction but I_2 flowing around the loop in a counterclockwise sense. What difference, if any, exists between the magnetic energies of the two systems?

8.10 A rectangular coil of side lengths a and b $(a > b)$ is coplanar with a long straight wire which is parallel to the long side of the rectangle. The side of the rectangle nearest the straight wire and the wire are separated by a distance c. The current in the straight wire is changing at a rate dI/dt. Calculate the emf induced in the rectangular loop.

8.11 A conducting spherical shell of radius R rotates with angular velocity ω about a diameter in a uniform magnetic field **B** which is perpendicular to the axis of rotation. Calculate the induced E-field at each point on the shell. If the shell has finite conductivity, indicate the direction of the induced current flow at each point on the shell.

8.12 Repeat Problem 8.11 for the case ω parallel to **B**.

9 | *Magnetostatics of Material Media*

The discussion of magnetostatics carried out so far has been concerned with physical effects produced by carriers of steady-state current residing in vacuum. It is the purpose of this chapter to indicate how the previous discussion may be modified to include effects associated with the presence of material media. The theory of magnetostatics involving material media is inherently a macroscopic theory. It consists, first of all, in a model of what transpires at a microscopic level; suitable space and time averages are then performed to produce a macroscopic theory. From the beginning, those materials will be ignored which possess nonvanishing magnetic dipole moments when no macroscopic current is flowing in them or in their neighborhood. Materials which possess permanent magnetic moments play a very important role in magnetic phenomena, but a discussion involving these materials will be temporarily postponed.

9.1 The Origin of Diamagnetism

Any medium is composed of atoms. For the present purposes these atoms may be considered as consisting of electrons moving in planar orbits about fixed nuclei. The possible intrinsic or permanent magnetic dipole moments of the electrons and nuclei will be ignored. As has been shown previously, a charged particle moving in a closed planar orbit in a force field has associated with it a magnetic dipole moment μ, the value of which is given by (see eq. 6.42)

$$\mu = \left(\frac{q}{2m}\right)l \tag{9.1}$$

where l is the angular momentum of the particle about the force center. In the present model the net magnetic dipole moment of an atom of the material is simply a sum over all the electrons in the atom of the expression in eq. 9.1:

$$\mu_{\text{atom}} = \left(\frac{e}{2m}\right)l_{\text{atom}}, \quad \text{where } e = \text{electron charge.} \tag{9.2}$$

There are two possibilities: (1) for an atom with an even number of electrons, close analysis shows that there is an electron with angular

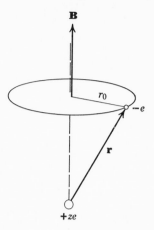

Fig. 9.1   A circle of radius r_0 is drawn with its center on a line parallel to a uniform applied **B**-field passing through the nucleus of an atom.   **r** is the distance from the nucleus to a point on the circle.   An electron at **r** experiences a force due to an induced emf if **B** changes in time.   The induced **E**-field at the electron is **E** $= \frac{1}{2}$**r** $\times$ $d\mathbf{B}/dt$.

momentum $\boldsymbol{l}$ for every electron with angular momentum $-\boldsymbol{l}$, that is, the electrons are "paired"; (2) for atoms in which this pairing effect is absent, an atom may have a net angular momentum, but it will be randomly oriented under normal conditions of temperature, etc., unless some external agency exists to align it; as a consequence, the net angular momentum associated with the randomly oriented magnetic dipoles of the electronic clouds of the atoms occupying a finite volume vanishes if the volume contains a large number of atoms.

What happens to an atom when the magnetic field at the atom is increased from zero to some finite value in some prescribed manner will now be examined.   It will be assumed that **B** is effectively constant over the extent of the atom.   As the **B**-field changes, an induced **E**-field is generated. This induced field may be calculated as follows.   Consider a circle of radius r_0 whose center is on a line parallel to **B** passing through the nucleus; the plane of the circle is perpendicular to **B** (see Fig. 9.1).   The magnitude of the induced **E**-field is constant on this circle, and its direction is tangential to the circle.   The induced emf associated with this circle is simply

$$E(2\pi r \sin \theta) = \oint \mathbf{E} \cdot \mathbf{dl} \quad \text{where } E = |\mathbf{E}| \quad \text{and} \quad r_0 = r \sin \theta. \quad (9.3)$$

The magnetic flux passing through any surface capping the circle is

$$\Phi_m = \pi r^2 \sin^2 \theta B. \quad (9.4)$$

The induced **E**-field and Φ_m are related via Faraday's law; this relationship is contained in eq. 9.5a:

$$\mathbf{E} = -\frac{d}{dt}\Phi_m \qquad (9.5a)$$

or
$$\mathbf{E} = -\frac{r\sin\theta}{2}\left(\frac{dB}{dt}\right)\hat{\phi} = \tfrac{1}{2}\mathbf{r}\times\frac{d\mathbf{B}}{dt}. \qquad (9.5b)$$

An electron in the atom at **r** will experience a force **F** associated with the induced **E**-field. The resultant acceleration of the electron is given by eq. 9.6

$$\mathbf{a} = \left(\frac{e}{2m}\right)\mathbf{r}\times\frac{d\mathbf{B}}{dt}. \qquad (9.6)$$

For normal time-varying fields, the magnitude of this acceleration is small. However, this acceleration caused by the changing **B**-field is a primary source of the alteration of the **B**-field in the presence of material media. Note that **a** depends on **r**, but not on the velocity of the electron at **r**; thus an electron moving with angular momentum l and another with $-l$, both of whose orbits pass through **r**, experience the same acceleration.

The net effect of this acceleration on all the electrons in an atom can be obtained as follows. The rate at which the angular momentum of an electron changes due to a time-varying **B**-field is given in eq. 9.7:

$$\frac{d\mathbf{l}}{dt} = \mathbf{r}\times\mathbf{F} = \frac{e}{2}\mathbf{r}\times\left(\mathbf{r}\times\frac{d\mathbf{B}}{dt}\right). \qquad (9.7)$$

Taking **B** in the polar direction and expanding the right-hand side of eq. 9.7 in Cartesian components yields

$$\frac{d\mathbf{l}}{dt} = \frac{e}{2}\left(\frac{dB}{dt}\right)\{xz\hat{\mathbf{x}} + yz\hat{\mathbf{y}} - (x^2+y^2)\hat{\mathbf{z}}\}. \qquad (9.8)$$

If **a** is assumed small compared to the normal centripetal acceleration of the electron in its orbit, the quantity of interest will be $d\mathbf{l}/dt$ averaged over the rapid internal motion of the electron around the nucleus. Representing this averaging process by the symbol $\langle\ \rangle$, it is noted that

$$\frac{d\mathbf{l}}{dt} = -\frac{e}{2}\left(\frac{dB}{dt}\right)\langle x^2 + y^2\rangle\hat{\mathbf{z}} \qquad (9.9)$$

since $\langle xz\rangle = \langle yz\rangle = 0$ for the rapid electron motion within the atom.

Equation 9.9 may now be integrated over the time t necessary to build up the **B**-field to its value **B**(t) starting from zero field. The result is

$$\langle\mathbf{l}(t)\rangle - \langle\mathbf{l}(0)\rangle = -\frac{e}{2}\langle x^2+y^2\rangle\mathbf{B}(t), \qquad (9.10)$$

where it is assumed that t is large compared to the characteristic periods of electrons in atomic orbits and the size and shape of the orbit are little disturbed by the accelerating action of the **B**-field.   Equation 9.10 must now be summed over all the electrons in an atom, designated by the number Z.   As mentioned before, the sum of $\langle l(0) \rangle$ will either be zero for a given atom or will be randomly oriented and thus average to zero when the average is taken over a sufficiently large number of atoms in the sample.   The net induced change in angular momentum may be written as

$$\sum_{k=1}^{Z} \langle l_k(t) \rangle = \mathbf{L}_{\text{ind}} \tag{9.11}$$

where

$$\mathbf{L}_{\text{ind}} = -\frac{e}{2} \mathbf{B}(t) \sum_{k=1}^{Z} \langle x^2 + y^2 \rangle_k$$

or

$$\mathbf{L}_{\text{ind}} = -\frac{e}{2\pi} \mathbf{B}(t) \sum_{k=1}^{Z} A_k$$

where $\pi \langle x^2 + y^2 \rangle_k \equiv A_k$ is the area of the orbit of the kth electron projected onto a plane perpendicular to the field direction.

Although eq. 9.11 has been derived using classical arguments and a rather simple model, it is essentially the same result that can be derived by quantum mechanical methods using a more realistic model.   In the more realistic quantum mechanical calculation, the averages in eq. 9.11 are to be interpreted as quantum mechanical averages or *expectation values* rather than as classical averages.   The essential features of the result—that $\mathbf{L}_{\text{ind}}$ is nonzero and is parallel to **B** (the electron charge e is intrinsically negative) —are independent of the specific model.

The result in eq. 9.11 may be interpreted in the following manner.   The time average *moment of inertia* of all the electrons in the atom with respect to an axis parallel to **B** and passing through the nucleus is

$$I_B \equiv m \sum_{k=1}^{Z} \langle x^2 + y^2 \rangle_k$$

and consequently $\mathbf{L}_{\text{ind}}$ may be expressed in terms of I_B and the field as

$$\mathbf{L}_{\text{ind}} = -\frac{e}{2m} I_B \mathbf{B}. \tag{9.12}$$

However, the source of the angular momentum of the atom can be thought of as a rigid rotational motion of the entire atom about the field direction, the rotational velocity or angular frequency $\boldsymbol{\omega}_L$ satisfying the relation:

$$\mathbf{L}_{\text{ind}} = I_B \boldsymbol{\omega}_L. \tag{9.13}$$

From eqs. 9.12 and 9.13, it is evident that the rotational velocity, the so-called *Larmor precessional velocity*, is given by the expression

$$\boldsymbol{\omega}_L = -\left(\frac{e}{2m}\right)\mathbf{B}. \tag{9.14}$$

The above discussion suggests the following physical picture. To a good approximation (assuming the accelerating effect of the induced **E**-field is small), the electrons in an atom move in the same orbits for a nonzero **B**-field as they do in a zero field; however, for nonzero field, superimposed upon the rapid orbital electronic motion is a slow uniform precessional motion of the entire atom about the field direction, the angular frequency of this motion being the Larmor precessional frequency.

According to the discussion immediately following eq. 6.42, the time average dipole moment associated with this precessional motion is just

$$\boldsymbol{\mu} = \left(\frac{e}{2m}\right)\mathbf{L}_{\text{ind}} = -\frac{1}{4}\left(\frac{e}{m}\right)^2\left(\sum_{k=1}^{Z}\langle x^2 + y^2\rangle_k\right)\mathbf{B}. \tag{9.15}$$

If there are N atoms per unit volume of the material under consideration, the induced magnetic dipole moment per unit volume, **M**, is

$$\mathbf{M} = N\boldsymbol{\mu} = -N\left(\frac{e}{2m}\right)^2\left(\sum_{k=1}^{Z}\langle x^2 + y^2\rangle_k\right)\mathbf{B} \tag{9.16}$$

or

$$\mathbf{M} = \frac{4\pi\chi}{\mu_0}\mathbf{B}$$

where χ = the *diamagnetic susceptibility* of the material.

$$\chi = -\left(\frac{\mu_0}{4\pi}\right)N\left(\frac{e}{2m}\right)^2\left(\sum_{k=1}^{Z}\langle x^2 + y^2\rangle_k\right) \tag{9.17}$$

and **B** = time and space average of the microscopic **B**-field. Such a material is said to behave diamagnetically because its magnetic susceptibility is intrinsically negative. If there are n species of atoms in the material, eq. 9.17 is modified in an obvious manner to read

$$\chi = -\left(\frac{\mu_0}{4\pi}\right)\left(\frac{e}{2m}\right)^2\sum_{j=1}^{n}N_j\left(\sum_{k=1}^{Z_1}\langle x^2 + y^2\rangle_k\right). \tag{9.18}$$

If the material is composed of polyatomic molecules, the entire molecule will precess about an axis parallel to the field direction passing through the center of mass of the molecule. However, the positively charged nuclei will precess with a much smaller precessional velocity (the Larmor frequency is inversely proportional to the mass). The resultant expression for the magnetic susceptibility will be much more complicated than that displayed in eq. 9.18. However, since the contribution to the susceptibility of the positively charged nuclei has the same sign as that of the negatively charged electrons, molecular susceptibilities whose origins may be attributed to the Larmor precessional phenomena are diamagnetic.

Diamagnetic susceptibilities are, in general, quite small. At room temperature and atmospheric pressure the diamagnetic susceptibility of nitrogen is approximately -4×10^{-10}, while that of hydrogen is approximately -1.5×10^{-10}. The diamagnetic susceptibility of solids is about 10^3 times as great as gases at room temperature.

9.2   The Origin of Paramagnetism

According to the discussion carried out above, all materials should exhibit diamagnetic behavior. However, there are many materials whose measured susceptibilities are positive. Materials with positive magnetic susceptibilities are called *paramagnetic* materials. The existence of paramagnetism is surprising if one considers the discussion that predicted diamagnetic behavior of all materials. However, paramagnetic behavior can be understood within the following simple model.

Atoms of some materials have a permanent magnetic dipole moment associated with them, a fact ignored in the discussion of diamagnetism. If there is no physical mechanism that tends to correlate the orientation of the dipoles of neighboring atoms, the atomic or molecular dipoles will be randomly oriented and the resultant moment of a volume containing many atoms will vanish. This was the situation considered in the previous discussion of the origin of diamagnetism. However, the presence of a magnetic field provides a mechanism to orient the individual atomic or molecular dipoles. This may be seen as follows. The orientation energy of an electric dipole in an applied **E**-field has been shown to be $U_{\text{int}} = -\mathbf{p} \cdot \mathbf{E}$; remembering the analogy between (E1) and (M1) moments on the one hand and the **E**- and **B**-fields on the other hand, it is not too surprising that the interaction energy between a magnetic dipole and an applied **B**-field turns out to be

$$U_{\text{int}} = -\mathbf{\mu} \cdot \mathbf{B}. \tag{9.19}$$

(The establishment of eq. 9.19 analytically will be delayed to a subsequent discussion.) This implies that the atomic or molecular (M1) moments will tend to orient in such a manner that U_{int} is a minimum; i.e., $\mathbf{\mu} \parallel \mathbf{B}$. The macroscopic (M1) moment per unit volume or *magnetization* **M** produced by this orientation will be parallel to **B** for linear materials, and thus the associated susceptibility will be positive. (This is precisely analogous to the behavior of electric dipoles in an applied E-field, yielding positive electric susceptibilities.)

In addition to the mechanism which tends to orient the submicroscopic dipoles, the dipoles tend to become disoriented due to collisions which occur through the mechanism of atomic and molecular motion. The frequency of these collisions is strongly temperature-dependent, and the collision disorientation mechanism becomes more effective at higher temperatures. For a paramagnetic gas such as oxygen at room temperature, the orientation effect of an applied field is not overpowered by the disorientation mechanism of molecular collisions.

In a material which has the possibility of paramagnetic behavior, diamagnetic reaction to an applied field also exists. The net effect of the two types of behavior cannot be predicted unless a microscopic theory of the material is constructed; this is beyond the intent of the present discussion. It suffices to remark that for many materials paramagnetic effects totally swamp the diamagnetic reaction of the material to an applied B-field.

Paramagnetic susceptibilities are usually of the same order of magnitude as diamagnetic susceptibilities at ordinary temperatures and pressures. A notable exception to this is molecular oxygen, which exhibits a paramagnetic susceptibility which is about 400 times larger than the diamagnetic susceptibility of molecular nitrogen at ordinary temperatures and pressures.

A brief but more thorough discussion of theories of magnetic susceptibilities is contained in Chapter 15 on magnetic and electric properties of materials.

A phenomenon related to paramagnetism is *ferromagnetism*. A ferromagnetic material is one which may possess a nonvanishing macroscopic dipole moment per unit volume even if no applied field is present. The most familiar ferromagnetic materials at ordinary temperature and pressure are iron and its various alloys, from which permanent magnets are made. The origin of ferromagnetism is complex, and an understanding of it is beyond the intent of the present discussion. The source of ferromagnetism is the mutual interaction of the atoms of a material which orients the dipole moments associated with the electronic motion over regions of the material which are macroscopic in size. This orienting mechanism is an internal one and does not depend upon the existence of an external applied field. The existence of ferromagnetic behavior in matter composed of atoms from one part of the periodic table of elements and not from other parts of the table suggests that ferromagnetism is intimately associated with rather specific features of the structure of the atomic electron clouds. A rather brief discussion of the physical origin of ferromagnetism will be given in Chapter 15.

9.3   Macroscopic Form of Ampère's Law

In Sections 9.1 and 9.2 it was seen how the atoms and molecules of a material behave in the presence of a magnetic field. The diamagnetic reaction consists in the induction of an atomic dipole moment associated with the Larmor precession of the atoms; the paramagnetic reaction consists in the alignment of the randomly oriented permanent dipole moments possessed by some atoms and molecules. If a time average is performed over a time interval long compared to characteristic atomic and molecular periods and if a space average is taken over a volume containing many atoms but small compared to ordinary measuring devices, both the diamagnetic and paramagnetic effects can be represented by attributing to a material a macroscopic magnetic dipole moment per unit volume **M**. This quantity is a macroscopic vector point function and is sometimes called the *magnetization field* or simply the *magnetization*. In general, **M** will be a function of the macroscopic (i.e., space- and time-averaged) **B**-field.[1]

It will now be possible to replace the material medium possessing an **M**-field in its interior by an equivalent distribution of current carriers residing in vacuum. Consider a current distribution with an (M1) moment (but vanishing moments of higher multipolarity) occupying an infinitesimal volume and located at the position **r'**. If the dipole moment of the distribution is **μ**, then the vector potential produced by the distribution at the point **r** is (see Fig. 9.2)

$$A(r) = \left(\frac{\mu_0}{4\pi}\right) \frac{\mu \times \hat{n}}{|r - r'|^2} \quad \text{where} \quad \hat{n} = \frac{r - r'}{|r - r'|}. \tag{9.20}$$

If the material medium under consideration is divided into subvolumes $d\tau$ each possessing a dipole moment per unit volume **M(r')**, the vector potential produced by the material medium will be

$$A(r) = \left(\frac{\mu_0}{4\pi}\right) \int d\tau' \frac{M(r') \times \hat{n}}{|r - r'|^2}. \tag{9.21}$$

Equation 9.21 may be simplified if it is noted that

$$\frac{\hat{n}}{|r - r'|^2} = \text{grad}' \frac{1}{|r - r'|}$$

---

[1] With ferromagnetism, **M** will not be a function of **B** but will depend in some complicated fashion on the past "history" of the material; that is, **M** will depend on the physical environment to which the material has been exposed.

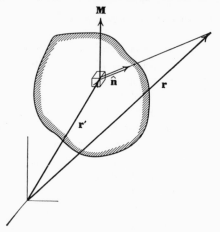

Fig. 9.2   A sample of material media has a dipole moment per unit volume **M**.   The vector potential **A** associated with this magnetized sample is given in eq. 9.21 in terms of **M**. $\mathbf{r}'$ is the position of a volume element of the material; **r** is the point at which the vector potential is to be evaluated. $\hat{\mathbf{n}}$ is a unit vector from the volume element to the field point.

where the derivatives in grad′ are with respect to the variables of integration (x', y', z'); consequently

$$A(\mathbf{r}) = \left(\frac{\mu_0}{4\pi}\right) \int d\tau' \mathbf{M}(\mathbf{r}') \times \mathrm{grad}' \frac{1}{|\mathbf{r} - \mathbf{r}'|}. \qquad (9.22)$$

The integrand in eq. 9.22 can be transformed by employing the following identity of the vector calculus:

$$\mathrm{curl}' \left\{ \frac{1}{|\mathbf{r} - \mathbf{r}'|} \mathbf{M} \right\} \equiv \frac{1}{|\mathbf{r} - \mathbf{r}'|} \mathrm{curl}' \, \mathbf{M} - \mathbf{M} \times \mathrm{grad}' \frac{1}{|\mathbf{r} - \mathbf{r}'|}.$$

Substituting from this identity into eq. 9.22 yields the result

$$A(\mathbf{r}) = \left(\frac{\mu_0}{4\pi}\right) \int d\tau' \frac{\mathrm{curl}' \, \mathbf{M}}{|\mathbf{r} - \mathbf{r}'|} - \left(\frac{\mu_0}{4\pi}\right) \int d\tau' \, \mathrm{curl}' \left\{ \frac{1}{|\mathbf{r} - \mathbf{r}'|} \mathbf{M} \right\}. \quad (9.23)$$

The second integral in eq. 9.23 can be transformed into an integral over a closed surface enveloping the material medium.   The necessary identity is listed in the Mathematical Appendix.

$$\int_v d\tau' \, \mathrm{curl}' \left\{ \frac{1}{|\mathbf{r} - \mathbf{r}'|} \mathbf{M} \right\} = \oiint_\Sigma dS' \frac{1}{|\mathbf{r} - \mathbf{r}'|} \hat{\mathbf{n}} \cdot \mathbf{M}.$$

Since **M** is identically zero outside of the material, the closed surface Σ may be expanded to envelop all space; since the material is finite, $\mathbf{M} \equiv 0$ on Σ, and thus the second integral vanishes identically.

The macroscopic vector potential produced by the material is then simply

$$\mathbf{A(r)} = \left(\frac{\mu_0}{4\pi}\right) \int d\tau' \frac{\text{curl}' \, \mathbf{M}}{|\mathbf{r} - \mathbf{r}'|}. \tag{9.24}$$

However, any real current distribution represented by a current density $\mathbf{j}$ produces a vector potential given by eq. 9.25:

$$\mathbf{A(r)} = \left(\frac{\mu_0}{4\pi}\right) \int d\tau' \frac{\mathbf{j(r')}}{|\mathbf{r} - \mathbf{r}'|}. \tag{9.25}$$

Comparison of eqs. 9.24 and 9.25 reveals that if the discussion is restricted to macroscopic phenomena, a sample of material may be replaced by an equivalent current distribution residing in vacuum; the relationship between the equivalent current distribution $\mathbf{j}_M$ and the magnetization of the material $\mathbf{M}$ is given by the expression

$$\mathbf{j}_M = \text{curl} \, \mathbf{M}. \tag{9.26}$$

The total effective current density is then the vector sum of the real current density $\mathbf{j}_{\text{real}}$ producing a macroscopic $\mathbf{B}$-field which polarizes the material and the magnetization current density $\mathbf{j}_M$ which results from the polarization of the material. It is then asserted that the macroscopic form of Ampère's law must be modified to read

$$\text{curl} \, \mathbf{B(r)} = \left(\frac{\mu_0}{4\pi}\right) 4\pi \{\mathbf{j}_{\text{real}} + \mathbf{j}_M\}. \tag{9.27}$$

Taking cognizance of eq. 9.26, Ampère's law can be rewritten as

$$\text{curl} \left(\frac{\mathbf{B}}{\mu_0} - \mathbf{M}\right) = \mathbf{j}_{\text{real}}. \tag{9.28}$$

Equation 9.28 can be used to define the macroscopic $\mathbf{H}$-field as

$$\mathbf{H} \equiv \frac{\mathbf{B}}{\mu_0} - \mathbf{M} \tag{9.29}$$

and Ampère's law then reads

$$\text{curl} \, \mathbf{H} = \mathbf{j}_{\text{real}}. \tag{9.30}$$

The integral form of Ampère's law for macroscopic phenomena can be developed from eq. 9.30 using methods which are by now quite familiar. The result is

$$\oint_{\Gamma} \mathbf{H} \cdot \mathbf{dl} = I_{\text{real}} \tag{9.31}$$

where I_{real} is the total real current passing through any area capping the closed contour Γ.

9.4   Boundary Conditions on the Macroscopic B- and H-Fields

The boundary conditions for **B** discussed previously when material media were not under consideration must be re-examined for the macroscopic theory. Gauss's magnetic law div **B** $\equiv 0$ is unmodified by the presence of material media. As has been previously shown, Gauss's magnetic law is equivalent to the statement that no magnetic monopoles exist; the diamagnetic and paramagnetic reaction of a material to an applied field does not alter this statement. Consequently the normal component of the macroscopic **B**-field across an interface separating regions 1 and 2 is continuous, that is,

$$\hat{n} \cdot \{\mathbf{B}_1(\mathbf{r}) - \mathbf{B}_2(\mathbf{r})\} = 0 \qquad (9.32)$$

where $\hat{n}$ = unit normal to the interface at the point **r**. The presence of material media does modify the behavior of the tangential component of **B** across an interface since this involves the application of Ampère's law:

$$\text{curl } \mathbf{H} = \mathbf{j}_{\text{real}}.$$

Proceeding in a fashion similar to that for vacuum magnetostatics, it is found that (see Fig. 9.3)

$$(\mathbf{H}_1 - \mathbf{H}_2) \cdot \hat{t} = (\mathbf{K}_{\text{real}} \times \hat{n}) \cdot \hat{t} \qquad (9.33)$$

where $\hat{t}$ = unit tangent to the interface

$\hat{n}$ = unit normal to the interface, pointing from region 2 to region 1.

$\mathbf{K}_{\text{real}}$ = real surface current density flowing across the interface.

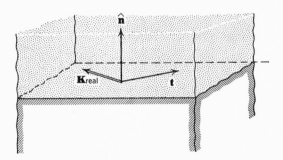

Fig. 9.3   Two media of different permeability are separated by an interface. The behavior of the tangential component of **H** across the interface is given in eq. 9.33. **t** is any vector tangent to the interface; $\hat{n}$ is a unit vector normal to the interface. $\mathbf{K}_{\text{real}}$ is the surface current density associated with the flow of real charge on the interface.

Gauss's law and Ampère's law have led to the behavior of the normal component of **B** and the tangential component of **H**, respectively, across an interface. The behavior of the tangential component of **B** and the normal component of **H** requires a knowledge of the functional dependence of **B** upon **H** (or vice versa).

The interrelationship between **B** and **H** can be introduced through the magnetic susceptibility discussed briefly at the beginning of this chapter. For linear homogeneous materials, **M** and **H** are related by

$$\mathbf{M} = 4\pi\chi\mathbf{H} \tag{9.34}$$

where χ = magnetic susceptibility.

(χ is introduced through a relationship between **M** and **H** and not **M** and **B**; in the electrostatic case, the susceptibility involved a relationship between **P** and **E**.) Substituting this expression for **M** into eq. 9.29 produces a relationship between **B** and **H**, namely

$$\mathbf{B} = \mu\mathbf{H} \tag{9.35}$$

where $\mu \equiv \mu_0(1 + 4\pi\chi)$ = magnetic permeability. It is necessary to realize that eq. 9.35 holds only for linear homogeneous materials. Since $\chi_{\text{para}} > 0$ and $\chi_{\text{dia}} < 0$, it follows that $\mu_{\text{para}} > \mu_0$ and $\mu_{\text{dia}} < \mu_0$. However, since para- and diamagnetic susceptibilities are usually very small, in many physical situations, it is sufficiently accurate to replace μ by μ_0.

For nonisotropic and nonlinear materials which behave either paramagnetically or diamagnetically, it is necessary to introduce a susceptibility matrix or tensor whose elements χ_{jk} are defined through eq. 9.36:

$$M_j = 4\pi \sum_{k=1}^{3} \chi_{jk} H_k, \quad j = 1, 2, 3 \tag{9.36}$$

where M_j = any Cartesian component of **M**. Equation 9.36 states that *any* component of **M** may be a function of *every* component of **H**. The proof that $\chi_{jk} = \chi_{kj}$ can be carried out in a manner completely analogous to that for the electric susceptibility matrix.

9.5 Interaction of a Dipole with an Applied Field; Energy of a Magnetized Medium in an Applied Field

In order to establish an expression for the magnetostatic energy of a system of current carriers and magnetic material, it is necessary to find the interaction energy of a dipole with an applied field. This is carried out as follows. The force on a charge q moving with velocity **v** in a **B**-field is given by

$$\mathbf{f} = q\mathbf{v} \times \mathbf{B}.$$

If the particle is located at position $\mathbf{r}$ when it is moving with velocity $\mathbf{v}$, the current density associated with the charge can be written down in the usual manner as

$$\mathbf{j}(\mathbf{r}') = q\mathbf{v}\, \delta(\mathbf{r} - \mathbf{r}').$$

This equation can be generalized to the motion of many charges producing a current density $\mathbf{j}$. The force will be the force on the system carrying the current and is given by

$$\mathbf{f} = \int_\tau \mathbf{j}(\mathbf{r}) \times \mathbf{B}(\mathbf{r})\, d\tau \qquad (9.37)$$

Equation 9.37 will now be applied to a small volume τ containing a current distribution with a magnetic dipole moment $\boldsymbol{\mu}$. It is assumed that $\mathbf{B}$ is essentially constant throughout the volume in which $\mathbf{j}$ is nonvanishing. The origin is located within τ and $\mathbf{B}$ is expanded in a Taylor series about its value at the origin:

$$\mathbf{B}(\mathbf{r}') = \mathbf{B}_0 + (\mathbf{r}' \cdot \nabla)\mathbf{B}_0 + \cdots$$
$$\mathbf{B}_0 = \mathbf{B}(0)$$

where
$$(\mathbf{r}' \cdot \nabla)\mathbf{B}_0 \equiv \sum_{j=1}^{3} x_j'\left(\frac{\partial}{\partial x_j}\mathbf{B}(\mathbf{r})\right)_0$$

It is now straightforward to establish the identity

$$(\mathbf{r}' \cdot \nabla)\mathbf{B}_0 \equiv \operatorname{grad}(\mathbf{r}' \cdot \mathbf{B}_0)$$

where the derivatives in grad operate on the variables in $\mathbf{B}_0$ and not upon $\mathbf{r}'$. In establishing this identity, use has been made of the fact that the source of $\mathbf{B}$ is external to τ, and therefore within τ, curl $\mathbf{B} \equiv 0$. Thus, the force on the current distribution can be written to a good approximation:

$$\mathbf{f} = -\mathbf{B}_0 \times \int_\tau d\tau'\mathbf{j}(\mathbf{r}') + \int_\tau d\tau'\mathbf{j}(\mathbf{r}') \times \operatorname{grad}(\mathbf{r}' \cdot \mathbf{B}_0). \qquad (9.38)$$

The integral in the first term vanishes identically since the current is confined to τ. The second integral may be transformed by use of another identity

$$\mathbf{j} \times \operatorname{grad}(\mathbf{r}' \cdot \mathbf{B}_0) = -\operatorname{curl}[\mathbf{j}(\mathbf{r}' \cdot \mathbf{B}_0)]$$

where the derivatives in the curl operate only on the components of $\mathbf{B}_0$. The force on the current distribution can therefore be written as

$$\mathbf{f} = -\int_\tau d\tau'\operatorname{curl}[\mathbf{j}(\mathbf{r}' \cdot \mathbf{B}_0)]. \qquad (9.39)$$

However, since the curl operator does not involve the variables of integration, it may formally be taken outside the integral sign, yielding

$$\mathbf{f} = -\operatorname{curl}\int d\tau'\mathbf{j}(\mathbf{r}')(\mathbf{r}' \cdot \mathbf{B}_0). \qquad (9.40)$$

In Chapter 6 it has already been shown (see discussion leading to eq. 6.32) that

$$\int d\tau' \mathbf{j}(\mathbf{r}' \cdot \mathbf{r}) = \boldsymbol{\mu} \times \mathbf{r}.$$

Replacing the constant vector $\mathbf{r}$ by the constant vector $\mathbf{B}_0$, eq. 9.40 can be written as

$$\mathbf{f} = -\operatorname{curl}(\boldsymbol{\mu} \times \mathbf{B}_0) \qquad (9.41)$$

where $\boldsymbol{\mu}$ is the dipole moment of the current distribution. (If more terms in the Taylor expansion of $\mathbf{B}$ had been employed, the force equation would have involved the higher multipole moments of the current distribution. However, eq. 9.41 will suffice to investigate the manner in which a magnetic dipole interacts with an applied field.)

Equation 9.41 is a useful form for the force on a dipole in an applied field. It can be transformed into an alternative expression employing the following chain of vector identities:

$$\operatorname{curl}(\boldsymbol{\mu} \times \mathbf{B}_0) = -(\boldsymbol{\mu} \cdot \nabla)\mathbf{B}_0$$
$$(\boldsymbol{\mu} \cdot \nabla)\mathbf{B}_0 = \operatorname{grad}(\boldsymbol{\mu} \cdot \mathbf{B}_0) - \boldsymbol{\mu} \times \operatorname{curl} \mathbf{B}_0$$

with the result that

$$\mathbf{f} = (\boldsymbol{\mu} \cdot \nabla)\mathbf{B}_0 \qquad (9.42a)$$

$$\mathbf{f} = \operatorname{grad}(\boldsymbol{\mu} \cdot \mathbf{B}_0) \qquad (9.42b)$$

where the term in curl $\mathbf{B}_0$ has been omitted since it is identically zero.

Equation 9.42b expresses $\mathbf{f}$ in a very useful form for consideration of the orientation energy of a dipole in an applied field. The force on a dipole in a $\mathbf{B}$-field is a conservative force since curl $\mathbf{f} = 0$. Consequently the orientation energy U_m can be related to $\mathbf{f}$ via

$$\mathbf{f} = -\operatorname{grad} U_m. \qquad (9.43)$$

Examination of eqs. 9.42b and 9.43 leads to the result

$$U_m = -\boldsymbol{\mu} \cdot \mathbf{B} \qquad (9.44)$$

where the subscript previously affixed to $\mathbf{B}$ has been dropped. This is the expression which has been written down previously by analogy with the equivalent electrostatic problem.

It is quite evident that the presence of material media will alter the expression for the energy residing in the magnetostatic field since in addition to any work done in establishing the field, a certain amount of work must be expended in orienting the dipole distributions associated with the material media. This can be seen as follows: the interaction energy of a system of current carriers in a field represented by a vector potential $\mathbf{A}$ is

$$U_m = \int \mathbf{j} \cdot \mathbf{A} \, d\tau \qquad (9.45)$$

(The quantity U_m of eq. 9.45 is the energy of the current carriers represented by a real current density $\mathbf{j}$ in an external field $\mathbf{A}$. This is not to be confused with the interaction energy among a number of current loops which contains an additional factor of $\frac{1}{2}$.) It is postulated that eq. 9.45 holds whether or not material media are present. The amount of work done by the external sources in producing an infinitesimal change in the vector potential is

$$\delta U_m = \int_\tau \mathbf{j} \cdot \delta\mathbf{A} \, d\tau. \tag{9.46}$$

It is possible to remove $\mathbf{j}$ and $\mathbf{A}$ from eq. 9.46 and obtain an expression involving only $\mathbf{B}$ and $\mathbf{H}$. This is done via Ampère's laws.

$$\text{curl } \mathbf{H} = \mathbf{j}$$

and the definition of $\mathbf{A}$ in terms of $\mathbf{B}$. Removing $\mathbf{j}$ from eq. 9.46 yields

$$\delta U_m = \int_\tau \text{curl } \mathbf{H} \cdot \delta\mathbf{A} \, d\tau.$$

The integrand can be further transformed by use of the vector calculus identity

$$\text{div} (\mathbf{H} \times \delta\mathbf{A}) = \delta\mathbf{A} \cdot \text{curl } \mathbf{H} - \mathbf{H} \cdot \text{curl } \delta\mathbf{A}.$$

Consequently

$$\delta U_m = \int_\tau \mathbf{H} \cdot \text{curl } \delta\mathbf{A} \, d\tau + \int_\tau \text{div} (\mathbf{H} \times \delta\mathbf{A}) \, d\tau.$$

In the first integrand, $\delta\mathbf{A}$ may be removed via the defining relationship:

$$\text{curl } \delta\mathbf{A} = \delta\mathbf{B}$$

where $\delta\mathbf{B}$ is the increment in the $\mathbf{B}$-field associated with the increment $\delta\mathbf{A}$ in the vector potential. In addition, the second integral can be transformed into an integral over Σ bounding τ by the divergence theorem:

$$\delta U_m = \int_\tau (\mathbf{H} \cdot \delta\mathbf{B}) \, d\tau + \oiint_\Sigma \hat{\mathbf{n}} \cdot (\mathbf{H} \times \delta\mathbf{A}) \, dS.$$

The integral over Σ vanishes if τ is allowed to encompass all space. Since the current distribution producing $\mathbf{H}$ is localized, $\mathbf{H}$ approaches zero on Σ at least as fast as a dipole field and therefore the integral over Σ vanishes. As a consequence

$$\delta U_m = \int (\mathbf{H} \cdot \delta\mathbf{B}) \, d\tau \tag{9.47}$$

where the integral is to be carried out over all space. Since δU_m is seen to depend explicitly on the field quantities $\mathbf{H}$ and $\mathbf{B}$, it is interpreted as the increment in the energy residing in the fields.

An expression for the field energy itself rather than the increment in the field energy can be obtained once a functional relationship between **H** and **B** is specified. For a linear homogeneous medium (**B** = μ**H**):

$$\mathbf{H} \cdot \delta\mathbf{B} = \tfrac{1}{2}\, \delta(\mathbf{H} \cdot \mathbf{B})$$

and consequently eq. 9.47 can be integrated directly, yielding

$$U_m = \tfrac{1}{2} \int \mathbf{H} \cdot \mathbf{B}\, d\tau \qquad (9.48)$$

where $U_m \equiv$ energy residing in the magnetostatic field.

The question now arises: suppose a system of current carriers resides in vacuum; the space between them is subsequently filled with linear material of magnetic permeability μ—what happens to the magnetostatic energy of the system? The magnetic material can be added in a variety of ways producing an equal variety of results. The only case to be considered here is the one in which the currents flowing in the conductors are kept constant as the material is added. Let $\mathbf{H}_0$ and $\mathbf{B}_0$ ($= \mu_0\mathbf{H}_0$) stand for the fields before the addition of the magnetic material and **H** and **B** ($= \mu$**H**) for the fields subsequent to the addition. According to Ampère's law

$$\oint_{\Gamma_i} \mathbf{H}_0 \cdot \mathbf{dl} = \oint_{\Gamma_i} \mathbf{H} \cdot \mathbf{dl} = I_i$$

where I_i = current threading through any loop Γ_i, and curl $\mathbf{H}_0$ = curl **H** = **j** at all points in the current-carrying region (and vacuum). Since **H** and $\mathbf{H}_0$ satisfy the same differential equation and the same boundary conditions,

$$\mathbf{H} = \mathbf{H}_0.$$

The energy in the field *before* the introduction of the material is given by

$$U_0 = \tfrac{1}{2} \int \mathbf{H}_0 \cdot \mathbf{B}_0\, d\tau = \tfrac{1}{2}\mu_0 \int H_0^2\, d\tau.$$

The energy in the field *after* the introduction of the material is

$$U = \tfrac{1}{2} \int \mathbf{H} \cdot \mathbf{B}\, d\tau = \tfrac{1}{2} \int \mu H^2\, d\tau.$$

However, since $\mathbf{H} = \mathbf{H}_0$, it follows immediately that the increase in energy in the fields due to the addition of the material is

$$\Delta U = U - U_0 = \tfrac{1}{2}(\mu - \mu_0) \int H_0^2\, d\tau$$

or
$$\Delta U = \left(\frac{\mu}{\mu_0} - 1\right) U_0.$$

It should be realized that this increase in field energy is produced by two effects: mechanical work W_1 must be done on the material as it is introduced into the region; in addition, energy W_2 must be supplied by the batteries in the conducting circuits to maintain the currents at their constant values as the material is introduced.   The change in field energy can be expressed as

$$\Delta U = W_1 + W_2.$$

If the material is paramagnetic ($\mu > \mu_0$), the field energy is increased by the introduction of the material; if the material is diamagnetic ($\mu < \mu_0$), the field energy is decreased.

9.6   *Body Forces in Magnetostatics*

In general, the material occupying a volume element $d\tau$ experiences a force when a **B** or **H**-field is present.   This force is a body force and is similar in origin to that occurring in electrostatics.   The body force or magnetostatic force per unit volume satisfies the equation

$$\frac{dU_m}{dt} + \int \mathbf{f}_m \cdot \mathbf{u} \, d\tau = 0 \tag{9.49}$$

where dU_m/dt is the increase in the magnetostatic energy of the system per unit time, $\mathbf{u}$ is the velocity of the material (this will be assumed small so that considerations of magnetostatics can be applied), and $\int \mathbf{f}_m \cdot \mathbf{u} \, d\tau$ is the rate at which mechanical forces do work on the system.   The magnetostatic energy U_m is known uniquely when $\mathbf{j}$, the current density, and μ, the magnetic permeability, are known.   Consequently changes in U_m must be accompanied by changes in $\mathbf{j}$ and/or μ.   An expression for $\mathbf{f}_m$ can be obtained by constructing arguments similar to those employed for the electrostatic body force.   These arguments will not be given here.   The result is

$$\mathbf{f}_m = \mathbf{j} \times \mathbf{B} - \tfrac{1}{2}H^2 \, \text{grad} \, \mu \tag{9.50}$$

where it has been assumed that changes in μ unaccompanied by bulk flow of material are negligible.   The magnetostatic body force is conservative and consequently may be expressed in terms of the equivalent hydrostatic pressure as

$$\mathbf{f}_m = -\text{grad} \, p.$$

The difference in pressure between any two points in the magnetostatic system may be therefore written as

$$p_2 - p_1 = - \int_\Gamma (\mathbf{j} \times \mathbf{B} - \tfrac{1}{2}H^2 \, \text{grad} \, \mu) \cdot \mathbf{dl} \tag{9.51}$$

where Γ is an arbitrary path connecting $\mathbf{r}_1$ with $\mathbf{r}_2$.

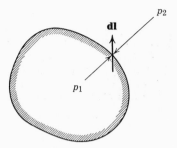

Fig. 9.4   A conductor carries a current with a current density **j**.   **dl** is an infinitesimal part of the path Γ whose extremities lie immediately inside and outside the surface of the conductor.   The current in the conductor produces a field **B**.   The integral $-\int_\Gamma \mathbf{j} \times \mathbf{B} \cdot \mathbf{dl}$ is the difference between the pressure outside and inside the conductor $p_2 - p_1 > 0$, which means that the field produced by the current exerts a pressure on the surface tending to decrease the cross-sectional area of the conductor.

EXAMPLE 9.1   Equation 9.51 may be used to calculate the pressure difference between points immediately outside and immediately inside the surface of a current-carrying conductor (see Fig. 9.4).   Here grad $\mu \approx 0$ since most conductors are weakly diamagnetic or paramagnetic (i.e., $\mu \approx \mu_0$).   The major contribution to the pressure difference comes from the term $\int \mathbf{j} \times \mathbf{B} \cdot \mathbf{dl}$.   Since **j** outside a conductor vanishes and since $\mathbf{j} \times \mathbf{B}$ inside the conductor points inward, it is seen that the integral $\int \mathbf{j} \times \mathbf{B} \cdot \mathbf{dl}$ is always negative.   Consequently

$$p_2 - p_1 > 0$$

where p_2, p_1 are the pressures immediately outside and inside the conductor respectively.   The fields exert a pressure on the surface of the conductor, tending to decrease the cross-sectional area of the conductor and thereby increase the current density.

An apparent paradox arises when one attempts to apply energy considerations to this problem.   In Example 8.1 the difference in magnetostatic energy per unit length of two long wires of circular cross-section with radii a and b each carrying a current I was calculated to be

$$\delta \tilde{U} = \tilde{U}_a - \tilde{U}_b = \left(\frac{\mu_0}{4\pi}\right) \frac{I^2}{16} \ln \frac{b}{a}$$

which is positive if $b > a$.   This implies that the energy residing in the fields of the wire of the *smaller* cross section is *greater* than the energy residing in the fields of the wire of the *larger* cross section.   Therefore a *decrease* in the cross-sectional area of a wire, keeping I fixed, involves an

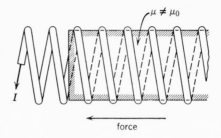

Fig. 9.5   A cylinder of permeability $\mu \neq \mu_0$ partially fills a long solenoid. **H** at the cylinder interface is perpendicular to the interface. The H-field immediately inside the material is different from the H-field immediately outside the cylinder, since the normal component of **H** suffers a discontinuity across the interface. The cylinder will experience a force tending to pull it into the solenoid if it is paramagnetic.

increase in the field energy. This paradox is removed by the observation that the battery supplies energy to the wire as its cross section is decreased to maintain the current at a constant value; an emf is induced in the wire as its cross section diminishes and this induced emf must be compensated by the emf causing the current to flow. The energy supplied by the battery plus the work (< 0) supplied by external forces to overcome the effect of the body force **j** × **B** as the conductor contracts just equals the increase in the field energy.

EXAMPLE 9.2   Consider the forces induced on a cylinder of material of permeability $\mu \neq \mu_0$ partially filling a long solenoid of the same cross section. (See Fig. 9.5.) The H-field at the face of the cylinder is normal to the cylinder face. The H-field on the vacuum side of the cylinder face is given by the result of Example 6.3 with $\mathbf{B} = \mu_0 \mathbf{H}_0$, namely

$$\mathbf{H}_0 = ni\hat{\mathbf{z}}$$

where n = number of turns per unit length of the solenoid
   i = current flowing in the wires of the solenoid
   $\hat{\mathbf{z}}$ = unit vector along the axis of the solenoid

The H-field immediately inside the cylinder face is different from $\mathbf{H}_0$, since the normal component of **B** is continuous across an interface. This implies that $\mathbf{H} = (\mu_0/\mu)\mathbf{H}_0$ inside the cylinder face. Equation 9.51 may now be solved to find the pressure difference acting across the cylinder face.

$$p_2 - p_1 = \int_\Gamma \tfrac{1}{2} H^2 \operatorname{grad} \mu \cdot \mathbf{dl}$$

where Γ is path connecting points $\mathbf{r}_1, \mathbf{r}_2$ immediately outside and inside

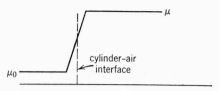

Fig. 9.6   The permeability of the material of the cylinder in Fig. 9.5 is assumed to vary linearly from μ_0 to μ (the value it attains within its interior) over a very small distance.

the cylinder, respectively.   Here grad $\mu \cdot \mathbf{dl} = (d\mu/dz)\,dz$.   The integral can be performed if it is assumed that μ does not change abruptly at the interface but in a linear fashion over a very small distance as illustrated in Fig. 9.6.   With this model the integral can be performed, yielding

$$p_2 - p_1 = \tfrac{1}{2}(ni)^2(\mu - \mu_0)$$

where μ = permeability within the cylinder.   Consequently there will be a net pressure tending to pull the cylinder into the solenoid if the cylinder is paramagnetic, and a net pressure tending to pull the cylinder out of the solenoid if the cylinder is diamagnetic.

9.7   Magnetostatics Involving Ferromagnets

Certain materials can become magnetized and remain magnetized in the absence of an applied field.   Such a material can be represented by a magnetization $\mathbf{M}$ which is not, however, a function of $\mathbf{B}$.   The vector potential produced by such a material is given by eq. 9.24:

$$\mathbf{A}(\mathbf{r}) = \left(\frac{\mu_0}{4\pi}\right) \int d\tau \, \frac{\text{curl}' \, \mathbf{M}}{|\mathbf{r} - \mathbf{r}'|}$$

and the resulting $\mathbf{B}$-field obtained from curl $\mathbf{A} = \mathbf{B}$.

Strictly speaking, it is not possible to define a magnetic permeability μ for a permanently magnetized material.   The equation $\mathbf{B} = \mu\mathbf{H}$ simply does not apply to such materials even if μ is allowed to be a complicated function of $\mathbf{B}$.   It is possible experimentally to define a quantity related to μ in the following manner.   A small sample of ferromagnetic material originally unmagnetized is placed in an initially field-free region.   A set of conductors is arranged which can produce a uniform field over the sample. The current in the conductors is then slowly increased from zero to some finite value in small increments, and the $\mathbf{B}$- and $\mathbf{H}$-fields present at the sample are plotted against one another as in Fig. 9.7.   The derivative of the $\mathbf{B}$-field with respect of $\mathbf{H}$ is then operationally defined as the permeability

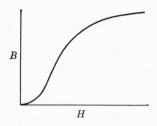

Fig. 9.7   An originally unmagnetized sample of ferromagnetic material is placed in the neighborhood of conducting coils.   As the current is increased in the coils, **B** and **H** in the sample behave as indicated.

of the material.   This operationally defined permeability will be field-dependent.   The experiment suggested is rather difficult to perform.   It consists in essence in two magnetic flux measurements (see Fig. 9.8): (1) the magnetic flux through a coil wound closely about the sample (this yields a value of **B** averaged over the sample); (2) the flux through a coil containing the sample but loosely wound about the sample (this flux minus that measured in step 1 yields $\mu_0\mathbf{H}$ immediately outside the sample).   The flux measurements can be made by a flux meter which measures the emf induced in a coil by the change in the flux of **B** threading through the coil; the flux meter is calibrated to convert measurements of emf to measurements of magnetic flux.

Some properties of **B** and **H** that exist inside a permanently magnetized medium can be obtained by examining an idealized bar magnet.   An idealized bar magnet sketched in Fig. 9.9 is a long circular cylinder of

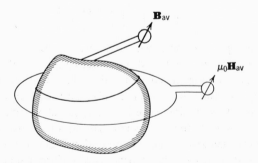

Fig. 9.8   Coil 1 is wound closely around a sample of ferromagnetic material.   The flux through this coil is a direct measure of the average value of **B** in the material. Coil 2 is wound loosely around the material.   The flux through coil 2 minus that through coil 1 is a measure of $\mu_0\mathbf{H}$ immediately outside the sample.

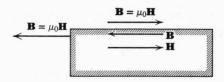

Fig. 9.9   The cylinder sketched is an "idealized bar magnet" with **M** uniform throughout the cylinder and in the direction indicated.   The direction of **B** and **H** are as indicated.

finite length with uniform magnetization **M** throughout the cylinder and parallel to the cylinder axis.   (In a real magnet of this type the magnetization will be uniform throughout most of the volume, but will deviate from uniformity at the cylinder faces.)   The boundary conditions on **B** and **H** can be employed to investigate the behavior of **B** and **H** near the cylinder's surfaces.   The **B**-field is continuous across the circular faces of the cylinder, since **B** is normal to the faces in this idealized case.   Immediately *outside* the circular faces, $\mathbf{B} = \mu_0 \mathbf{H}$ so that **H** is also normal to the cylinder faces in this region.   At the cylindrical surface where **H** is tangential to the surface, eq. 9.33 may be employed.   Since there is no real current flowing on the surface $\mathbf{H}_{\text{inside}} = \mathbf{H}_{\text{outside}}$.   However, $\mathbf{H}_{\text{outside}} = \dfrac{1}{\mu_0}\mathbf{B}_{\text{outside}}$, from which it follows that $\mathbf{H}_{\text{inside}}$ is antiparallel to $\mathbf{B}_{\text{inside}}$.   The **B**- and **H**-fields inside an idealized bar magnet point in opposite directions.   (Example 9.3 which appears subsequently is another illustration of the same result for the case of spherical geometry.)   Since **M** is known everywhere, eq. 9.24 can be used to obtain the vector potential everywhere.   It should be remembered that curl **M** is zero everywhere within the bar magnet and outside the magnet; however, curl **M** is infinite at the cylindrical surface. The abrupt change in **M** across the surface of the cylinder can be represented by a nonvanishing effective surface current density **K** flowing on this surface.   The **B**-field outside the magnet is then the same as that produced by a solenoid of the same volume V with dipole moment $\boldsymbol{\mu} = MV$.

The fields produced by a sample of material magnetized in a specified manner can be obtained by methods other than direct solution of eq. 9.24. These methods are based on the observation that for permanently magnetized media, with no carriers of real current, curl $\mathbf{H} = 0$; this implies that **H** can be derived from a potential; that is

$$\mathbf{H} = -\operatorname{grad} \Psi \tag{9.52}$$

where, in vacuum, Ψ is $1/\mu_0$ times the macroscopic magnetic scalar potential introduced in Section 7.3. It immediately follows that Ψ' of eq. 9.52 satisfies Laplace's equation everywhere:

$$\nabla^2\Psi' = 0. \tag{9.53}$$

This means that finding the fields produced by a magnetized medium reduces to a problem in potential theory; in particular, use can be made of the very general methods introduced in Chapter 3 to solve Laplace's equation in electrostatics. In addition, the uniqueness property of solutions to Laplace's equation is applicable to the solutions of eq. 9.53.

It should be remarked that Ψ' does not have an operational definition. Although Ψ' satisfies the same differential equation in any current free region that the electrostatic potential φ satisfies in a charge free region, φ has an operational definition in terms of work per unit charge. Therefore Ψ' is introduced as a calculation device without any physical interpretation.

These methods may also be used for magnetizable material in the presence of current carriers, since eq. 9.53 is still valid in any volume τ which may contain such material but no current carriers. The behavior of **B** and **H**, the physical fields, on the surface bounding τ must be specified, however. (See Fig. 9.10.) These remarks can be illustrated by the following examples.

EXAMPLE 9.3   Calculate the **B**- and **H**-fields due to a uniformly magnetized sphere of radius R (see Fig. 9.11). Since this physical problem has rotational symmetry about the direction parallel to **M**, eq. 3.54 may be employed for Ψ', namely,

$$\Psi'(r,\,\theta) = \sum_{l=0}^{\infty} (a_l r^l + b_l r^{-(l+1)})P_l(\cos\theta)$$

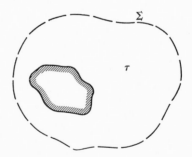

Fig. 9.10   The region τ contains magnetizable material but no current carriers. The magnetic scalar potential satisfies Laplace's equation in τ. In order to obtain solutions to Laplace's equation in τ, the behavior of **B** and **H** on the surface Σ bounding τ must be specified.

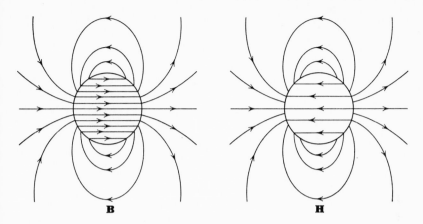

Fig. 9.11   A uniformly magnetized sphere resides in vacuum.   **H** and **B** within the sphere are uniform and oppositely directed.   **H** and **B** outside the sphere are those of a dipole of moment $\boldsymbol{\mu} = (4\pi R^3/3)\mathbf{M}$.

To find the fields it is convenient to consider the regions $r > R$ and $r < R$ separately.   At a very large distance from the sphere, the **H**- and **B**-fields must behave like a dipole field, since a uniformly magnetized sphere contains no other moment than a dipole moment.   Consequently in the region $r > R$, $a_l = 0$ for $l > 0$ and is undetermined for $l = 0$.

$$b_l = 0 \quad \text{for } l = 0, \text{ and } l > 1,$$

since Ψ' must behave as $1/r^2$ for large r; that is

$$\Psi'(r, \theta) = \frac{b_1}{r^2} P_1(\cos \theta) + a_0, \quad r > R. \tag{9.54}$$

In the region $r < R$, the condition that **H** and **B** are to be finite at $r = 0$ requires that $b_l = 0$ for all l.   Therefore in the region $r < R$

$$\Psi'(r, \theta) = \sum_{l=0}^{\infty} a_l r^l P_l(\cos \theta), \quad r < R. \tag{9.55}$$

The fields **B** and **H** must satisfy their continuity conditions at the spherical surface $r = R$; that is, H_θ and B_r must be continuous at $r = R$. H_θ is related to Ψ' via

$$H_\theta = -\frac{1}{r} \frac{\partial}{\partial \theta} \Psi'. \tag{9.56}$$

Employing this condition in both regions to the values of Ψ displayed in eqs. 9.54 and 9.55 yields

$$
\begin{aligned}
a_0 &= \text{undetermined constant} \\
a_1 &= b_1/R^3 \\
a_l &= 0 \quad \text{for } l > 1.
\end{aligned}
\tag{9.57}
$$

The undetermined constant a_0 appearing in eqs. 9.54 and 9.57 may be set equal to zero since its value does not affect **B** and **H**.   Finally, B_r at $r = R$ is calculated from Ψ from the chain of relations

$$
H_r = -\frac{\partial}{\partial r}\Psi
\tag{9.58}
$$

and
$$
\begin{aligned}
\mu_0 H_r &= B_r, \quad r > R \\
\mu_0(H_r + M_r) &= B_r, \quad r < R.
\end{aligned}
$$

These relations yield

$$
a_1 + \frac{2b_1}{R^3} = M.
\tag{9.59}
$$

Combining the results of eqs. 9.57 and 9.59 determines the values of a_1 and b_1, namely,

$$
\begin{aligned}
a_1 &= \tfrac{1}{3}M \\
b_1 &= \tfrac{1}{3}MR^3.
\end{aligned}
$$

Therefore the scalar potential produced by a uniformly magnetized sphere is

$$
\begin{aligned}
\Psi(r, \theta) &= \tfrac{1}{3}Mr \cos\theta, \quad &r < R \\
&= \tfrac{1}{3}M\left(\frac{R}{r}\right)^3 r \cos\theta, \quad &r > R.
\end{aligned}
$$

The **H**- and **B**-fields inside and outside the sphere are calculated via their definitions in terms of Ψ which are

$$
\mathbf{H} = -\left(\frac{\partial}{\partial r}\Psi\right)\hat{\mathbf{r}} - \frac{1}{r}\left(\frac{\partial}{\partial\theta}\Psi\right)\hat{\boldsymbol{\theta}}
$$
$$
\mathbf{B} = \mu_0(\mathbf{H} + \mathbf{M}).
$$

Carrying out the indicated operations yields

$$
\left.\begin{aligned}
\mathbf{H} &= -\tfrac{1}{3}\mathbf{M} \\
\mathbf{B} &= \left(\frac{\mu_0}{4\pi}\right)\left(\frac{8\pi}{3}\mathbf{M}\right)
\end{aligned}\right\} \quad r < R
$$

$$
\mathbf{B} = -\left(\frac{\mu_0}{4\pi}\right)\left\{\frac{\boldsymbol{\mu}}{r^3} - \frac{3(\boldsymbol{\mu}\cdot\mathbf{r})\mathbf{r}}{r^5}\right\}, \quad r > R
$$

with
$$
\boldsymbol{\mu} \equiv \left(\frac{4\pi}{3}R^3\right)\mathbf{M}
$$

and
$$
\mathbf{H} = \frac{1}{\mu_0}\mathbf{B}.
$$

The fields are constant within the sphere and are those of a magnetic dipole of moment $\mu = (4\pi R^3/3)\mathbf{M}$ outside the sphere.

EXAMPLE 9.4   The distortions produced in a uniform **B**-field by insertion of a linear nonferromagnetic sphere of radius R and permeability μ may be calculated by a method analogous to that employed in Chapter 3 for a conductor imbedded in an originally uniform **E**-field. The physical problem has symmetry about the direction of the originally uniform field $\mathbf{B}_0$, and Ψ can be written

$$\Psi(r, \theta) = \sum_{l=0}^{\infty} (a_l r^l + b_l r^{-(l+1)}) P_l(\cos \theta)$$

where the origin of coordinates is at the center of the sphere and the angle θ is measured from the direction of $\mathbf{B}_0$ (see Fig. 9.12).   Once again, space is divided into two regions; region 1 in which $r > R$ and region 2 in which $r < R$.

The boundary condition to be employed in region 1 is that the **B**-field calculated from Ψ approach $\mathbf{B}_0$ as $r \to \infty$; that is,

$$\lim_{r \to \infty} \Psi(r, \theta) = -\frac{1}{\mu_0} B_0 r \cos \theta$$

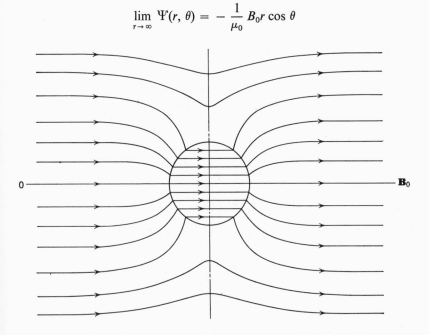

Fig. 9.12   A nonferromagnetic sphere of radius R and permeability μ is placed in a region of originally uniform $\mathbf{B}_0$.   Within the sphere the **B**-field is uniform and equal to $(3\mu/2\mu_0 + \mu)\mathbf{B}_0$, whereas outside the sphere the field is that of a dipole of moment $(4\pi R^3/\mu_0)(\mu - \mu_0/\mu + 2\mu_0)\mathbf{B}_0$ superimposed upon the uniform field $\mathbf{B}_0$.

where the arbitrary constant in Ψ' has been chosen to be zero. This condition immediately yields

$$r > R \quad \begin{cases} a_l = 0 \quad \text{for } l = 0 \text{ and } l > 1 \\ a_1 = \dfrac{1}{\mu_0} B_0. \end{cases}$$

Since the sphere is composed of a linear homogeneous nonferromagnetic material, the uniform field in which it is imbedded can induce no other multipole than a dipole.[1]   Therefore the only nonvanishing value of b_l in the region 1 is b_1.   Consequently in region 1

$$\Psi'(r, \theta) = \left(-\frac{B_0}{\mu_0} r + b_1 r^{-2} \right) \cos \theta, \quad r > R. \tag{9.60}$$

In region 2 the physical boundary condition employed is that **B** (and **H**) are finite at the origin.   Consequently

$$r < R, \quad b_l = 0 \text{ for all } l$$

and

$$\Psi'(r, \theta) = \sum_{l=1}^{\infty} a_l r^l P_l(\cos \theta), \quad r < R \tag{9.61}$$

where the arbitrary constant a_0 has been set equal to zero.   The boundary conditions at $r = R$ (the surface of the sphere) will suffice to determine b_1 and the a_l.   At $r = R$, the θ-component of **H** calculated from eqs. 9.60 and 9.61 must be equal and the r-component of **B** calculated from these equations must also be identical.   Consequently

$$a_l = 0 \quad \text{for } l > 1$$

and

$$-\frac{B_0}{\mu_0} R + b_1 R^{-2} = a_1 R$$

and

$$-B_0 R - 2\mu_0 b_1 R^{-2} = \mu a_1 R.$$

These two equations yield values of a_1 and b_1, namely,

$$a_1 = B_0 R^3 \frac{\mu - \mu_0}{\mu_0(\mu + 2\mu_0)}$$

$$b_1 = -\frac{3}{(\mu + 2\mu_0)} B_0$$

[1] This can be seen in the following way: the field $\mathbf{B}_0$ defines a direction (i.e., a vector) and since the sphere is magnetically isotropic, it does not introduce another direction into the problem.   Consequently the induced multipole moments must behave as vectors (there is no possibility of a monopole).   The only multipole which has the property of a vector is a dipole.

from which it follows that

region 1, $r > R$

$$\mathbf{B} = \mathbf{B}_0 - \left\{\frac{4\pi R^3}{\mu_0} \cdot \frac{\mu - \mu_0}{\mu + 2\mu_0}\right\}\left(\frac{\mu_0}{4\pi}\right)\left[\frac{\mathbf{B}_0}{r^3} - \frac{3(\mathbf{B}_0 \cdot \mathbf{r})\mathbf{r}}{r^5}\right]$$

region 2, $r < R$ $\qquad\qquad \mathbf{B} = \left(\frac{3\mu}{\mu + 2\mu_0}\right)\mathbf{B}_0.$

In the region exterior to the sphere the distortion of the field is that due to an induced dipole of moment:

$$\boldsymbol{\mu}_{\text{induced}} = \left(\frac{4\pi R^3}{\mu_0}\right)\frac{\mu - \mu_0}{\mu + 2\mu_0}\mathbf{B}_0.$$

The induced dipole is parallel to the applied field if the medium is paramagnetic ($\mu > \mu_0$) and is antiparallel to the applied field if the sphere is diamagnetic ($\mu < \mu_0$).

Other examples of fields produced by magnetic material are contained in the problems at the end of this chapter.

9.8 Hysteresis: Magnetic Irreversibility

Hysteresis or magnetic irreversibility arises in ferromagnetic materials but not in other magnetic materials.   To illustrate this phenomenon consider a ferromagnetic material in which **M** is initially zero in a field-free region.   If the material is placed in the neighborhood of an electric circuit and the electric current in the circuit is increased from an initial zero value, a magnetization will be induced within the material.   The **H**- and **B**-fields at a typical point in space will be produced by the current and the magnetization of the ferromagnetic material.   If the **H**- and **B**-fields are measured at a typical point within the ferromagnetic material, it is found that these fields increase as the current in the circuit increases.   The dashed curve in Fig. 9.13 is a representative plot of $|\mathbf{B}|$ vs. $|\mathbf{H}|$ at a point within the material as the current is increased to some maximum value, I_{max}; the relationship between **B** and **H** is nonlinear since the material is ferromagnetic.   If the current in the circuit is reduced to zero, the relationship between $|\mathbf{B}|$ and $|\mathbf{H}|$ will not be that of the dashed curve, but **B** will generally be finite when **H** becomes zero.   This arises from the essentially nonreversible physical mechanism that causes the submicroscopic dipoles of the ferromagnetic material to become locally oriented in the absence of an aligning field. As the current in the circuit is further reduced to $-I_{\text{max}}$ and subsequently increased to $+I_{\text{max}}$, the plot of $|\mathbf{B}|$ vs. $|\mathbf{H}|$ will be the loop-like pattern sketched in Fig. 9.13.   The area enclosed by this hysteresis loop is a direct

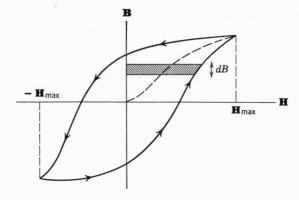

Fig. 9.13   An originally unmagnetized sample of ferromagnetic material is placed in the neighborhood of conducting coils. The current in the coils is increased slowly to some maximum value I_{max}. The dashed curve is a plot of **B** vs. **H** for this process. The current in the coils is then slowly reduced to $-I_{max}$ and increased again to I_{max}. The solid curve is a plot of **B** vs. **H** for this cyclic change in the current. The solid curve forms a loop which is the "hysteresis loop" for the ferromagnetic sample. The shaded area is the work done in incrementing the currents by an amount δI. The total area of the loop is the work done in the cyclic process.

measure of the irreversibility of the physical mechanism that causes local alignment of dipoles in ferromagnetic materials.

More analytically, consider eq. 9.47 which expresses the amount of work necessary to increment the current in the electric circuit by an amount δI, thereby causing an incremental change in $\delta \mathbf{B}$ in the presence of magnetic material:

$$\delta U_m = \int \mathbf{H} \cdot \delta \mathbf{B} \, d\tau. \tag{9.47}$$

Equation 9.47 (see page 204) is quite general, and the increment of work need not be reversible, that is, eq. 9.47 is valid even if the magnetic material is ferro-magnetic. The work per unit volume, δw_m expended in incrementing the current is

$$\delta w_m = \mathbf{H} \cdot \delta \mathbf{B}.$$

δw_m is the area crosshatched in Fig. 9.13.   The work done per unit volume in causing the current to change in a cyclic fashion is (see page 205)

$$w_m \equiv \oint \mathbf{H} \cdot \delta \mathbf{B} \text{ per cycle}, \tag{9.48}$$

where the symbol $\oint \cdots$ denotes integration over one cycle of the current. Examination of Fig. 9.13 and eq. 9.48 reveals that w_m is simply the area contained within the hysteresis loop. Since the material and the electric circuit return to the same magnetic and electric states at the end of one cycle which existed at the beginning of the cycle, it is clear that the cycling of the current involves an irreversible process. This, in turn, implies that the physical mechanism which causes ferromagnetism is irreversible.

The ferromagnetic material gains energy in the cycling of the current; this energy appears in the form of heat. Since heat is generated in this process, it is useful to recast eq. 9.48 in a form suitable to thermodynamic discussions involving ferromagnetic material. Since $\mathbf{B} = \mu_0(\mathbf{H} + \mathbf{M})$, w_m can be expressed as

$$w_m = \frac{\mu_0}{2} \oint \delta(H^2) + \left(\frac{\mu_0}{4\pi}\right) 4\pi \oint \mathbf{H} \cdot \delta\mathbf{M}. \qquad (9.48a)$$

The first integral vanishes identically, so that the work per unit volume done in a cyclic process (or the heat added in one cycle of the current) can be written as

$$w_m \equiv \left(\frac{\mu_0}{4\pi}\right) 4\pi \oint \mathbf{H} \cdot \delta\mathbf{M}. \qquad (9.48b)$$

Since $\mathbf{M}$ vanishes everywhere except within magnetic material, the total work done per cycle on a macroscopic sample of material is simply the integral of w_m over the volume of the material. In any process involving magnetic material the first law of thermodynamics must include not only the mechanical work, i.e., $p\,dV$, but also the *magnetic work*, i.e.,

$$\left(\frac{\mu_0}{4\pi}\right) 4\pi \mathbf{H} \cdot \delta\mathbf{M}.$$

Further discussion is postponed until Chapter 15.

9.9 Antiferromagnetism

Another physical phenomenon related to ferromagnetism is *antiferromagnetism*. Although individual atoms or molecules may possess non-vanishing magnetic dipole moments, most materials possess vanishing macroscopic dipole moments in the absence of applied fields. For ferromagnetic materials internal forces acting among the atoms can orient the dipoles to produce a net macroscopic dipole moment. In antiferromagnetic materials, however, the microscopic dipoles are not randomly oriented in time, but the internal forces are of such a nature that the time average dipole moments in neighboring subvolumes of the material are oriented antiparallel to one another. There is "order" in an antiferromagnetic material, although it is a different kind of order from that possessed by ferromagnetic materials. Time average magnetic dipole moments exist in both kinds of materials; however, space average dipole moments vanish for antiferromagnetic materials.[2]

9.10   The Meissner Effect and Superconductivity

Most metals at temperatures very near absolute zero ($0°$ K) undergo a phase transition in which the magnetic properties of the metals change in a remarkable way. Below the characteristic temperature or *transition temperature* for a given metal, the magnetic induction field **B** becomes zero within the metal independent of the existence and nature of current carriers in the neighborhood of the metal. This phenomenon is called the *Meissner effect*. The Meissner effect is intimately related to another effect discovered by Kamerlingh Onnes, namely, that at the transition temperature associated with the Meissner effect the electrical conductivity of the metal becomes infinite. The *repulsion* of the **B**-field from the interior of a metal is always accompanied by a vanishing electrical resistivity of the metal— superconductivity. (The reverse is not true, however; certain superconducting alloys do not exhibit the Meissner effect.) One of the major tasks of this section is to demonstrate that the existence of the Meissner effect in a metal implies the superconducting property.

The above description of the Meissner effect is an oversimplification. For a metal below the transition temperature, the **B**-field produced by an exterior agency is expelled from the interior of the metal but penetrates into the surface a distance of the order of optical distances, namely, $\sim 10^3$Å. It will be assumed here that the smallest linear dimension of the metal is large compared to this *penetration depth*, and to an excellent approximation the penetration depth can be set equal to zero. The discussion does not apply to very thin metallic films or other very small metallic samples.

The vanishing of **B** within a superconductor implies that the total current density **j** vanishes at every point within the superconductor. This follows immediately from the equation

$$\text{curl } \mathbf{B} = \left(\frac{\mu_0}{4\pi}\right)4\pi\mathbf{j}.$$

However, the normal component of **B** is continuous across the superconductor-vacuum interface, which implies that **B** immediately outside a superconductor is *tangential* to the superconductor. Furthermore, the

---

[2] For a more detailed discussion of the relationship between ferromagnetism and antiferromagnetism, see Landau and Lifshitz, *Electrodynamics of Continuous Media*, Addison–Wesley, pp. 116–119.

continuity relationship on the tangential component of **B** across the superconductor-vacuum interface implies the existence of a nonvanishing surface current density **K** on the superconductor. This continuity relation is

$$(\mathbf{B}_1 - \mathbf{B}_2) \cdot \hat{\mathbf{t}} = \left(\frac{\mu_0}{4\pi}\right) 4\pi (\mathbf{K} \times \hat{\mathbf{n}}) \cdot \hat{\mathbf{t}}$$

where region 2 is the superconductor and region 1 is the vacuum; i.e., $\mathbf{B}_2 = 0$ and $\mathbf{B}_1 = \mathbf{B}_{\text{ext}}$, and the remaining symbols have their usual meaning. This yields

$$\mathbf{K} = \left(\frac{4\pi}{\mu_0}\right)\left\{\frac{1}{4\pi} \hat{\mathbf{n}} \times \mathbf{B}_{\text{ext}}\right\}. \tag{9.62}$$

It is now possible to show that a *multiply-connected* body made of superconducting metal can carry a nonvanishing total current without including an emf within the body. The simplest form of a multiply-connected body is a torus or ring (a *doubly-connected* body). It will be the only form considered here.

The proof of this contention proceeds as follows. It is first demonstrated that the magnetic flux threading through any *open* surface Σ capping a contour Γ which lies on the ring is a constant independent of changes in the **B**-field produced by external sources (see Fig. 9.14). The integral form of Faraday's law applied to Σ and Γ is

$$\frac{d}{dt} \iint_\Sigma (\mathbf{B} \cdot \hat{\mathbf{n}}) \, dS = - \oint_\Gamma \mathbf{E} \cdot d\mathbf{l}.$$

Now **E** inside a superconductor vanishes since the superconductor is electrically neutral and **j** vanishes within it. Since the tangential component of **E** is continuous across the superconductor-vacuum interface, it implies that **E** is zero on Γ and consequently

$$\frac{d}{dt} \iint_\Sigma (\mathbf{B} \cdot \hat{\mathbf{n}}) \, dS = 0 \tag{9.63}$$

or $\Phi_m = $ constant, where Φ_m is the magnetic flux threading through Σ. Consider now a ring of metal *above* the transition temperature in an external field which produces a flux Φ_m. The temperature of the ring is reduced *below* the transition temperature, keeping the external field fixed. The external field is then altered. However, the magnetic flux threading through the ring must remain at Φ_m according to eq. 9.63. Consequently an amount of current I must flow around the ring to produce the flux necessary to compensate for the change in the external field. This current will maintain itself until the metal is raised once again above the transition temperature.

This bizarre behavior of a multiply-connected superconductor has interesting astrophysical applications. Consider a highly ionized dilute

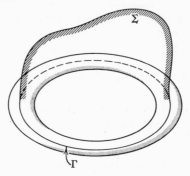

Fig. 9.14 A torus is constructed of superconducting material. The contour Γ is any closed curve lying on the torus; Σ is an arbitrary surface capping Γ.

gas cloud contained within a multiply connected region (see Fig. 9.13). Since the gas is ionized, it is conducting; further, since the gas is dilute, collisions between the ions within the cloud can be ignored and the conductivity of the cloud is therefore infinite. If this gas cloud was formed in the neighborhood of a star which produces a magnetic field, there will be a nonvanishing Φ_m through any open surface capping the cloud. As the cloud moves away from the star, it "drags the **B**-field with it"; that is, Φ_m is maintained at a constant value. Consequently the cloud carries with it some of the energy in the magnetic field of the neighboring star. This is an important agency for the propagation of magnetic fields and their associated energy through space. For example, the expulsion of ionized gas clouds from the surface of the sun causes the clouds to drag

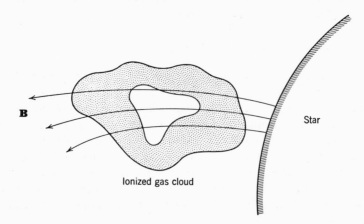

Fig. 9.15 An ionized gas cloud forms a multiply connected region in the neighborhood of a field-producing star. If the cloud is superconducting, it drags along with it the field of the star as it moves through space.

along with them the energy contained in the magnetic fields from the local regions where the ionized gas clouds are produced.

Another rather remarkable property of a superconducting ring is its self-inductance. The self-inductance of a circular loop composed of a wire of nonsuperconducting metal of zero cross section is infinite, as may be seen by direct calculation from eq. 8.13. However, as the temperature of the metal is reduced below the critical temperature, the self-inductance becomes finite. This may be seen as follows. The loop is originally above the critical temperature carrying zero current but is in an external field producing a flux Φ_m. The temperature is then reduced below the critical temperature and the source of the external field removed. Current I will flow around the loop to produce the flux Φ_m. The self-inductance L of the loop given by $L = \Phi_m/I$ will consequently be well defined.

Further properties of superconductors and some discussion concerning the microscopic origin of superconductivity are contained in Chapter 15.

PROBLEMS

9.1   A conducting material carries a steady-state current on its surface. If surface current is represented by a macroscopic surface current density **K**, calculate the discontinuity of the **H**-field across the conducting surface: establish eq. 9.33.

9.2   Two semi-infinite slabs of ferromagnetic material are separated by a gap of thickness d. The slabs are uniformly magnetized so that **M** is identical in both and perpendicular to the face of the slabs. A nonferromagnetic material of permeability μ is inserted to fill the gap partially. Calculate the force on the material. (Make an assumption about the variation of μ near the end of the paramagnetic slab.)

9.3   A magnetic dipole exists in a current-free region in a magnetic field **B**. Establish the following relationships:

$$\text{grad}\,(\boldsymbol{\mu} \cdot \mathbf{B}) = (\boldsymbol{\mu} \cdot \nabla)\mathbf{B} = -\text{curl}\,(\boldsymbol{\mu} \times \mathbf{B}).$$

9.4   Calculate the **H**- and **B**-fields inside and outside an infinitely long circular cylinder uniformly magnetized with **M** perpendicular to the cylinder axis.

9.5   Calculate the **H**- and **B**-fields inside and outside an infinitely long paramagnetic cylinder of circular cross section placed in an originally uniform field $\mathbf{B}_0$. The axis of the cylinder is oriented perpendicular to $\mathbf{B}_0$.

9.6   A paramagnetic spherical shell of inner radius a and outer radius b is placed in an originally uniform field $\mathbf{B}_0$. Calculate **H** and **B** everywhere.

9.7   Consider a superconducting body which is simply connected. Show that $\mathbf{K} = 0$ in the absence of an applied field. (Hint: Represent **B** outside the superconductor via the magnetic potential Ψ and use the boundary values of Ψ.)

10 | *Maxwell–Lorentz Theory of Electromagnetism*

Little attempt has been made in the material discussed so far to consider systematically electric and magnetic effects produced by charges whose positions vary with time. Among the phenomena considered were those of magnetostatics, in which the discussion was based on physical effects produced by charges in uniform motion. In addition, in discussing the magnetic energy of a system of current carriers, it was necessary to introduce Faraday's law (the law of induction) which relates explicitly time-dependent **B**-fields to equivalent or induced **E**-fields. Occasionally it has been necessary to apply Gauss's law to time-dependent phenomena with little or no justification, for example, in the derivation of the continuity relation for electric charge. As a consequence the theories of electrostatics and magnetostatics were developed as theories of unrelated electric and magnetic phenomena with only some tenuous connection evident through the medium of Faraday's law.

An attempt will now be made to develop a complete theory of time-dependent electric and magnetic phenomena. This theory, known as the Maxwell–Lorentz theory, will have electrostatic and magnetostatic theories as special cases. It shall be noted that no clear distinction can be made between electric and magnetic phenomena. The physical phenomena that will be considered in the complete theory are consequently called *electromagnetic* phenomena.

10.1   Generalization of the Two Gaussian Laws

In discussing the Maxwell–Lorentz theory, it will be assumed that there exist time-dependent electric and magnetic fields designated by $E(r, t)$ and $B(r, t)$, respectively, whose sources are arbitrarily moving charges. (Stationary charge and uniformly moving charge are special cases of charge in arbitrary motion.) In writing down the equation satisfied by these fields, guidance shall be provided by the condition that the time-dependent equations should reduce to those of electrostatics if the charges are stationary and to those of magnetostatics if the charges are in uniform motion.

224

Initially the discussion will be restricted to a microscopic theory so that the salient features of the theory will not be obscured by the complexities inherent in treating fields in physical media.

The two Gaussian laws for electrostatics and magnetostatics will be retained in electromagnetism, namely

$$\text{div } \mathbf{E}(\mathbf{r}, t) = \left(\frac{1}{4\pi\epsilon_0}\right) 4\pi\rho(\mathbf{r}, t) \left.\vphantom{\frac{1}{1}}\right\} \quad \text{differential} \tag{10.1}$$
$$\text{div } \mathbf{B}(\mathbf{r}, t) = 0 \qquad\qquad\qquad \text{form} \tag{10.2}$$

$$\oiint_{\Sigma} \mathbf{E}(\mathbf{r}, t) \cdot \hat{\mathbf{n}} \, dS = \left(\frac{1}{4\pi\epsilon_0}\right) 4\pi q_{\text{total}}(t) \left.\vphantom{\frac{1}{1}}\right\} \tag{10.3}$$
$$\oiint_{\Sigma} \mathbf{B}(\mathbf{r}, t) \cdot \hat{\mathbf{n}} \, dS = 0 \qquad\qquad\qquad \text{integral} \atop \text{form} \tag{10.4}$$

but will involve explicitly time-dependent quantities. The field quantities in eqs. 10.1–10.4 are the microscopic fields. (The changes brought about by the presence of material media which necessitate a reformulation in terms of macroscopic fields will be considered in Chapter 12.) The fields appearing in the above equations are to be thought of as being at least partially defined by these equations. As we shall see, at least two other equations are necessary before a complete *mathematical* description of $\mathbf{E}(\mathbf{r}, t)$ and $\mathbf{B}(\mathbf{r}, t)$ is possible. A *physical* description will only be available, however, whenever a method for measuring these fields is introduced.

It should be noted in eqs. 10.1–10.4 that the fields are uncoupled, that is, there is no relationship between $\mathbf{E}$ and $\mathbf{B}$ implied in these equations. A theory based on these equations alone would lead to phenomena which could be labeled "electric" and others which could be labeled "magnetic." The coupling of $\mathbf{E}$ and $\mathbf{B}$ is provided through two additional equations— Faraday's law and the time-dependent generalization of Ampère's law. The former has already been discussed. For completeness it is listed here:

$$\text{curl } \mathbf{E}(\mathbf{r}, t) = -\frac{\partial}{\partial t} \mathbf{B}(\mathbf{r}, t) \quad \text{(differential form)} \tag{10.5}$$

$$\oint_{\Gamma} \mathbf{E}(\mathbf{r}, t) \cdot \mathbf{dl} = -\frac{d}{dt} \iint_{\Sigma} \mathbf{B}(\mathbf{r}, t) \cdot \hat{\mathbf{n}} \, dS \quad \text{(integral form)} \tag{10.6}$$

10.2 Faraday and Ampère's Law: Induced Electromotive and Magnetomotive Forces

If eqs. 10.1 and 10.5 are examined, it is noted that the sources of a time-dependent E-field are charges (via Gauss's law) and time-varying magnetic fields (via Faraday's law).   On the other hand, Gauss's magnetic law (eq. 10.2) tells only that there is no magnetic analogue to electric charge, but does not give information concerning the source of the **B**-field. The necessary source equation for the time-dependent **B**-field is a generalization of Ampère's law for the case of steady-state phenomena.   The steady state Amperian law is

$$\text{curl } \mathbf{B}(\mathbf{r}) = \left(\frac{\mu_0}{4\pi}\right) 4\pi \mathbf{j}(\mathbf{r}). \tag{10.7}$$

The steady-state Amperian law implies that the source of a static **B**-field is steady-state current.   In taking cognizance of the above remarks concerning the sources of a time-dependent **E**-field, it would seem that a logical generalization of eq. 10.7 for a time-dependent **B** would contain an explicitly time-dependent current density $\mathbf{j}(\mathbf{r}, t)$ as well as effects of an explicitly time-varying **E**-field in analogy with Faraday's law.   The resulting generalization is

$$\text{curl } \mathbf{B}(\mathbf{r}, t) = \left(\frac{\mu_0}{4\pi}\right)\left\{ 4\pi \mathbf{j}(\mathbf{r}, t) + (4\pi\epsilon_0)\frac{\partial}{\partial t}\mathbf{E}(\mathbf{r}, t)\right\}. \tag{10.8}$$

Equations 10.1, 10.2, 10.5, and 10.8 give a complete description of the time-dependent **E**- and **B**-fields, but do not tell us how to measure these fields.   The ultimate justification of this set of equations, called Maxwell's equations, rests entirely upon their agreement with experiment.   Although the equations themselves have been introduced here in an *ad hoc* manner, Maxwell and others were led to their formulation through interpretation of experiments.   It is a great leap in logic to write down the time-dependent Gauss's law from knowledge of electrostatic phenomena alone.   Yet one must remember that the formulation of Maxwell theory to unify all classical physical phenomena of electromagnetism is one of the supreme creations of the human mind.

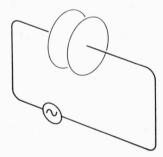

Fig. 10.1   A parallel plate capacitor is connected to a source of a time-varying emf. A current will flow in the wires which connect the source of the emf to the plates of the capacitor.

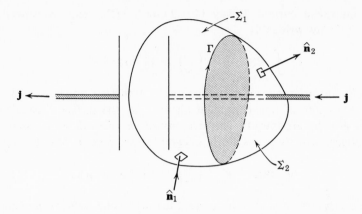

Fig. 10.2 A closed contour Γ encircles a conducting wire in the circuit sketched in Fig. 10.1. Two capping surfaces Σ_1 and Σ_2 for the contour Γ are indicated. Σ_1 passes through the nonconducting region between the plates of the capacitor; Σ_2 is pierced by the current-carrying wire. $\Sigma_1 + \Sigma_2$ forms a closed surface S. The flux of the real current density $\mathbf{j}$ through S is nonvanishing; however, the flux through Σ of $\mathbf{j}' = \mathbf{j} + (4\pi\epsilon_0)(1/4\pi)\partial\mathbf{E}/\partial t$ vanishes identically.

Before discussing the operational definition of the field quantities appearing in Maxwell's equations, an attempt shall be made to justify the arbitrary introduction of the term $(4\pi\epsilon_0)(1/4\pi)(\partial/\partial t)\mathbf{E}$ appearing as the source of an equivalent $\mathbf{B}$-field. For this purpose, consider a parallel plate capacitor in a simple electric circuit containing a source of a time-varying emf. This circuit is sketched in Fig. 10.1. Experience tells us that a time-varying current will flow in the conducting wires connecting the plates of the capacitor to the source of emf. However, this circuit is not "closed," since no electric current can flow in the nonconducting region (vacuum) separating the plates of the capacitor. If the nonconducting region is to be replaced by an equivalent conducting region, it is straightforward to show that the current density in this equivalent conducting region is related to the $\mathbf{E}$-field in the nonconducting region.

Let us examine closely what is happening in this circuit at some instant in time. In Fig. 10.2 an arbitrary closed contour Γ is allowed to encircle the conducting wire. Two capping surfaces Σ_1 and Σ_2 are constructed for the contour Γ; the surface Σ_1 passes through the nonconducting region between the plates of the capacitor, whereas the surface Σ_2 is pierced by the current-carrying conductor. It is possible to show that Ampère's law applied to the contour Γ and the surfaces Σ_1 and Σ_2 is consistent only if the current density appearing in Ampère's law is real current density $\mathbf{j}$ plus the equivalent current density $(4\pi\epsilon_0)(1/4\pi)(\partial/\partial t)\mathbf{E}$. (In magnetostatics Ampère's law written as

$$\oint_\Gamma \mathbf{B}(\mathbf{r}) \cdot \mathbf{dl} = \left(\frac{\mu_0}{4\pi}\right) 4\pi \iint_\Sigma \mathbf{j}(\mathbf{r}) \cdot \hat{\mathbf{n}} \, dS$$

held for any *arbitrary* surface Σ capping Γ. If this law is to be carried over into the realm of time-dependent phenomena, the surface Σ capping Γ must also be arbitrary.) This demonstration proceeds as follows: the time-dependent Ampère's law in integral form is postulated to be

$$\oint_\Gamma \mathbf{B}(\mathbf{r}, t) \cdot \mathbf{dl} = \left(\frac{\mu_0}{4\pi}\right) 4\pi \iint_\Sigma \mathbf{j}'(\mathbf{r}, t) \cdot \hat{\mathbf{n}} \, dS \qquad (10.9)$$

where $\mathbf{j}'(\mathbf{r}, t) \equiv$ total effective current density. The value of the integral on the left-hand side of eq. 10.9 depends only on Γ. Therefore

$$\iint_{\Sigma_1} \mathbf{j}'(\mathbf{r}, t) \cdot \hat{\mathbf{n}}_1 \, dS = \iint_{\Sigma_2} \mathbf{j}'(\mathbf{r}, t) \cdot \hat{\mathbf{n}}_2 \, dS \qquad (10.10)$$

where $\hat{\mathbf{n}}_1, \hat{\mathbf{n}}_2 =$ unit normals on the surfaces Σ_1 and Σ_2, respectively. If the convention is remembered for determining the positive direction of $\hat{\mathbf{n}}$ using the right-hand rule, it is noted that eq. 10.10 can be rewritten as

$$\iint_{\Sigma_1 + \Sigma_2} \mathbf{j}'(\mathbf{r}, t) \cdot \hat{\mathbf{n}} \, dS = \oiint_S \mathbf{j}'(\mathbf{r}, t) \cdot \hat{\mathbf{n}} \, dS = 0$$

where $\hat{\mathbf{n}}$ is the outward normal to the closed surface S formed by Σ_1 and Σ_2. Since S is a *closed* surface, the divergence theorem can be applied, yielding

$$\int_\tau \operatorname{div} \mathbf{j}'(\mathbf{r}, t) \, d\tau = 0.$$

Since the surfaces Σ_1 and Σ_2 are arbitrary except for the minor restrictions mentioned previously, it is evident that the volume τ is also arbitrary; hence the inference

$$\operatorname{div} \mathbf{j}'(\mathbf{r}, t) = 0. \qquad (10.11)$$

The effective current density $\mathbf{j}'$ is simply the sum of the real current density $\mathbf{j}$ and the equivalent current density $\mathbf{j}_e$; that is,

$$\mathbf{j}' = \mathbf{j} + \mathbf{j}_e. \qquad (10.12)$$

However, it has already been seen that the postulate of electric charge conservation implies that

$$\operatorname{div} \mathbf{j} = -\frac{\partial \rho}{\partial t}. \qquad (10.13)$$

(This was one of the instances of a time-dependent phenomenon discussed earlier in the context of steady-state phenomena.)   From eqs. 10.11–10.13 it is seen immediately that

$$\text{div } \mathbf{j}_e(\mathbf{r}, t) = + \frac{\partial}{\partial t} \rho(\mathbf{r}, t). \tag{10.14}$$

However, use may now be made of the time-dependent Gaussian electric law, eq. 10.1, to remove ρ from the right-hand side of eq. 10.14. This yields

$$\text{div } \mathbf{j}_e(\mathbf{r}, t) = (4\pi\epsilon_0) \frac{1}{4\pi} \frac{\partial}{\partial t} \text{div } \mathbf{E}(\mathbf{r}, t).$$

Interchanging the order of the space and time derivatives on the right-hand side leads to

$$\text{div } \mathbf{j}_e(\mathbf{r}, t) = \text{div } \left\{ (4\pi\epsilon_0) \frac{1}{4\pi} \frac{\partial}{\partial t} \mathbf{E}(\mathbf{r}, t) \right\}.$$

Consequently it is seen that

$$4\pi\mathbf{j}_e(\mathbf{r}, t) = (4\pi\epsilon_0) \frac{\partial}{\partial t} \mathbf{E}(\mathbf{r}, t) + \mathbf{h}(\mathbf{r}, t) \tag{10.15}$$

where $\mathbf{h}(\mathbf{r}, t)$ is an arbitrary vector function with vanishing divergence, and $\mathbf{h}$ is taken to be identically zero; hence the time-dependent Amperian law results.   The equivalent current density[1] can be thought of as leading to an induced magnetomotive force, since it is proportional to the time derivative of $\mathbf{E}$ and produces a $\mathbf{B}$-field with nonvanishing curl.   This is analogous to the case in which a time-varying $\mathbf{B}$-field produces an $\mathbf{E}$-field with nonvanishing curl and therefore an induced electromotive force.

10.3   Gauge Invariance and the Scalar and Vector Potentials

In electrostatics it was possible and convenient to introduce the scalar potential $\varphi(\mathbf{r})$ defined as

$$-\text{grad } \varphi(\mathbf{r}) = \mathbf{E}(\mathbf{r}) \tag{10.16}$$

and for similar reasons a vector potential $\mathbf{A}(\mathbf{r})$ was introduced in magnetostatics via the relation

$$\text{curl } \mathbf{A}(\mathbf{r}) = \mathbf{B}(\mathbf{r}). \tag{10.17}$$

In introducing these potential functions, care was taken to insure that no contradictions would ensue in the equations that the fields were known to

---

[1] The equivalent current density

$$4\pi\mathbf{j}_e(\mathbf{r}, t) = (4\pi\epsilon_0) \frac{\partial}{\partial t} \mathbf{E}(\mathbf{r}, t)$$

has been historically referred to as the *displacement current density*, but this name has little meaning.   It shall always be referred to as equivalent current density.

satisfy. The question now arises whether it is possible to define time-dependent scalar and vector potential functions which satisfy the time-dependent analogies of eqs. 10.16 and 10.17. The case of the vector potential will be examined first. Suppose $A(r, t)$ is defined through the analogue of eq. 10.17 namely

$$\text{curl } A(r, t) = B(r, t). \tag{10.18}$$

$B(r, t)$ must have vanishing divergence according to Gauss's magnetic law; this is automatically insured by eq. 10.18. However, it is straightforward to show that the time-dependent generalization of eq. 10.16 for the scalar potential is not valid; that is,

$$-\text{grad } \varphi(r, t) \neq E(r, t).$$

For this demonstration use is made of Faraday's law. According to Faraday's law, and the definition of $A(r, t)$,

$$\text{curl } E(r, t) = -\frac{\partial}{\partial t} \text{curl } A(r, t) \neq 0. \tag{10.19}$$

However, the curl $E(r, t)$ as calculated from the time-dependent generalization of eq. 10.16 leads to the result

$$\text{curl } E(r, t) = -\text{curl grad } \varphi(r, t) \equiv 0 \tag{10.20}$$

since curl grad of any scalar function vanishes identically. Consequently eqs. 10.19 and 10.20 exhibit an inconsistency which is traced back to the incompatibility of the time-dependent analogues of eqs. 10.16 and 10.17 defining A and φ. If we choose to redefine $E(r, t)$ in terms of A and φ as

$$E(r, t) = -\text{grad } \varphi(r, t) - \frac{\partial}{\partial t} A(r, t) \tag{10.21}$$

then the definitions of $E(r, t)$ and $B(r, t)$ in terms of $A(r, t)$ and $\varphi(r, t)$ are seen to be consistent. (Equation 10.21 illustrates that it is unwise and confusing to call $A(r, t)$ the *magnetic* vector potential since A yields a significant contribution to E. The simpler name *vector potential* will be adopted for this field quantity.)

A curious property of A and φ exists which has very profound implications in the structure of electromagnetic theory. This curious property may be exhibited as follows. Suppose $E(r, t)$ and $B(r, t)$ can be measured and an $A(r, t)$ and $\varphi(r, t)$ determined which leads to the correct $E(r, t)$ and $B(r, t)$. Further, suppose a new vector potential A_0 and scalar potential φ_0 are defined via eq. 10.22

$$\varphi(r, t) = \varphi_0(r, t) - \frac{\partial}{\partial t} \chi(r, t)$$

$$A(r, t) = A_0(r, t) + \text{grad } \chi(r, t) \tag{10.22}$$

where $\chi(\mathbf{r}, t)$ is some arbitrary scalar function of $\mathbf{r}$ and t. Calculating $\mathbf{E}$ and $\mathbf{B}$ from eqs. 10.18 and 10.21 and expressing the results in terms of $\mathbf{A}_0$, φ_0, and χ yields

$$\mathbf{E}(\mathbf{r}, t) = -\operatorname{grad} \varphi_0 + \operatorname{grad} \frac{\partial}{\partial t} \chi - \frac{\partial}{\partial t} \mathbf{A}_0 - \frac{\partial}{\partial t} \operatorname{grad} \chi \quad (10.23)$$

$$\mathbf{B}(\mathbf{r}, t) = \operatorname{curl} \mathbf{A}_0 + \operatorname{curl} \operatorname{grad} \chi. \quad (10.24)$$

However, in eq. 10.23 the order of the space and time derivatives acting on χ can be interchanged, causing χ to disappear from the expression for $\mathbf{E}$. In addition, since the operator curl grad acting on any scalar function produces zero as a result, χ disappears from the expression eq. 10.24 for $\mathbf{B}$. Consequently

$$\mathbf{E}(\mathbf{r}, t) = -\operatorname{grad} \varphi - \frac{\partial}{\partial t} \mathbf{A} = -\operatorname{grad} \varphi_0 - \frac{\partial}{\partial t} \mathbf{A}_0$$

$$\mathbf{B}(\mathbf{r}, t) = \operatorname{curl} \mathbf{A} = \operatorname{curl} \mathbf{A}_0.$$

Therefore if an $\mathbf{A}$ and a φ can be found that yield a given $\mathbf{E}$ and $\mathbf{B}$, it is always possible to find an infinitude of other potentials $\mathbf{A}_0$ and φ_0 which yield the same fields from eqs. 10.22, since $\chi(\mathbf{r}, t)$ is an arbitrary function. The definitions of $\mathbf{E}$ and $\mathbf{B}$ in terms of $\mathbf{A}$ and φ are said to be *invariant* with respect to a transformation of the kind exhibited in eq. 10.22. Such a transformation is called a *gauge transformation*, and the function χ is called the *gauge function*. (Note that it is always possible to find a gauge function χ such that $\varphi_0(\mathbf{r}, t) = 0$. The prescription is simply to choose χ such that $(\partial/\partial t)\chi = -\varphi$. This particular choice of the gauge function will allow the determination of $\mathbf{E}$ and $\mathbf{B}$ in terms of $\mathbf{A}_0$ alone; that is,

$$\mathbf{E}(\mathbf{r}, t) = -\frac{\partial}{\partial t} \mathbf{A}_0(\mathbf{r}, t)$$

$$\mathbf{B}(\mathbf{r}, t) = \operatorname{curl} \mathbf{A}_0(\mathbf{r}, t).$$

Other gauge functions can be chosen for convenience in a particular physical problem so that the desired results—the determination of $\mathbf{E}$ and $\mathbf{B}$—are obtained more easily.)

10.4 Maxwell's Equations in Vacuo

It is convenient at this point to write down Maxwell's equations in differential and integral form.

MAXWELL'S EQUATIONS IN DIFFERENTIAL FORM

$$\text{div } \mathbf{E} = \left(\frac{1}{4\pi\epsilon_0}\right)4\pi\rho \qquad (10.25)$$

$$\text{div } \mathbf{B} = 0 \qquad (10.26)$$

$$\text{curl } \mathbf{E} = -\frac{\partial}{\partial t}\mathbf{B} \qquad (10.27)$$

$$\left(\frac{4\pi}{\mu_0}\right)\text{curl } \mathbf{B} = 4\pi\mathbf{j} + (4\pi\epsilon_0)\frac{\partial}{\partial t}\mathbf{E}. \qquad (10.28)$$

MAXWELL'S EQUATIONS IN INTEGRAL FORM

$$\oiint_\Sigma \mathbf{E} \cdot \hat{\mathbf{n}} \, ds = \left(\frac{1}{4\pi\epsilon_0}\right)4\pi q \qquad (10.29)$$

$$\oiint_\Sigma \mathbf{B} \cdot \hat{\mathbf{n}} \, ds = 0 \qquad (10.30)$$

$$\oint_\Gamma \mathbf{E} \cdot d\mathbf{l} = -\frac{d}{dt}\iint_\Sigma (\mathbf{B} \cdot \hat{\mathbf{n}}) \, ds \qquad (10.31)$$

$$\left(\frac{4\pi}{\mu_0}\right)\oint_\Gamma \mathbf{B} \cdot d\mathbf{l} = 4\pi I + (4\pi\epsilon_0)\frac{d}{dt}\iint_\Sigma (\mathbf{E} \cdot \hat{\mathbf{n}}) \, ds. \qquad (10.32)$$

It should also be remembered that Maxwell's equations determine scalar and vector potential functions which are defined in terms of the fields as

$$\mathbf{E} = -\text{grad } \varphi - \frac{\partial}{\partial t}\mathbf{A}$$

$$\mathbf{B} = \text{curl } \mathbf{A}.$$

These potential functions are in no sense unique, and any other set φ_0, $\mathbf{A}_0$ which can be obtained via a gauge transformation indicated in eqs. 10.22 will yield the same fields. The question now arises whether the differential equation satisfied by $\varphi(\mathbf{r})$ for stationary charge and $\mathbf{A}(\mathbf{r})$ for uniformly moving charge hold in the time-dependent case. The equations satisfied by $\varphi(\mathbf{r})$ and $\mathbf{A}(\mathbf{r})$ have been shown to be, respectively,

$$\nabla^2\varphi(\mathbf{r}) = -\left(\frac{1}{4\pi\epsilon_0}\right)4\pi\rho(\mathbf{r})$$

$$\nabla^2\mathbf{A}(\mathbf{r}) = -\left(\frac{\mu_0}{4\pi}\right)4\pi\mathbf{j}(\mathbf{r}).$$

The equations satisfied by $\varphi(\mathbf{r}, t)$ and $\mathbf{A}(\mathbf{r}, t)$ can be obtained directly from Maxwell's equations. Gauss's magnetic law (eq. 10.26) and Faraday's law (eq. 10.27) have already been used to define $\mathbf{A}(\mathbf{r}, t)$ and $\varphi(\mathbf{r}, t)$ in terms of $\mathbf{E}(\mathbf{r}, t)$ and $\mathbf{B}(\mathbf{r}, t)$. Gauss's electric law and Ampère's law will yield the desired equations for the potential functions. Substituting the defining equations 10.21 and 10.18 for the potentials into eqs. 10.25 and 10.28 yields

$$\text{div grad } \varphi + \text{div } \frac{\partial}{\partial t} \mathbf{A} = -\left(\frac{1}{4\pi\epsilon_0}\right)4\pi\rho \tag{10.33}$$

$$-\left(\frac{4\pi}{\mu_0}\right) \text{curl curl } \mathbf{A} = -4\pi\mathbf{j} + (4\pi\epsilon_0)\frac{\partial}{\partial t}\text{ grad } \varphi + (4\pi\epsilon_0)\frac{\partial^2}{\partial t^2}\mathbf{A}. \tag{10.34}$$

Equations 10.33 and 10.34 may be simplified somewhat if one recalls the vector calculus identities:

$$\text{div grad} \equiv \nabla^2$$
$$\text{curl curl} \equiv -\nabla^2 + \text{grad div.}$$

However, the equations that result will still be coupled second-order differential equations in $\varphi(\mathbf{r}, t)$ and $\mathbf{A}(\mathbf{r}, t)$. To be explicit,

$$\nabla^2\varphi + \text{div } \frac{\partial}{\partial t}\mathbf{A} = -\left(\frac{1}{4\pi\epsilon_0}\right)4\pi\rho \tag{10.33a}$$

$$\nabla^2\mathbf{A} - \text{grad div } \mathbf{A} = -\left(\frac{\mu_0}{4\pi}\right)4\pi\mathbf{j} + (4\pi\epsilon_0)\left(\frac{\mu_0}{4\pi}\right)\frac{\partial}{\partial t}\text{ grad } \varphi$$
$$+ (4\pi\epsilon_0)\left(\frac{\mu_0}{4\pi}\right)\frac{\partial^2}{\partial t^2}\mathbf{A}. \tag{10.34a}$$

There is no way to produce uncoupled second-order differential equations for the potentials similar to Poisson's equations in electrostatics and magnetostatics unless some restrictions are placed upon $\mathbf{A}(\mathbf{r}, t)$ and $\varphi(\mathbf{r}, t)$ to remove some of the arbitrariness inherent because of the gauge invariance of the theory. Some restrictions will now be placed on the potentials: they shall be required to obey a "subsidiary condition" due to Lorentz. This condition is

$$\text{div } \mathbf{A} + (4\pi\epsilon_0)\left(\frac{\mu_0}{4\pi}\right)\frac{\partial}{\partial t}\rho(\mathbf{r}, t) = 0. \tag{10.35}$$

What restrictions this places upon the gauge function will be investigated shortly.

If the Lorentz condition is used to eliminate $\mathbf{A}(\mathbf{r}, t)$ from eq. 10.33a and $\varphi(\mathbf{r}, t)$ from eq. 10.34a, the desired time-dependent generalizations of the time-independent Poisson equations result:

$$\nabla^2\varphi - \epsilon_0\mu_0 \frac{\partial^2}{\partial t^2}\varphi = -\left(\frac{1}{4\pi\epsilon_0}\right)4\pi\rho \tag{10.36}$$

$$\nabla^2\mathbf{A} - \epsilon_0\mu_0 \frac{\partial^2}{\partial t^2}\mathbf{A} = -\left(\frac{\mu_0}{4\pi}\right)4\pi\mathbf{j}. \tag{10.37}$$

As remarked previously and as is obvious from eqs. 10.36 and 10.37, the product $\sqrt{\epsilon_0\mu_0}$ has the dimensions of a reciprocal velocity. A symbol shall be adopted for this constant and its physical significance investigated subsequently:

$$\sqrt{\epsilon_0\mu_0} \equiv c^{-1}. \tag{10.38}$$

The differential equations for the potentials then read:

$$\Box\varphi(\mathbf{r}, t) = -\left(\frac{1}{4\pi\epsilon_0}\right)4\pi\rho(\mathbf{r}, t) \tag{10.39}$$

$$\Box\mathbf{A}(\mathbf{r}, t) = -\left(\frac{\mu_0}{4\pi}\right)4\pi\mathbf{j}(\mathbf{r}, t) \tag{10.40}$$

where $\Box$ is a compact symbol for the operator

$$\Box \equiv \nabla^2 - \frac{1}{c^2}\frac{\partial^2}{\partial t^2} \tag{10.41}$$

and is called the d'Alembertian operator.

To return to the restriction on the gauge function χ implied by the Lorentz condition, $\mathbf{A}$ and φ are subjected to a gauge transformation and it is required that the transformed potentials $\mathbf{A}_0$ and φ_0 also satisfy the Lorentz condition. This yields from eqs. 10.22 and 10.35

$$\text{div grad } \chi - \epsilon_0\mu_0 \frac{\partial^2}{\partial t^2} \chi = 0$$

or more succinctly

$$\Box\chi(\mathbf{r}, t) = 0. \tag{10.42}$$

The gauge function satisfies the homogeneous counterpart of the differential equations satisfied by $\varphi(\mathbf{r}, t)$ and $\mathbf{A}(\mathbf{r}, t)$. The gauge function is still exceedingly arbitrary. For example, if ρ is identically zero everywhere (vacuum), an obvious solution of eq. 10.39 is that $\varphi(\mathbf{r}, t)$ equals a constant. This implies from the Lorentz condition that

$$\text{div } \mathbf{A}(\mathbf{r}, t) = 0.$$

As shall be seen, this is a very convenient gauge to employ in problems involving propagation of electromagnetic waves through vacuum.

10.5   Maxwell's Equations in Vacuo: d'Alembert's Equations

In vacuo, φ and $\mathbf{A}$ satisfy very simple differential equations. If ρ and $\mathbf{j}$ are identically zero (a microscopic vacuum), φ and $\mathbf{A}$ satisfy the homogeneous differential equations:

$$\Box\varphi(\mathbf{r}, t) = 0 \tag{10.43}$$

$$\Box\mathbf{A}(\mathbf{r}, t) = 0. \tag{10.44}$$

It is not difficult to show that under the same physical conditions, $\mathbf{E}(\mathbf{r}, t)$ and $\mathbf{B}(\mathbf{r}, t)$ also satisfy the same differential equations. If the curl of eqs. 10.27 and 10.28 is taken for the vacuum case, the results are

$$\text{curl curl } \mathbf{E} = -\text{curl}\frac{\partial}{\partial t}\mathbf{B}$$

$$\text{curl curl } \mathbf{B} = \frac{1}{c^2}\text{curl}\frac{\partial}{\partial t}\mathbf{E}.$$

After interchanging the order of the space and time derivatives in these equations, curl $\mathbf{B}$ can be eliminated from the right-hand side of the former equation by means of Ampère's law and curl $\mathbf{E}$ from the right-hand side of the latter by means of Faraday's law. The resulting equations are

$$-\nabla^2\mathbf{E} + \text{grad div }\mathbf{E} = -\frac{1}{c^2}\frac{\partial^2}{\partial t^2}\mathbf{E}$$

$$-\nabla^2\mathbf{B} + \text{grad div }\mathbf{B} = -\frac{1}{c^2}\frac{\partial^2}{\partial t^2}\mathbf{B}$$

where use has been made of the vector calculus identity

$$\text{curl curl} \equiv -\nabla^2 + \text{grad div.}$$

Both Gaussian laws say that $\mathbf{E}$ and $\mathbf{B}$ have vanishing divergence in vacuo. Therefore $\mathbf{E}$ and $\mathbf{B}$ satisfy d'Alembert's equations:

$$\Box\mathbf{E}(\mathbf{r}, t) = 0 \qquad (10.45)$$

$$\Box\mathbf{B}(\mathbf{r}, t) = 0. \qquad (10.46)$$

In vacuo, φ, $\mathbf{A}$, $\mathbf{E}$, and $\mathbf{B}$ all satisfy the same equation. For the vector functions $\mathbf{A}$, $\mathbf{E}$, and $\mathbf{B}$, this means that each component of these vector functions satisfies d'Alembert's equation. These results can be summarized symbolically in one equation:

$$\Box g(\mathbf{r}, t) = 0 \qquad (10.47)$$

where $\qquad g(\mathbf{r}, t) \begin{cases} \varphi(\mathbf{r}, t) \\ \\ \text{any component of} \begin{bmatrix} \mathbf{A}(\mathbf{r}, t) \\ \mathbf{B}(\mathbf{r}, t) \\ \mathbf{E}(\mathbf{r}, t) \end{bmatrix} \end{cases}.$

10.6 Plane Wave Solutions to d'Alembert's Equation

d'Alembert's equation has many different families of solutions. One family corresponds to the propagation of *waves of constant phase*, and the equation is therefore called the *wave equation*. The characteristics of solutions of this type may be expressed as follows: $g(\mathbf{r}, t)$ is taken to depend on only one Cartesian component of $\mathbf{r}$. For example,

$$\frac{\partial}{\partial x} g(\mathbf{r}, t) = \frac{\partial}{\partial y} g(\mathbf{r}, t) = 0. \tag{10.48}$$

Equation 10.48 implies that on planes defined by $z = $ constant, g is a constant at time t. Since $g(\mathbf{r}, t) = g(z, t)$, d'Alembert's equation simplifies to

$$\left\{ \frac{\partial^2}{\partial z^2} - \frac{1}{c^2} \frac{\partial^2}{\partial t^2} \right\} g(z, t) = 0. \tag{10.49}$$

For this discussion, it will be convenient to introduce a change of the variables upon which g depends explicitly. The new variables η^+ and η^- are related to the original variables z and t by the linear algebraic relations

$$\begin{aligned} \eta^+ &\equiv z + ct \\ \eta^- &\equiv z - ct. \end{aligned} \tag{10.50}$$

In terms of the new variables it is easy to show that d'Alembert's equation becomes

$$\frac{\partial}{\partial \eta^-} \frac{\partial}{\partial \eta^+} g(\eta^+, \eta^-) = 0. \tag{10.51}$$

It is quite evident from direct computation that one form of $g(\eta^+, \eta^-)$ can be written as a sum of two functions each depending on one variable only; that is,

$$g(\eta^+, \eta^-) = g^{(+)}(\eta^+) + g^{(-)}(\eta^-). \tag{10.52}$$

Equation 10.52 satisfies eq. 10.51 identically regardless of what form the functions $g^{(+)}$ and $g^{(-)}$ might assume.

The functions $g^{(+)}$ and $g^{(-)}$ lend themselves to an interesting physical interpretation. Consider the function $g^{(-)}(\eta^-) = g^{(-)}(z - ct)$. A priori, independent of the form of the function $g^{(-)}$, it assumes the same value at all points for which

$$z - ct = \alpha, \text{ a constant.} \tag{10.53}$$

Now $z - ct = \alpha$ is the equation of a plane at fixed t. The argument of $g^{(-)}$, namely, η^-, is called the *phase*; consequently the plane $z - ct = \alpha$ is called a *plane of constant phase*. The position in space of the plane of phase α at the time $t + dt$ is, according to eq. 10.53, $z + dz$ where $dz - c\, dt = 0$, or

$$\frac{dz}{dt} = c. \tag{10.54}$$

Therefore the plane on which $g^{(-)}$ takes on a constant value, $g^{(-)}(\alpha)$, moves in space with velocity c, according to eq. 10.54. Consequently c, the constant appearing in d'Alembert's equation, is seen to be the velocity with which the planes of constant phase move in time and is called the *phase velocity* of the plane wave solutions to d'Alembert's equations. (It is straightforward to show that the function $g^{(+)}(\eta^+)$ corresponds to planes of constant phase moving in the negative z-direction with speed c.)

Of course, there is no reason why solutions to d'Alembert's equations cannot occur which correspond to planes of constant phase moving along the X- or the Y-axes. In general, solutions are possible which correspond to planes of constant phase moving in the arbitrary direction $\hat{\mathbf{n}}$ (see Fig. 10.3). Here the variables η^+ and η^- are represented as

$$\eta^+ \equiv \hat{\mathbf{n}} \cdot \mathbf{r} + ct$$
$$\eta^- \equiv \hat{\mathbf{n}} \cdot \mathbf{r} - ct. \tag{10.55}$$

Suppose solutions of d'Alembert's equation for $\mathbf{A}$ which correspond to planes of constant phase moving with the phase velocity c in the direction $\hat{\mathbf{n}}$ are considered. Under these conditions $\mathbf{A}$ can be written as

$$\mathbf{A}(\mathbf{r}, t) = \mathbf{A}(\eta^-).$$

For convenience the gauge defined by

$$\operatorname{div} \mathbf{A}(\mathbf{r}, t) = 0 \quad \text{or} \quad \varphi(\mathbf{r}, t) = \text{constant} \tag{10.56}$$

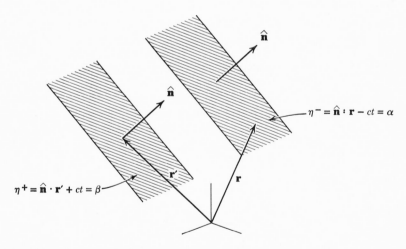

Fig. 10.3 The planes indicated are planes of constant phase $\eta^+ = \hat{\mathbf{n}} \cdot \mathbf{r} + ct$ and $\eta^- = \hat{\mathbf{n}} \cdot \mathbf{r} - ct$. The planes of constant phase η^+ move in the direction $-\hat{\mathbf{n}}$ with speed c; the planes of constant phase η^- move in the direction $+\hat{\mathbf{n}}$ with speed c. $\mathbf{E}$, $\mathbf{B}$, and $\mathbf{A}$ lie in the planes of constant phase.

will be employed.   Although this places some restriction on $\mathbf{A}(\mathbf{r}, t)$, this does not alter the values of $\mathbf{E}$ and $\mathbf{B}$, the field quantities, because of the gauge invariance of the Maxwell theory.   In this gauge, sometimes referred to as the *radiation gauge*, $\mathbf{E}(\mathbf{r}, t) = -(\partial/\partial t)\mathbf{A}(\mathbf{r}, t)$ or, physically, the planes of constant phase of $\mathbf{E}$ move parallel (or antiparallel) to the planes of constant phase of $\mathbf{A}$.

If for simplicity (this is completely arbitrary) the coordinate axes are oriented so that $\hat{\mathbf{z}} \parallel \hat{\mathbf{n}}$,

$$\frac{\partial}{\partial x} \mathbf{A}(\eta^-) = \frac{\partial}{\partial y} \mathbf{A}(\eta^-) = 0.$$

However, in the radiation gauge

$$\operatorname{div} \mathbf{A}(\eta^-) = \frac{\partial}{\partial x} A_x(\eta^-) + \frac{\partial}{\partial y} A_y(\eta^-) + \frac{\partial}{\partial z} A_z(\eta^-) = 0$$

and consequently

$$\frac{\partial}{\partial z} A_z(\eta^-) = 0 = \frac{\partial}{\partial \eta^-} A_z(\eta^-)$$

or more generally for arbitrary orientation of the coordinate axes

$$\frac{\partial}{\partial \eta^-} (\hat{\mathbf{n}} \cdot \mathbf{A}) = 0. \tag{10.57}$$

Equation 10.57 states that the component of $\mathbf{A}$ perpendicular to the planes of constant phase does not depend on $\mathbf{r}$ (i.e., x, y, and z), and is thus a constant (in space).   Since $\mathbf{B}$ depends only on the space derivatives of $\mathbf{A}$ through $\mathbf{B} = \operatorname{curl} \mathbf{A}$, $\mathbf{B}$ cannot depend upon the value of this component of $\mathbf{A}$.   In addition, this component of $\mathbf{A}$ (namely, A_z) satisfies d'Alembert's equation:

$$\left(\frac{\partial^2}{\partial z^2} - \frac{1}{c^2} \frac{\partial^2}{\partial t^2}\right) A_z(\eta^-) = 0.$$

Consequently

$$\frac{\partial}{\partial t} A_z(\eta^-)$$

is independent of t or, more generally,

$$\frac{\partial}{\partial t} [\hat{\mathbf{n}} \cdot \mathbf{A}(\eta^-)]$$

is independent of t.   However, the field quantity $E_z(\eta^-)$ is related to $\mathbf{A}$ via

$$E_z(\eta^-) = - \frac{\partial}{\partial t} A_z(\eta^-)$$

and is a constant (in time). Since only time-varying solutions to d'Alembert's equations are under consideration, $E_z(\eta^-)$ can be set equal to zero or, more generally,

$$\hat{n} \cdot \mathbf{E}(\mathbf{r}, t) = 0. \tag{10.58}$$

Equation 10.58 states that the planes of constant phase of $\mathbf{E}$ move so that $\mathbf{E}$ is always perpendicular to the direction of propagation of the planes. Such solutions to d'Alembert's equation are called *transverse solutions*. The relationships that must exist in these transverse solutions between $\mathbf{E}$ and $\mathbf{B}$ will now be examined. The transverse solution under consideration depends only on $\eta^- = z - ct$. According to Faraday's law in vacuum

$$\text{curl } \mathbf{B} = \frac{1}{c^2} \frac{\partial}{\partial t} \mathbf{E}.$$

$\mathbf{E}$ is perpendicular to the direction of propagation of the planes of constant phase, z in this case. The choice $\mathbf{E} = E\hat{x}$ will be made; this choice is perfectly arbitrary and does no violence to what has already been demonstrated.

Information about $\mathbf{B}$ can be obtained by looking at its definition in terms of $\mathbf{A}$, curl $\mathbf{A} = \mathbf{B}$:

$$\text{curl}_x \mathbf{A} = \frac{\partial}{\partial y} A_z - \frac{\partial}{\partial z} A_y = B_x.$$

However, A_z does not depend on y, and A_y is zero since $\mathbf{E} = E\hat{x}$ and $\mathbf{A}$ is parallel to $\mathbf{E}$ in the gauge chosen. Consequently $B_x = 0$. The equation for the y-component of $\mathbf{B}$ leads to eq. 10.59.

$$B_y(\eta^-) = \frac{1}{c} E(\eta^-). \tag{10.59}$$

The z-component of $\mathbf{B}$ satisfies

$$\text{curl}_z \mathbf{A} = \frac{\partial}{\partial x} A_y - \frac{\partial}{\partial y} A_x = B_z.$$

Since A_y and A_x are functions of $\eta^- = z - ct$ only, it follows that $B_z = 0$. Combining all these results, if $\mathbf{A}(\mathbf{r}, t) = \mathbf{A}(z - ct) = \mathbf{A}(\eta^-)$, then

$$\hat{z} \cdot \mathbf{A}(\eta^-) = \hat{z} \cdot \mathbf{E}(\eta^-) = \hat{z} \cdot \mathbf{B}(\eta^-) = 0.$$

Further, if $\mathbf{E}(\eta^-) = E(\eta^-)\hat{x}$, then

$$\mathbf{B}(\eta^-) = B(\eta^-)\hat{y}$$

and
$$B(\eta^-) = \frac{1}{c} E(\eta^-). \tag{10.60}$$

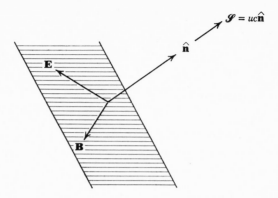

Fig. 10.4   The plane indicated is a plane of constant phase moving in the direction
$\hat{n}$.   **E, B,** and the direction of propagation of the plane form a right-handed orthogonal system of vectors.   In addition, $cB = E$ in rationalized mks units.   The
Poynting vector $\mathscr{S}$ associated with the propagation of the plane of constant phase is
parallel to $\hat{n}$; $\mathscr{S} = uc\hat{n}$ where u = electromagnetic energy density.

E, B, $\hat{z}$ form a right-handed orthogonal system.   In general, for a wave
traveling in the direction $\hat{n}$, the result is

$$c\mathbf{B}(\eta^-) = \hat{n} \times \mathbf{E}(\eta^-). \tag{10.61}$$

(In Gaussian units the factor c does not appear in eqs. 10.60 and 10.61.
In Gaussian units these transverse solutions **E** and **B** to d'Alembert's
equation are equal in magnitude.)   The situation displayed in eq. 10.61 is
illustrated in Fig. 10.4.   These results can be summarized as follows: the
planes of constant phase move with the velocity c; **E** and **B** lie in the
planes of constant phase and in the order **E, B,** $\hat{n}$ form a right-handed
orthogonal system of vectors.   In Gaussian units the magnitude of **E** and
B are equal; in rationalized mks units $cB = E$.

10.7   *The Lorentz Force Law; Electromagnetic Energy*

So far the functional dependence of **E** and **B** upon η^- (and η^+) has been
perfectly arbitrary.   None of the conclusions derived above depends on
this functional form.   In Chapter 11, some particularly simple functional
forms of **E** and **B** corresponding to *traveling* and *standing* waves will be
considered.   Here, however, we close with an investigation of how energy
is transported through space by planes of constant phase.

Consider Faraday's and Ampère's laws in differential form:

$$\text{curl } \mathbf{E} = -\frac{\partial}{\partial t}\,\mathbf{B} \tag{10.27}$$

$$\left(\frac{4\pi}{\mu_0}\right)\text{curl } \mathbf{B} = 4\pi\mathbf{j} + (4\pi\epsilon_0)\frac{\partial}{\partial t}\,\mathbf{E}. \tag{10.28}$$

For the present purposes it will be convenient to take the scalar product of both sides of eq. 10.27 with $\mathbf{B}(4\pi/\mu_0)$ and both sides of eq. 10.28 with $\mathbf{E}$:

$$\left(\frac{4\pi}{\mu_0}\right)\mathbf{B} \cdot \text{curl } \mathbf{E} = \left(\frac{4\pi}{\mu_0}\right)\mathbf{B} \cdot \frac{\partial}{\partial t}\,\mathbf{B}$$

$$\left(\frac{4\pi}{\mu_0}\right)\mathbf{E} \cdot \text{curl } \mathbf{B} = 4\pi\mathbf{j} \cdot \mathbf{E} + (4\pi\epsilon_0)\mathbf{E} \cdot \frac{\partial}{\partial t}\,\mathbf{E}.$$

Subtracting these two equations and rearranging terms, eq. 10.62 is obtained:

$$(4\pi\epsilon_0)\frac{1}{2}\frac{\partial}{\partial t}\,E^2 + \left(\frac{4\pi}{\mu_0}\right)\frac{1}{2}\frac{\partial}{\partial t}\,B^2 + 4\pi\mathbf{j} \cdot \mathbf{E}$$

$$+ \left(\frac{4\pi}{\mu_0}\right)\{\mathbf{B} \cdot \text{curl } \mathbf{E} - \mathbf{E} \cdot \text{curl } \mathbf{B}\} = 0, \tag{10.62}$$

since, for example,

$$\frac{1}{2}\frac{\partial}{\partial t}\,E^2 = \frac{1}{2}\frac{\partial}{\partial t}\,\mathbf{E} \cdot \mathbf{E} = \mathbf{E} \cdot \frac{\partial}{\partial t}\,\mathbf{E}.$$

The vector calculus identity introduced previously (see, for example, eq. 8.26)

$$\mathbf{B} \cdot \text{curl } \mathbf{E} - \mathbf{E} \cdot \text{curl } \mathbf{B} = \text{div } (\mathbf{E} \times \mathbf{B})$$

employed here yields

$$\frac{\partial}{\partial t}\left\{\frac{1}{2}(4\pi\epsilon_0)E^2 + \frac{1}{2}\left(\frac{4\pi}{\mu_0}\right)B^2\right\} + 4\pi\mathbf{j} \cdot \mathbf{E} + \left(\frac{4\pi}{\mu_0}\right)\text{div } \mathbf{E} \times \mathbf{B} = 0. \tag{10.63}$$

Each term in eq. 10.63 can be given some physical meaning if it is multiplied by an element of volume $d\tau$ and integrated over a volume whose enclosing surface is designated by Σ. The result is

$$\frac{d}{dt}\left\{(4\pi\epsilon_0)\int_\tau d\tau\,\frac{E^2}{8\pi} + \left(\frac{4\pi}{\mu_0}\right)\int_\tau d\tau\,\frac{B^2}{8\pi}\right\} + \int_\tau d\tau\mathbf{j} \cdot \mathbf{E} + \frac{1}{\mu_0}\int_\tau d\tau\,\text{div } (\mathbf{E} \times \mathbf{B}) = 0.$$

In the electrostatic and magnetostatic cases integrals of the type appearing as the first two integrals above were shown to be the energy residing in the electrostatic and magnetostatic fields, respectively. It is now *assumed* that the energy in the electromagnetic fields has the same form; that is, the energy in the electromagnetic fields is defined as

$$U \equiv (4\pi\epsilon_0) \int_\tau d\tau \frac{E^2}{8\pi} + \left(\frac{4\pi}{\mu_0}\right) \int_\tau d\tau \frac{B^2}{8\pi} \qquad (10.64)$$

and thus the time rate of change of the electromagnetic energy obeys the equation

$$\frac{d}{dt} U + \int_\tau d\tau \mathbf{j} \cdot \mathbf{E} + \int_\tau d\tau \, \text{div} \left\{\frac{1}{\mu_0} \mathbf{E} \times \mathbf{B}\right\} = 0. \qquad (10.65)$$

Before interpreting the remaining two terms in eq. 10.65, it should be noted that the last term can be converted into an integral over Σ, using the divergence theorem:

$$\frac{d}{dt} U + \int_\tau d\tau \mathbf{j} \cdot \mathbf{E} + \oiint_\Sigma ds \hat{\mathbf{n}} \cdot \left\{\frac{1}{\mu_0} \mathbf{E} \times \mathbf{B}\right\} = 0. \qquad (10.66)$$

It is impossible to give a physical interpretation to the latter two terms in eq. 10.66 using Maxwell's equations alone. It is necessary to introduce a force law which gives some connection between physically measurable quantities and the fields. This force law is due to Lorentz:

$$\mathbf{f}(\mathbf{r}, t) = q\mathbf{E}(\mathbf{r}, t) + q\mathbf{v} \times \mathbf{B}(\mathbf{r}, t). \qquad (10.67)$$

The Lorentz force law is a straightforward generalization of the force laws used in electrostatics and magnetostatics. The fields in the Lorentz force law are the time-dependent microscopic fields. The Lorentz force law allows a physical interpretation to be given to the second term in eq. 10.66. If the scalar product of both sides of the Lorentz force equations is taken with $\mathbf{v}$, it is noted that

$$\mathbf{f} \cdot \mathbf{v} = q\mathbf{v} \cdot \mathbf{E} \qquad (10.68)$$

since

$$\mathbf{v} \cdot (\mathbf{v} \times \mathbf{B}) \equiv 0.$$

The left-hand side of eq. 10.68 is the rate at which the fields $\mathbf{E}$ and $\mathbf{B}$ are doing work on the charge q or the power delivered to the charge by the fields. Note, as in the magnetostatic case, $\mathbf{B}$ itself does no work on a moving charge. For simplicity, assume that the current density in eq. 10.68 is due to one charge q located instantaneously at $\mathbf{r}'$ moving with velocity $\mathbf{v}(\mathbf{r}')$. Then

$$\mathbf{j}(\mathbf{r}) = q\mathbf{v}(\mathbf{r}') \, \delta(\mathbf{r} - \mathbf{r}')$$

and

$$\int_\tau d\tau \mathbf{j} \cdot \mathbf{E} = q \int_\tau d\tau \mathbf{v}(\mathbf{r}') \cdot \mathbf{E}(\mathbf{r}) \, \delta(\mathbf{r} - \mathbf{r}')$$

$$= q\mathbf{v} \cdot \mathbf{E} = \frac{d}{dt} W$$

where $(d/dt)W$ = rate at which work is done by the fields on the charge. This treatment also follows through when $\mathbf{j}$ is due to the motion of many charges. Consequently

$$\frac{d}{dt} U + \frac{d}{dt} W + \oiint_\Sigma ds\hat{\mathbf{n}} \cdot \mathscr{S} = 0, \tag{10.69}$$

where

$$\mathscr{S} \equiv \frac{1}{\mu_0} \mathbf{E} \times \mathbf{B}. \tag{10.70}$$

Equation 10.69 may be stated in the form of an energy conservation law which allows a physical interpretation of $\mathscr{S}$. The rate at which the field energy is *increasing* in τ $\left(\dfrac{d}{dt} U\right)$ plus the rate at which work is being done *on* the charges in τ $\left(\dfrac{d}{dt} W\right)$ plus the rate at which energy is flowing *out* of τ through Σ $\left(\oiint_\Sigma ds\hat{\mathbf{n}} \cdot \mathscr{S}\right)$ must vanish if energy is to be conserved. Therefore $\mathscr{S}$ may be interpreted as the rate of outward flow of energy per unit area oriented normal to the flow. It is an energy flux vector (energy per unit time per unit area). $\mathscr{S} = \dfrac{1}{\mu_0} \mathbf{E} \times \mathbf{B}$ is often called the Poynting vector.

The Poynting or flux vector for the transverse solutions to d'Alembert's equation can be evaluated immediately

$$\mathscr{S} = \frac{1}{\mu_0} \mathbf{E} \times \mathbf{B} = \frac{1}{\mu_0} \mathbf{E} \times \left(\frac{1}{c} \hat{\mathbf{n}} \times \mathbf{E}\right)$$

$$= \frac{1}{\mu_0 c} E^2\hat{\mathbf{n}} = \frac{c}{\mu_0} B^2\hat{\mathbf{n}}.$$

However,

$$\frac{1}{\mu_0 c} = c\epsilon_0$$

or

$$\mathscr{S} = 2c(4\pi\epsilon_0) \frac{E^2}{8\pi} \hat{\mathbf{n}} = 2c\left(\frac{4\pi}{\mu_0}\right) \frac{B^2}{8\pi} \hat{\mathbf{n}}$$

from which it follows immediately that

$$(4\pi\epsilon_0) \frac{1}{8\pi} E^2 = \left(\frac{4\pi}{\mu_0}\right) \frac{1}{8\pi} B^2. \tag{10.71}$$

The content of eq. 10.71 is that the energy density in the **E**-field is equal to the energy density in the **B**-field for transverse solutions to d'Alembert's

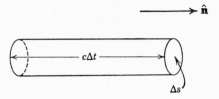

Fig. 10.5   The cylinder with base area Δs and height $c\Delta t$ is oriented with its base perpendicular to the direction of propagation of the wave.   The total electromagnetic energy which flows through the base of the cylinder per unit area per unit time is the magnitude of the Poynting vector $\mathscr{S}$.

equation.   Calling the energy density in the electromagnetic field u, it is noted that the energy flux vector is given simply by

$$\mathscr{S} = cu\hat{\mathbf{n}}. \tag{10.72}$$

This is not a surprising result.   It can be derived in another manner, which gives added credence to the physical interpretation of the Poynting vector.   Consider as in Fig. 10.5 a small cylinder constructed in space with its base area ΔS perpendicular to the direction of energy flow.   The height of the cylinder is taken to be $c\,\Delta t$ where Δt is the time interval in which the energy flow through the cylinder base is to be calculated. Δt is chosen small enough so that the energy density is essentially uniform throughout the cylinder.   The amount of energy, ΔU, which flows through ΔS in time Δt is the energy density within the sphere u multiplied by the volume of the sphere $(c\,\Delta t\,\Delta S)$.   The amount of energy flowing through ΔS per unit area per unit time is then

$$\frac{\Delta U}{\Delta t\,\Delta S} = |\mathscr{S}| = \frac{uc\,\Delta t\,\Delta S}{\Delta t\,\Delta S} = uc,$$

in agreement with eq. 10.72.

10.8   Linear and Angular Momentum in the Electromagnetic Fields

In the previous section it was shown how it is possible and why it is useful to assign energy to the electromagnetic fields.   It will now be shown how it is also possible to assign linear and angular momentum to the fields.   In Chapter 1 the observation was made that the law of force between two moving charged particles does not satisfy Newton's third law of motion.

Since the third law is essential in order that the momentum conservation theorems hold, it is obvious why it is desirable to find a way to assign momentum to the fields in such a way that the total momentum (fields plus charges) is conserved in an interaction process.

Consider an arbitrary region of volume V surrounded by a surface Σ and containing charges and currents. The total force on the matter in the region is given by the Lorentz force law, namely;

$$\mathbf{F} = \int_V d\tau \{\rho \mathbf{E} + \mathbf{j} \times \mathbf{B}\}. \tag{10.73}$$

Both ρ and $\mathbf{j}$ can be removed from the integrand in eq. 10.73 using the appropriate Maxwell equations, namely

$$\rho = \epsilon_0 \, \text{div} \, \mathbf{E}$$

and

$$\mathbf{j} = \frac{1}{\mu_0} \left(\text{curl} \, \mathbf{B} - \mu_0 \epsilon_0 \frac{\partial \mathbf{E}}{\partial t} \right)$$

that is,

$$\mathbf{F} = \int_V d\tau \left\{ \epsilon_0 \mathbf{E} \, \text{div} \, \mathbf{E} + \frac{1}{\mu_0} \left(\text{curl} \, \mathbf{B} - \mu_0 \epsilon_0 \frac{\partial \mathbf{E}}{\partial t} \right) \times \mathbf{B} \right\}.$$

The integrand can be put in an ultimately more useful form by adding and subtracting the term

$$\epsilon_0 \mathbf{E} \times \frac{\partial \mathbf{B}}{\partial t} = \epsilon_0 \mathbf{E} \times \text{curl} \, \mathbf{E} \quad \text{(via Faraday's law)}.$$

Consequently the force on the matter within V can be written in terms of the fields as

$$\mathbf{F} = \int_V d\tau \left\{ \epsilon_0 (\mathbf{E} \, \text{div} \, \mathbf{E} - \mathbf{E} \times \text{curl} \, \mathbf{E}) \right.$$
$$\left. + \frac{1}{\mu_0} (\mathbf{B} \, \text{div} \, \mathbf{B} - \mathbf{B} \times \text{curl} \, \mathbf{B}) - \epsilon_0 \frac{\partial}{\partial t} (\mathbf{E} \times \mathbf{B}) \right\} \tag{10.74}$$

where the term $\mathbf{B} \, \text{div} \, \mathbf{B} (= 0)$ has been added to the integrand to produce an expression with some degree of symmetry with respect to an interchange of $\mathbf{E}$ and $\mathbf{B}$. To facilitate the evaluation of the integral on the right-hand side of eq. 10.74, consider the x-component only. The x-component of $(\mathbf{E} \, \text{div} \, \mathbf{E} - \mathbf{E} \times \text{curl} \, \mathbf{E})$ can be evaluated by straightforward expansion in Cartesian coordinates. The result is

$$(\mathbf{E} \, \text{div} \, \mathbf{E} - \mathbf{E} \times \text{curl} \, \mathbf{E}) \cdot \hat{\mathbf{x}} = \frac{\partial}{\partial x} (E_x^2 - \tfrac{1}{2} E^2) + \frac{\partial}{\partial y} (E_x E_y) + \frac{\partial}{\partial z} (E_x E_z).$$

The same result holds for the term in **B**.   The generalization of the above to the kth component of the integrand can be written as

$$\sum_{j=1}^{3} \frac{\partial}{\partial x_j} S_{kj} - \epsilon_0 \frac{\partial}{\partial t} (\mathbf{E} \times \mathbf{B})_k$$

where[2]

$$S_{kj} \equiv \epsilon_0 [E_k E_j - \tfrac{1}{2} E^2 \, \delta_{k,j}] + \frac{1}{\mu_0} [B_k B_j - \tfrac{1}{2} B^2 \, \delta_{k,j}].$$

Consequently the kth component of **F** may be expressed as

$$F_k = \int_V d\tau \left\{ \sum_{j=1}^{3} \frac{\partial}{\partial x_j} S_{kj} - \epsilon_0 \frac{\partial}{\partial t} (\mathbf{E} \times \mathbf{B})_k \right\}$$

or
$$\left[\mathbf{F} + \int_V \epsilon_0 \frac{\partial}{\partial t} (\mathbf{E} \times \mathbf{B}) \, d\tau \right]_k = \int_V d\tau \sum_{j=1}^{3} \frac{\partial}{\partial x_j} S_{kj}. \qquad (10.75)$$

The right-hand side of eq. 10.75 can be converted into an integral over the closed surface Σ bounding V as follows: define a vector $\mathbf{G}^{(k)}$ (there is a separate vector for each Cartesian direction).   Then the right-hand side of eq. 10.75 can be rewritten as

$$\int_V d\tau \sum_{j=1}^{3} \frac{\partial}{\partial x_j} S_{kj} = \int_V d\tau \sum_{j=1}^{3} \frac{\partial}{\partial x_j} (\mathbf{G}^{(k)} \cdot \hat{\mathbf{x}}_j) = \int_V d\tau \, \text{div} \, \mathbf{G}^{(k)}.$$

The divergence theorem can then be applied to yield

$$\int_V d\tau \sum_{j=1}^{3} \frac{\partial}{\partial x_j} S_{kj} = \oiint_\Sigma \mathbf{G}^{(k)} \cdot \hat{\mathbf{n}} \, ds.$$

The vector $\mathbf{G}^{(k)}$ is quadratic in the fields, and therefore if the sources of **E** and **B** are confined to a finite volume and V is of all space,

$$\oiint_\Sigma \mathbf{G}^{(k)} \cdot \hat{\mathbf{n}} \, ds = \int_{\substack{\text{all space}}} d\tau \sum_{j=1}^{3} \frac{\partial}{\partial x_j} S_{kj} = 0.$$

Consequently, when V is allowed to envelop all space, eq. 10.75 becomes

$$\mathbf{F} + \frac{d}{dt} \int_{\substack{\text{all space}}} \epsilon_0 (\mathbf{E} \times \mathbf{B}) \, d\tau = 0. \qquad (10.76)$$

The total momentum of charges (matter) plus the fields can be defined as

$$\mathbf{p}^{(\text{total})} = \mathbf{p}^{(\text{matter})} + \mathbf{p}^{(\text{fields})}$$

with
$$\frac{d\mathbf{p}^{(\text{matter})}}{dt} = \mathbf{F}$$

and
$$\mathbf{p}^{(\text{fields})} = (4\pi\epsilon_0) \int_{\substack{\text{all space}}} \frac{(\mathbf{E} \times \mathbf{B})}{4\pi} \, d\tau. \qquad (10.77)$$

---

[2] The S_{kj} are the elements of a 3×3 matrix; this matrix is usually referred to as the electromagnetic stress-energy tensor.

Consequently with eq. 10.77 as the definition of the linear momentum in the fields, the conservation theorem for linear momentum is restored.

It is therefore natural to define the linear momentum density in the fields as

$$\mathbf{g} = (4\pi\epsilon_0)\frac{(\mathbf{E} \times \mathbf{B})}{4\pi} = \frac{1}{c^2}\mathscr{S} \tag{10.78}$$

where $\mathscr{S}$ = Poynting vector. For a plane electromagnetic wave in vacuum, eqs. 10.72 and 10.78 yield

$$\mathbf{g} = \frac{u}{c}\,\hat{\mathbf{n}}. \tag{10.79}$$

It is also natural to define the angular momentum density $\mathscr{L}$ as in mechanics, namely,

$$\mathscr{L} \equiv \mathbf{r} \times \mathbf{g} = (4\pi\epsilon_0)\frac{1}{4\pi}\mathbf{r} \times (\mathbf{E} \times \mathbf{B}) \tag{10.80}$$

where $\mathbf{r}$ is measured from the point with respect to which the angular momentum is to be measured.

10.9 Superposition Principle

The Maxwell equations are a set of linear partial differential equations in which the fields are the quantities to be determined. Since the equations are linear, a solution $(\mathbf{E}_1, \mathbf{B}_1)$ can be combined with another solution $(\mathbf{E}_2, \mathbf{B}_2)$ to form a third solution $(\mathbf{E}_3, \mathbf{B}_3)$ where

$$\mathbf{E}_3(\mathbf{r}, t) = \mathbf{E}_1(\mathbf{r}, t) + \mathbf{E}_2(\mathbf{r}, t)$$
$$\mathbf{B}_3(\mathbf{r}, t) = \mathbf{B}_1(\mathbf{r}, t) + \mathbf{B}_2(\mathbf{r}, t).$$

This is sometimes referred to as the *superposition principle*. If $(\mathbf{E}_1, \mathbf{B}_1)$ are produced by source 1 and $(\mathbf{E}_2, \mathbf{B}_2)$ by source 2, then the sources 1 plus 2 acting as a single source produce the fields $(\mathbf{E}_3, \mathbf{B}_3)$.

If two electromagnetic waves are propagating through space, the resultant electromagnetic fields at $\mathbf{r}$ at the time t are the vector sums of the fields of the two waves. The two electromagnetic waves propagate independently of one another, although the fields at a given point are the sums of the fields associated with the two waves. There are several interesting physical consequences of the superposition principle which are useful to discuss at this point (although all the physical results of electromagnetic theory discussed so far are themselves consequences since linearity has been tacitly assumed): it is not possible to scatter one electromagnetic wave from another (i.e., no momentum transfer can occur between the two waves) and it is not possible to alter the direction of propagation of an electromagnetic wave by a static field.   These consequences are well established by experiments at the macroscopic level.

However, when Maxwell theory is incorporated into a quantum mechanical treatment of the behavior of charged particles, it turns out that the two physical processes mentioned above—the scattering of light by light and the scattering of light in a Coulomb field (Delbruck scattering)—are possible processes although they have never been convincingly observed experimentally.   They are necessary consequences of quantum theory, and the failure to observe them is due solely to their very low probability of occurrence or their small cross section.   For example, in quantum theory the energy in an electromagnetic wave can be used to create an electron-position pair.   If this is done in the neighborhood of an atomic nucleus, one or both members of the pair can transfer momentum to the nuclear source of the Coulomb field.   The pair can then recombine or annihilate in the Coulomb field producing an outgoing electromagnetic wave which has different momentum from the incoming wave because of the scattering of the intermediate pair by the nucleus.   (See Fig. 10.6.) Delbruck scattering is due to the nonlinearities introduced into the theory by the quantum-mechanical processes of pair creation and annihilation.

These nonlinear effects which cause the breakdown of the superposition principle in the subatomic domain can be taken care of by adding nonlinear correction terms to Maxwell's equations.   How this might be done has

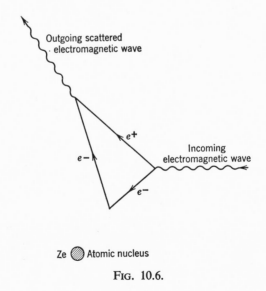

Ze ⊘ Atomic nucleus

FIG. 10.6.

been pointed out by H. Euler.[3] He showed that the nonlinear effects could be taken care of by assigning to the vacuum equivalent charge and current densities which are given by the expressions (Gaussian units are employed following Euler):

$$\rho = -\frac{1}{360\pi^2} \left(\frac{e^2}{\hbar c}\right)^2 \left(\frac{\hbar}{mc}\right)^3 (mc^2) \operatorname{div}[4(E^2 - B^2)\mathbf{E} + 14(\mathbf{E} \cdot \mathbf{B})\mathbf{B}]$$

$$\mathbf{j} = \frac{1}{360\pi^2} \left(\frac{e^2}{\hbar c}\right)^2 \left(\frac{\hbar}{mc}\right)^3 (mc^2)\left\{\frac{\partial}{\partial t}[4(E^2 - B^2)\mathbf{E} + 14(\mathbf{E} \cdot \mathbf{B})\mathbf{B}] \right.$$
$$\left. -c \operatorname{curl}[4(E^2 - B^2)\mathbf{B} - 14(\mathbf{E} \cdot \mathbf{B})\mathbf{E}]\right\}$$

where m = electron mass.

The nonlinear sources are extremely weak; the appearance of Planck's constant is a manifestation of the quantum mechanical origin of the nonlinearities.

These phenomena will not be discussed further, and the validity of the superposition principle will be assumed throughout the text.

[3] H. Euler, *Annalen der Physik*, **26** (1936).

11 | Plane Waves in Vacuum; Wave Guides and Resonators

In Chapter 10 Maxwell's equations were introduced as the generalization of the field equations valid in the realm of electrostatics and magnetostatics. These time-dependent field equations, which are coupled linear first-order partial differential equations involving the fields $\mathbf{E}$ and $\mathbf{B}$, could be recast in the form of uncoupled second-order partial differential equations which in vacuum are known as d'Alembert's equations. A particular class of solutions to d'Alembert's equation was examined in Chapter 10, namely, plane waves of constant phase. In this chapter attention will be focused on traveling and standing wave solutions to d'Alembert's equation valid in vacuum. The discussion of wave propagation in material media is reserved for Chapter 12.

11.1 Monochromatic Plane Waves

The solutions to d'Alembert's equations for $\mathbf{E}$ and $\mathbf{B}$ which have been discussed have the following property,

$$c\mathbf{B}(\eta^{\pm}) = \hat{\mathbf{n}} \times \mathbf{E}(\eta^{\pm})$$

where
$$\eta^{\pm} \equiv \hat{\mathbf{n}} \cdot \mathbf{r} \pm ct.$$

These solutions correspond to planes of constant phase propagating with the speed c. No restrictions are imposed on the functional form of these solutions by d'Alembert's equation itself. A particularly simple form of solutions of this type which has wide application is the *monochromatic plane wave*:

$$\mathbf{E}(\eta^{-}) = \mathbf{E}_0 \exp\left\{ i \frac{2\pi}{\lambda} (\hat{\mathbf{n}} \cdot \mathbf{r} - ct) \right\}. \tag{11.1}$$

Since $\mathbf{E}$ is measurable and therefore a physical field, eq. 11.1 must be interpreted in such a manner that the real part of the right-hand side is understood to represent the physical $\mathbf{E}$-field. The real part of $\mathbf{E}$ is

250

obtained as follows: $\exp(i\vartheta)$ is, in general, a complex number whose real part is $\cos\vartheta$ and whose imaginary part is $\sin\vartheta$; that is,

$$\exp(i\vartheta) \equiv \cos\vartheta + i\sin\vartheta, \quad i \equiv \sqrt{-1}.$$

The amplitude vector $\mathbf{E}_0$ may also be taken quite generally to be complex and may be written as

$$\mathbf{E}_0 = (\mathrm{Re}\ \mathbf{E}_0) + i(\mathrm{Im}\ \mathbf{E}_0).$$

A particular Cartesian component of the physical field, for example the x-component, is then

$$\mathbf{E}_{\mathrm{physical}} \cdot \hat{\mathbf{x}} = \mathrm{Re}\ E_x = (\mathrm{Re}\ E_{0x}) \cos\left[\frac{2\pi}{\lambda}(\hat{\mathbf{n}} \cdot \mathbf{r} - ct)\right]$$
$$- (\mathrm{Im}\ E_{0x}) \sin\left[\frac{2\pi}{\lambda}(\hat{\mathbf{n}} \cdot \mathbf{r} - ct)\right],$$

which may be rewritten in the form

$$\mathrm{Re}\ E_x = \sqrt{|\mathrm{Re}\ E_{0x}|^2 + |\mathrm{Im}\ E_{0x}|^2}\ \cos\left[\frac{2\pi}{\lambda}(\hat{\mathbf{n}} \cdot \mathbf{r} - ct) + \beta\right]$$

where
$$\beta \equiv \arctan\frac{\mathrm{Im}\ E_{0x}}{\mathrm{Re}\ E_{0x}}.$$

The real constant λ appearing in eq. 11.1 is called the *wavelength*. For *fixed t*, $\mathbf{E}$ takes on the same value at all pairs of points for which $\hat{\mathbf{n}} \cdot \mathbf{r}$ differs by $m\lambda$, where m is an integer. For *fixed* $\mathbf{r}$, $\mathbf{E}$ has the same value for all pairs of times which differ by mc/λ; c/λ is called the *period* of the monochromatic wave. Symbols and associated definitions which will be of some use in discussing monochromatic plane waves appear in Table 11.1.

Table 11.1.

Name	Symbol	Definition
Phase velocity	c	—
Wavelength	λ	—
Angular frequency	ω	$2\pi c/\lambda$
Period	T	λ/c
Wave vector	$\mathbf{k}$	$\frac{2\pi}{\lambda}\hat{\mathbf{n}}$
Wave number	k	$\frac{2\pi}{\lambda}$

The monochromatic plane wave solution for $\mathbf{E}$ can be written alternatively in terms of the wave vector and the angular frequency as

$$\mathbf{E}(\eta^-) = \mathbf{E}_0 \exp\{i(\mathbf{k} \cdot \mathbf{r} - \omega t)\} \qquad \text{with } kc = \omega. \qquad (11.2)$$

In addition to such attributes as frequency, wavelength, etc., a monochromatic plane wave possesses an attribute designated as its state of *polarization*. For a plane wave propagating in the z-direction, i.e., $\mathbf{k} = k\hat{\mathbf{z}}$, it is convenient to write

$$\mathbf{E}_0 = E_a\hat{\mathbf{x}} - iE_b\hat{\mathbf{y}}.$$

The physical field which is the real part of $\mathbf{E}(\eta^-)$ becomes

$$\text{Re } \mathbf{E} = E_a \cos(\mathbf{k} \cdot \mathbf{r} - \omega t)\hat{\mathbf{x}} + E_b \sin(\mathbf{k} \cdot \mathbf{r} - \omega t)\hat{\mathbf{y}} \qquad (11.3)$$

from which it is apparent that

$$\frac{(\hat{\mathbf{x}} \cdot \text{Re } \mathbf{E})^2}{E_a^2} + \frac{(\hat{\mathbf{y}} \cdot \text{Re } \mathbf{E})^2}{E_b^2} = 1 \qquad (11.4)$$

where $(\hat{\mathbf{x}} \cdot \text{Re } \mathbf{E})$ and $(\hat{\mathbf{y}} \cdot \text{Re } \mathbf{E})$ are the x- and y-components of the physical field. Consequently a plane wave is said to be *elliptically polarized* in general. From eq. 11.3 it is evident that the x- and y-components of the physical field oscillate with angular frequency ω but 90° out of phase and, in general, different amplitudes. The $\mathbf{E}$-vector can therefore be thought of as rotating with angular frequency ω in a plane of constant phase with its tip moving on the ellipse defined by eq. 11.4. There are two special cases of elliptical polarization, namely, *circular polarization* in which the x- and y-components of the physical field have the same amplitude, and *linear polarization* in which one of the components of the physical field vanishes. The characteristics of these states of polarization are listed in Table 11.2.

Table 11.2.   States of Polarization

Elliptical	$E_a \neq E_b$
Circular	$E_a = E_b$
Linear	E_a or $E_b = 0$

If the wave is circularly polarized, the tip of the $\mathbf{E}$-vector will trace out a right-handed or left-handed helix in a system in which the planes of constant phase move with velocity c; circularly polarized waves are consequently characterized as either right circularly polarized or left circularly polarized (see Fig. 11.1). For a plane wave propagating in the z-direction, there are two independent states of linear polarization; these may be represented by unit vectors parallel to the x- and y-axes.

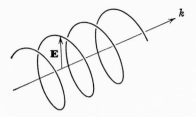

Fig. 11.1 A plane electromagnetic wave propagates in the direction indicated. The wave is "right circularly polarized"; i.e., the tip of the **E** vector traces out a right-handed helix in the laboratory system.

Two waves traveling in the z-direction polarized perpendicular to one another are independent of each other in the sense that all quantities which are quadratic or bilinear in the fields such as energy density (u), energy flux density ($\mathscr{S}$), etc., can be expressed in terms of each wave separately. This is seen as follows: suppose wave 1 is polarized in the x-direction and wave 2 in the y-direction; then

$$\mathbf{E}_{\text{total}} = E_1\hat{\mathbf{x}} + E_2\hat{\mathbf{y}}$$
$$\mathbf{B}_{\text{total}} = B_1\hat{\mathbf{y}} - B_2\hat{\mathbf{x}}$$

and consequently

$$u_{\text{total}} = (4\pi\epsilon_0)\frac{E_1^2 + E_2^2}{8\pi} + \left(\frac{4\pi}{\mu_0}\right)\frac{B_1^2 + B_2^2}{8\pi}$$

and

$$\mathscr{S}_{\text{total}} = \frac{1}{\mu_0}(E_1B_1 + E_2B_2)\hat{\mathbf{z}}$$

where E_1, B_1, E_2, B_2 are the physical fields associated with the waves and therefore are real quantities. The two kinds of circular polarization are also independent of each other in the same sense: a right circularly polarized wave traveling in the z-direction may be represented by

$$\mathbf{E}_{\text{R}}(\eta^-) = E_{0\text{R}}\left(\frac{\hat{\mathbf{x}} - i\hat{\mathbf{y}}}{\sqrt{2}}\right)\exp\{i(kz - \omega t)\} \tag{11.5a}$$

and a left circularly polarized wave by

$$\mathbf{E}_{\text{L}}(\eta^-) = E_{0\text{L}}\left(\frac{\hat{\mathbf{x}} + i\hat{\mathbf{y}}}{\sqrt{2}}\right)\exp\{i(kz - \omega t)\}. \tag{11.5b}$$

The unit polarization vectors corresponding to right and left circularly polarized waves are, respectively,

$$\hat{\boldsymbol{\epsilon}}_R \equiv \frac{\hat{\mathbf{x}} - i\hat{\mathbf{y}}}{\sqrt{2}}, \qquad |\hat{\boldsymbol{\epsilon}}_R| = 1 \qquad (11.6a)$$

$$\hat{\boldsymbol{\epsilon}}_L \equiv \frac{\hat{\mathbf{x}} + i\hat{\mathbf{y}}}{\sqrt{2}}, \qquad |\hat{\boldsymbol{\epsilon}}_L| = 1 \qquad (11.6b)$$

with the properties $\hat{\boldsymbol{\epsilon}}_R \cdot \hat{\boldsymbol{\epsilon}}_L^* = \hat{\boldsymbol{\epsilon}}_R^* \cdot \hat{\boldsymbol{\epsilon}}_L = 0$ where * stands for complex conjugation. Since the unit polarization vectors for circularly polarized waves are complex, a theorem is needed to show that no interference terms appear in u_{total} and $\mathscr{S}_{\text{total}}$ when $\mathbf{E}_{\text{total}}$ and $\mathbf{B}_{\text{total}}$ are composed of a superposition of a right and a left circularly polarized wave traveling in the same direction. The interference terms in the energy density will be of the form $(\text{Re } \mathbf{E}_R) \cdot (\text{Re } \mathbf{E}_L)$ and $(\text{Re } \mathbf{B}_R) \cdot (\text{Re } \mathbf{B}_L)$, whereas for the energy flux vector, terms such as $(\text{Re } \mathbf{E}_R) \times (\text{Re } \mathbf{B}_L)$ and $(\text{Re } \mathbf{E}_L) \times (\text{Re } \mathbf{B}_R)$ will appear. As an example of the value of these interference terms, consider

$$\begin{aligned} (\text{Re } \mathbf{E}_R) \cdot (\text{Re } \mathbf{E}_L) &= E_{0R}E_{0L}(\hat{\mathbf{x}} \cos \alpha + \hat{\mathbf{y}} \sin \alpha) \cdot (\hat{\mathbf{x}} \cos \alpha - \hat{\mathbf{y}} \sin \alpha) \\ &= E_{0R}E_{0L}(\cos^2 \alpha - \sin^2 \alpha) \end{aligned}$$

where
$$\alpha \equiv kz - \omega t.$$

Such an interference term does not vanish instantaneously at a point since $\cos^2 \alpha - \sin^2 \alpha \neq 0$, in general. However, the interference term averaged in time over one period of the wave vanishes since $\langle \cos^2 \alpha \rangle_T = \langle \sin^2 \alpha \rangle_T$ where $\langle \cdots \rangle_T$ stands for time average over one period. All other interference terms averaged in the same manner can be shown to vanish.

The vanishing of the interference terms when a time averaging is performed is a manifestation of the following theorem: if f and g are two complex functions with a time dependence given by $\exp(-i\omega t)$, then

$$\langle \text{Re} f \text{ Re} g \rangle_T \equiv \tfrac{1}{2} \text{Re}(f^*g). \qquad (11.7)$$

The theorem can be proved as follows:

$$f = f_0 \exp(-i\omega t) \quad \text{and} \quad g = g_0 \exp(-i\omega t);$$

then

$$\begin{aligned} \text{Re} f \text{ Re} g = [(\text{Re} f_0) \cos \omega t + (\text{Im} f_0) \sin \omega t] \\ \times [(\text{Re} g_0) \cos \omega t + (\text{Im} g_0) \sin \omega t] \end{aligned}$$

and

$$\langle \text{Re} f \text{ Re} g \rangle_T \equiv \tfrac{1}{2}[(\text{Re} f_0)(\text{Re} g_0) + (\text{Im} f_0)(\text{Im} g_0)]$$

since

$$\frac{1}{T} \int_{t=0}^{t=2\pi/\omega} \cos^2 \omega t \, dt = \frac{1}{T} \int_{t=0}^{t=2\pi/\omega} \sin^2 \omega t \, dt = \frac{1}{2}$$

and

$$\int_{t=0}^{t=2\pi/\omega} \sin \omega t \cos \omega t \, dt \equiv 0.$$

However, $f^*g = f_0^*g_0$, and

$$\operatorname{Re} f^*g = (\operatorname{Re} f_0)(\operatorname{Re} g_0) + (\operatorname{Im} f_0)(\operatorname{Im} g_0).$$

Consequently $\langle \operatorname{Re} f \operatorname{Re} g \rangle_T \equiv \frac{1}{2} \operatorname{Re} f^*g$ and the theorem is proved.
This means that

$$\langle u \rangle_T = \frac{1}{2} \left\{ (4\pi\epsilon_0) \frac{\operatorname{Re} \mathbf{E}^* \cdot \mathbf{E}}{8\pi} + \left(\frac{4\pi}{\mu_0}\right) \frac{\operatorname{Re} \mathbf{B}^* \cdot \mathbf{B}}{8\pi} \right\} \qquad (11.8)$$

and

$$\langle \mathscr{S} \rangle_T = \frac{1}{2} \left\{ \frac{1}{\mu_0} \operatorname{Re} (\mathbf{E}^* \times \mathbf{B}) \right\}, \qquad (11.9)$$

when complex fields are used. As a consequence the interference terms in u when a right and a left circularly polarized wave are added will contain terms such as $\hat{\boldsymbol{\epsilon}}_R^* \cdot \hat{\boldsymbol{\epsilon}}_L$ and $\hat{\boldsymbol{\epsilon}}_L^* \cdot \hat{\boldsymbol{\epsilon}}_R$ which are identically zero. (An examination of the interference terms in $\mathscr{S}$ is left as an exercise for the reader.)

11.2   Wave Packets

Since Maxwell's equations are linear partial differential equations, it is possible to obtain a traveling plane wave solution to these equations by superposing monochromatic waves of different frequency. For example,

$$\mathbf{E} = \mathbf{E}_1 \exp \{i(\mathbf{k}_1 \cdot \mathbf{r} - \omega_1 t)\} + \mathbf{E}_2 \exp \{i(\mathbf{k}_2 \cdot \mathbf{r} - \omega_2 t)\}$$

is a plane wave solution to d'Alembert's equation, but it is not monochromatic. A solution of d'Alembert's equation composed of a superposition of many monochromatic wave solutions is called a *wave packet*. A wave packet is represented in general by eq. 11.10:

$$\mathbf{E} = \sum_{j=1}^{N} \mathbf{E}_j \exp \{i(\mathbf{k}_j \cdot \mathbf{r} - \omega_j t)\} \qquad (11.10)$$

where $\omega_j/k_j = c$, independent of j.

Figure 11.2 contains several examples of wave packets constructed in this manner. Such a wave packet will travel undistorted through vacuum since the phase velocity of each frequency component is the same, namely, c. The vacuum is said to be a *nondispersive* medium for electromagnetic waves. (In Chapter 12, the dispersive nature of material media will be

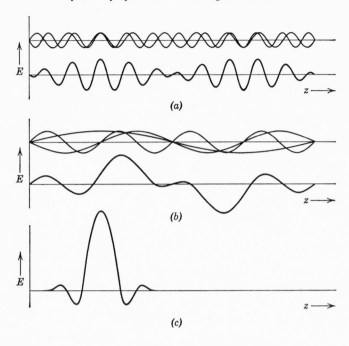

Fig. 11.2   Several wave packets traveling in the z direction are indicated at time $t = 0$. Packet (a) is composed of two waves with nearly the same frequency; packet (b) is composed of three waves of widely varying frequencies; packet (c) is composed of many waves of differing frequencies and is highly "localized" in space.

discussed and the spreading of wave packets in material media examined in terms of the dependence of phase velocity upon the wavelength.) As a consequence of the nondispersive nature of the vacuum, the behavior of wave packets is completely understood whenever the behavior of a monochromatic wave is known.

11.3   Reflection From a Conducting Surface

A plane electromagnetic wave incident upon a conducting surface will be reflected.   Consider a plane wave traveling in the z-direction incident upon a plane conducting surface (see Fig. 11.3).   Initially normal incidence will be considered, and the material of the plane surface will be assumed to have infinite conductivity.   (Finite conductivity and zero conductivity, i.e., a dielectric, are considered in Chapter 12.)   The physical situation in vacuum in steady state consists of an incident wave

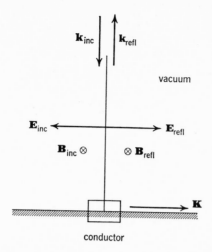

Fig. 11.3 A plane wave is incident normally upon a slab of infinite conductivity; i.e., $E \equiv 0$ in the medium. The flux of **B** through the infinitesimal loop vanishes, and therefore $E = 0$ immediately outside the conductor. The directions of **E** and **B** for both incident and reflected waves are sketched as is the direction of the required surface current **K**.

traveling in the positive z-direction and a reflected wave, i.e., a wave traveling in the negative z-direction. The physical characteristics of the reflected wave can be obtained by applying the boundary conditions on **E** and **B** at the conductor-vacuum interface. At this interface the E-field must be identically zero. This follows from the following observations: **E** immediately *inside* the conductor vanishes (the conductivity is assumed to be infinite in this example). Faraday's law applied to the rectangular loop sketched in Fig. 11.3 yields the information that the tangential component of **E** is continuous across the interface, since the flux of **B** through this infinitesimal loop vanishes. Since **E** of the incident wave is tangential to the interface (the incident wave is transverse), the **E** of the reflected wave must be equal in magnitude and opposite in direction to **E** of the incident wave. (There can be no normal component of **E** since the conducting surface is uncharged.) However, $c\mathbf{B} = \hat{n} \times \mathbf{E}$ for both incident and reflected waves, which implies that $\mathbf{B}_{incident} = \mathbf{B}_{reflected}$ since $\hat{n}_{incident} = -\hat{n}_{reflected}$ and $\mathbf{E}_{incident} = -\mathbf{E}_{reflected}$. Within the conductor there is no transverse wave, since **E** is identically zero in the conductor; this implies that $\mathbf{B} = 0$ within the conductor. **B** suffers a discontinuity across the vacuum-conductor interface. This implies that an instantaneous current must be flowing *on* the interface to account for this discontinuity in **B**. This surface current may be obtained from the continuity relationship on the tangential component of **B**, which reads

$$(\mathbf{B}_{\text{vacuum}} - \mathbf{B}_{\text{conductor}}) \cdot \hat{\mathbf{t}} = \left(\frac{\mu_0}{4\pi}\right) 4\pi (\hat{\mathbf{n}} \times \mathbf{K}) \cdot \hat{\mathbf{t}}$$

where $\hat{\mathbf{n}}$ = unit vector normal to the interface pointing toward the vacuum,
$\quad\hat{\mathbf{t}}$ = unit tangent to the interface.
This may be solved for **K**, yielding

$$\mathbf{K} = 2\left(\frac{4\pi}{\mu_0}\right)\hat{\mathbf{n}} \times \mathbf{B}_{\text{incident}}(\eta^- = -\omega t) \tag{11.11}$$

where the conducting plane is taken to be the plane $z = 0$. Naturally there is no net flow of charge over the surface; **K** oscillates with the same frequency as the electromagnetic wave.

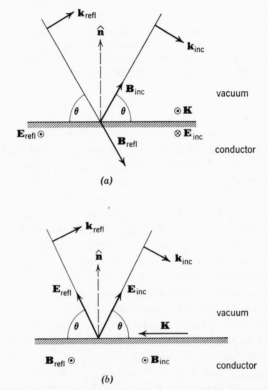

(a)

(b)

Fig. 11.4 A plane wave is incident from the vacuum upon a plane slab of infinite conductivity at an arbitrary angle of incidence. The directions of k, E, and B for both incident and reflected waves are indicated, as is the direction of the induced current density K. Two cases are considered: (a) $\mathbf{E}_{\text{inc}}$ perpendicular to the plane of incidence; (b) $\mathbf{E}_{\text{inc}}$ in the plane of incidence.

The reflection of a plane wave which is incident at some angle with respect to the normal to the conducting plane is treated in a manner similar to that for normal incidence. However, for non-normal incidence there are two distinct cases which must be considered: (*a*) **E** of the incident wave is perpendicular to the plane of incidence defined by the normal to the surface and the direction of propagation of the incident wave; (*b*) **E** of the incident wave lies in the plane of incidence. (See Fig. 11.4.) Once again, Faraday's law requires that the tangential component of the total field at the conducting surface must vanish. In case (*a*), examination of Fig. 11.4 reveals that upon reflection the wave vector of the plane wave is rotated through an angle of $\pi-2\theta$, the **E**-field is rotated through π, and the **B**-field through an angle $2\pi-2\theta$ in the same sense as the rotation of the wave vector. This implies an oscillating surface current density perpendicular to the plane of incidence. In case (*b*), examination of Fig. 11.4 reveals that upon reflection both the wave vector and the **E**-field of the incident wave are rotated through an angle of $\pi-2\theta$, whereas the **B**-field remains unaltered in direction. This implies an oscillating surface current density in the plane of incidence.   (Implicit in the above discussion is the assumption that the wave vector of the incident wave makes the same angle with respect to the surface normal as the wave vector of the reflected wave.   This must be true in order that no energy be lost (or gained) in the reflection process for which it is necessary that $|\mathbf{E}_{\text{incident}}| = |\mathbf{E}_{\text{reflected}}|$. This, coupled with the vanishing of the tangential component of **E** at the conducting surface, leads to equality of the angles of incidence and reflection.)

11.4   Guided Waves

The traveling wave solutions to d'Alembert's equation considered thus far have been plane waves, i.e., waves in which the components of **E** and **B** depend on only *one* Cartesian component of **r**.   There are, of course, other solutions to d'Alembert's equation which correspond to traveling waves, but for which this restriction is not imposed upon the dependence of **E** and **B** on **r**.   A specific example of traveling waves of this more general character is wave propagation in a given direction, say, *z*, with the three Cartesian components of the fields depending on *all* three Cartesian components of **r**.   Such a wave is called a *guided wave*.   A wave may be guided, for example, by a long conducting cylindrical sheet and propagated parallel to the axis of the cylinder.   In general, a guided wave is characterized by the boundary conditions that **E** and **B** satisfy in the plane perpendicular to the direction of propagation of the guided wave.   In particular, if the wave guide is made of material of infinite conductivity, the component of **E** tangential to the walls of the guide must vanish.

Guided waves of the kind to be considered are displayed in eqs. 11.12; more general kinds of guided waves will not be discussed here.

$$\mathbf{E} = (E_{0x}\hat{\mathbf{x}} + E_{0y}\hat{\mathbf{y}} + E_{0z}\hat{\mathbf{z}}) \exp\{i(k_g z - \omega t)\} \qquad (11.12a)$$

$$\mathbf{B} = (B_{0x}\hat{\mathbf{x}} + B_{0y}\hat{\mathbf{y}} + B_{0z}\hat{\mathbf{z}}) \exp\{i(k_g z - \omega t)\} \qquad (11.12b)$$

where ω = angular frequency of the guided wave,

k_g = wave number of the guided wave.

Note that no assumptions have been made concerning the transversality of the wave, and a longitudinal component of the wave has been introduced. In addition, the wave is being guided in the z-direction with a velocity $v = \omega/k_g$. This wave velocity is not necessarily equal to the phase velocity of a plane wave of angular frequency ω in vacuum, namely, c. In fact, one of the questions to be answered in an analysis of guided waves is what restrictions, if any, are placed upon k_g by the assumed form of the wave and the boundary conditions that it must satisfy.

Gauss's electric and magnetic laws may be used to obtain relationships involving the Cartesian components of the amplitudes of $\mathbf{E}$ and $\mathbf{B}$; specifically

$$\frac{\partial}{\partial x} E_{0x} + \frac{\partial}{\partial y} E_{0y} + ik_g E_{0z} = 0 \qquad (11.13a)$$

$$\frac{\partial}{\partial x} B_{0x} + \frac{\partial}{\partial y} B_{0y} + ik_g B_{0z} = 0, \qquad (11.13b)$$

where it has been assumed that the guide is infinite in the z-direction and that the cross section of the guide in the x-y plane is independent of z; this implies that the Cartesian components of $\mathbf{B}_0$ and $\mathbf{E}_0$ depend on x and y only. Further relationships may be obtained by invoking Faraday's and Ampère's laws, namely,

$$\left.\begin{aligned} \frac{\partial}{\partial y} E_{0z} - ik_g E_{0y} &= i\omega B_{0x} \\[2mm] ik_g E_{0x} - \frac{\partial E_{0z}}{\partial x} &= i\omega B_{0y} \\[2mm] \frac{\partial E_{0y}}{\partial x} - \frac{\partial}{\partial y} E_{0x} &= i\omega B_{0z} \end{aligned}\right\} \quad \text{Faraday's law} \qquad (11.14a)$$

$$\left.\begin{aligned} \frac{\partial}{\partial y} B_{0z} - ik_g B_{0y} &= -\frac{i\omega}{c^2} E_{0x} \\[2mm] ik_g B_{0x} - \frac{\partial}{\partial x} B_{0z} &= -\frac{i\omega}{c^2} E_{0y} \\[2mm] \frac{\partial}{\partial x} B_{0y} - \frac{\partial}{\partial y} B_{0x} &= -\frac{i\omega}{c^2} E_{0z} \end{aligned}\right\} \quad \text{Ampère's law} \qquad (11.14b)$$

These equations may be solved for the transverse components of **E** and **B**. After some algebra, the following results are obtained:

$$E_{0x} = \frac{ick}{k^2 - k_g^2} \left[\frac{\partial}{\partial y} B_{0z} + \frac{1}{c} \left(\frac{k_g}{k} \right) \frac{\partial}{\partial x} E_{0z} \right] \tag{11.15a}$$

$$E_{0y} = \frac{ick}{k^2 - k_g^2} \left[-\frac{\partial}{\partial x} B_{0z} + \frac{1}{c} \left(\frac{k_g}{k} \right) \frac{\partial}{\partial y} E_{0z} \right] \tag{11.15b}$$

$$B_{0x} = \frac{ik/c}{k^2 - k_g^2} \left[-\frac{\partial}{\partial y} E_{0z} + c \left(\frac{k_g}{k} \right) \frac{\partial}{\partial x} B_{0z} \right] \tag{11.15c}$$

$$B_{0y} = \frac{ik/c}{k^2 - k_g^2} \left[\frac{\partial}{\partial x} E_{0z} + c \left(\frac{k_g}{k} \right) \frac{\partial}{\partial y} B_{0z} \right] \tag{11.15d}$$

where $k = \omega/c$ is the wave number of a plane wave of angular frequency ω propagating through vacuum.

Examination of eqs. 11.15 yields the important result that the *transverse* components of the fields of a guided wave are independent of one another and depend only on the values of the *longitudinal* components of the guided wave. (Note that eqs. 11.15 are meaningless for a plane wave since $k_g = k$ for a plane wave. In addition, eqs. 11.15 are meaningless for those guided waves for which $k_g = k$.)

Since the transverse components of **E** *or* **B** depend on the longitudinal components of **E** *and* **B**, any guided wave may be considered as a linear superposition of two independent waves: transverse electric (TE), in which **E** · $\mathbf{k}_g$ = 0 but **B** · $\mathbf{k}_g$ ≠ 0; and transverse magnetic (TM), in which **B** · $\mathbf{k}_g$ = 0 but **E** · $\mathbf{k}_g$ ≠ 0. TE and TM waves have interesting general properties. Consider the transverse components of **E** and **B** defined as

$$\hat{z} \times \mathbf{E} = (E_{0x}\hat{y} - E_{0y}\hat{x}) \exp \{i(k_g z - \omega t)\}$$
$$\hat{z} \times \mathbf{B} = (B_{0x}\hat{y} - B_{0y}\hat{x}) \exp \{i(k_g z - \omega t)\}.$$

The scalar product formed from the transverse components of **E** and **B** is

$$(\hat{z} \times \mathbf{E}) \cdot (\hat{z} \times \mathbf{B}) = (E_{0x}B_{0x} + E_{0y}B_{0y}) \exp \{2i(k_g z - \omega t)\}. \tag{11.16}$$

For either TE or TM waves, substitution from eqs. 11.15 yields the result that

$$(\hat{z} \times \mathbf{E}) \cdot (\hat{z} \times \mathbf{B}) = 0 \quad \text{(TE and TM waves)}. \tag{11.17}$$

Therefore the transverse components of **E** and **B** for TE and TM waves are perpendicular to one another, a property they share with plane waves.

The transverse components of $\mathbf{E}$ and $\mathbf{B}$ for TE and TM waves have another general property: from eq. 11.15 it is straightforward to establish that

$$\frac{|\hat{z} \times \mathbf{E}|}{|\hat{z} \times \mathbf{B}|} = c\left(\frac{k}{k_g}\right) \quad \text{(TE waves)} \tag{11.18a}$$

$$\frac{|\hat{z} \times \mathbf{E}|}{|\hat{z} \times \mathbf{B}|} = c\left(\frac{k_g}{k}\right) \quad \text{(TM waves).} \tag{11.18b}$$

Equations 11.18 are to be compared with the analogous expression for plane waves for which

$$\frac{|\hat{z} \times \mathbf{E}|}{|\hat{z} \times \mathbf{B}|} = c \quad \text{(plane waves).}$$

To obtain more specific information about the transverse components of guided waves, an expression must be developed for the longitudinal components upon which the transverse components depend through eqs. 11.15. The most convenient expression involving the longitudinal components of $\mathbf{E}$ and $\mathbf{B}$ is d'Alembert's equation:

$$\square \, \mathbf{E} = 0 \quad \text{and} \quad \square \, \mathbf{B} = 0.$$

Substituting the form of $\mathbf{E} \cdot \hat{z}$ and $\mathbf{B} \cdot \hat{z}$ from eqs. 11.12 into d'Alembert's equation yields

$$\left(\frac{\partial^2}{\partial x^2} + \frac{\partial^2}{\partial y^2}\right)E_{0z} = (k_g^2 - k^2)E_{0z} \tag{11.19a}$$

$$\left(\frac{\partial^2}{\partial x^2} + \frac{\partial^2}{\partial y^2}\right)B_{0z} = (k_g^2 - k^2)B_{0z}. \tag{11.19b}$$

Equations 11.19 must be solved, taking cognizance of the boundary conditions that E_{0z} and B_{0z} must satisfy. It is not possible, in general, to obtain solutions to eqs. 11.19 for an arbitrary value of k_g; only certain values of k_g will yield solutions to these equations consistent with the boundary conditions. Therefore the important result is obtained that the wave number of the guided wave is determined by the geometry of the guide and may not be specified *ab initio*. Equations of the general type of which eqs. 11.19 are specific examples are called *eigenvalue* equations; thus the values of $(k_g^2 - k^2)$ which satisfy eqs. 11.19 are eigenvalues of the equation. The boundary conditions that must be invoked to obtain the TE and TM solutions to d'Alembert's equation are the following. For TM waves, $(\mathbf{E} \cdot \hat{z})$ must vanish at the walls of the guide which are assumed to possess infinite conductivity. For TE waves $(\mathbf{E} \cdot \hat{z})$ is identically zero everywhere so that the boundary condition must be expressed in terms of $(\mathbf{B} \cdot \hat{z})$. However, since the normal component of $\mathbf{E}$ must vanish at the walls of the guide (the guide is assumed to be uncharged), examination of eqs. 11.15 yields the result that at the walls of the guide

$$(\hat{\mathbf{n}} \cdot \nabla)(\mathbf{B} \cdot \hat{\mathbf{z}}) = \frac{\partial}{\partial n}(\mathbf{B} \cdot \hat{\mathbf{z}}) = 0$$

where $\hat{\mathbf{n}} \cdot \nabla \equiv \partial/\partial n$ is the derivative evaluated with respect to the direction perpendicular to the walls. To summarize the boundary conditions,

$$\mathbf{E} \cdot \hat{\mathbf{z}} = 0 \quad \text{(TM waves)} \tag{11.20a}$$

$$\frac{\partial}{\partial n}(\mathbf{B} \cdot \hat{\mathbf{z}}) = 0 \quad \text{(TE waves)}. \tag{11.20b}$$

It is now possible to determine the properties of waves propagating down a guide possessing a given cross section. Once the geometry of the guide is specified (i.e., the cross section of the guide in the z-plane), eqs. 11.15 may be solved, using the results obtained from eqs. 11.19 with the appropriate boundary conditions of eqs. 11.20.

EXAMPLE 11.1 TE Modes in a Rectangular Guide. For the first application of the analysis of guided waves, consider a guided wave traveling in an infinitely long guide whose cross section is a rectangle (see Fig. 11.5). Since the TE modes are under consideration, eqs. 11.19b and 11.20b must be first solved for B_{0z}.

$$\left(\frac{\partial^2}{\partial x^2} + \frac{\partial^2}{\partial y^2} + \gamma^2\right) B_{0z} = 0 \quad \text{where } \gamma^2 \equiv k^2 - k_g^2$$

$$\frac{\partial}{\partial x} B_{0z}\bigg)_{x=0} = \frac{\partial}{\partial x} B_{0z}\bigg)_{x=a} = 0$$

$$\frac{\partial}{\partial y} B_{0z}\bigg)_{y=0} = \frac{\partial}{\partial y} B_{0z}\bigg)_{y=b} = 0$$

The solution to the differential equation which satisfies the stated boundary conditions is

$$B_{0z}(x, y) = B_0 \cos\left(\frac{l\pi x}{a}\right) \cos\left(\frac{m\pi y}{b}\right) \tag{11.21}$$

where l, m are positive integers, including zero. (This solution can be verified by direct substitution.) The values of γ^2 which correspond to this form of B_{0z} are

$$\gamma_{lm}^2 = \pi^2\left(\frac{l^2}{a^2} + \frac{m^2}{b^2}\right) = k_{lm}^2 - k_g^2 \tag{11.22}$$

or

$$k_g = \sqrt{\left(\frac{\omega_{lm}}{c}\right)^2 - \pi^2\left(\frac{l^2}{a^2} + \frac{m^2}{b^2}\right)}.$$

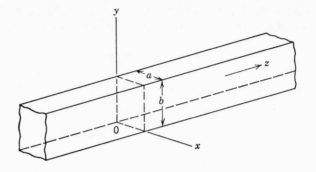

Fig. 11.5   A wave guide of rectangular cross section is sketched.   The walls of the guide are of infinite conductivity.

For a nontrivial solution to the problem, l and m cannot both be equal to zero; otherwise there will be no wave propagation.   If $a > b$, the lowest value of γ_{lm} is $\gamma_{10} = \pi/a$ with the corresponding angular frequency ω_{10}, which must satisfy

$$c\sqrt{k_g^2 + \frac{\pi^2}{a^2}} = \omega_{10}.$$

The minimum frequency which can be maintained by the guide operating in this so-called TE(10) mode is obtained when $k_g = 0$; that is,

$$(\omega_{10})_{\min} = \frac{\pi}{a} c.$$

It is impossible to propagate a wave down the guide in the TE(10) mode with a frequency less than $\pi c/a$.   At frequency above $(\omega_{01})_{\min} \equiv \pi c/b$, the guide can operate in the TE(01) mode.   It is evident that for each value of the pair l, m there is a frequency below which the guide will not operate. This is called the *cut-off* frequency for the mode and is given by

$$(\omega_{lm})_{\text{cut-off}} \equiv \pi c\sqrt{\frac{l^2}{a^2} + \frac{m^2}{b^2}}.$$

The fields in the TE(10) mode are obtained from eq. 11.21; the longitudinal component of **B** is explicitly

$$B_z = B_0 \cos\left(\frac{\pi x}{a}\right) \exp\{i(k_g z - \omega t)\}.$$

Noting that E_z is zero in any TE mode and employing eqs. 11.15, it is straightforward to verify the following results:

$$E_x = 0$$

$$E_y = \frac{ick}{k^2 - k_g^2} \frac{\pi}{a} B_0 \sin\left(\frac{\pi x}{a}\right) \exp\{i(k_g z - \omega t)\}$$

$$E_z = 0$$

$$B_x = \frac{-ik_g}{k^2 - k_g^2} \frac{\pi}{a} B_0 \sin\left(\frac{\pi x}{a}\right) \exp\{i(k_g z - \omega t)\} \qquad (11.23)$$

$$B_y = 0$$

$$B_z = B_0 \cos\left(\frac{\pi x}{a}\right) \exp\{i(k_g z - \omega t)\}.$$

Since $\pm i = \exp(\pm i\pi/2)$, the explicit factor of i appearing in the transverse components of $\mathbf{E}$ and $\mathbf{B}$ corresponds to a 90° phase difference between these transverse fields and the longitudinal component of $\mathbf{B}$. The analysis of the TM modes for a rectangular guide proceeds in a manner analogous to that employed for the TE modes; this analysis is left as an exercise.

It is straightforward to give a physical interpretation of the transverse components of $\mathbf{E}$ and $\mathbf{B}$ in the TE(10) mode. For example, ignoring the constant factors, the spatial dependence of both E_y and B_x from eqs. 11.23 contains the term

$$i \sin\left(\frac{\pi x}{a}\right) \exp\{ik_g z\}.$$

Expressing the sine function in exponential form, this spatial factor becomes

$$\exp\left\{i\left(k_g z + \frac{\pi x}{a}\right)\right\} - \exp\left\{i\left(k_g z - \frac{\pi x}{a}\right)\right\}.$$

Since $k_g < k_{10}(= \omega_{10}/c)$, it is possible to write

$$k_g = k_{10} \cos\theta$$

which merely serves to define the angle θ. Since k_g and ω_{10} are related via

$$k_g^2 = \left(\frac{\omega_{10}}{c}\right)^2 - \frac{\pi^2}{a^2}$$

it is seen that $\pi/a = k_{10} \sin\theta$. Therefore, the spatial dependence of the transverse components of $\mathbf{E}$ and $\mathbf{B}$ is

$$\exp\{ik_{10}(z\cos\theta + x\sin\theta)\} - \exp\{ik_{10}(z\cos\theta - x\sin\theta)\}.$$

This is evidently a linear superposition of two plane waves of angular frequency ω_{10} whose wave vectors make an angle $\pm\theta$ with respect to the

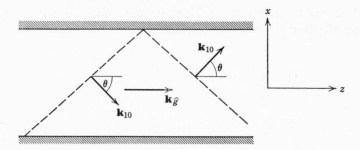

Fig. 11.6   A wave is propagating down a guide of rectangular cross section in the TE(10) mode.   The wave is a linear superposition of two plane waves whose wave vectors make angles $\pm\,\theta$ with respect to the z-axis in the x-z plane.   These component waves suffer optical reflection from the conducting planes parallel to the y-z plane.

z-axis in the x-z plane.   In other words, the wave traveling in the z-direction consists in a linear superposition of plane waves incident upon and reflected from the (y-z) conducting planes.   (See Fig. 11.6.)   At the cut-off frequency $k_{10} = k_g$, and therefore $\theta = 90°$; that is, these plane waves are incident normally upon the conducting (y-z) planes, and no propagation results.

Before proceeding to examine a guide with a different geometry, it is useful to remark that the *phase velocity* of the guided wave is defined as

$$v \equiv \frac{\omega}{k_g} = \frac{c}{\sqrt{1 - \dfrac{c^2\gamma^2}{\omega^2}}} \geqslant c. \tag{11.24}$$

Just as with a plane wave, the phase velocity for a guided wave is the velocity with which the plane defined by $\alpha = k_g z - \omega t$ moves down the axis of the guide; this is given in eq. 11.24.   The rate at which energy is propagating down the guide is given by the ratio $\mathscr{S} \cdot \hat{z}/u$, called the *group velocity* and designated by the symbol v_g; that is,

$$v_g \equiv \frac{\dfrac{1}{\mu_0} \operatorname{Re} (\mathbf{E^*} \times \mathbf{B})}{\dfrac{(4\pi\epsilon_0) \operatorname{Re} (\mathbf{E^*} \cdot \mathbf{E}) + \left(\dfrac{4\pi}{\mu_0}\right) \operatorname{Re} (\mathbf{B^*} \cdot \mathbf{B})}{8\pi}}$$

$$\tag{11.25}$$

$$v_g = \frac{2c^2 \operatorname{Re} (\mathbf{E^*} \times \mathbf{B})}{\operatorname{Re} (\mathbf{E^*} \cdot \mathbf{E}) + c^2 \operatorname{Re} (\mathbf{B^*} \cdot \mathbf{B})}$$

It is possible to show in general that $v_g \leqslant c$ and that the product of the phase and group velocities is simply[1]

$$v_g v = c^2. \tag{11.26}$$

Using eq. 11.23 for a rectangular cavity operating in the TE(10) mode and eq. 11.25, it is possible to verify that

$$v_g = c\sqrt{1 - \frac{c^2\gamma^2}{\omega^2}} \leqslant c.$$

This also is left as an exercise. Since the phase velocity is always greater than c, it is apparent that electromagnetic energy is propagated by a guide at a velocity less than c. The group velocity of the guide approaches c only at very high frequency.

EXAMPLE 11.2 TM Modes in a Circular Guide. For a cylindrical wave guide with circular cross section, it is convenient to express the differential equation satisfied by the longitudinal amplitudes of **E** and **B** in polar coordinates:

$$\left\{\frac{1}{\rho}\frac{\partial}{\partial\rho}\left(\rho\frac{\partial}{\partial\rho}\right) + \frac{1}{\rho^2}\frac{\partial^2}{\partial\phi^2} + \gamma^2\right\}\begin{pmatrix}E_{0z}(\rho, \phi)\\B_{0z}(\rho, \phi)\end{pmatrix} = 0. \tag{11.27}$$

For the TM modes, the associated boundary condition is

$$E_{0z}(a, \phi) = 0$$

where a is the radius of the circular cross section. Equation 11.27 may be solved by defining a new variable $\xi \equiv \gamma\rho$ and expressing $E_{0z}(\rho, \phi)$ as

$$E_{0z}(\rho, \phi) = J(\xi)\Phi(\phi).$$

Substituting this form of E_{0z} into eq. 11.27 yields

$$\Phi\frac{1}{\xi}\frac{d}{d\xi}\left(\xi\frac{d}{d\xi}J\right) + J\frac{1}{\xi^2}\frac{d^2}{d\phi^2}\Phi + J\Phi = 0.$$

Multiplying this equation by $\xi^2(J\Phi)^{-1}$ and rearranging terms leads to

$$\left\{\frac{1}{J}\xi\frac{d}{d\xi}\left(\xi\frac{d}{d\xi}J\right) + \xi^2\right\} = -\frac{1}{\Phi}\frac{d^2}{d\phi^2}\Phi. \tag{11.28}$$

[1] See, for example, Section 8.5 of *Classical Electrodynamics*, by J. D. Jackson, John Wiley & Sons, New York, 1962.

The left-hand side of eq. 11.28 is a function of ξ only, whereas the right-hand side is a function of ϕ only; therefore the separation constant l^2 may be introduced and defined as

$$l^2 = -\frac{1}{\Phi}\frac{d^2}{d\phi^2}\Phi, \tag{11.29a}$$

$$\frac{1}{J}\xi\frac{d}{d\xi}\left(\xi\frac{d}{d\xi}J\right) + \xi^2 = l^2. \tag{11.29b}$$

The solution of equation 11.29a is simply

$$\Phi_l(\phi) = A_l\cos(l\phi) + B_l\sin(l\phi)$$

where $l = 0, 1, 2, 3, \ldots$ since Φ must be a single-valued function of the azimuth angle. Equation 11.29b yields the radial dependence of $E_{0z}(\rho, \phi)$, namely,

$$\left[\xi^2\frac{d^2}{d\xi^2} + \xi\frac{d}{d\xi} + (\xi^2 - l^2)\right]J_l(\xi) = 0.$$

There are two linearly independent solutions to this equation for a given value of l. Only one of these solutions is regular at $\xi = 0$; this is the so called "lth order Bessel function." The number $\xi_{lm} \equiv a\gamma_{lm}$ is the mth "zero" of J_l or the mth root of the equation

$$J_l(\xi_{lm}) = 0. \tag{11.30}$$

Figure 11.7 is a plot of J_l for the first few values of l. Table 11.3 contains the zeros of some of the Bessel functions of low order. Tables

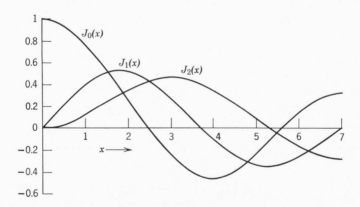

Fig. 11.7   The Bessel function $J_l(x)$ is plotted as a function of x. The values $l = 0$, 1, 2 are included.

of Bessel functions are quite numerous, since Bessel's equation appears frequently in many branches of physics.[1]

Table 11.3. *Zeros of Bessel Functions*

l	m	ξ_{lm}
	1	2.405
0	2	5.520
	3	8.654
	$\vdots$	—
	1	3.832
1	2	7.016
	3	10.173
	$\vdots$	—
	1	5.136
2	2	8.417
	3	11.620
	$\vdots$	—

(For $l > 2$, the approximate expression $\xi_{lm} \simeq m\pi + (l - \tfrac{1}{2})\pi/2$ gives three-figure accuracy for these zeros.)

The lowest TM mode is the TM(01) mode. For this mode the lowest value of γ_{lm} is $\gamma_{01} = 2.405/a$ with corresponding angular frequency ω_{01}, which satisfies

$$\omega_{01}^2 = c^2 k_g^2 + \left(\frac{2.405}{a}\right)^2 c^2.$$

The cut-off frequency for this mode is obtained when $k_g = 0$; that is,

$$(\omega_{01})_{\text{cut-off}} = \frac{2.405}{a}\, c.$$

In the TM(01) mode the explicit expressions for the fields are

$$E_\rho = \frac{-ik_g}{k^2 - k_g^2}\left(\frac{2.405}{a}\right)E_0 J_1\!\left(\frac{2.405\rho}{a}\right)\exp\{i(k_g z - \omega t)\}$$
$$E_\phi = 0$$
$$E_z = E_0 J_0\!\left(\frac{2.405\rho}{a}\right)\exp\{i(k_g z - \omega t)\}$$
$$B_\rho = 0 \tag{11.31}$$
$$B_\phi = \frac{-ik/c}{k^2 - k_g^2}\left(\frac{2.405}{a}\right)E_0 J_1\!\left(\frac{2.405\rho}{a}\right)\{i(k_g z - \omega t)\}$$
$$B_z = 0$$

[1] See, for example, Jahnke and Emde, *Tables of Functions*, Dover Press, New York.

where use has been made of the transformations of eqs. 1.21, namely,

$$E_\rho = E_x \cos \phi + E_y \sin \phi$$
$$E_\phi = -E_x \sin \phi + E_y \cos \phi$$

and the identity $(d/d\xi)J_0(\xi) = J_1(\xi)$.

An analysis of the TE modes of a guide with circular cross section is left as an exercise.

Before terminating the discussion of traveling guided waves, it is interesting to investigate the general conditions for which *transverse electromagnetic guided waves* or TEM waves may exist. TEM waves are those for which *both* E_{0z} and B_{0z} are identically zero. The first observation is that eqs. 11.15 yield nonvanishing values for the transverse components of **E** and **B** only if k_g is identical with k. Another property of TEM waves is obtained from the two Gaussian laws and the z-component of Faraday's and Ampère's laws (see eqs. 11.13 and 11.14 with $k = k_g$):

$$\frac{\partial}{\partial x}\left(\frac{E_{0x}}{B_{0x}}\right) + \frac{\partial}{\partial y}\left(\frac{E_{0y}}{B_{0y}}\right) = 0$$

$$\frac{\partial}{\partial x}\left(\frac{E_{0y}}{B_{0y}}\right) - \frac{\partial}{\partial y}\left(\frac{E_{0x}}{B_{0x}}\right) = 0. \tag{11.32}$$

These equations are consistent with the following relations:

$$\left(\frac{E_{0x}}{B_{0x}}\right) = -\frac{\partial}{\partial x}\varphi$$

$$\left(\frac{E_{0y}}{B_{0y}}\right) = -\frac{\partial}{\partial y}\varphi \tag{11.33}$$

that is, for TEM waves the transverse components of **E** and **B** (the only nonvanishing components) are *derivable from a potential*. Since **E** at the conducting walls must vanish and since **B** at the walls is related to **E** via Faraday's and Ampère's laws, a glance at eqs. 11.14 reveals that $\varphi(x, y)$ must satisfy the boundary condition

$$\varphi(x, y) = \text{constant, at the conducting walls.}$$

Since the interior of a guide is completely enclosed by a conductor, it is an equipotential region and for this case the transverse components of **E** and **B** vanish identically. Therefore for a guide whose cross section is bounded by a simple closed curve, no TEM solutions exist. However, if the cross section of the guide is bounded by more than one closed curve (for example, coaxial cables and transmission lines), TEM solutions do exist when there is a potential difference between the conducting surfaces bounding the guiding region. (See Fig. 11.8.) The field pattern set up between the conducting surfaces in the TEM case is identical with that in

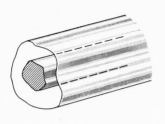 

Transmission line   Coaxial cable

Fig. 11.8 Sketched are wave guides whose cross section is bounded by more than one closed curve. The region in which the guided wave exists for a coaxial cable is the region contained between the two conducting cylinders; for a transmission line this region lies outside the two conductors.

the two-dimensional electrostatic and magnetostatic case, except that the amplitude of **E** and **B** and therefore the potential difference between the bounding conductors oscillates with frequency ω.

11.5 Standing Waves: Resonant Cavities

In the previous discussion of waves guides, it was assumed that the guide was infinite in extent in the direction in which the waves propagate. If the guide is terminated at both ends by conducting surfaces so that it becomes finite in all its dimensions, the guide will no longer support *traveling* waves in steady state, but becomes instead a cavity in which *standing* waves may be sustained. This is not at all surprising. In the simple mechanical analogue system, a string, traveling transverse waves propagate on the string in steady state only if the string is infinite in extent. If the string is finite in extent and terminated at both ends by rigid supports, standing waves will be set up on the string when the string is set in motion. These standing waves are a linear superposition of traveling waves propagating in opposite directions on the string. The string will not support standing waves composed of traveling waves of arbitrary wavelength. In fact, only waves of particular wavelengths or frequencies related to the length of the string will result in standing waves. The string is said to *resonate*, i.e., display standing waves, at these special frequencies. In the same manner a cavity will only support standing electromagnetic waves of particular frequencies; the cavity is therefore commonly called a *resonant cavity*.

A simple kind of resonant cavity is a rectangular box with a base of dimensions a and b and height L whose walls are made of material of infinite conductivity.   This will be the only cavity that will be analyzed here.   In addition to the boundary conditions invoked for traveling waves, the TM and TE boundary conditions for standing waves must be applied at the ends of the cavity; that is,

$$\text{TM:} \quad E_z = 0, \quad z = 0 \text{ and } L$$
$$\text{TE:} \quad \frac{\partial}{\partial z} B_z = 0, \quad z = 0 \text{ and } L \tag{11.34}$$

where the ends of the cavity are the planes $z = 0$ and $z = L$.   These boundary conditions can be satisfied only if $\exp(ik_g z)$ in the expression for traveling waves, eqs. 11.12, is replaced by

$$\alpha \sin(k_g z) + \beta \cos(k_g z)$$

for standing waves.   The TM modes are characterized by

$$\beta = 0, \quad k_g = \frac{s\pi}{L}, \quad s = 0, 1, 2, \ldots \tag{11.35a}$$

and the TE modes by

$$\alpha = 0, \quad k_g = \frac{s\pi}{L}, \quad s = 0, 1, 2, \ldots \tag{11.35b}$$

(obviously other characterizations of the modes in terms of α and β are possible since the sine and cosine functions are 90° out of phase.   Other methods of characterization are equivalent, however, to eqs. 11.35.) In the TE mode the differential equation for B_{0z} and the boundary conditions are satisfied by

$$B_{0z}(x, y, z) = B_0 \cos\left(\frac{l\pi x}{a}\right) \cos\left(\frac{m\pi y}{b}\right) \cos\left(\frac{s\pi z}{L}\right)$$

where l, m, and s are positive integers including zero.   The resonant frequencies may be obtained from eq. 11.22 with k_g replaced by $s\pi/L$; that is,

$$\omega_{lms}^2 = \pi^2 c^2 \left[\frac{l^2}{a^2} + \frac{m^2}{b^2} + \frac{s^2}{L^2}\right]. \tag{11.36}$$

Although it is possible to solve the field equations for any positive integral values of l, m, and s including zero, it is evident from eqs. 11.15 that l and m cannot both be zero in a TE mode since E_{0x}, E_{0y}, E_{0z}, B_{0x}, B_{0y} would all be identically zero.   A similar analysis holds for the TM modes for which the differential equation for E_{0z} and the boundary conditions are satisfied by

$$E_{0z}(x, y, z) = E_0 \cos \left(\frac{l\pi x}{a}\right) \cos \left(\frac{m\pi y}{b}\right) \sin \left(\frac{s\pi z}{L}\right).$$

Further discussion of guides and resonant cavities is deferred to Chapter 13 when the wave equations for the macroscopic fields are considered.

PROBLEMS

11.1 A monochromatic plane wave for **E** can be written in trigonometric form as $\mathbf{E}(\eta^-) = \mathbf{E} \cos \{(2\pi/\lambda)(\hat{\mathbf{n}} \cdot \mathbf{r} - ct) + \alpha\}$ where $\mathbf{E}$ = vector amplitude, and α = phase angle. Express $\mathbf{E}(\eta^-)$ in exponential form.

11.2 A plane monochromatic wave propagating through vacuum can be represented by a linear superposition of left and right circularly polarized waves. Calculate the Poynting vector for this wave and show that $\mathscr{S}$ averaged over one period of the wave is a sum of the Poynting vectors for the left and right circularly polarized components.

11.3 A wave packet is represented by a sum of plane monochromatic waves (see eq. 11.10). Show that the total energy contained in the wave packet may be represented as a sum of the energies contained in the component monochromatic waves.

11.4 A general solution of d'Alembert's equation for the vector potential in vacuum can be represented by a sum of monochromatic plane wave solutions. This can be written as

$$\mathbf{A}(\mathbf{r}, t) = \sum_\lambda q_\lambda(t) \mathbf{A}_\lambda(\mathbf{r})$$

where
$$\left[\nabla^2 + \left(\frac{\omega_\lambda}{c}\right)^2\right] \mathbf{A}_\lambda(\mathbf{r}) = 0$$

$$\left(\frac{d^2}{dt^2} + \omega_\lambda^2\right) q_\lambda(t) = 0$$

and div $\mathbf{A}_\lambda(\mathbf{r}) = 0$.

(λ is an index which labels the frequency.) Calculate **E** and **B** in terms of q_λ and $\mathbf{A}_\lambda$ and from these develop an expression for the energy and momentum in the fields in terms of q_λ. Show that the energy is formally equivalent to the energy of an ensemble of linear harmonic oscillators where q_λ is the coordinate of the λth oscillator.

11.5 In many instances it is not possible to set div $\mathbf{A} = 0$, but one must work instead in a gauge for which div $\mathbf{A} \neq 0$. **A** may be written generally as $\mathbf{A} = \mathbf{A}_1 + \mathbf{A}_2$ where div $\mathbf{A}_1 = 0$, and curl $\mathbf{A}_2 = 0$. $\mathbf{A}_2$ may be represented by a series similar to $\mathbf{A}_1(\mathbf{r}, t)$; that is,

$$\mathbf{A}_1 = \sum_\lambda q_\lambda \mathbf{A}_\lambda$$

$$\mathbf{A}_2 = \sum_\sigma q_\sigma \mathbf{A}_\sigma.$$

Show that the waves representing A_2 are orthogonal to the waves representing A_1; that is,

$$\int_{\text{all space}} d\tau(A_\sigma \cdot A_\lambda) \equiv 0.$$

11.6   Figures 11.4(a) and 11.4(b) illustrate the relative orientation of the E- and B-fields in the reflection of a plane wave incident upon a conductor at nonnormal incidence. Analytically establish these relative orientations.

11.7   Perform the necessary algebraic details to arrive at the relations between the components of the E- and B-fields for a wave guided in the z-direction; that is, establish eqs. 11.15.

11.8   Carry out the necessary steps to establish the relationships among the components TE and TM waves in a guided wave; that is, establish eqs. 11.17 and 11.18.

11.9   Prove that the correct boundary conditions at the wall of the wave guide for TE waves is $(\partial/\partial n)B_{\text{long}} = 0$.

11.10 Carry out a detailed analysis of TM modes in a guide with rectangular cross section. How does the minimum frequency of the TM modes which the guide will propagate compare with the minimum frequency for the TE modes?

11.11 Construct a physical interpretation of the transverse components of E and B for a rectangular guide operating in the lowest TM mode.

11.12 Show that the wave velocity for a rectangular guide operating in the TE(10) mode is

$$v_g = c\sqrt{1 - \frac{c^2\gamma^2}{\omega^2}}.$$

11.13 Find analytic expressions for the components of E and B for a wave guide of circular cross section operating in a TE mode.

11.14 Find the resonant frequencies of a rectangular box cavity operating in the TM mode.

11.15 Find the resonant frequencies of a resonant cavity consisting of a circular cylinder of height h operating in the TE and TM modes.

12 | *Maxwell's Equations for Material Media*

In Chapters 10 and 11 the equations satisfied by the microscopic electromagnetic fields were introduced and several applications of these field equations were discussed. As in the case of static and steady-state phenomena, it is useful to consider the effects of the interaction of electromagnetic fields with material media which necessitate the introduction of simple models of material media. Realizing that simple models will ignore the inherent complexities of the structure of matter and concentrate on the essential features of the structure, it is necessary to develop a macroscopic theory of electromagnetism which will, in a sense, average out these complexities.

In the macroscopic theory space averages of all field quantities are performed over distances large compared to characteristic atomic sizes and small compared to the size or space resolution of the devices introduced to measure the fields. In addition, averages of all field quantities are performed over time intervals long compared to characteristic atomic and molecular periods but small compared to the time resolution of the field measuring devices. The macroscopic fields that result from these averaging processes may then be considered *coarse-grained* functions of position *and* time rather than the *fine-grained* functions of these variables in a microscopic theory. Care must be exercised in the application of the ensuing macroscopic theory to physical processes; an initial analysis should always be performed to determine whether the process is accurately handled by a macroscopic, that is, approximate, theory.

12.1 Macroscopic Field Equations

Maxwell's equations of the microscopic theory form a guide for the construction of appropriate equations for a macroscopic theory. Consider the two microscopic Gaussian laws:

$$\text{div } \mathbf{E}(\mathbf{r}, t) = \frac{1}{(4\pi\epsilon_0)} 4\pi\rho(\mathbf{r}, t)$$

$$\text{div } \mathbf{B}(\mathbf{r}, t) = 0$$

(time-dependent microscopic)

and their two static macroscopic limits, i.e.,

$$\text{div } \mathbf{D}(\mathbf{r}) = \rho_{\text{real}}(\mathbf{r})$$
$$\text{div } \mathbf{B}(\mathbf{r}) = 0. \quad \text{(static macroscopic)}$$

The postulate is now made that the time dependent macroscopic Gaussian laws have the same form as the static macroscopic Gaussian laws:

$$\text{div } \mathbf{D}(\mathbf{r}, t) = \rho_{\text{real}}(\mathbf{r}, t) \qquad \text{(12.1)}$$
$$\text{(time-dependent macroscopic).}$$
$$\text{div } \mathbf{B}(\mathbf{r}, t) = 0. \qquad \text{(12.2)}$$

Equation 12.1 implies the existence of a coarse-grained space and time-dependent polarization field defined as in electrostatics as

$$\mathbf{D}(\mathbf{r}, t) \equiv \epsilon_0 \mathbf{E}(\mathbf{r}, t) + \mathbf{P}(\mathbf{r}, t).$$

Equation 12.2 implies the absence in macroscopic theory of a macroscopic magnetic equivalent to electric charge.

The remaining macroscopic field equations are introduced as follows. The microscopic Faraday law is

$$\text{curl } \mathbf{E}(\mathbf{r}, t) = -\frac{\partial}{\partial t} \mathbf{B}(\mathbf{r}, t) \quad \text{(time-dependent microscopic and macroscopic).}$$
$$\text{(12.3)}$$

The postulate is now made that eq. 12.3 holds for the macroscopic as well as the microscopic fields. Equation 12.3 certainly has the correct static limit for the macroscopic fields. It implies further that the macroscopic **E**-field is conservative except for effects due to time-varying macroscopic **B**-fields.

Finally the macroscopic form of Ampère's law must be introduced. The microscopic Amperian law is:

$$\left(\frac{4\pi}{\mu_0}\right) \text{curl } \mathbf{B}(\mathbf{r}, t) = 4\pi \mathbf{j}(\mathbf{r}, t) + (4\pi\epsilon_0) \frac{\partial}{\partial t} \mathbf{E}(\mathbf{r}, t) \quad \text{(time-dependent microscopic)}$$

and the static macroscopic Ampèrian law is

$$\text{curl } \mathbf{H}(\mathbf{r}) = \mathbf{j}_{\text{real}}(\mathbf{r}) \quad \text{(static macroscopic).}$$

The arguments leading to the static macroscopic Ampèrian law carried out in Chapter 9 through the introduction of the magnetization field **M** as a model to represent the para- and diamagnetic behaviors of material are now postulated to be valid for the time-dependent macroscopic theory. In addition, the arguments of Chapter 10 which lead to introduction of a time-varying microscopic **E**-field as the source of a microscopic magnetomotive force are postulated to be valid for the time-dependent macroscopic fields. Therefore the time-dependent macroscopic Ampèrian law is taken to be

$$\text{curl } \mathbf{H}(\mathbf{r}, t) = \mathbf{j}_{\text{real}}(\mathbf{r}, t) + \frac{\partial}{\partial t} \mathbf{D}(\mathbf{r}, t) \quad \text{(time-dependent macroscopic)}.$$

$$(12.4)$$

Equations 12.1–12.4 are Maxwell's equations for the macroscopic electromagnetic fields. (Some rationale is now apparent in the introduction of rationalized mks units. In this system of units no factors of 4π or physical constants appear in the equations. This is certainly an advantage over Gaussian units, where factors of 4π and c appear liberally in the equations. Whether this advantage outweighs the cumbersome nature of the static and microscopic time-dependent field equations expressed in rationalized mks units is a matter of personal taste.)

The macroscopic field equations are not sufficient in themselves for a physical theory because they do not allow for "measurement" processes. As in the microscopic theory, these measurement possibilities are supplied by the Lorentz force equation which is postulated to have the identical form in both theories, namely,

$$\mathbf{f}(\mathbf{r}, t) = q\mathbf{E}(\mathbf{r}, t) + q\mathbf{v} \times \mathbf{B}(\mathbf{r}, t) \quad \text{(time-dependent microscopic}$$
$$\text{and macroscopic)}. \quad (12.5)$$

For convenience of future reference, Table 12.1 contains the differential form of the macroscopic Maxwell–Lorentz equations.

Table 12.1

$\text{div } \mathbf{D} = \rho_{\text{real}}$	Gauss's electric law
$\text{div } \mathbf{B} = 0$	Gauss's magnetic law
$\text{curl } \mathbf{E} = -\dfrac{\partial}{\partial t} \mathbf{B}$	Faraday's law
$\text{curl } \mathbf{H} = \mathbf{j}_{\text{real}} + \dfrac{\partial}{\partial t} \mathbf{D}$	Ampère's law
$\mathbf{f} = q\mathbf{E} + q\mathbf{v} \times \mathbf{B}$	Lorentz law

One more observation is necessary before the macroscopic Maxwell–Lorentz theory is applied to physical problems. It is convenient to consider that the real current density, $\mathbf{j}_{\text{real}}$, appearing in the Ampèrian law is due to real charge moving under the influence of a macroscopic $\mathbf{E}$-field; it is postulated that normal conducting media behave linearly and isotropically; that is,

$$\mathbf{j}_{\text{real}}(\mathbf{r}, t) \equiv \sigma \mathbf{E}(\mathbf{r}, t) \quad \text{where } \sigma \equiv \text{conductivity of the medium}. \quad (12.6)$$

If the medium is linear but nonisotropic, a conductivity matrix must be introduced and defined as

$$j_l(\mathbf{r}, t) = \sum_{n=1}^{3} \sigma_{ln} E_n(\mathbf{r}, t), \quad l = 1, 2, 3.$$

However, any applications in the following discussion will assume that eq. 12.6 holds.

12.2   Wave Equation for a Nonconducting Medium

Here it will be assumed that any material present in space is non-conducting, uncharged, linear, and isotropic.   Under these circumstances the Maxwell equations read

$$\text{div} \, (\epsilon \mathbf{E}) = 0 \qquad \text{curl} \, \mathbf{E} = - \frac{\partial}{\partial t} \mathbf{B}$$

$$\text{div} \, \mathbf{B} = 0 \qquad \text{curl} \left(\frac{1}{\mu} \mathbf{B} \right) = \frac{\partial}{\partial t} (\epsilon \mathbf{E}).$$

A wave equation for $\mathbf{E}$ is obtained by taking the curl of Ampère's law:

$$\text{curl curl} \, \mathbf{E} = - \text{curl} \left(\frac{\partial}{\partial t} \mathbf{B} \right).$$

For an isotropic medium:[1]

$$\text{curl} \left(\frac{1}{\mu} \mathbf{B} \right) = \frac{1}{\mu} \text{curl} \, \mathbf{B}$$

and Ampère's law may be used to write

$$\text{curl curl} \, \mathbf{E} = - \frac{\partial}{\partial t} \mu \frac{\partial}{\partial t} (\epsilon \mathbf{E}).$$

However, μ and ϵ are physical constants characteristic of the material and thus independent of the time.   Therefore

$$\left(\nabla^2 - \mu \epsilon \frac{\partial^2}{\partial t^2} \right) \mathbf{E}(\mathbf{r}, t) = 0 \tag{12.7}$$

where explicit use has been made of the identity: curl curl $\equiv$ grad div $- \nabla^2$ and Gauss's electric law, namely, div $\mathbf{E} \equiv 0$.   A similar equation involving $\mathbf{B}$ may be developed with the same set of assumptions concerning the nature of the material.

[1] $\text{curl} \left(\dfrac{1}{\mu} \mathbf{B} \right) \equiv \left(\text{grad} \dfrac{1}{\mu} \right) \times \mathbf{B} + \dfrac{1}{\mu} \text{curl} \, \mathbf{B}.$ For an isotropic medium grad $\left(\dfrac{1}{\mu} \right) \equiv 0.$

Equation 12.7 is d'Alembert's equation for the macroscopic E-field. The constant $\mu\epsilon$ has the dimensions of the square of a reciprocal velocity and is written as

$$\mu\epsilon = \frac{1}{v^2} \tag{12.8}$$

where v is the phase velocity of plane waves of constant phase propagating through the medium. It is straightforward to show by repeating the arguments of Chapter 10 that plane wave solutions to d'Alembert's equations exist and that for these solutions $v\mathbf{B} = \hat{\mathbf{n}} \times \mathbf{E}$. In general, μ and ϵ are functions of frequency (a simple model of a gaseous medium introduced later in the chapter will illustrate this comment explicitly), and therefore the phase velocity of a monochromatic wave in the medium depends upon the wavelength of the wave. Material media therefore act in a dispersive manner, that is, a wave packet composed of plane waves of various frequencies:

$$\mathbf{E}(\mathbf{r}, t) = \sum_{l=1}^{N} \mathbf{E}_l \exp\{i(\mathbf{k}_l \cdot \mathbf{r} - \omega_l t)\}$$

will alter its shape as it propagates through material media since the phase velocity for each component wave, $v_l \equiv \omega_l/k_l$, depends upon l. The exact nature of the alteration of the shape of the packet depends on how ω depends upon k; this must be gleaned from a model of the material medium.

12.3   A Model of a Nonconducting Gas

A very simple model can be constructed for a nonconducting isotropic gas. That the model has some validity is borne out by its success in describing the behavior of the propagation of electromagnetic waves through gases. Consider the Lorentz force law for a particle of charge q acted upon by a plane electromagnetic wave of frequency ω:

$$\mathbf{f} = q\mathbf{E}_0 \exp\{i\omega t\} + q\mathbf{v} \times \mathbf{B}_0 \exp\{i\omega t\}$$

where $\mathbf{E}_0$ and $\mathbf{B}_0$ are the space-dependent amplitudes of the fields. However, in a plane wave, $|\mathbf{B}_0| = (1/c)|\mathbf{E}_0|$. Therefore, unless the charged particle attains a velocity approaching that of the speed of light, the second or magnetic term can be neglected. To approximate a real gas, the charged particle is assumed to be an electron of a typical gas atom. (The acceleration effects on the atomic nuclei are negligible since $m_{\text{atom}} \geqslant 2000 m_{\text{electron}}$.) The electron may be considered to be elastically bound to its nucleus with an elastic constant k_0, where $\sqrt{k_0/m_e} = \omega_0$ the characteristic angular frequency of the electron. The energy that is transferred by the electron to its surroundings is represented by a viscous damping force proportional to the velocity of the electron. Naturally this is a very crude model, but it turns out to represent most of the salient features of the interaction of an atom with an electromagnetic wave. In this model the equation of motion of the electron is

$$\frac{d^2x}{dt^2} = -\frac{k_0}{m_e} x - \kappa \frac{dx}{dt} + \frac{q}{m_e} E_0 \exp\{i\omega t\} \qquad (12.9)$$

where the electromagnetic wave is considered to be polarized in the x-direction. A quasi-steady-state solution to eq. 12.9 is assumed of the form

$$x(t) = x_0 \exp\{i\omega t\}.$$

Substituting this form of the solution into eq. 12.9 yields the algebraic equation

$$-\omega^2 x_0 = -\frac{k_0}{m_e} x_0 - i\omega\kappa x_0 + \frac{q}{m_e} E_0$$

which when solved for x_0 yields

$$x_0 = \frac{\left(\dfrac{q}{m_e}\right) E_0[(\omega_0^2 - \omega^2) - i\omega\kappa]}{[(\omega_0^2 - \omega^2)^2 + \omega^2\kappa^2]} \quad \text{where } \omega_0^2 \equiv k_0/m_e. \quad (12.10)$$

The action of the electromagnetic wave upon the electron induces an electric dipole moment in the atom of amplitude qx_0. If there are n atoms per unit volume, this corresponds to an oscillating polarization field **P** and a consequent oscillating **D**-field of amplitude

$$D_0 = \epsilon_0 E_0 + mqx_0. \qquad (12.11)$$

Substituting the value of x_0 from 12.10 and noting that the gas behaves in a linear fashion to the applied field, i.e., $D_0 = \epsilon E_0$ yields a complex electric permittivity given by the expression

$$\epsilon = \epsilon_0 \left\{ 1 + \left(\frac{1}{4\pi\epsilon_0}\right) \frac{4\pi n \dfrac{q^2}{m_e} [(\omega_0^2 - \omega^2) - i\omega\kappa]}{[(\omega_0^2 - \omega^2)^2 + \omega^2\kappa^2]} \right\}. \qquad (12.12)$$

The zero-frequency limit of eq. 12.12 is the static permittivity

$$\epsilon_{\text{static}} = \epsilon_0 \left\{ 1 + \left(\frac{1}{4\pi\epsilon_0}\right) \frac{4\pi nq^2}{m_e\omega_0^2} \right\}. \qquad (12.13)$$

The *index of refraction* of the gas for an electromagnetic wave of angular frequency ω is defined as

$$\nu(\omega) \equiv \frac{c}{v(\omega)} = \sqrt{\frac{\epsilon\mu}{\epsilon_0\mu_0}}. \tag{12.14}$$

To a very high degree of accuracy for normal gases $\mu = \mu_0$ and consequently

$$\nu(\omega) = \sqrt{1 + \left(\frac{1}{4\pi\epsilon_0}\right)\frac{4\pi n \dfrac{q^2}{m_e}[(\omega_0^2 - \omega^2) - i\omega\kappa]}{[(\omega_0^2 - \omega^2)^2 + \omega^2\kappa^2]}}. \tag{12.15}$$

The index of refraction of gases under normal conditions is approximately unity, so that the expression $\sqrt{1 + y} \approx 1 + 1/2y$ (for $y < 1$) may be employed to obtain

$$\nu(\omega) = 1 + \left(\frac{1}{4\pi\epsilon_0}\right)\frac{2\pi n \dfrac{q^2}{m_e}[\omega_0^2 - \omega^2]}{[(\omega_0^2 - \omega^2)^2 + \omega^2\kappa^2]}$$

$$- i\left(\frac{1}{4\pi\epsilon_0}\right)\frac{2\pi n\left(\dfrac{q^2}{m_e}\right)\omega\kappa}{[(\omega_0^2 - \omega^2)^2 + \omega^2\kappa^2]}. \tag{12.16}$$

The index of refraction is a complex function of the frequency of the electromagnetic wave propagating through the gas. The real part of $\nu(\omega)$ is the source of the dispersion of an electromagnetic wave packet as it propagates through the gas. The real part of $\nu(\omega)$ is plotted in Fig. 12.1 as a function ω. At very low frequencies, Re $\nu(\omega)$ is slightly greater than unity; Re $\nu(\omega)$ increases with increasing ω, reaching a maximum value at approximately $\omega \approx \omega_0 - \kappa/2$ falling rapidly to one at $\omega = \omega_0$. Re $\nu(\omega)$ continues to decrease rapidly until $\omega_0 + \kappa/2$, whereupon it increases again and approaches unity asymptotically for large value of ω. The imaginary part of $\nu(\omega)$ also plotted in Fig. 12.1 corresponds to absorption of the electromagnetic wave propagating through the gas. The amplitude of an electromagnetic wave decreases exponentially as it penetrates into the gas. The imaginary part of $\nu(\omega)$ has a typical *resonance* shape. Im $\nu(\omega)$ is a maximum at $\omega = \omega_0$, where Re $\nu(\omega)$ is unity, and has a width at half maximum approximately equal to κ. Therefore in the region where Re $\nu(\omega)$ changes rapidly, the gas is relatively highly absorbing.

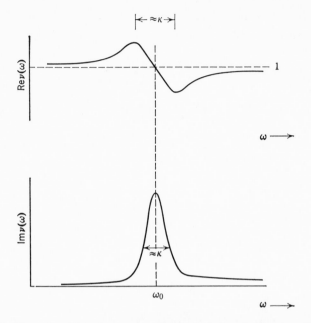

Fig. 12.1   The real and imaginary parts of $\nu(\omega)$, the index of refraction of the model gas, are plotted as a function of ω.   Re $\nu(\omega)$ varies rapidly in the neighborhood of ω_0; Im $\nu(\omega)$ is a maximum at $\omega = \omega_0$ and has a width at half maximum equal approximately to κ.   The frequency region of rapid variation in Re $\nu(\omega)$ corresponds to the region of high absorptivity of the gas.

For any real gas there exist many resonant frequencies ω_0 and corresponding damping coefficients κ.   Assuming that only electron interactions with an electromagnetic wave contribute to ϵ, eq. 12.12 may be generalized to

$$\epsilon = \epsilon_0 \left\{ 1 + \left(\frac{1}{4\pi\epsilon_0} \right) \frac{q^2}{m_e} \sum_{j=1}^{N} \frac{n_j[(\omega_{0j}^2 - \omega^2) - i\omega\kappa_j]}{[(\omega_{0j}^2 - \omega^2)^2 + \omega^2\kappa_j^2]} \right\} \tag{12.17}$$

where $\omega_{0j} = j^{\text{th}}$ resonant angular frequency

$\kappa_j \equiv j^{\text{th}}$ absorption coefficient

$n_j \equiv$ number of electrons per unit volume which contribute to the jth absorption mode.

The behavior of the real and imaginary parts of the index of refraction for this more realistic model of a gas is illustrated in Fig. 12.2.   (The electrons in an atom or molecule should be described quantum mechanically.   A quantum mechanical treatment of this problem yields a result

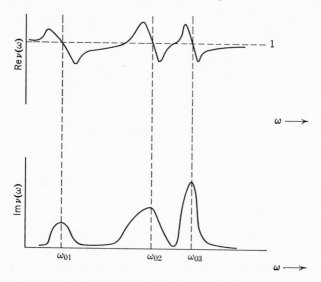

Fig. 12.2   The real and imaginary parts of $\nu(\omega)$ are plotted as a function of ω for a gas in which the electrons have more than one resonance frequency.   The Re $\nu(\omega)$ varies rapidly in the neighborhood of each resonance frequency ω_{0j}, and the gas is highly absorptive in the neighborhood of each resonance frequency.   The width at half maximum for the jth absorption peak in Im $\nu(\omega)$ is κ_j.

similar to eq. 12.17.   The ω_{0j} are the frequency differences between the various electronic states, and the κ_j are the absorption widths for the jth atomic transition.)

12.4   Kramers' Dispersion Theory

H. A. Kramers was one of the first to conjecture that the real and imaginary parts of the complex index of refraction were related to one another. The theory of Kramers has recently been extended into the realm of quantum field theory where it has had widespread application in the construction of theories which govern the quantum behavior of elementary particles.   The simple form of Kramers' theory for classical electromagnetism can be formulated in terms of the "polarizability" of a medium for which a simple model of optical dispersion was introduced in the preceding section.   The polarizability α is defined by the equation

$$\mathbf{P} = \alpha\mathbf{E}. \tag{12.18}$$

Writing α as $\alpha' + i\alpha''$, the real and imaginary parts of α induced by an

E-field with angular frequency ω may be readily obtained from eqs. 12.11 and 12.17:

$$\alpha'(\omega) = \frac{1}{4\pi} \frac{nq^2}{m_e} \sum_j f_j \frac{(\omega_{0j}^2 - \omega^2)}{[(\omega_{0j}^2 - \omega^2)^2 + \kappa_j^2 \omega^2]} \tag{12.19}$$

$$\alpha''(\omega) = -\frac{1}{4\pi} \frac{nq^2}{m_e} \sum_j f_j \frac{\kappa_j \omega_j}{[(\omega_{0j}^2 - \omega^2)^2 + \kappa_j^2 \omega^2]} \tag{12.20}$$

where $n \equiv$ total number of electrons per unit volume

and $f_j \equiv n_j/n$ is the relative number of electrons which participate in the jth resonance.

The symbol f_j is sometimes called the *oscillator strength*; the name is a relic of an era in physics when it was conjectured that every atom could be represented by a series of oscillators—the relative strength of each oscillator for absorption was designated as the oscillator strength.   The average rate at which the medium absorbs energy per unit volume at the angular frequency ω is given by the equivalent expressions:

$$\langle w \rangle = -\tfrac{1}{2} \text{Re} \, (\mathbf{E}^* \cdot \mathbf{j}) = -\tfrac{1}{2} \, \text{Re} \left(\mathbf{E}^* \cdot \frac{d\mathbf{P}}{dt} \right). \tag{12.21}$$

Writing $\mathbf{E}(\mathbf{r}, t)$ and $\mathbf{P}(\mathbf{r}, t)$ as

$$\mathbf{E}(\mathbf{r}, t) = \mathbf{E}_0 \exp \{i(\mathbf{k} \cdot \mathbf{r} - \omega t)\}$$

$$\mathbf{P}(\mathbf{r}, t) = (\alpha' + i\alpha'')\mathbf{E}(\mathbf{r}, t)$$

yields for $\langle w \rangle$

$$\langle w \rangle = -\tfrac{1}{2} \omega \alpha'' |\mathbf{E}_0|^2. \tag{12.22}$$

The rate at which the medium absorbs energy is proportional to the intensity I of the incident wave.   (The intensity is defined as the energy passing normal across a surface per second divided by the area of the surface.) If u is the energy density in the electric part of the incident wave, then

$$I = uc = (4\pi\epsilon_0) \frac{E^2}{8\pi} c,$$

which, when substituted into eq. 12.22, yields

$$\langle w \rangle = -\left(\frac{1}{4\pi\epsilon_0} \right) \frac{4\pi\omega\alpha''}{c} I. \tag{12.23}$$

Equation 12.23 may be recast in terms of the *atomic absorption cross section* $\sigma(\omega)$, defined by

$$\sigma(\omega) \equiv \frac{\langle w \rangle}{nI}$$

or

$$\sigma(\omega) = \left(\frac{1}{4\pi\epsilon_0}\right)\left(\frac{\omega^2}{c}\right)\left(\frac{q^2}{m_e}\right) \sum_j f_j \frac{\kappa_j}{[(\omega_{0j}^2 - \omega^2)^2 + \kappa_j^2\omega^2]} \qquad (12.24)$$

$$= \sum_j \sigma_j(\omega)$$

where $\sigma_j(\omega)$ is the contribution to the atomic absorption cross section of the jth resonance.

It is now possible to obtain an approximate expression for the oscillator strength f_j, which appears in the definition of both α' and α'', and consequently to obtain a relationship between α' and α''. This proceeds as follows. The *absorption intensity* S_j of the jth resonance is defined as

$$S_j \equiv \int_0^\infty \sigma_j(\omega)\, d\omega = \left(\frac{1}{4\pi\epsilon_0}\right)\left(\frac{q^2}{m_e c}\right) f_j \kappa_j \int_0^\infty \frac{\omega^2\, d\omega}{[(\omega_{0j}^2 - \omega^2)^2 + \kappa_j^2\omega^2]}. \qquad (12.25)$$

The integral on the right-hand side of eq. 12.25 can be evaluated in a simple manner if it is assumed that κ_j is small, i.e., the resonance is narrow. Under this assumption the following replacements can be made in the integrand:

$$\omega^2 \to \omega_{0j}^2$$

$$(\omega_{0j}^2 - \omega^2)^2 = [(\omega_{0j} + \omega)(\omega_{0j} - \omega)]^2 \to 4\omega_{0j}^2(\omega_{0j} - \omega)^2,$$

yielding

$$S_j \simeq \left(\frac{1}{4\pi\epsilon_0}\right)\left(\frac{q^2}{m_e c}\right)\left(\frac{f_j}{\kappa_j}\right) \int_0^\infty \frac{d\omega}{1 + 4\frac{(\omega_{0j} - \omega)^2}{\kappa_j^2}}. \qquad (12.26)$$

Although the lower limit on ω is zero, the range of integration in eq. 12.26 can be formally extended to $-\infty$ without introducing appreciable error since the jth resonance lies in the region of positive ω and is narrow. Consequently to a good approximation

$$S_j \simeq \left(\frac{1}{4\pi\epsilon_0}\right)\left(\frac{q^2}{2m_e c}\right) f_j \int_{-\infty}^\infty \frac{dx}{1 + x^2} = \left(\frac{1}{4\pi\epsilon_0}\right)\frac{\pi q^2}{2m_e c} f_j, \qquad (12.27)$$

or solving for the oscillator strength,

$$f_j = (4\pi\epsilon_0) \frac{2m_e c}{\pi q^2} S_j.$$

This value of the oscillator strength is substituted into eq. 12.19 to yield for α' the expression

$$\alpha'(\omega) = (4\pi\epsilon_0) \frac{nc}{2\pi^2} \sum_j S_j \frac{(\omega_{0j}^2 - \omega^2)}{[(\omega_{0j}^2 - \omega^2)^2 + \kappa_j^2 \omega^2]}. \qquad (12.28)$$

Equation 12.28 is a *dispersion relation* in that it relates the real part of the polarizability to the imaginary part through the absorption strength S_j. This relation can be transformed into one which is more useful if the assumption is made that the resonances are *nonoverlapping*, i.e., the separation of the resonances is large compared with their widths. Under this assumption $S_j = \sigma_j(\omega_{0j}) \Delta_j$. (This replacement is schematically indicated in Fig. 12.3.) With this substitution and neglecting the term in κ_j in the denominator, eq. 12.28 becomes

$$\alpha'(\omega) = (4\pi\epsilon_0) \frac{nc}{2\pi^2} \sum_j \frac{\sigma_j(\omega_{0j}) \Delta_j}{(\omega_{0j}^2 - \omega^2)}. \qquad (12.29)$$

It is reasonable to assume further that for any real material there are very many resonances j and that the separation of the resonances is small compared to the resolution of the devices used to measure the polarizability. (Once again, this is a coarse-grained determination of an inherently macroscopic entity α.) With these assumptions the sum of eq. 12.29 can be converted into an integral; that is,

$$\alpha'(\omega) = (4\pi\epsilon_0) \frac{nc}{2\pi^2} \int_0^\infty \frac{\sigma(\omega') \, d\omega'}{(\omega'^2 - \omega^2)} \qquad (12.30)$$

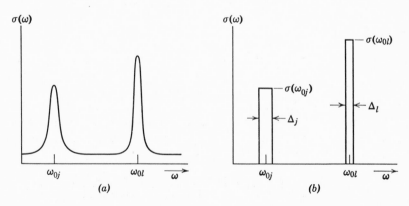

Fig. 12.3   The absorption cross section $\sigma(\omega)$ in the neighborhood of two narrow nonoverlapping levels is illustrated in (*a*). If the cross section is measured by a device whose resolution is poor so that the isolated resonances cannot be detected, $\int \sigma(\omega) \, d\omega$ can be replaced by the area under the rectangles in (*b*).

where $\sigma(\omega')$ is a "poor resolution" determination of the absorption cross section. $\sigma(\omega')$ may be expressed in terms of $\alpha''(\omega')$ via eqs. 12.23 and 12.24 to yield for $\alpha'(\omega)$ the expression

$$\alpha'(\omega) = -\frac{2}{\pi} \int_0^\infty \frac{\omega' \alpha''(\omega') \, d\omega'}{(\omega'^2 - \omega^2)}. \tag{12.31}$$

Equation 12.31 can be further simplified if the definitions of α' and α'' are extended to negative frequencies; the conventional definitions are

$$\alpha'(-\omega) = \alpha'(\omega) \qquad \text{and} \qquad \alpha''(-\omega) = -\alpha''(\omega).$$

With the latter definition the integral in eq. 12.31 can be transformed by the following steps:

$$\int_0^\infty \frac{\omega' \alpha''(\omega') \, d\omega'}{(\omega'^2 - \omega^2)} = \frac{1}{2} \left[\int_0^\infty \frac{\alpha''(\omega') \, d\omega'}{\omega' - \omega} + \int_0^\infty \frac{\alpha''(\omega') \, d\omega'}{\omega' + \omega} \right]$$

$$= \frac{1}{2} \int_{-\infty}^\infty \frac{\alpha''(\omega') \, d\omega'}{\omega' - \omega}.$$

This yields the Kramers result, namely,

$$\alpha'(\omega) = -\frac{1}{\pi} \int_{-\infty}^\infty \frac{\alpha''(\omega') \, d\omega'}{\omega' - \omega}. \tag{12.32}$$

This equation which relates the real and imaginary parts of the complex polarizability is so simple that it is tempting to conjecture that it has validity far beyond what the simple model employed to obtain it would suggest. In fact, it has been shown that such an equation is a fundamental

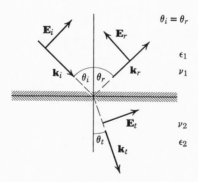

Fig. 12.4 A plane of angular frequency ω is incident upon a plane interface separating a medium of permittivity ϵ_1 from a second medium of permittivity ϵ_2. The wave vectors of the incident reflected and transmitted waves are $\mathbf{k}_i$, $\mathbf{k}_r$, $\mathbf{k}_t$ and these make angles θ_i, θ_r, and θ_t with respect to the normal to the interface. $\mathbf{E}$ of the incident wave lies in the plane of incidence. (If region 2 is a region of high conductivity, $\theta_t \to 0$. See Section 12.7.)

relation which must be satisfied by any dispersive system.   A discussion of the model independence of the Kramers relation is beyond the scope and intent of this text, however.

12.5   Optical Reflection From a Dielectric Interface

As an application of d'Alembert's macroscopic field equations for a dielectric medium, the laws of optical reflection from an interface separating two dielectrics will be examined.   The physical situation is illustrated in Fig. 12.4.   A plane wave of angular frequency ω is incident upon a plane interface separating a medium of permittivity ϵ_1 from a second medium of permittivity ϵ_2.   In the steady state both an *incident* and a *reflected* wave will be present in medium 1, whereas a *transmitted* wave will exist in medium 2.   The wave vectors of the incident, reflected, and transmitted waves are, respectively, $\mathbf{k}_i$, $\mathbf{k}_r$, and $\mathbf{k}_t$, and these wave vectors make angles of θ_i, θ_r, and θ_t with respect to the normal to the interface.

Assuming the wave to be linearly polarized, there are two cases to consider: (1) $\mathbf{E}$ of the incident wave ($\mathbf{E}_i$) in the plane of incidence; (2) $\mathbf{E}_i$ perpendicular to the plane of incidence.   Only case (1) will be considered here.   Both media are linear, isotropic, and nonabsorptive, and the interface between the media is uncharged.   The boundary conditions on the macroscopic fields yield the various laws of optical reflection.   The E-fields of the three waves present are represented analytically by

$$\mathbf{E}_i = E_{i_0}(\sin \theta_i \hat{\mathbf{z}} + \cos \theta_i \hat{\mathbf{x}}) \exp \{i(\mathbf{k}_i \cdot \mathbf{r} - \omega t)\}$$

$$\mathbf{E}_r = E_{r_0}(\sin \theta_r \hat{\mathbf{z}} - \cos \theta_r \hat{\mathbf{x}}) \exp \{i(\mathbf{k}_r \cdot \mathbf{r} - \omega t)\} \qquad (12.33)$$

$$\mathbf{E}_t = E_{t_0}(\sin \theta_t \hat{\mathbf{z}} + \cos \theta_t \hat{\mathbf{x}}) \exp \{i(\mathbf{k}_t \cdot \mathbf{r} - \omega t)\}$$

with

$$\mathbf{k}_i \equiv \frac{\omega}{v_1} (-\cos \theta_i \hat{\mathbf{z}} + \sin \theta_i \hat{\mathbf{x}})$$

$$\mathbf{k}_r \equiv \frac{\omega}{v_1} (\cos \theta_r \hat{\mathbf{z}} + \sin \theta_r \hat{\mathbf{x}}) \qquad (12.34)$$

$$\mathbf{k}_t \equiv \frac{\omega}{v_2} (\cos \theta_t \hat{\mathbf{z}} + \sin \theta_t \hat{\mathbf{x}})$$

and

$$v_1^{-1} = \sqrt{\epsilon_1 \mu_1}, \qquad v_2^{-1} = \sqrt{\epsilon_2 \mu_2}. \qquad (12.35)$$

The relationship between θ_r and θ_i (the law of reflection) and between θ_t and θ_i (Snell's law) may be obtained by examining the boundary conditions on **E** at the dielectric interface, the plane $z = 0$. Across this interface the tangential component (here the x-component) is continuous; consequently

$$\mathbf{E}_i \cdot \hat{\mathbf{x}} + \mathbf{E}_r \cdot \hat{\mathbf{x}} = \mathbf{E}_t \cdot \hat{\mathbf{x}}$$

or

$$E_{i_0} \cos \theta_i \exp \left\{ i\omega \left(\frac{x}{v_1} \sin \theta_i - t \right) \right\} - E_{r_0} \cos \theta_r \exp \left\{ i\omega \left(\frac{x}{v_1} \sin \theta_r - t \right) \right\}$$
$$= E_{t_0} \cos \theta_t \exp \left\{ i\omega \left(\frac{x}{v_2} \sin \theta_t - t \right) \right\}. \quad (12.36)$$

The only way to satisfy eq. 12.36 for *all* x is to require that

$$\frac{1}{v_1} \sin \theta_i = \frac{1}{v_1} \sin \theta_r = \frac{1}{v_2} \sin \theta_t. \quad (12.37)$$

The first of these equalities is the law of reflection, i.e., $\theta_i = \theta_r$. The second equality is Snell's law:

$$v_1 \sin \theta_i = v_2 \sin \theta_t. \quad (12.38)$$

The remaining content of eq. 12.36 is the relation

$$E_{i_0} \cos \theta_i - E_{r_0} \cos \theta_r = E_{t_0} \cos \theta_t. \quad (12.39)$$

An equation independent of eq. 12.39 is obtained from Gauss's law applied to the **D**-vector. This equation is the continuity of the *normal* component of **D** across the plane $z = 0$ or, employing eq. 12.37,

$$\epsilon_1 (E_{i_0} \sin \theta_i + E_{r_0} \sin \theta_r) = \epsilon_2 (E_{t_0} \sin \theta_t). \quad (12.40)$$

Equations 12.39 and 12.40 are two linear algebraic equations in two unknowns, namely;

$$R \equiv E_{r_0}/E_{i_0} \quad \text{and} \quad T \equiv E_{t_0}/E_{i_0}.$$

Noting that $\theta_i = \theta_r$ and that for most media it is sufficiently accurate to write $\mu = \mu_0$, the equations satisfied by R and T are

$$(1 - R) \cos \theta_i = T \cos \theta_t$$

$$(1 + R) \sin \theta_i = \left(\frac{v_2}{v_1} \right)^2 T \sin \theta_t$$

with solutions

$$T = \frac{2 \sin \theta_i \cos \theta_i}{\sin \theta_i \cos \theta_t + \left(\dfrac{v_2}{v_1} \right)^2 \sin \theta_t \cos \theta_i} \quad (12.41)$$

$$R = \frac{\left(\dfrac{v_2}{v_1} \right)^2 \cos \theta_i \sin \theta_t - \sin \theta_i \cos \theta_t}{\left(\dfrac{v_2}{v_1} \right)^2 \cos \theta_i \sin \theta_t + \sin \theta_i \cos \theta_t} \quad (12.42)$$

The indices of refraction ν_1 and ν_2 may be removed from eq. 12.42 using Snell's law to obtain

$$R = \frac{\cos \theta_i \sin \theta_i - \cos \theta_t \sin \theta_t}{\cos \theta_i \sin \theta_i + \cos \theta_t \sin \theta_t} \tag{12.43}$$

or
$$R = \frac{\sin (\theta_i - \theta_t) \cos (\theta_i + \theta_t)}{\sin (\theta_i + \theta_t) \cos (\theta_i - \theta_t)} = \frac{\tan (\theta_i - \theta_t)}{\tan (\theta_i + \theta_t)},$$

in which the following trigonometric identity has been employed:

$$\sin (a \pm b) \cos (a \mp b) \equiv \sin a \cos a \pm \sin b \cos b.$$

The reflected wave has zero amplitude (i.e., $R = 0$) if $\theta_i + \theta_t = \pi/2$, which is Brewster's law. (The other condition for which $R = 0$ is $\theta_i = \theta_t$, which is not consistent with Snell's law.) The angle of incidence for which $R = 0$ is called Brewster's angle. Using the facts that $\theta_i + \theta_t = \pi/2$ and $\nu_1 \sin \theta_i = \nu_2 \sin \theta_t$, Brewster's angle is easily shown to satisfy the relation

$$\theta_{iB} \equiv \arctan \left(\frac{\nu_2}{\nu_1}\right). \tag{12.44}$$

Brewster's law was introduced into optics in a somewhat different context. The above analysis applied to case (2)—$\mathbf{E}_i$ perpendicular to the plane of incidence—yields the result that R is always different from zero. Therefore if unpolarized light is incident upon a plane dielectric interface at Brewster's angle, the reflected light will be linearly polarized with $\mathbf{E}_r$ perpendicular to the plane of incidence.

It should be observed that the analysis yields complete information about the state of the reflected and transmitted waves without involving the boundary conditions on $\mathbf{B}$ and $\mathbf{H}$ at the dielectric interface. It is left as an exercise to show that these boundary conditions yield the same equations as the boundary conditions on $\mathbf{E}$ and $\mathbf{D}$.

12.6   Wave Equations for a Conducting Medium

Maxwell's equations for a linear, isotropic, conducting medium may be cast in the form of wave equations for $\mathbf{E}$ and $\mathbf{B}$. Throughout the following discussion it will be assumed that the medium is uncharged. For a linear, isotropic, conducting medium the macroscopic Maxwell equations are

$$\text{div } \mathbf{E} = 0 \qquad\qquad \text{div } \mathbf{B} = 0$$

$$\text{curl } \mathbf{E} = -\frac{\partial}{\partial t} \mathbf{B} \qquad \frac{1}{\mu} \text{curl } \mathbf{B} = \sigma \mathbf{E} + \epsilon \frac{\partial}{\partial t} \mathbf{E}.$$

The curl of Faraday's law coupled with Ampère's law yields

$$\text{curl curl } \mathbf{E} = -\mu\sigma \frac{\partial}{\partial t} \mathbf{E} - \mu\epsilon \frac{\partial^2}{\partial t^2} \mathbf{E}.$$

This may be converted to the form of an inhomogeneous wave equation using the identity

$$\text{curl curl} \equiv \text{grad div} - \nabla^2,$$

the definition

$$v^2 = (\mu\epsilon)^{-1}$$

and the Gauss electric law

$$\left(\nabla^2 - \frac{1}{v^2} \frac{\partial^2}{\partial t^2}\right) \mathbf{E} = \mu\sigma \frac{\partial}{\partial t} \mathbf{E}. \tag{12.45}$$

Solutions of the monochromatic plane wave type exist, that is,

$$\mathbf{E}(\mathbf{r}, t) = \mathbf{E}_0 \exp\{i(\mathbf{k} \cdot \mathbf{r} - \omega t)\} \quad \text{with } \mathbf{k} = \beta \mathbf{k}_0 \tag{12.46}$$

where the constant β is determined by eq. 12.45 and $\mathbf{k}_0$ is the wave vector of a plane wave of angular frequency ω propagating through a medium of zero conductivity, i.e., $k_0 \equiv \omega/v$. Substituting this solution into eq. 12.45 yields the following algebraic equation for β:

$$\beta^2 = 1 + i \left(\frac{v^2}{\omega}\right) \mu\sigma. \tag{12.47}$$

β is a complex number with

$$(\text{Re } \beta) = \left[1 + \left(\frac{v^2}{\omega} \mu\sigma\right)^2\right]^{1/4} \cos \vartheta$$

$$(\text{Im } \beta) = \left[1 + \left(\frac{v^2}{\omega} \mu\sigma\right)^2\right]^{1/4} \sin \vartheta \quad \text{with } \vartheta \equiv \frac{1}{2} \arctan\left(\frac{v^2\mu\sigma}{\omega}\right). \tag{12.48}$$

β is a complicated function of ω and constants of the material. There are two limiting cases of some interest which are quite simple. For a material of low conductivity the imaginary part of (βk_0) is small and therefore

$$(\beta k_0) \approx k_0 + i \frac{v^2 k_0}{2\omega} \mu\sigma.$$

Substituting this approximate expression for (βk_0) into the monochromatic plane wave solution yields

$$\mathbf{E}(\mathbf{r}, t) = \mathbf{E}_0 \exp\{i(\mathbf{k}_0 \cdot \mathbf{r} - \omega t)\} \exp\left\{-\frac{v^2\mu\sigma}{2\omega} \mathbf{k}_0 \cdot \mathbf{r}\right\} \quad \text{(low conductivity)}. \tag{12.49}$$

The plane wave is exponentially damped as it propagates through the medium. The *skin depth* or *attenuation length* δ is defined as

$$\exp\left\{-\frac{v^2\mu\sigma}{2\omega}\,\mathbf{k}_0\cdot\mathbf{r}\right\} = \exp\left\{-\frac{z}{\delta}\right\} \quad \text{where } \mathbf{k}_0 = k_0\hat{\mathbf{z}}.$$

This yields for the attenuation length a value

$$\delta = \frac{2}{v\mu\sigma} \quad \text{(low conductivity)}.$$

The simple model of a conductor introduced in the next section produces a conductivity which decreases with frequency. Therefore a wave packet propagating through a poor conductor has its low frequency components attenuated more rapidly than its high frequency components.

The other limiting case which can be handled with some ease is that of a very good conductor. For a material of high conductivity ϑ of eq. 12.48 is approximately $\pi/4$. Consequently the imaginary part of β is approximately

$$\text{Im }\beta \approx \sqrt{\frac{v^2\mu\sigma}{2\omega}}.$$

The attenuation length is therefore

$$\delta \approx \frac{1}{k_0}\sqrt{\frac{2\omega}{v^2\mu\sigma}} = \sqrt{\frac{2}{\omega\mu\sigma}} \quad \text{(high conductivity)}.$$

The model of a conductor introduced in the next section produces a conductivity that varies as ω^{-2} for very high frequencies. In this region the attenuation length of a good conductor increases with frequency. However, for low frequencies σ is essentially constant, and therefore the attenuation length decreases with frequency in this region.

In general, for a medium of finite conductivity the conductivity is frequency-dependent and various frequency components of a wave packet will be preferentially absorbed, thereby producing a dispersion of the packet.

12.7 A Simple Model of a Linear Conductor

The model of a nonconducting gas introduced in Section 12.3 may be modified to apply to a conducting gas by setting $\omega_0 = 0$. This produces a simple model of a conductor as a gas of electrons moving through the field of stationary positive ions and losing energy to them in collisions. The equation of motion for one of the conduction electrons interacting with a monochromatic plane wave is

$$\frac{d}{dt}v = -\kappa v + \left(\frac{q}{m_e}\right)E_0\exp\{i\omega t\} \tag{12.50}$$

where only one mode of dissipation is assumed.   The steady-state solution to eq. 12.50 is postulated to be

$$v = v_0 \exp\{i\omega t\}$$

which, when substituted into eq. 12.50 yields for v_0 the value

$$v_0 = \left(\frac{q}{m_e}\right)\frac{E_0}{\kappa + i\omega}.$$

Associated with the electron velocity is a time-dependent current density

$$j(t) = j_0 \exp\{i\omega t\} \quad \text{with } j_0 = nqv_0.$$

The resulting conductivity is

$$\sigma = n\left(\frac{q^2}{m_e}\right)\frac{\kappa - i\omega}{\kappa^2 + \omega^2}, \tag{12.51}$$

which can be generalized to include more than one dissipative mode of energy loss for the conduction electrons:

$$\sigma = \left(\frac{q^2}{m_e}\right)\sum_{l=1}^{N} n_l\left(\frac{\kappa_l - i\omega}{\kappa_l^2 + \omega^2}\right). \tag{12.52}$$

This conductivity is frequency-dependent.   The index of refraction of the conducting gas is given by eq. 12.16 with ω_0 set equal to zero:

$$\text{Re } \nu(\omega) = 1 - \left(\frac{1}{4\pi\epsilon_0}\right)\left(\frac{2\pi}{\omega^2}\right)\left(\frac{q^2}{m_e}\right)\sum_{l=1}^{N} n_l \frac{1}{1 + \left(\frac{\kappa_l}{\omega}\right)^2} \tag{12.53}$$

$$\text{Im } \nu(\omega) = -\left(\frac{1}{4\pi\epsilon_0}\right)\left(\frac{2\pi}{\omega^2}\right)\left(\frac{q^2}{m_e}\right)\sum_{l=1}^{N} n_l \frac{\left(\frac{\kappa_l}{\omega}\right)}{1 + \left(\frac{\kappa_l}{\omega}\right)^2}.$$

The fact that Re $\nu(\omega)$ is less than unity corresponds to the *optical density* of an electron gas being less than that of vacuum.   As a result a plane wave incident from vacuum on a conducting gas can suffer total internal reflection.   This allows the ionosphere to act as a reflector of radio waves.   The existence of the imaginary part of $\nu(\omega)$ corresponds to an attenuation of an electromagnetic wave propagating through a conducting gas.   Outside of a trivial numerical factor, the imaginary part of the index of refraction is equal to the real part of the conductivity, as may be seen by examining eqs. 12.52 and 12.53.

12.8   Optical Reflection From a Good Conductor

As an example of the application of the ideas developed in the previous sections concerning wave propagation in conducting media, consider the reflection of a plane monochromatic electromagnetic wave incident from the vacuum upon a plane slab of high conductivity.   As in the case of reflection from a dielectric interface considered in Section 12.5, only the situation where **E** of the incident wave is in the plane of incidence will be analyzed.   Using the same notation as in that section, the identical conclusion can be drawn concerning the law of reflection, namely, $\theta_i = \theta_r$. Snell's law, eq. 12.38, is also valid:

$$\nu_1 \sin \theta_i = \nu_2 \sin \theta_t.$$

In addition, however, it is possible to demonstrate that $\theta_t \to 0$ according to Section 12.6 as long as the conductivity of the slab from which the wave is reflected is high enough.

For a good conductor the wave number has been shown to be

$$k_t = \beta k_0 = \sqrt{\frac{\omega\mu\sigma}{2}}\,(1 + i).$$

From this expression a value of the velocity of the wave in the conductor may be gleaned:

$$v_{\text{cond}} = \frac{\omega}{\text{Re}\,(\beta k_0)} = \sqrt{\frac{2\omega}{\mu\sigma}}$$

from which, in turn, the index of refraction defined as

$$\nu_2 = \frac{c}{v_{\text{cond}}} = c\sqrt{\frac{\mu\sigma}{2\omega}}$$

may be obtained.   Since the wave is incident on the conducting slab from the vacuum ($\nu_1 = 1$), Snell's law becomes

$$\sin \theta_i = c\sqrt{\frac{\mu\sigma}{2\omega}} \sin \theta_t. \tag{12.54}$$

Since σ is assumed very large, it is seen that θ_t must be very small in order that Snell's law be satisfied.   Therefore, independent of the angle of incidence, the wave in the conducting medium will propagate approximately perpendicular to the interface.   Of course, the transmitted wave will be highly attenuated since the skin depth for a good conductor is proportional to $\sigma^{-1/2}$.

It is evident from eq. 12.44 that Brewster's angle for a good conductor is approximately 90°.   Therefore unpolarized light incident on a good conductor becomes polarized on reflection only for grazing incidence.

12.9 Energy Density and the Poynting Vector in Material Media

With suitable restrictions it has been possible to derive expressions for the energy residing in the fields in both the static and stationary macroscopic theories and in the time-dependent microscopic theory; that is

$$U = \tfrac{1}{2} \int\limits_{\text{all space}} d\tau \mathbf{E} \cdot \mathbf{D} + \tfrac{1}{2} \int\limits_{\text{all space}} d\tau \mathbf{B} \cdot \mathbf{H} \quad \text{(static macroscopic)}. \qquad (12.55a)$$

$$U = (4\pi\epsilon_0)\left[\frac{1}{8\pi} \int\limits_{\text{all space}} E^2 \, d\tau \right]$$

$$+ \left(\frac{4\pi}{\mu_0}\right)\left[\frac{1}{8\pi} \int\limits_{\text{all space}} B^2 \, d\tau \right] \quad \text{(time-dependent microscopic)}. \qquad (12.55b)$$

In addition, in order to preserve the concept of energy conservation within a finite volume V, it was found useful for time-dependent microscopic fields to introduce the energy flux or Poynting vector $\mathscr{S} \equiv (1/\mu_0)\mathbf{E} \times \mathbf{B}$. It will now be shown that these concepts can be generalized to time-dependent macroscopic fields in a linear, isotropic medium. The demonstration proceeds as follows. The scalar product of Faraday's law is taken with $\mathbf{H}$, and the result is subtracted from the scalar product between Ampère's law and $\mathbf{E}$:

$$\mathbf{E} \cdot \text{curl } \mathbf{H} - \mathbf{H} \cdot \text{curl } \mathbf{E} = \mathbf{E} \cdot \mathbf{j}_{\text{real}} + \tfrac{1}{2}\frac{\partial}{\partial t}(\mathbf{E} \cdot \mathbf{D}) + \tfrac{1}{2}\frac{\partial}{\partial t}(\mathbf{H} \cdot \mathbf{B})$$

Use is then made of the vector calculus identity

$$\text{div } (\mathbf{E} \times \mathbf{H}) = \mathbf{H} \cdot \text{curl } \mathbf{E} - \mathbf{E} \cdot \text{curl } \mathbf{H}$$

and on rewriting

$$\text{div } (\mathbf{E} \times \mathbf{H}) + \mathbf{E} \cdot \mathbf{j}_{\text{real}} + \frac{\partial}{\partial t}[\tfrac{1}{2}(\mathbf{E} \cdot \mathbf{D} + \mathbf{H} \cdot \mathbf{B})] = 0. \qquad (12.56)$$

Multiplying eq. 12.56 by the volume element $d\tau$, integrating over a finite volume V, and converting the volume integral of the divergence into an integral over the surface Σ bounding V yields

$$\int_V d\tau(\mathbf{E} \cdot \mathbf{j}_{\text{real}}) + \frac{d}{dt}\left\{ \int_V d\tau \, \frac{\mathbf{E} \cdot \mathbf{D}}{2} + \int_V d\tau \, \frac{\mathbf{B} \cdot \mathbf{H}}{2}\right\}$$

$$+ \oiint_\Sigma ds \, \hat{\mathbf{n}} \cdot (\mathbf{E} \times \mathbf{H}) = 0. \qquad (12.57)$$

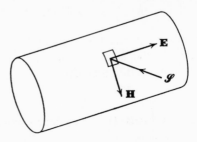

Fig. 12.5 A long wire of circular cross section of radius R carries a current distributed uniformly over its cross section. The directions of **E**, **H**, and $\mathscr{S}$ (the Poynting vector) at the surface of the wire are indicated. The rate at which electromagnetic energy flows into the wire across the surface of the wire is numerically equal to the rate at which Joule heat is developed in the wire.

The first term is the rate at which the fields do work on the real charges in V (the Lorentz force law holds for the macroscopic as well as the microscopic fields); the second term is interpreted as the energy in V in the macroscopic fields (this term has the correct time-dependent microscopic and static macroscopic limits); the last term must be the macroscopic equivalent to the energy flux in order to preserve the concept of energy conservation in the time-dependent macroscopic theory. The Poynting vector for the macroscopic theory is defined as

$$\mathscr{S} = \mathbf{E} \times \mathbf{H}. \tag{12.58}$$

EXAMPLE 12.1 As a very simple example of the energy balance made possible by the above interpretation of the various field quantities in eq. 12.57, consider a long wire of circular cross section (radius R) carrying a uniform current I. (See Fig. 12.5.) If the material of the wire is linear, then $j = \sigma E$. In addition, it has been shown previously that the magnitude of the H-field at the surface of such a wire is $H = 1/2jR$. The direction of **E** and **H** are such that they are perpendicular to one another, and the resulting Poynting vector is perpendicular to the surface of the wire and inward. As a consequence the integral of the Poynting vector over a length l of the wire yields

$$\int \mathscr{S} \cdot \hat{\mathbf{n}} \, ds = -\left(\frac{j}{\sigma}\right) (\tfrac{1}{2} jR) \int ds = -\frac{j^2 R}{2\sigma} 2\pi R l$$

$$\int \mathscr{S} \cdot \hat{\mathbf{n}} \, ds = -\frac{j^2}{\sigma} (\pi R^2 l)$$

Therefore electromagnetic energy flows *into* the wire at the same rate as Joule heat is developed *in* the wire. The Joule heating is seen as a necessary consequence of the interpretation of eq. 12.57, and since the energy density and the Poynting vector depend on the fields alone and not on the agencies producing the fields, the Joule heating is independent of the specific emf providing for the current flow in the wire.

PROBLEMS

12.1 Obtain plane wave solutions to d'Alembert's equations for the electromagnetic fields in nonconducting uncharged material media. Calculate the ratio between the energy contained in the electric and magnetic parts of the wave.

12.2 Calculate the width at half-maximum of the imaginary part of the frequency dependent index of refraction as given in eq. 12.16.

12.3 A plane electromagnetic wave is incident from a medium of index of refraction ν_1 upon a plane interface separating this medium from another of index of refraction ν_2. The incident wave is linearly polarized with E perpendicular to the plane of incidence. Calculate the ratio between the transmitted, reflected, and incident intensities. Show that the reflected intensity is always greater than zero.

12.4 In the text, the laws of optical reflection and transmission were derived examining the boundary conditions on E and D at the interface between two media. Repeat the arguments, using instead the boundary conditions on B and H.

12.5 For a plane electromagnetic wave polarized parallel to the plane of incidence, the wave reflected from an interface separating two dielectrics will be in phase with the incident wave if R defined in eq. 12.42 or 12.43 is greater than zero. Discuss the situation in which the reflected and incident waves are in phase in terms of θ_i and θ_t. (Note there are two distinct cases; $\theta_i < \theta_t$ and $\theta_i > \theta_t$.)

12.6 A plane electromagnetic wave is incident from vacuum upon a dielectric slab with index of refraction ν which rests upon a slab of material of infinite conductivity. Derive a relationship that must be satisfied by the angle of incidence at the vacuum-dielectric interface such that no reflection occurs at the dielectric-vacuum interface after the wave has been reflected from the dielectric-conductor interface.

12.7 Derive an expression for the linear momentum flux density carried by a plane electromagnetic wave propagating through a nonconducting medium with electric and magnetic permeabilities equal to ϵ and μ. Calculate the pressure exerted by such a wave on a plane conducting surface imbedded in the nonconductor.

13 | *Electromagnetic Radiation*

Chapters 10–12 were concerned with the development of the electromagnetic field equations and their application to the propagation of electromagnetic waves in vacuum and material media. However, no attempt was made to discuss how the electromagnetic waves are generated. The present chapter will investigate the generation of such waves by moving charges. The discussion will be based on the equations satisfied by the time-dependent microscopic potential functions, eqs. 10.39 and 10.40:

$$\Box \varphi(\mathbf{r}, t) = -\left(\frac{1}{4\pi\epsilon_0}\right) 4\pi \rho(\mathbf{r}, t),$$

$$\Box \mathbf{A}(\mathbf{r}, t) = -\left(\frac{\mu_0}{4\pi}\right) 4\pi \mathbf{j}(\mathbf{r}, t),$$

with the Lorentz subsidiary condition, eq. 10.35,

$$\operatorname{div} \mathbf{A}(\mathbf{r}, t) + \frac{1}{c^2}\frac{\partial}{\partial t}\varphi(\mathbf{r}, t) = 0.$$

It has already been shown that wave solutions to these equations exist in vacuum (i.e., ρ and $\mathbf{j} \equiv 0$). These wave solutions are generated in the regions where ρ and $\mathbf{j}$ are nonzero. The explicit demonstration of this is carried out by solving the inhomogeneous partial differential equations satisfied by the potentials, and showing that the solutions obtained correspond to electromagnetic waves propagating in those regions which are sufficiently distant from the source. It turns out to be easier to work with the equations for φ and $\mathbf{A}$ rather than those for $\mathbf{E}$ and $\mathbf{B}$; of course, $\mathbf{E}$ and $\mathbf{B}$ can be obtained very simply from φ and $\mathbf{A}$ via the relations

$$\mathbf{E} = -\operatorname{grad}\varphi - \frac{\partial}{\partial t}\mathbf{A}.$$
$$\mathbf{B} = \operatorname{curl}\mathbf{A}.$$

13.1 The Retarded and Advanced Potentials

It is possible to solve the potential equations by very elegant methods, but the method here will be somewhat intuitive. Whatever this method

298

lacks in elegance will be compensated for by its very close connection with the methods already employed in solving the equations satisfied by the static potentials. Only the equation for $\mathbf{A}(\mathbf{r}, t)$ will be discussed in any detail since it has already been shown that in the limiting region in which wave solutions exist, the gauge can always be chosen so that $\varphi = 0$. The equation satisfied by $\mathbf{A}(\mathbf{r}, t)$ is

$$\left(\nabla^2 - \frac{1}{c^2}\frac{\partial^2}{\partial t^2}\right)\mathbf{A}(\mathbf{r}, t) = -\left(\frac{\mu_0}{4\pi}\right)4\pi\mathbf{j}(\mathbf{r}, t). \tag{13.1}$$

Before attempting to solve eq. 13.1, consider the case in which $\mathbf{j}$ and $\mathbf{A}$ take on steady-state values:

$$\nabla^2\mathbf{A}(\mathbf{r}) = -\left(\frac{\mu_0}{4\pi}\right)4\pi\mathbf{j}(\mathbf{r}). \tag{13.2}$$

This equation was discussed in Chapter 6, and the solution obtained of the form

$$\mathbf{A}(\mathbf{r}) = \left(\frac{\mu_0}{4\pi}\right)\int d\tau\,\frac{\mathbf{j}(\mathbf{r}')}{|\mathbf{r} - \mathbf{r}'|}. \tag{13.3}$$

Whatever solutions are obtained for the time-dependent equation, eq. 13.1 must reduce to eq. 13.3 in the steady-state limit.

To obtain the solution of eq. 13.1 which has the correct steady-state limit and which corresponds to electromagnetic waves in the regions of space far from the source, it will be assumed initially that $\mathbf{j}(\mathbf{r}, t)$ is due to a single charge in motion; that is,

$$\mathbf{j}(\mathbf{r}, t) = q\mathbf{v}\,\delta(\mathbf{r} - \mathbf{r}'(t)) \tag{13.4}$$

where $\mathbf{r}'(t)$ is the instantaneous location of the charge at time t. $\mathbf{A}(\mathbf{r}, t)$ satisfies the equation

$$\left(\nabla^2 - \frac{1}{c^2}\frac{\partial^2}{\partial t^2}\right)\mathbf{A}(\mathbf{r}, t) = -\left(\frac{\mu_0}{4\pi}\right)4\pi q\mathbf{v}\,\delta(\mathbf{r} - \mathbf{r}'(t)). \tag{13.5}$$

This is really a set of three equations involving the Cartesian components of $\mathbf{A}$ and $\mathbf{v}$. Any one component, say, the x-component, satisfies

$$\left(\nabla^2 - \frac{1}{c^2}\frac{\partial^2}{\partial t^2}\right)A_x = 0 \quad \text{for } \mathbf{r} \neq \mathbf{r}'$$

with the associated boundary condition

$$-\left(\frac{\mu_0}{4\pi}\right)4\pi q v_x(t) = \int_{\Delta\tau} d\tau\left\{\nabla^2 - \frac{1}{c^2}\frac{\partial^2}{\partial t^2}\right\}A_x$$

where $\Delta\tau$ is a small volume surrounding the charge q.   Since the source of A_x, namely,

$$-\left(\frac{\mu_0}{4\pi}\right)4\pi q v_x\, \delta(\mathbf{r} - \mathbf{r}')$$

is *spherically symmetric*, that is, depends only on the magnitude of the vector $\mathbf{r} - \mathbf{r}'$, $\mathbf{A}$ will depend only upon the magnitude of $\mathbf{r} - \mathbf{r}'$.   Employing the change of variables $\mathbf{R} \equiv \mathbf{r} - \mathbf{r}'$ enables the Laplacian operator to be written simply in spherical polar coordinates since $\mathbf{A}(\mathbf{r}, t) = \mathbf{A}(R, t)$:

$$\left[\frac{1}{R^2}\frac{\partial}{\partial R} R^2 \frac{\partial}{\partial R} - \frac{1}{c^2}\frac{\partial^2}{\partial t^2}\right]A_x(R, t) = 0, \quad R \neq 0. \tag{13.6}$$

The equation for (RA_x) is somewhat simpler than that of eq. 13.6.   It is straightforward to demonstrate that RA_x satisfies the equation

$$\left(\frac{\partial^2}{\partial R^2} - \frac{1}{c^2}\frac{\partial^2}{\partial t^2}\right)[RA_x(R, t)] = 0, \quad R \neq 0. \tag{13.7}$$

Equation 13.7 is a one-dimensional wave equation with a general wave solution of the form

$$RA_x(R, t) = h(R + ct) + g(R - ct). \tag{13.8}$$

The functions g and h are constant on spherical surfaces of radius R centered at $\mathbf{r}'$ at time t.   These functions maintain these values on the spherical surface as the radius of the surface changes in time at the rates $+c$ for g and $-c$ for h, respectively. $A_x(R, t)$ is composed of terms g/R and h/R, which correspond to *outgoing* and *incoming* spherical waves, respectively.

The precise form of the functions g and h can be obtained by examining the condition that A_x must satisfy at $R = 0$ or $\mathbf{r} = \mathbf{r}'$.   Remembering that $\mathbf{r}'$ is the position of the moving charge at some fixed time t, it is seen that A_x must match the solution to Laplace's equation at $\mathbf{r} = \mathbf{r}'$ for a point source of strength $-(\mu_0/4\pi)4\pi q v_x$ located there; that is, A_x must approach the value $(\mu_0/4\pi)q v_x/R$ as $R \to 0$.   Consequently A_x may be written as a linear combination of the terms

$$\left(\frac{\mu_0}{4\pi}\right)\frac{q}{R}v_x(t') \quad \text{and} \quad \left(\frac{\mu_0}{4\pi}\right)\frac{q}{R}v_x(t'') \tag{13.9}$$

where $t' \equiv t - R/c$, and $t'' \equiv t + R/c$.

It is seen that the first contribution to A_x at the field point $\mathbf{r}$ at the time t depends explicitly on the location and the velocity of the charge at an "earlier" or "retarded" time t', whereas the second contribution to A_x depends explicitly on the location and velocity of the charge at a "later"

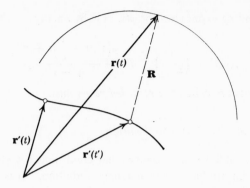

Fig. 13.1 At the time $t' = t - R/c$, the charge q is the source of an outgoing spherical wave which passes the field point at the time t. The electromagnetic fields at $\mathbf{r}$ at time t are due to the behavior of the charge at time t' and position $\mathbf{r}'$.

or "advanced" time t''. This second contribution is "unphysical" in the sense that it defies elementary notions of *causality*; that is, the present behavior of the potential is due to future behavior of the source. On these grounds, the "advanced" solutions will be discarded.

This discussion may be repeated unaltered for the other two Cartesian components of $\mathbf{A}$. Keeping only the retarded part of the solution, $\mathbf{A}(\mathbf{r}, t)$ due to a moving point charge is

$$\mathbf{A}(\mathbf{r}, t) = \left(\frac{\mu_0}{4\pi}\right) q \left[\frac{\mathbf{v}}{R}\right]_{t' = t - R/c} \tag{13.10}$$

where the quantities within the brackets are to be evaluated at the retarded time $t - R/c$.

Equation 13.10 can be given the following physical interpretation (see Fig. 13.1). At the time $t - R/c$, the moving charge is the source of a spherical wave which propagates outward from the point $\mathbf{r}'$ with a velocity c. This spherical wave front passes the point $\mathbf{r}$ at the time t, an interval R/c after the wave front was originated by the moving charge. The potential and the fields derived from it are consequently related causally to the motion of the charge. The charges do not instantaneously establish the fields. The generalization of eq. 13.10 to an ensemble of moving charges occupying a finite volume τ is

$$\mathbf{A}(\mathbf{r}, t) = \left(\frac{\mu_0}{4\pi}\right) \int_\tau d\tau' \, \frac{\mathbf{j}\left(\mathbf{r}', t - \frac{1}{c}|\mathbf{r} - \mathbf{r}'|\right)}{|\mathbf{r} - \mathbf{r}'|}. \tag{13.11}$$

The corresponding expression for $\varphi(\mathbf{r}, t)$ is by analogy

$$\varphi(\mathbf{r}, t) = \left(\frac{1}{4\pi\epsilon_0}\right) \int_\tau d\tau' \frac{\rho\left(\mathbf{r}', t - \frac{1}{c}|\mathbf{r} - \mathbf{r}'|\right)}{|\mathbf{r} - \mathbf{r}'|}. \tag{13.12}$$

These potentials are called the *retarded potentials*.

13.2   The Wave Zone Approximation

It is now possible to show under what conditions a system of charges and currents can produce electromagnetic radiation.   It is supposed that all charges and currents are confined to a finite volume τ.   A coordinate system is located with its origin within τ, and all position vectors are referred to this coordinate system.   Here the field point will be assumed far enough from the origin so that its distance is larger than the largest linear dimension of the source.   Accordingly the quantity $R \equiv |\mathbf{r} - \mathbf{r}'|$, which appears explicitly in the expression for $\mathbf{A}$ and implicitly through the retarded time, can be expanded.   Here only the first two terms in the expansion need be considered (see Fig. 13.2):

$$R \simeq r - \hat{\mathbf{n}} \cdot \mathbf{r}'. \tag{13.13}$$

This approximate value of R may be substituted into the expressions for the retarded potentials.   Two observations should be made.   First, R appears explicitly as the denominator in the integrands of the potentials

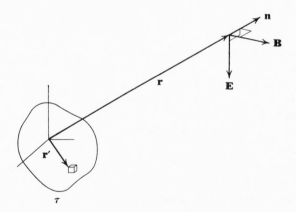

Fig. 13.2   The source of the radiation field is confined to the volume τ.   A coordinate system is erected with its origin within τ. $\mathbf{r}'$ is the position vector of an element of the source; $\mathbf{r}$ is the field point in the wave zone. $\hat{\mathbf{n}}$ is the unit vector from the origin to the field point.   The fields in the wave zone satisfy the wave condition, namely, $c\mathbf{B} = \hat{\mathbf{n}} \times \mathbf{E}$.

and it will barely affect the value of the integrand if the denominator is replaced by the first term in the expansion:

$$\mathbf{A}(\mathbf{r}, t) = \left(\frac{\mu_0}{4\pi}\right)\frac{1}{r}\int_\tau d\tau' \mathbf{j}\left(\mathbf{r}', t - \frac{r}{c} + \frac{\hat{\mathbf{n}} \cdot \mathbf{r}'}{c}\right), \tag{13.14}$$

$$\varphi(\mathbf{r}, t) = \left(\frac{1}{4\pi\epsilon_0}\right)\frac{1}{r}\int_\tau d\tau' \rho\left(\mathbf{r}', t - \frac{r}{c} + \frac{\hat{\mathbf{n}} \cdot \mathbf{r}'}{c}\right). \tag{13.15}$$

Second, the neglect of $\hat{\mathbf{n}} \cdot \mathbf{r}'/c$ cannot be tolerated in the arguments of $\mathbf{j}$ and ρ, since $\mathbf{j}$ and ρ may change significantly in times of the order of r'/c. Equations 13.14 and 13.15 for the potentials may be called the *wave zone* or *radiation zone* values for the potentials since $\mathbf{E}$ and $\mathbf{B}$ derived from them satisfy the wave conditions

$$c\mathbf{B} = \hat{\mathbf{n}} \times \mathbf{E}.$$

To demonstrate that the fields derived from these potentials correspond to waves outgoing from the source, note that after the integration indicated in eq. 13.14 is performed, $\mathbf{A}$ will be a function of $t_0 \equiv t - r/c$; that is,

$$\mathbf{A} = \frac{1}{r}\mathbf{g}(t_0). \tag{13.16}$$

The field $\mathbf{B}$ may be obtained from eq. 13.16 as follows:

$$\mathbf{B} = \operatorname{curl}\left[\frac{1}{r}\mathbf{g}(t_0)\right] = \frac{1}{r}\operatorname{curl}\mathbf{g}(t_0) + \operatorname{grad}\left(\frac{1}{r}\right) \times \mathbf{g}(t_0)$$

where the term in grad $(1/r)$ may be dropped in the wave zone as negligible compared to the term in $1/r$. However, since $t_0 = t - r/c$,

$$\operatorname{curl}\mathbf{g}(t_0) = (\operatorname{grad} t_0) \times \frac{d\mathbf{g}}{dt_0} = -\frac{1}{c}\hat{\mathbf{n}} \times \frac{d\mathbf{g}}{dt_0}.$$

Therefore the magnetic field in the wave zone is

$$\mathbf{B} = -\frac{1}{rc}\hat{\mathbf{n}} \times \frac{d\mathbf{g}}{dt_0}$$

which may be written in terms of $\mathbf{A}$, employing eq. 13.16,

$$\mathbf{B} = -\frac{1}{c}\hat{\mathbf{n}} \times \left(\frac{d\mathbf{A}}{dt_0}\right) \qquad \text{wave zone approximation.} \tag{13.17}$$

In a similar fashion, using the relation

$$\mathbf{E} = -\operatorname{grad}\varphi - \frac{\partial\mathbf{A}}{\partial t},$$

it is possible to show that in the wave zone

$$\mathbf{E} = \hat{\mathbf{n}} \times \left(\hat{\mathbf{n}} \times \frac{d\mathbf{A}}{dt_0}\right) \qquad \text{wave zone approximation.} \tag{13.18}$$

(The establishment of eq. 13.18 is left as an exercise.) Examination of eqs. 13.17 and 13.18 reveals that the wave condition is satisfied in the wave zone; that is,

$$c\mathbf{B} = \hat{\mathbf{n}} \times \mathbf{E}.$$

The properties of the source which lead to radiation will now be examined, using an approximation method similar to the multipole approximation employed in electrostatics and magnetostatics.

13.3   Multipole Expansion of the Radiation Field

The multipole approximation to the retarded potential $\mathbf{A}$ in the wave zone consists in the expansion of $\mathbf{j}(\mathbf{r}', t - r/c + \hat{\mathbf{n}} \cdot \mathbf{r}'/c)$ in the *time variable* $t - r/c + \hat{\mathbf{n}} \cdot \mathbf{r}'/c$ about the time appropriate to the origin of coordinates, t_0:

$$\mathbf{j}\left(\mathbf{r}', t_0 + \frac{\hat{\mathbf{n}} \cdot \mathbf{r}'}{c}\right) \simeq \mathbf{j}(\mathbf{r}', t_0) + \frac{\hat{\mathbf{n}} \cdot \mathbf{r}'}{c}\left(\frac{\partial}{\partial t_0} \mathbf{j}(\mathbf{r}', t_0)\right). \tag{13.19}$$

(*Note:* It is actually not consistent to include higher-order terms in this expansion of $\mathbf{j}$, since the terms in $(\hat{\mathbf{n}} \cdot \mathbf{r}'/c)^2$, for example, are of the same order as the terms neglected in approximating the retarded time t' by $t_0 + (\hat{\mathbf{n}} \cdot \mathbf{r}')/c$.)

Using this approximate expression for $\mathbf{j}$ and substituting into eq. 13.14, an approximate expression for $\mathbf{A}$ in the wave zone is obtained, namely,

$$\mathbf{A}(\mathbf{r}, t) \simeq \left(\frac{\mu_0}{4\pi}\right)\frac{1}{r}\int_\tau d\tau' \mathbf{j}(\mathbf{r}', t_0) + \left(\frac{\mu_0}{4\pi}\right)\frac{1}{r}\int_\tau d\tau' \frac{\hat{\mathbf{n}} \cdot \mathbf{r}'}{c}\left(\frac{\partial}{\partial t_0} \mathbf{j}(\mathbf{r}', t_0)\right), \tag{13.20}$$
$$\simeq \mathbf{A}_{E1}(\mathbf{r}, t) + [\mathbf{A}_{M1}(\mathbf{r}, t) + \mathbf{A}_{E2}(\mathbf{r}, t)],$$

where

$$\mathbf{A}_{E1}(\mathbf{r}, t) \equiv \left(\frac{\mu_0}{4\pi}\right)\frac{1}{r}\int_\tau d\tau' \mathbf{j}(\mathbf{r}', t_0) \tag{13.21}$$

$$\mathbf{A}_{M1}(\mathbf{r}, t) + \mathbf{A}_{E2}(\mathbf{r}, t) \equiv \left(\frac{\mu_0}{4\pi}\right)\frac{1}{r}\int_\tau d\tau' \frac{\hat{\mathbf{n}} \cdot \mathbf{r}'}{c}\left(\frac{\partial}{\partial t_0} \mathbf{j}(\mathbf{r}', t_0)\right), \tag{13.22}$$

in which the physical characteristics of the source which appear in these terms in $\mathbf{A}$ have been anticipated in the notation.

13.4   Electric Dipole Radiation

The leading contribution to $\mathbf{A}$ is given in eq. 13.21 as

$$\mathbf{A}_{E1}(\mathbf{r}, t) \equiv \left(\frac{\mu_0}{4\pi}\right)\frac{1}{r}\int_\tau d\tau' \mathbf{j}(\mathbf{r}', t_0).$$

This integral can be performed immediately since the "time" variable in the integrand is not a function of the integration variable:

$$\int_\tau d\tau' \mathbf{j}(\mathbf{r}', t_0) = \sum_{i=1}^{N} q\mathbf{v}_i(t_0) = \frac{d}{dt_0} \sum_{i=1}^{N} q_i \mathbf{r}_i$$

or

$$\mathbf{A}_{\mathrm{E1}}(\mathbf{r}, t) \equiv \left(\frac{\mu_0}{4\pi}\right) \frac{1}{r} \left(\frac{d}{dt_0} \mathbf{p}\right) \tag{13.23}$$

where $\mathbf{p} \equiv$ time-dependent (E1) moment of the charge distribution. $\mathbf{A}_{\mathrm{E1}}$ is the (E1) contribution to the vector potential in the wave zone. This contribution is produced by the time-varying (E1) moment of the source. The electric dipole contribution to the **B**-field is obtained directly from eq. 13.17 with the result

$$\mathbf{B} = -\frac{1}{c} \left(\frac{\mu_0}{4\pi}\right) \frac{1}{r} \hat{\mathbf{n}} \times \left(\frac{d^2}{dt_0^2} \mathbf{p}\right) \quad \text{(E1) radiation field.} \tag{13.24}$$

Note that **B** vanishes in the direction parallel to the instantaneous orientation of the (E1) moment of the source and attains a maximum in the plane perpendicular to the instantaneous dipole. Since $|\mathbf{E}| = c|\mathbf{B}|$, these statements apply to **E** as well as to **B** for a radiating dipole. (See Fig. 13.3.) Defining ϑ as the angle between $\hat{\mathbf{n}}$ (the direction to the field point) and **p**, it is seen that the magnitude of the energy flux (the Poynting vector) from a radiating electric dipole is proportional to $\sin^2 \vartheta$. This is the characteristic *radiation pattern* for a time-varying electric dipole distribution. The amount of energy per unit time radiated by an electric dipole can be calculated using eqs. 13.17, 13.18, and 13.24 and the definition of the Poynting vector $\mathscr{S}$,

$$\mathscr{S} = \left(\frac{\mu_0}{4\pi}\right) \frac{1}{c} \frac{1}{4\pi r^2} \left|\frac{d^2}{dt_0^2} \mathbf{p}\right|^2 \sin^2 \vartheta \, \hat{\mathbf{n}}. \tag{13.25}$$

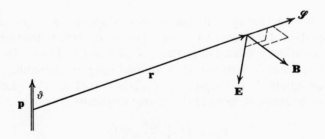

Fig. 13.3 The **E**- and **B**-fields in the wave zone due to a radiating electric dipole **p** are indicated.

The flux of the Poynting vector through a sphere of radius r centered at the origin is the power radiated by the (E1) distribution; that is,

$$P = \oiint_S \mathscr{S} \cdot \hat{n} \, dS \quad \text{where } S = \text{spherical surface of radius } r. \quad (13.26)$$

Substituting the value for $\mathscr{S}$ from eq. 13.25 yields the result

$$P = \left(\frac{\mu_0}{4\pi}\right) \frac{1}{c} \left|\frac{d^2}{dt_0^2} \mathbf{p}\right|^2 \left\{\frac{1}{4\pi r^2}\left[\int_0^{2\pi} r \, d\phi \int_0^{\pi} \sin^2 \vartheta (r \sin \vartheta \, d\vartheta)\right]\right\}$$

$$P = \left(\frac{\mu_0}{4\pi}\right) \frac{2}{3c} \left|\frac{d^2}{dt_0^2} \mathbf{p}\right|^2. \quad (13.27)$$

The rate at which energy flows outward through any spherical surface centered at the source is independent of the radius of the surface. This is intuitively evident since there are no sources or sinks of radiant energy in the region contained between any two spherical surfaces in the radiation zone. All the energy passing a given surface was radiated from the source confined to a finite volume τ.

There are two special applications of eq. 13.27: (1) an oscillating dipole; (2) an arbitrarily moving charge. An oscillating dipole is defined via the expression

$$\mathbf{p}(t_0) = \mathbf{p}_0 \cos (\omega t_0 + \alpha).$$

For an oscillating dipole

$$P = \left(\frac{\mu_0}{4\pi}\right)\left(\frac{2\omega^4}{3c} p_0^2\right) \cos^2 (\omega t_0 + \alpha).$$

The average power radiated in one cycle of dipole oscillation, P_{av}, is obtained by replacing $\cos^2 (\omega t_0 + \alpha)$ by its average over one period, namely, $1/2$. Consequently

$$P_{av} = \left(\frac{\mu_0}{4\pi}\right)\left(\frac{\omega^4 p_0^2}{3c}\right) \quad \text{(oscillating electric dipole).} \quad (13.28)$$

A simple model for an oscillating dipole is a charge q moving according to the equation of motion: $l(t_0) = l_0 \cos (\omega t_0 + \alpha)$ where l_0, the amplitude of the oscillation, is related to p_0 via $p_0 = q l_0$ (see Fig. 13.4). The oscillating charge may be represented by an oscillating or alternating current whose amplitude I_0 is simply $I_0 = (\omega/2\pi)q = (\omega/2\pi)(p_0/l_0)$. Equation 13.28 may be recast in terms of the current amplitude I_0 as

$$P_{av} = \left(\frac{\mu_0}{4\pi}\right) \frac{4\pi^2}{3c} \omega^2 l_0^2 I_0^2.$$

However, the wavelength λ of the radiation emitted is given by the

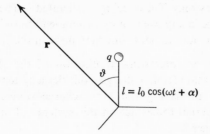

Fig. 13.4   A charge q oscillates with angular frequency ω. The position of the charge from the origin at any time is $l(t) = l_0 \cos(\omega t + \alpha)$. Such an oscillating charge emits dipole radiation of angular frequency ω.

expression $\lambda = 2\pi c/\omega$. Consequently, in terms of the wavelength of the emitted dipole radiation, the average value of the power emitted over one cycle of the oscillation is

$$P_{av} = \left[\left(\frac{\mu_0}{4\pi} \right) \frac{4\pi^2 c}{3} \right] 4\pi^2 \left(\frac{l_0}{\lambda} \right)^2 I_0^2. \tag{13.29}$$

This dependence on λ is characteristic of (E1) radiation. In rationalized mks units power is measured in *watts*. (The watt is the rate at which a force of one newton does work on an object moving at a velocity of one meter per second.) The numerical value of the constant contained in the brackets is 10.0. If the amplitude of the current is expressed in amperes, the constant has the dimensions of ohms. Since the current is oscillating, its root-mean-square value I_{rms} is just $(1/\sqrt{2})I_0$. Consequently eq. 13.29 can be written as

$$P_{av} = (4\pi^2)(20.0)\left(\frac{l_0}{\lambda} \right)^2 I_{rms}^2. \tag{13.30}$$

The quantity

$$R_{rad} = (4\pi^2)(20.0)\left(\frac{l_0}{\lambda} \right)^2$$

is conventionally called the *radiation resistance* of an oscillating dipole. (Note: P_{av} may be written in terms of the *reduced* wavelength $\lambdabar \equiv (1/2\pi)\lambda$. Here the radiation resistance is simply $20.0\ (l_0/\lambdabar)^2$ ohms.)

As previously indicated, a moving charge can radiate electric dipole radiation. The instantaneous power appearing in the form of electric dipole radiation is obtained from eq. 13.27, using the following notation:

$$\mathbf{p} = q\mathbf{r}, \qquad \mathbf{a} = \frac{d^2}{dt_0^2}\mathbf{r}, \qquad c^2 = (\mu_0\epsilon_0)^{-1},$$

$$P = \left(\frac{1}{4\pi\epsilon_0} \right) \frac{2q^2 a^2}{3c^3}. \tag{13.31}$$

The charge radiates only if it is being accelerated. The changing dipole moment of a charge in *uniform* motion cannot lead to radiation, since such a charge is at rest in an inertial frame moving with the charge.

EXAMPLE 13.1   As an interesting application of the above analysis of electric dipole radiation from a charge, consider a system of N interacting charged particles all having the same charge-to-mass-ratio. Assume further that no external forces act on this system. The (E1) moment of the system of charges is

$$\mathbf{p} = \sum_{i=1}^{N} q_i \mathbf{r}_i,$$

which can be written in the following manner:

$$\mathbf{p} = \sum_{i=1}^{N} \left(\frac{q_i}{m_i}\right) m_i \mathbf{r}_i.$$

However, q_i/m_i has been assumed independent of i and will be designated by the constant α. Therefore

$$\mathbf{p} = \alpha \sum_{i=1}^{N} m_i \mathbf{r}_i = \alpha M \mathbf{R}$$

where $M = \sum_{i=1}^{N} m_i$ (total mass of the system)

$$\mathbf{R} = \frac{1}{M} \sum_{i=1}^{N} m_i \mathbf{r}_i \text{ (coordinate of the center of mass).}$$

Since by hypothesis no external forces act upon the system, the velocity of the center of mass, namely, $d\mathbf{R}/dt$ is a constant. Consequently $(d^2/dt^2)\mathbf{p} \equiv 0$, and no electric dipole radiation is emitted by the system.

Finally, it is possible to recast in other terms the criterion for the validity of the (E1) approximation to $\mathbf{A}$, namely, that changes in $\mathbf{j}$ in times of the order of magnitudes of L/c (where L is the largest linear dimension of the volume τ containing all the charge) are negligible. A characteristic charge within τ will move within the volume τ with a characteristic period $T \approx L/v$ where v is its average speed. The (E1) criterion may then be restated as follows:

(1) $L/c \ll T$ or $v/c \ll 1$; that is, the charge must be moving slowly compared to c;

(2) $L \ll cT$ or $L \ll \lambda$ where λ is the characteristic wavelength of the radiation emitted by the moving charge; that is, the wavelength of the

emitted radiation must be large compared to the linear dimensions of the source. The electric dipole approximate is essentially a *nonrelativistic* and *long wavelength* approximation.

13.5 Magnetic Dipole and Electric Quadrupole Radiation

The second term in the multipole expansion of $\mathbf{A}$ has been written in eq. 13.22 as

$$\mathbf{A}_{M1}(\mathbf{r}, t) + \mathbf{A}_{E2}(\mathbf{r}, t) = \left(\frac{\mu_0}{4\pi}\right)\frac{1}{r}\int_\tau d\tau' \left(\frac{\hat{\mathbf{n}} \cdot \mathbf{r}'}{c}\right)\left(\frac{\partial}{\partial t_0}\mathbf{j}(\mathbf{r}', t_0)\right).$$

It is now possible to show that the integral in this expression can be written in terms of the (M1) and (E2) moments of the charge distribution producing the fields. This is accomplished as follows: Since the factor $[(\hat{\mathbf{n}} \cdot \mathbf{r}')/c]$ in the integrand is not a function of t_0, the partial derivative with respect to t_0 in the integrand may be replaced by the total derivative with respect to t_0 of the integral:

$$\mathbf{A}_{M1}(\mathbf{r}, t) + \mathbf{A}_{E2}(\mathbf{r}, t) = \left(\frac{\mu_0}{4\pi}\right)\frac{1}{r}\frac{d}{dt_0}\int_\tau d\tau' \left(\frac{\hat{\mathbf{n}} \cdot \mathbf{r}'}{c}\right)\mathbf{j}(\mathbf{r}', t_0).$$

Writing $\mathbf{j}(\mathbf{r}', t_0)$ as

$$\mathbf{j}(\mathbf{r}', t_0) = \sum_{i=1}^{N} q_i \mathbf{v}_i(t_0)\, \delta(\mathbf{r}_i - \mathbf{r}'),$$

the above contribution to the vector potential can be expressed as

$$\mathbf{A}_{M1}(\mathbf{r}, t) + \mathbf{A}_{E2}(\mathbf{r}, t) = \left(\frac{\mu_0}{4\pi}\right)\frac{1}{rc}\frac{d}{dt_0}\sum_{i=1}^{N} q_i \mathbf{v}_i(\hat{\mathbf{n}} \cdot \mathbf{r}_i). \tag{13.32}$$

The summand in eq. 13.32 can be transformed using the following simple identity which may be verified by direct calculation

$$\mathbf{v}_i(\hat{\mathbf{n}} \cdot \mathbf{r}_i) = \frac{1}{2}(\mathbf{r}_i \times \mathbf{v}_i) \times \hat{\mathbf{n}} + \frac{1}{2}\frac{d}{dt_0}[\mathbf{r}_i(\hat{\mathbf{n}} \cdot \mathbf{r}_i)].$$

Applying this identity to eq. 13.32 yields

$$\mathbf{A}_{M1}(\mathbf{r}, t) + \mathbf{A}_{E2}(\mathbf{r}, t) = \left(\frac{\mu_0}{4\pi}\right)\frac{1}{r}\frac{1}{2c}\frac{d}{dt_0}\sum_{i=1}^{N} q_i(\mathbf{r}_i \times \mathbf{v}_i) \times \hat{\mathbf{n}}$$

$$+ \left(\frac{\mu_0}{4\pi}\right)\frac{1}{r}\frac{1}{2c}\frac{d^2}{dt_0^2}\sum_{i=1}^{N} q_i \mathbf{r}_i(\hat{\mathbf{n}} \cdot \mathbf{r}_i). \tag{13.33}$$

In the first term on the right-hand side of eq. 13.33 is recognized the (M1) moment of the source, namely,

$$\boldsymbol{\mu} \equiv \tfrac{1}{2} \sum_{i=1}^{N} q_i(\mathbf{r}_i \times \mathbf{v}_i).$$

Consequently, $\mathbf{A}_{M1}(\mathbf{r}, t)$ is identified with

$$\mathbf{A}_{M1}(\mathbf{r}, t) \equiv \left(\frac{\mu_0}{4\pi}\right) \frac{1}{rc} \left(\frac{d}{dt_0} \boldsymbol{\mu}\right) \times \hat{\mathbf{n}}. \tag{13.34}$$

The **B**-field associated with the magnetic dipole contribution to **A** is obtained from eq. 13.17 and is

$$\mathbf{B}(\mathbf{r}, t) = \left(\frac{\mu_0}{4\pi}\right) \frac{1}{rc^2} \left[\left(\frac{d^2}{dt_0^2} \boldsymbol{\mu}\right) \times \hat{\mathbf{n}}\right] \times \hat{\mathbf{n}} \quad \begin{array}{l} \text{(M1) contribution to} \\ \text{radiation field.} \end{array} \tag{13.35}$$

The magnitude of the (M1) contribution to **B** contains the factor $\sin \vartheta$ where ϑ is the angle between the magnetic dipole moment and the direction to the field point. The radiation pattern, i.e. the dependence of $\mathscr{S}$ on ϑ, is the same for both (E1) and (M1) radiation, namely $\sin^2 \vartheta$. Consequently, it is not possible to distinguish (E1) radiation from (M1) radiation by observing the radiation pattern. The orientation of the **E** and **B** vectors for magnetic dipole radiation is indicated in Fig. 13.5; this should be compared with Fig. 13.3 for a radiating electric dipole.

The amount of energy radiated per unit time by a magnetic dipole can be expressed via the Poynting vector which is here

$$\mathscr{S} = \left(\frac{\mu_0}{4\pi}\right) \frac{1}{c^3} \frac{1}{4\pi r^2} \left|\frac{d^2}{dt_0^2} \boldsymbol{\mu}\right|^2 \sin^2 \vartheta \hat{\mathbf{n}} \tag{13.36}$$

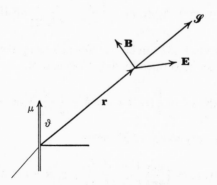

Fig. 13.5 The **E**- and **B**-fields in the wave zone due to a radiating magnetic dipole $\boldsymbol{\mu}$ are indicated.

which is similar to eq. 13.25 for a radiating electric dipole. The instantaneous power radiated by the dipole is the flux of $\mathscr{S}$ through a large spherical surface surrounding the dipole. The result is

$$P = \left(\frac{\mu_0}{4\pi}\right) \frac{2}{3c^2} \left|\frac{d^2}{dt_0^2} \boldsymbol{\mu}\right|^2. \tag{13.37}$$

An interesting observation can be made concerning the (M1) radiation from a system of charged particles all of which have the same charge-to-mass ratio. It has already been shown in Chapter 6 that the magnetic dipole moment of such a system is proportional to the total angular momentum of the system. Since the total angular momentum is a constant of the motion for such a charged system, it cannot emit (M1) radiation. Therefore, an isolated system of such interacting charges cannot emit either (E1) or (M1) radiation.

The introduction of the concept of the radiation resistance of a magnetic dipole can be made in a fashion similar to that employed in the case of the electric dipole. A magnetic dipole of moment $\boldsymbol{\mu}$ can be replaced by a circular loop of radius r_0 carrying a current I via the expression $\mu = \pi r^2 I$. Assuming the current to be oscillating with frequency ω, that is, $I = I_0 \cos(\omega t + \alpha)$, leads to an average power loss given by

$$P_{av} = \left[\left(\frac{\mu_0}{4\pi}\right) \frac{2\pi^2}{3} \frac{\omega^4 r_0^4}{c^3}\right] I_{rms}^2$$

where the quantity in brackets is the radiative resistance. Expressed in terms of the wavelength of the emitted (M1) radiation, the radiative resistance is:

$$R_{rad}(M1) = \left(\frac{\mu_0}{4\pi}\right)\left(\frac{32\pi^6 c}{3}\right)\left(\frac{r_0}{\lambda}\right)^4 = 320\pi^6 \left(\frac{r_0}{\lambda}\right)^4 \text{ ohms}.$$

The wavelength dependence of P_{av}, i.e., λ^{-4}, is characteristic of (M1) radiation.

The second term on the right-hand side of eq. 13.33 can be transformed in such a manner that the elements of the (E2) matrix appear explicitly. This is done as follows: in the wave zone $\mathbf{E}$ and $\mathbf{B}$ can be written in terms of the vector potential as

$$\mathbf{B} = -\frac{1}{c}\hat{\mathbf{n}} \times \frac{d\mathbf{A}}{dt_0},$$

$$\mathbf{E} = \hat{\mathbf{n}} \times \left(\hat{\mathbf{n}} \times \frac{d\mathbf{A}}{dt_0}\right).$$

Consequently since $\mathbf{E}$ and $\mathbf{B}$ are both perpendicular to $\mathbf{A}$, it is possible to add to $\mathbf{A}$ any term proportional to $\hat{\mathbf{n}}$ without changing the values of

E and **B** in the wave zone.   Without altering the value of the fields, it is possible to add to the summand of the second term on the right-hand side of eq. 13.33 the term

$$-\tfrac{1}{3}q_i r_i^2 \hat{\mathbf{n}}$$

with the result that $\mathbf{A}_{E2}(\mathbf{r}, t)$ may be expressed as

$$\mathbf{A}_{E2}(\mathbf{r}, t) = \left(\frac{\mu_0}{4\pi}\right) \frac{1}{6rc} \frac{d^2}{dt_0^2} \sum_{i=1}^{N} \{3q_i \mathbf{r}_i(\hat{\mathbf{n}} \cdot \mathbf{r}_i) - q_i r_i^2 \hat{\mathbf{n}}\} \qquad (13.38)$$

$$= \left(\frac{\mu_0}{4\pi}\right) \frac{1}{6rc} \frac{d^2}{dt_0^2} \mathbf{X}.$$

It should be recalled that the α-β element of the (E2) matrix has been defined as

$$Q_{\alpha\beta} = \sum_{i=1}^{N} [3q_i(r_i)_\alpha(r_i)_\beta - q_i r_i^2 \, \delta_{\alpha\beta}].$$

Calling n_α the α-Cartesian component of $\hat{\mathbf{n}}$ and $\mathbf{X}_\beta$ the β-Cartesian component of $\mathbf{X}$, it is noted that[1]

$$\sum_{\alpha=1}^{3} n_\alpha Q_{\alpha\beta} = \sum_{i=1}^{N} \sum_{\alpha=1}^{3} (3q_i n_\alpha r_{i\alpha} r_{i\beta} - q_i r_i^2 n_\alpha \, \delta_{\alpha\beta})$$

$$= \sum_{i=1}^{N} [3q_i(\hat{\mathbf{n}} \cdot \mathbf{r}_i)r_{i\beta} - q_i r_i^2 n_\beta] = \mathbf{X}_\beta.$$

Consequently the components of the vector **X** contain the elements of the electric quadrupole matrix $Q_{\alpha\beta}$. The vector **X** appearing in eq. 13.38 for $\mathbf{A}_{E2}$ depends on the vector $\hat{\mathbf{n}}$, and therefore the angular distribution of the (E2) radiation emitted by the charge distribution can be expressed in terms of the angle between $\hat{\mathbf{n}}$ and the orientation of the quadrupole.   It has already been remarked in electrostatics that it is always possible to orient the coordinate axes so that the quadrupole matrix is diagonal. Assuming this to be done, the components of the vector **X** can be expressed as

$$X_\beta = \sum_{\alpha=1}^{3} n_\alpha Q_{\alpha\beta} = \sum_{\alpha=1}^{3} n_\alpha Q_\beta \, \delta_{\alpha\beta} = n_\beta Q_\beta.$$

The components of $\mathbf{A}_{E2}$ will then depend on the corresponding components of $\hat{\mathbf{n}}$; i.e., $n_x \equiv \sin\theta \cos\phi$, $n_y \equiv \sin\theta \sin\phi$; $n_z \equiv \cos\theta$. The **E**- and **B**-fields derived from the vector potential can be expressed in terms of spherical harmonics of order two.   If the source has rotational symmetry about one of the coordinate axes, the **E**- and **B**-fields will not depend on

---

[1] In matrix notation the column matrix or vector **X** can be obtained from the column matrix **n** and the square matrix **Q** by the operation $\mathbf{X} = \mathbf{Qn}$.

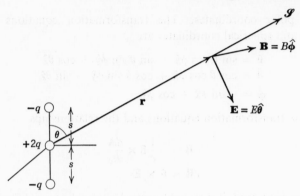

Fig. 13.6 An electric quadrupole consists in the charge distribution indicated. The distance s varies in time as $s = s_0 \cos \omega t$. With the axes indicated, the quadrupole matrix is diagonal with nonvanishing elements $Q_{33} = -2Q_{22} = -2\,Q_{11} = Q \cos^2 \omega t$, with $Q = -4qs_0{}^2$. The **E**- and **B**-fields in the wave zone are as indicated.

azimuthal angle. Although these statements about (E2) radiation will not be proved in general, these features will become evident in the particular case of the radiating quadrupole in Example 13.2 and in the problems at the end of the chapter.

EXAMPLE 13.2   Consider the quadrupole source of Fig. 13.6 in which $s = s_0 \cos \omega t$. With the choice of the axes shown, the (E2) matrix is diagonal. The diagonal elements are

$$Q_{33} = -4qs_0^2 \cos^2 \omega t = -2Q_{11} = -2Q_{22} = Q \cos^2 \omega t.$$

Since $Q_{\alpha\beta}$ is diagonal, it follows that $X_\beta = n_\beta Q_\beta$, or, in particular,

$$\hat{\mathbf{x}} \cdot \mathbf{X} = \hat{\mathbf{x}} \cdot \hat{\mathbf{n}}(-1/2Q \cos^2 \omega t) = -1/2Q \sin \theta \cos \phi \cos^2 \omega t$$
$$\hat{\mathbf{y}} \cdot \mathbf{X} = \hat{\mathbf{y}} \cdot \hat{\mathbf{n}}(-1/2Q \cos^2 \omega t) = -1/2Q \sin \theta \sin \phi \cos^2 \omega t$$
$$\hat{\mathbf{z}} \cdot \mathbf{X} = \hat{\mathbf{z}} \cdot \hat{\mathbf{n}}(Q \cos^2 \omega t) = +Q \cos \theta \cos^2 \omega t.$$

The corresponding Cartesian components of $\mathbf{A}_{\text{E2}}$ are

$$\hat{\mathbf{x}} \cdot \mathbf{A}_{\text{E2}} = \left(\frac{\mu_0}{4\pi}\right) \frac{\omega^2}{6rc} Q \sin \theta \cos \phi \cos 2\omega t$$

$$\hat{\mathbf{y}} \cdot \mathbf{A}_{\text{E2}} = \left(\frac{\mu_0}{4\pi}\right) \frac{\omega^2}{6rc} Q \sin \theta \sin \phi \cos 2\omega t$$

$$\hat{\mathbf{z}} \cdot \mathbf{A}_{\text{E2}} = -\left(\frac{\mu_0}{4\pi}\right) \frac{\omega^2}{3rc} Q \cos \theta \cos 2\omega t.$$

The **B**- and **E**-fields derived from $\mathbf{A}_{\text{E2}}$ are most conveniently expressed in spherical polar coordinates. The transformation equations between Cartesian and spherical coordinates are

$$\hat{n} = \sin\theta\cos\phi\hat{x} + \sin\theta\sin\phi\hat{y} + \cos\theta\hat{z}$$
$$\hat{\theta} = \cos\theta\cos\phi\hat{x} + \cos\theta\sin\phi\hat{y} - \sin\theta\hat{z}$$
$$\hat{\phi} = -\sin\phi\hat{x} + \cos\phi\hat{y}.$$

Using these transformation equations and the relationships

$$\mathbf{B} = -\frac{1}{c}\hat{n}\times\frac{d\mathbf{A}}{dt_0}$$
$$c\mathbf{B} = \hat{n}\times\mathbf{E}$$

valid in the wave zone, it is straightforward although somewhat tedious to show that

$$\mathbf{B}\cdot\hat{n} = 0 \qquad\qquad\qquad \mathbf{E}\cdot\hat{n} = 0$$

$$\mathbf{B}\cdot\hat{\theta} = 0 \qquad\qquad\qquad \mathbf{E}\cdot\hat{\theta} = \left(\frac{\mu_0}{4\pi}\right)\frac{\omega^3}{2rc}Q(\sin 2\theta)(\sin 2\omega t)$$

$$\mathbf{B}\cdot\hat{\phi} = \left(\frac{\mu_0}{4\pi}\right)\frac{\omega^3}{2rc^2}Q(\sin 2\theta)(\sin 2\omega t) \quad \mathbf{E}\cdot\hat{\phi} = 0.$$

The Poynting vector calculated from these values for $\mathbf{E}$ and $\mathbf{B}$ is

$$\mathscr{S} = \left(\frac{\mu_0}{4\pi}\right)\frac{1}{4\pi r^2}\left(\frac{\omega^6 Q^2}{4c^3}\right)(\sin^2 2\theta)(\sin^2 2\omega t)\hat{n}.$$

The instantaneous and average power emission associated with the source are, respectively,

$$P = \left(\frac{\mu_0}{4\pi}\right)\frac{2\omega^6}{15c^3}Q^2\sin^2 2\omega t$$

$$P_{\mathrm{av}} = \left(\frac{\mu_0}{4\pi}\right)\frac{\omega^6 Q^2}{15c^3}.$$

13.6　Further Remarks on Multipole Radiation

It is possible to expand the radiation fields keeping higher order terms in $[(\hat{n}\cdot\mathbf{r}')/c]$ than those considered so far which would yield components of $\mathbf{A}$ which could be expressed in terms of the higher multipole moments of the radiating charge and current distributions such as magnetic quadrupole (M2), electric octupole (E3), etc. The method employed above in the case of (E1), (M1), and (E2) emission is not particularly tractable for these higher multipole terms. However, convenient methods do exist for the calculation of radiation fields of arbitrarily high multipolarity and the reader is referred to more advanced texts for the description of such methods.

For an oscillating system, the rate at which energy is emitted in a given multipole order is dependent on the frequency of the source in a manner characteristic of the multipole order. It has already been shown that

$$P_{E1} \sim \omega^4 \qquad P_{M1} \sim \omega^4.$$
$$P_{E2} \sim \omega^6$$

It can be further shown that the frequency dependence of the rate of emission can be expressed as

$$P_l \sim \omega^{2(l+1)} \tag{13.39}$$

where l = multipole order. The frequency dependence of the emission rate depends on the multipole order and is the same for (El) emission as it is for (Ml) emission.

In the discussion of (E1), (M1), and (E2) radiation, it was implicitly assumed that there were no "interference" terms in the emission rate; i.e., the instantaneous power was expressed as a sum of terms of the form

$$P = P_{E1} + P_{M1} + P_{E2} + \cdots,$$

This assumption can be verified as follows. For simplicity, although the argument is quite general, consider a source whose time-dependent multipole moments vanish except for the (E1) and (M1) moments. The **B**- and **E**-fields for these sources have been obtained previously in this chapter and may be expressed as

$$\begin{aligned}
\mathbf{B} &= \hat{\mathbf{n}} \times \boldsymbol{\alpha} + \hat{\mathbf{n}} \times (\hat{\mathbf{n}} \times \boldsymbol{\beta}) \\
\mathbf{E} &= -c\hat{\mathbf{n}} \times (\hat{\mathbf{n}} \times \boldsymbol{\alpha}) - c\hat{\mathbf{n}} \times [\hat{\mathbf{n}} \times (\hat{\mathbf{n}} \times \boldsymbol{\beta})]
\end{aligned} \tag{13.40}$$

where

$$\boldsymbol{\alpha} \equiv -\frac{1}{c}\left(\frac{\mu_0}{4\pi}\right)\frac{1}{r}\frac{d^2}{dt_0^2}\mathbf{p}$$

$$\boldsymbol{\beta} \equiv \frac{1}{c^2}\left(\frac{\mu_0}{4\pi}\right)\frac{1}{r}\frac{d^2}{dt_0^2}\boldsymbol{\mu}.$$

It is straightforward to show that those terms in the rate of emission which depend on both $\mathbf{p}$ and $\boldsymbol{\mu}$ vanish. For this purpose, consider the cross terms that appear in the Poynting vector; these will be designated by $\mathscr{S}(\boldsymbol{\mu}, \mathbf{p})$ and are:

$$\mathscr{S}(\boldsymbol{\mu}, \mathbf{p}) = -\frac{c}{\mu_0}\{[\hat{\mathbf{n}} \times (\hat{\mathbf{n}} \times \boldsymbol{\alpha})] \times [\hat{\mathbf{n}} \times (\hat{\mathbf{n}} \times \boldsymbol{\beta})]$$
$$+ [\hat{\mathbf{n}} \times [\hat{\mathbf{n}} \times (\hat{\mathbf{n}} \times \boldsymbol{\beta})]] \times [\hat{\mathbf{n}} \times \boldsymbol{\alpha}]\}. \tag{13.41}$$

The following vector identities which can be established by direct evaluation are useful in simplifying eq. 13.41:

$$\hat{n} \times [\hat{n} \times (\hat{n} \times \boldsymbol{\beta})] \equiv -(\hat{n} \times \boldsymbol{\beta})$$
$$[\hat{n} \times (\hat{n} \times \boldsymbol{\alpha})] \times [\hat{n} \times (\hat{n} \times \boldsymbol{\beta})] \equiv (\hat{n} \times \boldsymbol{\alpha}) \times (\hat{n} \times \boldsymbol{\beta})$$

where liberal use of the identity

$$\mathbf{a} \times (\mathbf{b} \times \mathbf{c}) = (\mathbf{a} \cdot \mathbf{c})\mathbf{b} - (\mathbf{a} \cdot \mathbf{b})\mathbf{c}$$

has been made. The interference term in the Poynting vector is then expressible as

$$\mathscr{S}(\boldsymbol{\mu}, \mathbf{p}) = \frac{-2c}{\mu_0} (\hat{n} \times \boldsymbol{\alpha}) \times (\hat{n} \times \boldsymbol{\beta}) = \frac{-2c}{\mu_0} [\hat{n} \cdot (\boldsymbol{\alpha} \times \boldsymbol{\beta})]\hat{n}. \quad (13.42)$$

The Poynting vector thus contains an interference term proportional to $\cos \vartheta$ where $\vartheta \equiv$ angle between $\hat{n}$ and $(\boldsymbol{\alpha} \times \boldsymbol{\beta})$. The flux of this interference term through a large sphere surrounding the source must be calculated in order to see the effect of the term of the instantaneous power emission of the source. This involves the integral

$$\int_0^\pi \cos \vartheta [\sin \vartheta \, d\vartheta],$$

which vanishes identically. Therefore although the intensity of radiation emitted in a given direction does contain an interference term, the intensity integrated over all directions of emission does not. This result can be traced back ultimately to the fact that whereas $\mathbf{p}$ is a polar vector, $\boldsymbol{\mu}$ is an axial vector.

Finally, it should be remarked that the multipole expansion of the radiation fields is an inherently non-relativistic approximation involving as it does an expansion in powers of (v/c) of the charged particles in the source. Consequently it is not suitable in inherently relativistic situations where other methods must be employed.

PROBLEMS

13.1   If $\mathbf{B}$ is given in the wave zone by eq. 13.17, i.e., $c\mathbf{B} = -\hat{n} \times d\mathbf{A}/dt$, show from the expressions for φ and $\mathbf{A}$ that $\mathbf{E}$ is given by $\mathbf{E} = \hat{n} \times (\hat{n} \times d\mathbf{A}/dt)$.

13.2   Using the wave zone expressions for $\mathbf{E}$ and $\mathbf{B}$ given in Problem 13.1, calculate an explicit expression for the Poynting vector $\mathscr{S}$ in terms of $d\mathbf{A}/dt$.

13.3   Express the wave zone values for the (E1) contribution to $\mathbf{E}$ and $\mathbf{B}$ in spherical polar coordinates.

13.4   In radiation problems, it is sometimes useful to introduce an auxiliary field called the Hertz field $\boldsymbol{\pi}$ defined as

$$c^2\mathbf{A}(\mathbf{r}, t) = \frac{\partial}{\partial t} \boldsymbol{\pi}(\mathbf{r}, t).$$

Find expressions for **E** and **B** in terms of the Hertz vector. Calculate the (E1) approximation to π.

13.5 Calculate the total cross section σ_T for the scattering of a plane electromagnetic wave by a point particle of charge q and mass m. Assume that the charge can be treated nonrelativistically. Demonstrate that the cross section, sometimes called the Thomson cross section, is independent of the frequency of the incident wave. Express σ_T in terms of the "classical electromagnetic radius" of the charge, $r_0 \equiv q^2/mc^2$. (Note: The total cross section is defined by the expression

$$\sigma_T \equiv \frac{\text{power scattered (or emitted)}}{\text{flux of incident energy}}.$$

13.6 Express the wave zone values for the (M1) contribution to **E** and **B** in spherical polar coordinates. Compare these results with the analogous expressions for the (E1) fields.

13.7 A charge q moves according to the equation $r = r_0 \cos \omega t$. Another charge q moves in a circular orbit of radius r_0 with angular frequency ω. Calculate the ratio between the rates of radiation from these two charges.

13.8 A charge distribution consists in a magnetic dipole $\boldsymbol{\mu}$ and an electric dipole **p** which are parallel. Using the expressions for **E** and **B** calculated in Problems 13.3 and 13.6 in spherical polar coordinates, calculate the Poynting vector in the wave zone for this distribution. Repeat the calculation assuming that **p** and $\boldsymbol{\mu}$ make an angle β with respect to one another.

13.9 Using the expression for $\mathscr{S}$ calculated in the previous problem, show that the total power radiated by the distribution described in that problem does *not* contain terms depending on both **p** and $\boldsymbol{\mu}$, i.e., interference terms.

13.10 Calculate the radiation pattern for an (E2) distribution which does not possess rotational symmetry. (Note: For such a distribution, the diagonalized (E2) matrix has *two* linearly independent elements.)

13.11 Two electric dipoles each consist in charges $+q$ and $-q$ separated by a fixed distance l. The two dipoles are positioned in such a way that their centers coincide. The dipoles rotate in the same plane with angular frequency ω but in opposite directions. Calculate the radiation pattern from these dipoles and discuss the multipole nature of the radiation.

13.12 An excellent semiclassical model of moderately heavy nuclei is a liquid drop of uniform charge density whose surface can be approximated by the expression: $R(\theta) = R_0[1 + \beta P_2(\cos \theta)]$. The total charge of such a nucleus is Ze where e is the magnitude of the electronic charge. The internal motion of this liquid drop can be represented by $\beta = \beta_0 \cos \omega t$. Calculate the rate of radiation from such a nucleus in the long wave length limit discussing the multipolarity of the radiation.

14 | *Motion of Charged Particles in Electromagnetic Fields; Plasmas*

The discussion in previous chapters has centered almost solely in the properties of electromagnetic fields and their interaction with matter. The present chapter, however, is devoted to a discussion of the behavior of charged particles in electric and magnetic fields. The first part of the discussion will examine the trajectories of individual charged particles in such fields; the latter part of the chapter will consider the behavior of an ensemble or system of charged particles.

14.1 Motion of a Charge in a Static E-Field

The behavior of a charge in an electric field is governed by the relatively simple equation of motion defining the E-field:

$$\mathbf{f} = m\frac{d^2\mathbf{r}}{dt^2} = q\mathbf{E}. \tag{14.1}$$

The acceleration of a charged particle in an E-field is proportional to the field, the constant of proportionality being the charge-to-mass ratio of the particle. For a uniform E-field it is convenient to write the instantaneous velocity of the particle as

$$\mathbf{v} = \mathbf{v}_\| + \mathbf{v}_\perp$$

where $\mathbf{v}_\|$, $\mathbf{v}_\perp$ are the components of $\mathbf{v}$ parallel and perpendicular to the E-field, respectively. Referring to eq. 14.1, the following statements may be made:

(a) $\mathbf{v}_\perp$ is a constant in time;

(b) $\mathbf{v}_\| = \mathbf{v}_0 + \left(\dfrac{q}{m}\right) t\mathbf{E}$

$$\tag{14.2}$$

where $\mathbf{v}_0$ is the value of $\mathbf{v}_\|$ at time $t = 0$. The distance covered by the charge in the time t may also be conveniently decomposed into parallel and perpendicular components as $\mathbf{d} = \mathbf{d}_\perp + \mathbf{d}_\parallel$. From eqs. 14.2 it follows that

(a) $\mathbf{d}_\perp = \mathbf{v}_\perp t$

(b) $\mathbf{d}_\parallel = \mathbf{v}_0 t + \dfrac{1}{2}\left(\dfrac{q}{m}\right)t^2\mathbf{E}$

$$(14.3)$$

which can be rewritten, eliminating the time variable, as a relationship between $d_\parallel$ and $d_\perp$:

$$d_\parallel = \left(\frac{v_0}{v_\perp}\right) d_\perp + \frac{1}{2}\left(\frac{q}{m}\right)\frac{E}{v_\perp^2}\, d_\perp^2. \tag{14.4}$$

When $d_\perp$ is plotted as a function of $d_\parallel$, Eq. 14.4 is that of a parabola. The trajectory of a charged particle in a uniform E-field is the same as that of a projectile in a uniform gravitational field.

The trajectory of a charged particle in a nonuniform but static E-field is generally complicated. In the examples in Section 14.2 the nonuniform E-field is assumed to be axially symmetric. This allows for certain simplifications, but serves to illustrate the salient effects of nonuniformity.

14.2 Electrostatic Lens with Axial Symmetry

As an example of the behavior of charged particles in a nonuniform field, consider an electrostatic potential which is axially symmetric, that is, adopting cylindrical coordinates

$$\varphi(\mathbf{r}) = \varphi(z, \rho). \tag{14.5}$$

The E-field derived from such a potential has two components, E_z and E_ρ. The equation of motion for the radial component of $\mathbf{r}$ is

$$\frac{d^2\rho}{dt^2} = \frac{q}{m}\, E_\rho. \tag{14.6}$$

To analyze the possible trajectories of a charged particle in an axially symmetric E-field, it is convenient to remove the time-variable in eq. 14.6 by the following transformation:

$$\frac{d}{dt} = \left(\frac{dz}{dt}\right)\frac{\partial}{\partial z} + \left(\frac{d\rho}{dt}\right)\frac{\partial}{\partial \rho}. \tag{14.7}$$

In the discussion that follows, it will be assumed that the radial velocity,

$d\rho/dt$, attained by the charge is negligible compared to the axial velocity, dx/dt. Therefore to a good approximation,

$$\frac{d}{dt} = v \frac{d}{dx} \quad \text{where} \quad v = \frac{dx}{dt}.$$

In terms of the new variables, eq. 14.6 becomes

$$v \frac{d}{dx} \left(v \frac{d}{dx} \rho \right) = \frac{q}{m} E_\rho. \tag{14.8}$$

According to the definition of the electrostatic potential, the change in kinetic energy of the particle as it moves from some initial position designated by the subscript zero to some final position is

$$\tfrac{1}{2}mv^2 - \tfrac{1}{2}mv_0^2 = q(\varphi - \varphi_0).$$

If the initial velocity of the charge moving in the field is zero and the electrostatic potential is arbitrarily chosen to be zero at this point, then

$$v^2 = v_x^2 + v_\rho^2 = \frac{2q}{m} \varphi.$$

However, it has been assumed that the radial component of the particle velocity is always small compared to the axial component, i.e., $v \approx v_x$, and therefore eq. 14.8 can be rewritten as

$$\sqrt{\frac{2q}{m} \varphi} \frac{d}{dx} \left(\sqrt{\frac{2q}{m} \varphi} \frac{d}{dx} \rho \right) = \frac{q}{m} E_\rho. \tag{14.9}$$

(Although φ is a function of both x and ρ, it has been assumed in writing eq. 14.9 that the derivatives of φ with respect to ρ are negligible compared

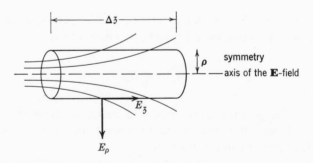

Fig. 14.1   A small cylinder of length Δx is constructed with its axis as the axis of symmetry of the electrostatic potential.   Gauss's law applied to this cylinder yields a relation between E_ρ and E_x near the symmetry axis.   This relation is given in eq. 14.10 as $E_\rho = -(\rho/2) \, \partial E_x/\partial x$.

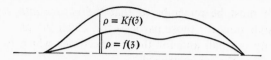

Fig. 14.2   Two possible trajectories of charged particles in an electrostatic lens are sketched.   The trajectories can be expressed as: $\rho = f(z)$ and $\rho = Kf(z)$, respectively, where K is a constant.

to the corresponding derivatives with respect to z.) E_ρ can be expressed in terms useful for this discussion by application of Gauss's law to a small cylinder of length Δz whose axis is the axis of symmetry of the potential. (See Fig. 14.1.)   The net outward radial flux through the cylinder is $2\pi\rho \, \Delta z E_\rho$.   The net outward axial flux is

$$\pi\rho^2[E_z(z + \Delta z) - E_z(z)] = \pi\rho^2 \frac{\partial E_z}{\partial z}\Delta z.$$

Since there is no charge contained within the cylinder, it follows that

$$E_\rho = -\frac{\rho}{2}\frac{\partial E_z}{\partial z}. \tag{14.10}$$

Consistent with the assumptions already made concerning the relative orders of magnitude of the various derivatives of φ, this expression can be written as

$$E_\rho = \frac{\rho}{2}\frac{d^2\varphi}{dz^2}.$$

Equation 14.10 holds only in the neighborhood of the symmetry axis, i.e., $\rho \approx 0$.   Therefore

$$\sqrt{\frac{2q}{m}}\,\varphi\,\frac{d}{dz}\left(\sqrt{\frac{2q}{m}}\,\varphi\,\frac{d}{dz}\rho\right) = \rho\left(\frac{q}{2m}\right)\frac{d^2}{dz^2}\,\varphi$$

$$\tag{14.11}$$

or

$$\sqrt{\varphi}\,\frac{d}{dz}\left(\sqrt{\varphi}\,\frac{d}{dz}\rho\right) = \frac{\rho}{4}\frac{d^2}{dz^2}\,\varphi.$$

Equation 14.11 has several interesting properties (1) q and m do not explicitly appear, and thus all charged particles behave similarly in the field; (2) the equation is *homogeneous* in ρ.   The latter property of the equation implies that if $\rho = f(z)$ is the equation of a given charged particle trajectory in the field, $\rho = Kf(z)$ where K is a constant is also the equation of a possible charged particle trajectory.   (See Fig. 14.2.)   This is just the property required for a *lens*.   All charged particles which start out from a point on the axis ($\rho = 0$) will return to the axis at the same point.

Of course, it must be remembered that the *electrostatic lens equation,* eq. 14.11, holds only for those particles for which the radial component of the velocity is small and for those trajectories which do not depart significantly from the symmetry axis.

EXAMPLE 14.1   Consider the effect on charged particle trajectories of a small circular hole in one plate of a parallel plate capacitor. (See Fig. 14.3.)   The potential at the plate ($x = x_1$) with the hole is taken to be φ_1, whereas the potential at the other plate ($x = x_0$) is zero.   If the hole did not exist, the field in the region between the plates would be uniform.   A charged particle starting at rest from $x = x_0$ would travel in a straight line toward the other plate and reach the plate with a kinetic energy $q\varphi_1$.   But because of the hole in the plate at x_1, a charged particle which passes through the hole will be deflected and pass into the region $x > x_1$. Here it is assumed to an excellent approximation that $\varphi = \varphi_1(x > x_1)$. The lens equation may be employed directly in this case:

$$\sqrt{\varphi}\,\frac{d}{dx}\left(\sqrt{\varphi}\,\frac{d}{dx}\,\rho\right) = \frac{\rho}{4}\frac{d}{dx}\left(\frac{d}{dx}\,\varphi\right). \tag{14.12}$$

To a first approximation, the variation of φ with x may be neglected, but the variation of $d\varphi/dx$ with x will be kept.   In this approximation eq. 14.12 may be integrated directly to yield

$$\left.\frac{d\rho}{dx}\right)_{x_1}^{x_2} = \frac{\rho}{4\varphi_1}\left.\frac{d\varphi}{dx}\right)_{x_1}^{x_2} = \frac{-\rho}{4\varphi_1}\,[E(x_2) - E(x_1)].$$

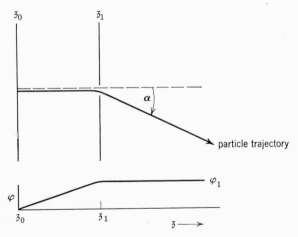

Fig. 14.3   A parallel plate capacitor has a hole in one plate.   This system acts as a diverging electrostatic lens for charged particles traveling from x_0 to x_1.   In the region $x > x_1$, the electrostatic potential is assumed to have a constant value φ_1, whereas the electrostatic field between the plates is assumed to be constant, $\mathbf{E}_0$.

At $x = x_2$, the E-field is zero, whereas at $x = x_1$ the field is approximately that which exists between the plates, which shall be designated as E_0. Therefore

$$\frac{d\rho}{dx}\bigg)_{x_1}^{x_2} = \frac{\rho}{4\varphi_1} E_0. \tag{14.13}$$

The left-hand side of eq. 14.13 is the tangent of the angle α that the straight line trajectory in the region $x > x_1$ makes with the symmetry axis. Consequently

$$\tan \alpha = \frac{\rho}{4\varphi_1} E_0.$$

Since the lens equation is valid only for those trajectories which lie near the symmetry axis, α must be small and consequently $\tan \alpha \approx \alpha$; that is,

$$\alpha = \frac{\rho}{4\varphi_1} E_0.$$

The hole thus acts like a diverging lens for a bundle of parallel trajectories close to the symmetry axis. The *focal length* of the lens is defined as

$$f = \frac{\rho}{\alpha} = \frac{4\varphi_1}{E_0}.$$

14.3   *Motion of a Charge in a Static* **B**-*Field*

The behavior of a charge in a static **B**-field is governed by the equation of motion:

$$\mathbf{f} = q\mathbf{v} \times \mathbf{B}. \tag{14.14}$$

The rate at which the **B**-field does work on the charge is

$$\mathbf{f} \cdot \mathbf{v} = q\mathbf{v} \cdot (\mathbf{v} \times \mathbf{B}) \equiv 0.$$

This implies that the force due to a static magnetic field can change the direction in which the particle is moving, but cannot change the magnitude of its velocity. It is convenient to write **v** as

$$\mathbf{v} = \mathbf{v}_\parallel + \mathbf{v}_\perp$$

where $\mathbf{v}_\parallel$ and $\mathbf{v}_\perp$ are the components of **v** parallel and perpendicular to the field direction, respectively. The force equation is then

$$\frac{d^2\mathbf{r}}{dt^2} = \frac{d}{dt}\mathbf{v}_\perp + \frac{d}{dt}\mathbf{v}_\parallel = \left(\frac{q}{m}\right)\mathbf{v}_\perp \times B$$

from which it follows that $\mathbf{v}_\parallel$ is constant in time. In a coordinate system moving with velocity $\mathbf{v}_\parallel$, the charged particle moves in a circle since $\mathbf{f}$ is always perpendicular to $\mathbf{v}_\perp$. The radius of the circle is obtained by equating the Lorentz force to the centrifugal force; that is,

$$\frac{mv_\perp^2}{R} = qv_\perp B$$

yielding

$$R = \frac{mv_\perp}{qB}. \tag{14.15}$$

The angular velocity associated with this circular orbit is defined as

$$\omega_c \equiv \frac{v_\perp}{R} = \left(\frac{q}{m}\right)B$$

which is the so-called *cyclotron frequency*. Note that the magnitude of the cyclotron frequency is *twice* the Larmor frequency ω_L introduced previously. In the stationary system the trajectory of the charged particle is a helix. (See Fig. 14.4.)

Associated with the motion of the particle perpendicular to the field direction is an effective magnetic moment whose magnitude $|\boldsymbol{\mu}|$ is given by

$$|\boldsymbol{\mu}| = \text{effective current} \times \text{cross-sectional area of helix}$$
$$|\boldsymbol{\mu}| = \left(\frac{qv_\perp}{2\pi R}\right) \times \pi R^2 = \frac{mv_\perp^2}{2B}.$$

In terms of $K_\perp =$ kinetic energy due to tranverse motion $= \tfrac{1}{2}mv_\perp^2$, this effective moment is written as

$$|\boldsymbol{\mu}| = \frac{K_\perp}{B}. \tag{14.16}$$

In a nonuniform axially symmetric **B**-field which is slowly varying in the axial direction, it is possible to prove an interesting theorem: a charged particle will move such that its effective magnetic moment is a constant of the motion. For the proof of this theorem we write

$$\mathbf{B}(\mathbf{r}) = B_z(\rho, z)\hat{\mathbf{z}} + B_\rho(\rho, z)\hat{\boldsymbol{\rho}}.$$

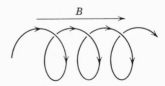

Fig. 14.4   The trajectory of a charged particle in a uniform **B**-field is a helix. The angular frequency associated with this motion is the cyclotron frequency $\omega_c = (q/m)B$.

The total kinetic energy K of a charged particle in a **B**-field is constant; consequently

$$\frac{d}{dt}\left(\frac{1}{2}mv_x^2\right) = -\frac{d}{dt}K_\perp$$

where $K_\perp$ is now, more generally, the contribution to K due to motion perpendicular to x, the axis of symmetry. However, if the field is slowly varying, the motion of a particle perpendicular to x is to a very good approximation circular; that is, in a time of the order of the cyclotron period, the charged particle has moved a distance in which the change in B_x is negligible—v_ρ is small compared to v_ϕ. Consequently eq. 14.16 may be used for $K_\perp$, yielding

$$\frac{d}{dt}\left(\frac{1}{2}mv_x^2\right) = -\frac{d}{dt}(|\boldsymbol{\mu}|B_x). \qquad (14.17)$$

It is possible to derive an alternative expression for the left-hand side of eq. 14.17 which will produce the desired theorem. Consider the axial or x-component of the equation of motion:

$$m\frac{d}{dt}v_x = qv_\phi B_\rho. \qquad (14.18)$$

Applying Gauss's law to a cylinder parallel to the x-axis yields (see Fig. 14.5)

radial flux through cylinder sides + axial flux through ends = 0

$$(2\pi\rho)\Delta xB_\rho + \pi\rho^2[B_x(x + \Delta x) - B_x(x)] = 0$$

or
$$B_\rho = -\frac{1}{2}\rho\frac{\partial B_x}{\partial x}. \qquad (14.19)$$

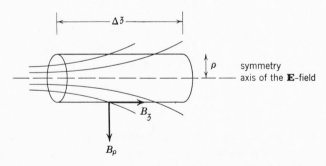

Fig. 14.5   A small cylinder of length Δx is constructed with its axis as the axis of symmetry of a non-uniform axially symmetric **B**-field. Gauss's law applied to this cylinder yields a relation between B_ρ and B_x near the symmetry axis. This relation is given in eq. 14.19 as $B_\rho = -\frac{1}{2}\rho(\partial B_x/\partial x)$.

Combining eqs. 14.18 and 14.19 yields

$$m \frac{d}{dt} v_x = -\frac{1}{2} q\rho v_\Phi \frac{\partial B_x}{\partial x}.$$

However, according to the definition of the effective magnetic moment $|\boldsymbol{\mu}|$,

$$\tfrac{1}{2} q\rho v_\Phi = |\boldsymbol{\mu}|$$

and therefore:

$$m \frac{d}{dt} v_x = -|\boldsymbol{\mu}| \frac{\partial B_x}{\partial x}. \tag{14.20}$$

Multiplying both sides of eq. 14.20 by v_x yields

$$\frac{d}{dt} \left(\frac{1}{2} m v_x^2 \right) = -|\boldsymbol{\mu}| \left(\frac{\partial}{\partial x} B_x \right) v_x = -|\boldsymbol{\mu}| \frac{d}{dt} B_x. \tag{14.21}$$

Comparing eqs. 14.17 and 14.21 yields the desired result, namely,

$$\frac{d|\boldsymbol{\mu}|}{dt} = 0.$$

It is important to remember that this result was proved only for a slowly varying axially symmetric **B**-field.

Equation 14.17 may be integrated directly to yield

$$\tfrac{1}{2} m v_x^2 + |\boldsymbol{\mu}| B_x = \text{constant} = a. \tag{14.22}$$

This equation coupled with the constancy of $|\boldsymbol{\mu}|$ is the basis of an important phenomenon called *magnetic mirrors*. If a charged particle exists with a given longitudinal kinetic energy and $|\boldsymbol{\mu}|$ in a field containing region, as it moves toward a region of increasing B_x its kinetic energy will decrease. The particle cannot exist, however, in a region for which $B_x > a/|\boldsymbol{\mu}|$ as its longitudinal kinetic energy would have to be negative in this region. Consequently the charged particle is reflected from the *barrier* $B_x \approx a/|\boldsymbol{\mu}|$ and is confined to the region for which $B_x < a/|\boldsymbol{\mu}|$.

14.4   Magnetic Lens

A slowly varying axially symmetric magnetic field has the properties of a lens for parallel beams of charged particles. It will be assumed that all charged particle trajectories remain close to the axis of symmetry of the fields; as for an electrostatic or an optical lens, this assumption will eliminate discussion of the aberration of the lens due to its finite "thickness". It will also be assumed that the radial component of **v** is negligible.

Newton's equations of motion in cylindrical coordinates are

$$f_\rho = m\left[\frac{d^2\rho}{dt^2} - \rho\left(\frac{d\phi}{dt}\right)^2\right] \tag{14.23a}$$

$$\rho f_\phi = m\frac{d}{dt}\left(\rho^2\frac{d\phi}{dt}\right) \tag{14.23b}$$

$$f_z = m\frac{d^2z}{dt^2}. \tag{14.23c}$$

The **B**-field is assumed to be axially symmetric

$$\mathbf{B(r)} = B_\rho\hat{\boldsymbol{\rho}} + B_z\hat{\mathbf{z}}$$

from which it follows that

$$q\mathbf{v} \times \mathbf{B} = q\left\{\rho\frac{d\phi}{dt}B_z\hat{\boldsymbol{\rho}} + \left[\frac{dz}{dt}B_\rho - \frac{d\rho}{dt}B_z\right]\hat{\boldsymbol{\phi}} + \rho\frac{d\phi}{dt}B_\rho\hat{\mathbf{z}}\right\}.$$

However, to a good approximation the major components of **B** and **v** are the axial ones, and therefore the term in $\rho(d\phi/dt)B_\rho = v_\phi B_\rho$ can be disregarded. Consequently eqs. 14.23 become

$$m\left[\frac{d^2\rho}{dt^2} - \rho\left(\frac{d\phi}{dt}\right)^2\right] = qB_z\rho\frac{d\phi}{dt}, \tag{14.24a}$$

$$m\frac{d}{dt}\left(\rho^2\frac{d\phi}{dt}\right) = q\rho\left[B_\rho\frac{dz}{dt} - B_z\frac{d\rho}{dt}\right], \tag{14.24b}$$

$$m\frac{d^2z}{dt^2} = 0. \tag{14.24c}$$

Equation 14.24b may be used to solve for $(d\phi/dt)$. This proceeds as follows. As shown in Section 14.3, Gauss's law for a slowly varying axially symmetric magnetic field may be expressed as (see eq. 14.19)

$$B_\rho = -\frac{1}{2}\rho\frac{\partial B_z}{\partial z}$$

which, when substituted into eq. 14.24b yields

$$\frac{d}{dt}\left(\rho^2\frac{d\phi}{dt}\right) = -\left(\frac{q}{m}\right)\rho\left[\frac{1}{2}\rho\left(\frac{dz}{dt}\right)\left(\frac{\partial B_z}{\partial z}\right) + \left(\frac{d\rho}{dt}\right)B_z\right].$$

Consistent with the approximation already introduced, the derivatives with respect to time may be converted into derivatives with respect to z by the transformation

$$\frac{d}{dt} = v\frac{d}{dz} \quad \text{where} \quad v = \left(\frac{dz}{dt}\right).$$

The equation of motion becomes

$$\frac{d}{dz}\left(\rho^2 v \frac{d\phi}{dz}\right) = -\left(\frac{q}{m}\right)\left[\frac{\rho^2}{2}\frac{dB_z}{dz} + \rho\left(\frac{d\rho}{dz}\right)B_z\right]$$

where it has been assumed that radial derivatives are negligible compared with axial derivatives. This equation can be immediately integrated to yield

$$\rho^2 \frac{d\phi}{dz}\bigg)_{z_0}^{z} = -\frac{q}{2mv}\left(\rho^2 B_z\right)_{z_0}^{z}.$$

The assumption is now made that the lens is "short"; that is, the **B**-field is confined to a finite region. At z_0 where the particle enters the lens, $B_z = 0$ and $d\phi/dz = 0$; that is, the particle is traveling in a straight line. Therefore at z, a typical point within the lens,

$$\frac{d\phi}{dz} = -\frac{q}{2mv}B_z$$

or

$$\frac{d\phi}{dt} = -\frac{q}{2m}B_z. \tag{14.25}$$

The angular frequency of a charged particle within the lens is just the Larmor frequency or one-half the cyclotron frequency.

To complete the analysis of the trajectories within the lens, the value of $d\phi/dt$ is substituted back into the equation for radial motion, eq. 14.24a.

$$\frac{d^2\rho}{dt^2} = -\left(\frac{q}{2m}\right)^2 \rho B_z^2. \tag{14.26}$$

Once again, making the substitution $d/dt = v(d/dz)$ transforms eq. 14.26 into

$$\frac{d^2\rho}{dz^2} = -\left(\frac{q}{2mv}\right)^2 \rho B_z^2$$

which can be integrated immediately on the assumption that ρ changes little within the lens:

$$\frac{d\rho}{dz} = -\left(\frac{q}{2mv}\right)^2 \rho \int_{-\infty}^{\infty} B_z \, dz. \tag{14.27}$$

where the integral in eq. 14.27 extends over all z since B_z is zero outside the lens. The left-hand side of eq. 14.27 is evaluated at a value of z on the far side of the lens ($d\rho/dz = 0$ at the near side of the lens where the charged particle enters the lens). As in an electrostatic lens, $d\rho/dz$ is just the angle of deflection α of the trajectory, assuming small deflections. Note that α is proportional to ρ, and therefore the lens brings all axial rays to a point focus. Since the right-hand side of eq. 14.27 is negative, the lens is converging. The focal length of the lens depends on the velocity of the charged particles and is defined by eq. 14.28:

$$\frac{1}{f} \equiv \frac{|\alpha|}{\rho} = \left(\frac{q}{2mv}\right)^2 \int_{-\infty}^{\infty} B_x^2 \, dx. \tag{14.28}$$

14.5 Motion of a Charge in Static E- and B-Fields

The motion of a charge in a static E- *or* a static B-field has been considered previously. The present section will concern itself with the motion of a charge when a static B- *and* a static E-field are present.

The force equation governing the behavior of the charge is the Lorentz force law:

$$\mathbf{f} = q\mathbf{E} + q\mathbf{v} \times \mathbf{B}. \tag{14.29}$$

If E and B are parallel and uniform, the force equation becomes, in Cartesian coordinates,

$$m\frac{d^2x}{dt^2} = qv_yB,$$

$$m\frac{d^2y}{dt^2} = -qv_xB, \quad \text{where } \begin{aligned} \mathbf{E} &= E\hat{z} \\ \mathbf{B} &= B\hat{z}. \end{aligned}$$

$$m\frac{d^2z}{dt^2} = qE;$$

In other words, the effects of E and B may be treated independently.

If E and B are not parallel in the laboratory but uniform, the problem may be viewed in another coordinate system moving with velocity $\mathbf{v}_0$. The velocity is chosen in such a way that the component of E perpendicular to B does not explicitly appear in the equations of motion. Writing $\mathbf{E} = \mathbf{E}_\| + \mathbf{E}_\perp$ where $\mathbf{E}_\|$ and $\mathbf{E}_\perp$ are the components of E parallel and perpendicular to B, respectively;

$$\mathbf{f} = q\mathbf{E}_\| + q\mathbf{v}' \times \mathbf{B} + (q\mathbf{E}_\perp + q\mathbf{v}_0 \times \mathbf{B}) \tag{14.30}$$

and $\mathbf{v}'$ is the velocity of the charge with respect to the moving system. $\mathbf{v}_0$ is chosen so that the terms in parentheses in eq. 14.30 vanish; that is,

$$\mathbf{v}_0 = \frac{\mathbf{E}_\perp \times \mathbf{B}}{B^2}. \tag{14.31}$$

The problem therefore reduces to that discussed previously, where the effects of the fields can be considered independently. An important comment should be made at this point: the above argument is inherently

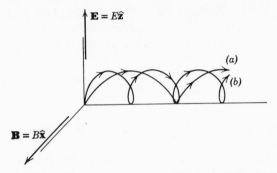

Fig. 14.6   A charged particle moves in uniform **E**- and **B**-fields which are perpendicular.   To an observer moving with the velocity $v_0 = (E/B)\hat{y}$, the particle will move in a circle if its initial velocity was in the *y-z* plane.   To an observer in the laboratory, the trajectory is a cycloid.   Two separate cases are sketched: (*a*) initial $V_y \geq 0$; (*b*) initial $V_y < 0$.

nonrelativistic since only in the limit $v/c \ll 1$ can **v** be written as $v_0 + v'$. Consequently eq. 14.31 is valid only when $|E_\perp| \ll c|B|$.   The velocity v_0 is called the *drift velocity* of the charged particle.

EXAMPLE 14.2   Consider **E** and **B** to be uniform and perpendicular to one another.   If $E = E\hat{z}$ and $B = B\hat{x}$, then $v_0 = (E/B)\hat{y}$.   With respect to an observer moving with velocity $(E/B)\hat{y}$, the particle motion is, in general, a helix.   If the initial velocity of the particle is in the *y-z* plane, the particle will move in a circle in the *y'-z'* plane.   To an observer in the laboratory, the trajectory is a cycloid (see Fig. 14.6).

14.6   Charged Particle Accelerators

The behavior of charged particles in electric and magnetic fields suggests several possibilities for imparting large energies to elementary particles. Fast moving particles are often used as probes to study the properties of atoms and nuclei.   The accelerating devices analyzed here are the *cyclotron*, which uses an alternating **E**-field for acceleration and a static **B**-field to confine the accelerated charge, and the *betatron* which employs a time-varying **B**-field both for acceleration and confinement.   The discussion will be highly simplified, merely illustrating the salient physical principles involved.   In addition, a brief discussion of a *linear accelerator* is included.

THE CYCLOTRON

The cyclotron is based on the principle that a charged particle performs circular motion in a static uniform **B**-field with an angular frequency independent of the velocity of the particle. The angular frequency is the cyclotron frequency ω_c previously introduced:

$$\omega_c = \left(\frac{q}{m}\right)B.$$

Figure 14.7 is a schematic view of a cyclotron. A short flat circular conducting cylindrical box is split along a diameter, and an oscillator is connected between the two D-shaped cavities, thereby producing a time-dependent E-field of angular frequency ω_c in the gap between the "dees." A uniform static B-field is applied normal to the plane of the "dees." A charged particle residing within one of the dees is electrostatically shielded and experiences only the effect of the uniform B-field. A charged particle within the gap between the dees generally experiences the accelerating effect of the electric field.

A charged ion created in the center of the dee-gap is accelerated towards one of the dees. It enters the dee with nonzero velocity and travels in a semicircular arc with constant speed. It re-enters the gap in the time

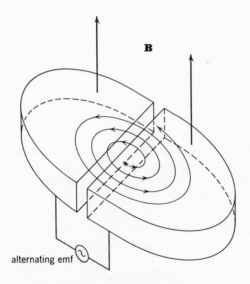

Fig. 14.7 The dee cavities of a cyclotron are sketched. An alternating emf is placed across the dees with angular frequency equal to the cyclotron frequency of the charged particle being accelerated. A uniform B-field perpendicular to the plane of the dees is supplied by electromagnets. A source of positive ions exists at the center of the dees. A typical charged particle trajectory is indicated; for simplicity, however, the number of turns in the sketched trajectory is much smaller than that of an actual trajectory.

interval $\Delta t = \pi/\omega_c$, i.e., one-half the cyclotron period.   The E-field in the gap is now reversed and the particle accelerated across the gap to the other dee, where it circulates with the cyclotron frequency and re-enters the gap for further acceleration after the time $\Delta t = \pi/\omega_c$.   This process will continue, the particle picking up more energy (q times the potential difference across the dees) every time it crosses the dee gap.   The particle orbit expands after each acceleration until the particle reaches the edges of the dees where it either strikes a target or is deflected by some electric or magnetic field to enter a scattering or reaction chamber outside the cyclotron.

The cyclotron operates because the cyclotron frequency of a charged particle is independent of its velocity.   This statement about ω_c is only strictly true, however, in the nonrelativistic limit since ω_c is proportional to the charge-to-mass ratio of the particle being accelerated.   As the particle velocity approaches the speed of light, its mass and, therefore, its cyclotron frequency becomes dependent on its velocity.   Unless steps are taken to alter the frequency of the oscillating E-field in the dee-gap as the particle velocity approaches c, the circulating particles will rapidly get out of phase with the accelerating field and the particles will become decelerated.   The critical velocities occur at particle energies in the neighborhood of 100–200 Mev for protons.   To operate proton cyclotrons at these energies, the accelerating field must be modulated to compensate for the change in ω_c with velocity.   Such frequency-modulated or FM cyclotrons are operative and produce protons of energy in the hundreds of Mev region.

Naturally, the dee cavities of the cyclotron must be evacuated to prevent loss of energy of the particles in the accelerator to the residual gas in the dee cavities.   Any momentum imparted to the accelerated particles in the radial direction or in the direction perpendicular to the plane of the dees will cause the particle beam to blow up.   To examine the stability of the particle beam, two effects must be considered: (1) motion in the radial direction (in-and-out stability), (2) motion perpendicular to the dee-plane (up-and-down stability).

The radial equation of motion for the charged particle is

$$m\left(\frac{d^2\rho}{dt^2} - \frac{v^2}{\rho}\right) = -qvB. \tag{14.32}$$

If the confining magnetic field is essentially uniform, it can be adequately represented by the expression

$$B = B_0\left(\frac{\rho_0}{\rho}\right)^n \tag{14.33}$$

in the neighborhood of ρ_0. (B_0 is the value of B at $\rho = \rho_0$.) B can be approximated by the first two terms in the Taylor's expansion of eq. 14.33 as

$$B \simeq B_0\left(1 - n\frac{\rho - \rho_0}{\rho_0}\right) = \left(\frac{m}{q}\right)\omega_0\left(1 - n\frac{\rho - \rho_0}{\rho_0}\right) \tag{14.34}$$

where
$$\omega_0 \equiv \left(\frac{q}{m}\right)B_0,$$

which upon substitution into the radial equation of motion yields

$$\frac{d^2\rho}{dt^2} - \frac{v^2}{\rho} = -v\omega_0\left(1 - n\frac{\rho - \rho_0}{\rho_0}\right). \tag{14.35}$$

In the neighborhood of ρ_0, the following approximations may be made:

$$v \approx \omega_0\rho_0$$
$$\rho^{-1} \approx \rho_0^{-1}\left(1 - \frac{\rho - \rho_0}{\rho_0}\right)$$

Substituting these expressions into eq. 14.35 and rearranging terms yields the equation of radial motion:

$$\frac{d^2(\rho - \rho_0)}{dt^2} + \omega_0^2(1 - n)(\rho - \rho_0) = 0. \tag{14.36}$$

Equation 14.36 is the differential equation for small vibrations in the radial motion about $\rho = \rho_0$ of angular frequency

$$\omega_\rho = \omega_0\sqrt{1 - n}. \tag{14.37}$$

The cyclotron orbits are stable against small radial disturbances as long as $1 > 1 - n > 0$. If $1 - n \leqslant 0$, departure from the correct radial position will increase in time. If $n = 0$, the period of radial oscillation will be in resonance with the cyclotron frequency in the uniform field.

The effect of a radial dependence in the field illustrated in eq. 14.33 must be considered in a discussion of the possible motion of the particle perpendicular to the dee plane. Since for radial stability $1 > n > 0$, the **B**-field is weaker near the edges of the dees than it is in the center (see Fig. 14.8). The guiding field is chosen to have reflectional symmetry about the plane of the equilibrium orbit of the accelerating charges. This equilibrium or symmetry plane is designated by $x = 0$. For x near the equilibrium plane, B_ρ is in general nonvanishing but small; that is,

$$B_\rho(x) \simeq B_\rho(0) + x\left(\frac{\partial}{\partial x}B_\rho\right)_0.$$

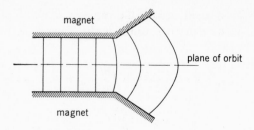

Fig. 14.8   The "fringing" of the field lines in a cyclotron to produce stability in the cyclotron orbits is indicated.

However, since $z = 0$ in the equilibrium or symmetry plane, $B_\rho(0) = 0$, and therefore

$$B_\rho(z) = z\left(\frac{\partial}{\partial z} B_\rho\right)_0.$$

However, curl $\mathbf{B} = 0$ and thus $(\partial/\partial z)B_\rho = (\partial/\partial \rho)B_z$, from which it follows that

$$B_\rho(z) = z\left(\frac{\partial}{\partial \rho} B_z\right)_0. \tag{14.38}$$

Near the symmetry plane the components of $\mathbf{B}$ other than the z-component are small, and to a good approximation

$$B_z = B_0\left(\frac{\rho_0}{\rho}\right)^n \simeq B_0\left(1 - n\frac{\rho - \rho_0}{\rho_0}\right)$$

or

$$B_\rho(z) = \frac{-nz}{\rho_0} B_0.$$

The equation for motion perpendicular to the symmetry plane becomes

$$m\frac{d^2z}{dt^2} = -qvB_\rho(z) = \frac{n}{\rho_0} qvB_0.$$

However, as before,

$$\omega_0 = \frac{q}{m} B_0, \quad v = \omega_0\rho_0,$$

and consequently

$$\frac{d^2z}{dt^2} + n\omega_0^2 z = 0. \tag{14.39}$$

Equation 14.39 is the differential equation for small vibrations of the orbit about the equilibrium plane. The frequency of the up-and-down oscillations is

$$\omega_z = \omega_0\sqrt{n}. \tag{14.40}$$

If $n = 1/2$, the frequencies of radial and axial oscillations are identical. The cyclotron orbits are therefore stable against small disturbances in the radial and axial directions, provided that any departure from uniformity in the guiding field is small and corresponds to a weakening of the field as ρ increases.

THE BETATRON

The betatron makes use of an alternating **B**-field as both a guiding field and an accelerating field (through the induced **E**-field). According to Faraday's law, the induced **E**-field produced by a changing magnetic flux is in magnitude.

$$E = \frac{1}{2\pi\rho_0} \frac{d\Phi}{dt} \tag{14.41}$$

where ρ_0 is the distance of the particle being accelerated from the axis of symmetry of the betatron (see Fig. 14.9). The magnetic flux Φ can be written as

$$\Phi = \pi\rho_0^2 \langle B \rangle$$

so that

$$E = \frac{\rho_0}{2} \frac{d\langle B \rangle}{dt} \tag{14.42}$$

where $\langle B \rangle$ is the average **B**-field threading the orbit of the charged particle.

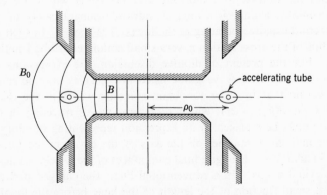

Fig. 14.9 Sketched is a cross section of a betatron. The charged particles are accelerated in an evacuated torus in a circular orbit of radius ρ_0. The guiding field at ρ_0 is B_0. The average value of the accelerating field threading through the plane capping the circle of radius ρ_0 is $\langle B \rangle$. In order for acceleration to occur, the betatron condition must hold at all times, namely, $B_0 = \frac{1}{2}\langle B \rangle$ + constant.

Unlike the cyclotron, the charged particle in a betatron remains a *fixed distance* from the axis of the accelerator; i.e., ρ_0 = constant. The charge being accelerated experiences a force tangential to the circle of radius ρ_0 due to the induced **E**-field given by

$$f_{\text{ind}} = \frac{q\rho_0}{2} \frac{d\langle B \rangle}{dt}. \tag{14.43}$$

However, if B_0 is the value of the **B**-field at ρ_0, the particle will be guided by the field if $mv = q\rho_0 B_0$ or

$$f_{\text{guiding}} = \frac{d}{dt}(mv) = q\rho_0 \frac{dB_0}{dt}. \tag{14.44}$$

Equations 14.43 and 14.44 are consistent only if

$$B_0 = \tfrac{1}{2}\langle B \rangle + \text{constant.} \tag{14.45}$$

Equation 14.45 must hold at all times if the betatron is to operate; the **B**-field at the particle orbit must always equal one-half the average field threading through the orbit. The electromagnets producing the accelerating field ($\langle B \rangle$) and the guiding field (B_0) are pulsed simultaneously. Since $B_0 < \langle B \rangle$, the discussion of stability of orbits in a cyclotron holds also for a betatron in the neighborhood of the equilibrium orbit $\rho = \rho_0$.

LINEAR ACCELERATOR

Of the many other types of accelerators used to impart large amounts of energy to charged particles, one of the simplest, at least in principle, is the linear accelerator or *linac*. As the name suggests, linacs are linear machines in contrast to cyclotrons and betatrons which are circular. Fundamentally, a linac is a long cylindrical resonant cavity of circular cross section usually operating in the lowest TM mode. In such a linac, the radius of the cross section is very small compared to the length of the cavity. For the present qualitative discussion, the expressions for the fields in a cylindrical wave guide listed in eq. 11.31 may be employed, remembering that in order to obtain standing waves in the cavity the function $\exp\{i(k_g z - \omega t)\}$ which represents waves traveling in the $+z$ direction must be replaced by an expression representing standing waves. The magnetic field vanishes on the axis of the cavity in the lowest TM mode; in addition, the longitudinal component of the **E**-field is a maximum on the cylinder axis. In a conventional linac, the charged particle only travels a small fraction of the length of the linac before the longitudinal component of the **E**-field changes sign. Consequently, unless special measures are taken, the acceleration attained by the particle in the first half-cycle of the oscillating field which drives the resonant cavity will be lost in the second half-cycle. This is prevented by allowing the charged particle to enter a conducting cylinder coaxial with the cavity during the second half cycle where it is shielded from the resonant electromagnetic field. It emerges from this cylinder, called a *drift-tube*, when the field has reversed itself again and is able to further accelerate the particle. It is not the purpose of these brief remarks to give a detailed description of the operation of a linac. However, it should be remarked that although the drift tubes are essential, they perturb the fields particularly in the neighborhood of the cylinder axis causing defocussing of the charged particle beam. Such effects can be minimized by installation of suitable electrostatic lens which counteract the defocussing effects of the drift tubes.

14.7 Systems of Charged Particles: The Magnetohydrodynamic Equations

So far the trajectories of single charged particles in **E**- and **B**-fields have been considered. The remainder of this chapter is concerned with a brief discussion of the behavior of systems of charged particles in **E**- and **B**-fields. It will be assumed that the number of particles in the system is so large, the time scale of the phenomena so long, etc., that a macroscopic approach is valid; that is, it will be assumed that to the system can be assigned such macroscopic quantities as current density (**j**), mass density (η), conductivity (σ), etc.

In the consideration of the behavior of systems of charges in electromagnetic fields, a distinction is usually made between two different physical situations: (1) a neutral system in which the negative electrons and positive ions move as a single fluid; (2) a neutral system in which the negative electrons and positive ions move as separate fluids. Situation 1 is usually referred to as the *magnetohydrodynamic* or MHD limit, whereas situation 2 is referred to as the *plasma* limit, although this is an oversimplification. There is very little to distinguish the MHD system from a plasma, the basic physical principles being identical.

The starting point of the discussion of the physics of a neutral[1] fluid composed of electrons and positive ions is the so-called MHD system of equations:

$$\frac{\partial \eta}{\partial t} + \text{div}\,(\eta \mathbf{v}) = 0 \quad \text{(conservation of matter or matter-continuity)} \quad (14.46)$$

$$\eta \frac{d\mathbf{v}}{dt} = -\text{grad}\,p + \mathbf{j} \times \mathbf{B} + \mathbf{f}_v \quad \text{(force equation)} \quad (14.47)$$

---

[1] It will be assumed that local departures from electric neutrality are small and can be ignored. However, as in a metal conductor, the macroscopic charge density may be zero (considering both the electrons and positive ions), but the current density may be finite.

where $\mathbf{f}_v \equiv$ velocity dependent or viscous force per unit volume,

$p \equiv$ fluid pressure (assumed to be associated with a conservative force),

and
$$\frac{d}{dt} \equiv \frac{\partial}{\partial t} + \mathbf{v} \cdot \mathbf{\nabla} \equiv \frac{\partial}{\partial t} + \sum_{j=1}^{3} v_j \frac{\partial}{\partial x_j}.$$

Within the fluid, the electromagnetic fields satisfy Maxwell's equations. For simplicity it will be assumed that the fields vary slowly enough in time so that the displacement current can be ignored with respect to the conduction current. (This is the magnetohydrodynamic limit.) In this low frequency limit eqs. 14.48 are valid:

$$\text{curl } \mathbf{E} = -\frac{\partial}{\partial t} \mathbf{B}$$

$$\text{curl } \mathbf{B} = \left(\frac{\mu_0}{4\pi}\right) 4\pi \mathbf{j} \tag{14.48}$$

$$\text{div } \mathbf{j} = 0.$$

The MHD equations are not complete in an electromagnetic sense even when the restrictions of eqs. 14.48 are imposed, since eqs. 14.48 are not enough to determine $\mathbf{j}$ in terms of the electromagnetic fields. The missing condition can be introduced phenomenologically for a simple conducting fluid as Ohm's law, namely,

$$\mathbf{j}' = \sigma \mathbf{E}'$$

where $(\mathbf{j}', \mathbf{E}')$ are the current density and E-field measured in the system moving with the fluid. The effect of the motion of the fluid may be taken care of by Faraday's law, the Ohm's law relation in the laboratory system or rest frame being

$$\mathbf{j} = \sigma(\mathbf{E} + \mathbf{v} \times \mathbf{B}) \tag{14.49}$$

where all quantities are measured in the laboratory system. The MHD equations are then complete both electromagnetically and mechanically as soon as the relation between p, the mechanical pressure, and η, the mass density is given; such a relation is called an *equation of state*.

Faraday's law may be used to recast the magnetic force term $\mathbf{j} \times \mathbf{B}$ in the MHD equations in other terms;

$$\mathbf{j} \times \mathbf{B} = -\left(\frac{4\pi}{\mu_0}\right) \frac{1}{4\pi} \mathbf{B} \times \text{curl } \mathbf{B}. \tag{14.50}$$

The right-hand side of eq. 14.50 can be transformed, using the vector calculus identity

$$\mathbf{B} \times \text{curl } \mathbf{B} \equiv -(\mathbf{B} \cdot \nabla)\mathbf{B} + 1/2 \text{ grad } B^2 \tag{14.51}$$

where $$(\mathbf{B} \cdot \nabla)\mathbf{B} \equiv \left[B_x \frac{\partial}{\partial x} + B_y \frac{\partial}{\partial y} + B_z \frac{\partial}{\partial z} \right] \mathbf{B}.$$

Substitution of eq. 14.51 into eq. 14.50 yields

$$\mathbf{j} \times \mathbf{B} = -\text{grad } u_B + \left(\frac{4\pi}{\mu_0} \right) \frac{1}{4\pi} (\mathbf{B} \cdot \nabla)\mathbf{B}, \tag{14.52}$$

where $$u_B \equiv \left(\frac{4\pi}{\mu_0} \right) \frac{1}{8\pi} B^2.$$

The magnetic energy volume density is, as far as the MHD equations are concerned, equivalent to a *magnetic pressure*, p_B. For many simple geometric configurations, for example, a unidirectional field, the second term on the right-hand side of eq. 14.52 vanishes and the magnetic force is simply

$$\mathbf{j} \times \mathbf{B} = -\text{grad } p_B.$$

In the static limit $[d\mathbf{v}/dt = 0, \mathbf{f}_v = 0]$ the MHD equation (eq. 14.47) is equivalent to the relation

$$p + p_B = \text{constant}. \tag{14.53}$$

In order for the fluid to remain in static equilibrium, any variation in the *mechanical* fluid pressure p must be compensated by an opposite variation in the magnetic pressure p_B.

14.8 Confined Plasmas: The Pinch Effect

The existence of a magnetic pressure makes it possible for a plasma to confine itself. Only the most simple case of a confined plasma will be considered here, namely, a plasma which has axial symmetry and which is superconducting. It is straightforward to demonstrate that such a plasma will confine itself to a cylindrical sheath of radius R. Qualitatively this may be understood as follows. Within the plasma, $(\rho \leqslant R)$ the Meissner effect insures that $\mathbf{B} = 0$. Within the plasma itself the total pressure is simply the mechanical pressure due to the motion of the constituent particles of the plasma. However, outside the plasma, $\mathbf{B}$ is nonzero, and the total pressure is the magnetic pressure due to the finite $\mathbf{B}$. Consequently R (the sheath radius) is determined by equating the mechanical pressure at the surface of the sheath to the magnetic pressure immediately outside the sheath.

No attempt will be made here to give a dynamical description of the formation of a confined plasma or, as it is sometimes called more picturesquely, the *pinch effect*. However, assuming the existence of a steady-state cylindrical sheath carrying a current I, it is possible to evaluate certain relationships between the static properties of the sheath, for example, the average mechanical pressure within the sheath, the mechanical pressure outside the sheath, the average particle density within the sheath, the effective temperature of the sheath, etc., without giving a detailed description of the formation of the sheath.

The magnitude of the **B**-field at a point outside the sheath is given by Ampère's law:

$$B(\rho) = \left(\frac{\mu_0}{4\pi}\right) \frac{2}{\rho} \int_0^R (2\pi\rho' \, d\rho') j(\rho') \tag{14.54}$$

From this, it is possible to demonstrate using eq. 14.52 that in the steady state, i.e., $d/dt \, \mathbf{v} = 0$, the MHD equation reduces to

$$0 = -\frac{dp}{d\rho} - \frac{d}{d\rho}\left[\left(\frac{4\pi}{\mu_0}\right)\frac{B^2}{8\pi}\right] - \frac{B^2}{4\pi\rho}\left(\frac{4\pi}{\mu_0}\right).$$

This equation can be rewritten in a more useful form as

$$\frac{dp}{d\rho} = -\left(\frac{4\pi}{\mu_0}\right)\frac{1}{8\pi\rho^2}\frac{d}{d\rho}(\rho^2 B^2), \tag{14.55}$$

which may be integrated directly to yield

$$p(\rho) = p(0) - \left(\frac{4\pi}{\mu_0}\right)\frac{1}{8\pi}\int_0^\rho \frac{1}{\rho'^2}\frac{d}{d\rho'}(\rho'^2 B^2)\, d\rho' \tag{14.56}$$

where $p(0)$ is the mechanical pressure on the axis of the sheath. $p(0)$ may be evaluated by noting that at $\rho = R$ the mechanical pressure drops to zero and

$$p(0) = \left(\frac{4\pi}{\mu_0}\right)\frac{1}{8\pi}\int_0^R \frac{1}{\rho'^2}\frac{d}{d\rho'}(\rho'^2 B^2)\, d\rho'. \tag{14.57}$$

Substituting this expression into eq. 14.56 yields

$$p(\rho) = \left(\frac{4\pi}{\mu_0}\right)\frac{1}{8\pi}\int_\rho^R \frac{1}{\rho'^2}\frac{d}{d\rho'}(\rho'^2 B^2)\, d\rho'. \tag{14.58}$$

The average pressure within the sheath $\langle p \rangle$ may be calculated as follows. By definition

$$\langle p \rangle \equiv \frac{1}{\pi R^2}\int_0^R 2\pi\rho p(\rho)\, d\rho. \tag{14.59}$$

However, integrating eq. 14.59 by parts yields

$$\langle p \rangle = \frac{1}{\pi R^2}\left\{\frac{2\pi\rho^2}{2}p(\rho)\bigg]_0^R - \pi\int_0^R d\rho\rho^2\left(\frac{dp}{d\rho}\right)\right\}. \tag{14.60}$$

The first term in eq. 14.60 vanishes since $\rho^2 = 0$ at the lower limit and $p(\rho) = 0$ at the upper limit. Consequently

$$\langle p \rangle = -\frac{1}{R^2} \int_0^R d\rho \rho^2 \left(\frac{dp}{d\rho}\right)$$

which can be evaluated using eq. 14.55 for $dp/d\rho$:

$$\langle p \rangle = \left(\frac{4\pi}{\mu_0}\right) \frac{1}{R^2} \int_0^R \frac{d\rho}{8\pi} \frac{d}{d\rho} (\rho^2 B^2) = \left(\frac{4\pi}{\mu_0}\right) \frac{1}{8\pi} B^2(R). \tag{14.61}$$

The average mechanical pressure within the sheath is just equal to the magnetic pressure at the surface of the sheath. Furthermore, if I is the total current flowing in the confined plasma,

$$B(R) = \left(\frac{\mu_0}{4\pi}\right) \frac{2I}{R}$$

which when substituted into eq. 14.61, yields a relation between $\langle p \rangle$, I, and R, namely,

$$\langle p \rangle = \left(\frac{\mu_0}{4\pi}\right) \frac{I^2}{2\pi R^2}. \tag{14.62}$$

A very important application of the pinch effect is the possible production of useful power in a thermonuclear reactor of the fusion type. Very light nuclei of atoms can combine (fuse) to form nuclei of heavier atoms with the release of energy. For example, the nuclei of two deuterium atoms (H_1^2) are heavier than the nucleus of a helium atom (He_2^4) and, consequently, the nuclear reaction: $H_1^2 + H_1^2 \rightarrow He_2^4$ is an exothermic fusion reaction with an energy release of about 23 Mev. This reaction does not proceed in a normal gas of atomic deuterium for two reasons: (1) the number of collisions per unit time between deuterium atoms under normal conditions is very small; (2) the Coulomb repulsion between the nuclei of two deuterium atoms causes the cross section for the reaction to be exceedingly small since there are a negligible number of atoms with energies sufficiently high to penetrate the electrostatic barrier. Consequently it is necessary to pinch an atomic deuterium plasma to high densities and to produce a high temperature within the plasma to insure a large collision rate between sufficiently high velocity deuterium nuclei. To obtain an approximate order of magnitude of the quantities involved, it is sufficiently accurate to consider the plasma as an ideal gas for which the internal pressure is related to the absolute temperature Θ of the plasma via eq. 14.63:

$$\langle p \rangle = Nk\Theta \tag{14.63}$$

where N = particle density in the plasma,
  k = Boltzmann's constant
  $= 1.38 \times 10^{-23}$ joule/°K $= 0.86 \times 10^{-7}$ kev/°K.

Combining equations 14.62 and 14.63 yields a relationship between the thermal energy $k\Theta$ of the particle plasma and the other physical properties of the plasma,

$$k\Theta = \left(\frac{\mu_0}{4\pi}\right)\frac{I^2}{2\pi R^2 N}. \tag{14.64}$$

To obtain sufficiently high energy particles in the plasma for the nuclear fusion reaction (10–100 kev) requires a plasma temperature of about 10^8–$10^{9\circ}$K. Plasma currents of the order of 10^6–10^7 amperes are required to produce such temperatures in plasmas of reasonable densities ($N \simeq 10^{21}$–10^{22} particles/m^3) and practically obtainable size ($\pi R^2 \simeq 10^2$ cm^2).

Although it is possible for a plasma to confine itself by its self-generated magnetic field, a confined plasma has very serious inherent instabilities. These instabilities can be discussed in a qualitative manner. Two basic types of instability are caused by so-called *neck* and *kink* distortions of the sheath. A neck instability occurs whenever part of the plasma is compressed radially at a given point (see Fig. 14.10a). Since the **B**-field at the surface of the plasma sheath is inversely proportional to the radius of the sheath, the magnetic pressure is greater at the neck of the plasma than it is elsewhere, causing a net inward pressure at the neck, causing further distortion of the plasma at the neck. For a plasma of finite but large conductivity, the plasma can maintain an axial **B**-field of external origin which is pinched at the neck distortion causing a net outward magnetic pressure to compensate for the net inward magnetic pressure produced by the neck distortion. In this way the plasma may be stabilized. A kink instability is illustrated in Fig. 14.10b. Since the magnetic field lines are crowded more closely together at the concave part of the kink and moved further apart at the convex part it is evident that the resulting imbalance of the magnetic pressures enhances the distortion which is the source of the kink distortion. Once again, for a plasma of finite conductivity, this distortion can be stabilized by an externally supplied axial

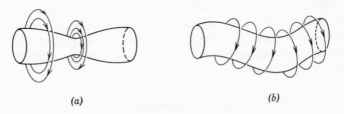

(a)   (b)

Fig. 14.10   Two simple distortions of a cylindrical plasma are indicated. Distortion (*a*) is a "neck" or pinch distortion, whereas (*b*) is a "kink" distortion.

B-field within the plasma sheath. A quantitative treatment of the stabilization of confined plasmas is beyond the scope of this discussion.

14.9 Magnetohydrodynamic Waves

In the low frequency limit in which the previous discussion of plasmas has been carried out, it has been possible to consider a plasma as a neutral current carrying fluid in which account is taken of any internally produced or externally applied magnetic fields. Since a plasma acts as a neutral fluid for low frequencies, it is intuitively evident that such a fluid will support wave motion. The waves maintained by such a fluid will differ in some respects from mechanical waves in a nonconducting fluid due to the effects of the **B**-field. In the MHD limit, the equations describing the behavior of a superconducting current carrying fluid are eqs. 14.46–14.49 which for present purposes can be written:

$$\frac{\partial \eta}{\partial t} + \operatorname{div}(\eta \mathbf{v}) = 0,$$

$$\eta \frac{\partial \mathbf{v}}{\partial t} + \eta (\mathbf{v} \cdot \nabla) \mathbf{v} = -\operatorname{grad} p - \left(\frac{4\pi}{\mu_0}\right) \frac{1}{4\pi} \mathbf{B} \times \operatorname{curl} \mathbf{B}, \qquad (14.65)$$

$$\frac{\partial B}{\partial t} = \operatorname{curl}(\mathbf{v} \times \mathbf{B}).$$

It is now assumed that there exist equilibrium values of the quantities **v**, **B**, and η designated by $\mathbf{v}_0$, $\mathbf{B}_0$, and η_0 which are constant in space and time. Furthermore, the plasma will be examined in a system which is at rest with respect to the equilibrium value of **v**. It is then supposed that some disturbance in the plasma causes **v**, **B**, and η to differ from these equilibrium values by small amounts $\delta\mathbf{v}$, $\delta\mathbf{B}$, and $\delta\eta$ so that

$$\mathbf{v} = \delta\mathbf{v}(\mathbf{r}, t)$$
$$\mathbf{B} = \mathbf{B}_0 + \delta\mathbf{B}(\mathbf{r}, t)$$
$$\eta = \eta_0 + \delta\eta(\mathbf{r}, t).$$

Accompanying these small departures from the equilibrium values of η, **B**, and **v** will be a change in the fluid pressure p from its equilibrium value p_0. Assuming that the fluid pressure depends in some known way upon the mass density η through the equation of state, the change in the fluid pressure may be written

$$p - p_0 = \delta p \approx +\left(\frac{\partial p}{\partial \eta}\right)_0 \delta\eta.$$

Consequently the mechanical properties of the fluid enter into the equations only through the equilibrium mass density η_0 and the quantity $(\partial p/\partial \eta)_0$ which is the square of the velocity of sound waves in the fluid. These values are substituted into eq. 14.65 and only terms linear in the δ quantities are kept, yielding

$$\frac{\partial}{\partial t}(\delta\eta) + \eta_0 \operatorname{div}(\delta\mathbf{v}) = 0, \tag{14.66a}$$

$$\eta_0 \frac{\partial}{\partial t}(\delta\mathbf{v}) = -\left(\frac{\partial p}{\partial \eta}\right)\operatorname{grad}(\delta\eta) - \frac{4\pi}{\mu_0}\mathbf{B}_0 \times \operatorname{curl}\delta\mathbf{B}, \tag{14.66b}$$

$$\frac{\partial}{\partial t}(\delta\mathbf{B}) = \operatorname{curl}(\delta\mathbf{v} \times \mathbf{B}_0). \tag{14.66c}$$

Equations 14.66 may be converted into a second order partial differential equation for $\delta\mathbf{v}$ alone by the following series of steps: the partial derivative with respect to t is taken of eq. 14.66b, yielding

$$\frac{\partial^2}{\partial t^2}(\delta\mathbf{v}) = -\left(\frac{\partial p}{\partial \eta}\right)_0 \frac{1}{\eta_0}\frac{\partial}{\partial t}\operatorname{grad}(\delta\eta) - \left(\frac{4\pi}{\mu_0}\right)\frac{1}{4\pi\eta_0}\mathbf{B}_0 \times \operatorname{curl}\frac{\partial}{\partial t}\delta\mathbf{B}. \tag{14.67}$$

The first term on the right-hand side of eq. 14.67 is expressed in terms of $\delta\mathbf{v}$ by taking the gradient of eq. 14.66a and substituting the resulting expression for $(\partial/\partial t)\operatorname{grad}(\delta\eta)$ into eq. 14.67; the second term is expressed in terms of $\delta\mathbf{v}$ through direct substitution from eq. 14.66c, i.e., Faraday's law for a superconducting fluid. The resulting equation satisfied by $\delta\mathbf{v}$ is

$$\frac{\partial^2}{\partial t^2}(\delta\mathbf{v}) = v_s^2 \operatorname{grad}\operatorname{div}(\delta\mathbf{v}) + \mathbf{v}_A \times \operatorname{curl}\operatorname{curl}(\mathbf{v}_A \times \delta\mathbf{v}) \tag{14.68}$$

where $v_s \equiv \sqrt{\left(\dfrac{\partial p}{\partial \eta}\right)_0} = $ velocity of compressional waves (sound) in the fluid.

$\mathbf{v}_A = \sqrt{\dfrac{4\pi}{\mu_0}}\dfrac{\mathbf{B}_0}{\sqrt{4\pi\eta_0}} = $ the Alfvén velocity.

Equation 14.68 can be converted into an algebraic equation by assuming a plane wave monochromatic solution of the form

$$\delta\mathbf{v} = \mathbf{v}\exp\{i(\mathbf{k}\cdot\mathbf{r} - \omega t)\} \tag{14.69}$$

which, upon substitution into eq. 14.68, yields

$$\omega^2\mathbf{v} = (v_s^2 + v_A^2)(\mathbf{k}\cdot\mathbf{v})\mathbf{k} + (\mathbf{v}_A\cdot\mathbf{k})\{(\mathbf{v}_A\cdot\mathbf{k})\mathbf{v} - (\mathbf{v}_A\cdot\mathbf{v})\mathbf{k} - (\mathbf{k}\cdot\mathbf{v})\mathbf{v}_A\}. \tag{14.70}$$

Equation 14.70 has a particularly simple solution for $\mathbf{k} \perp \mathbf{v}_A$ (i.e., $\mathbf{k} \perp \mathbf{B}_0$). The wave solution propagates perpendicular to the equilibrium value of **B** and the direction of propagation is parallel to **v**; therefore this solution is a longitudinal wave.   In this case, eq. 14.70 simplifies to

$$\omega^2\mathbf{v} = (v_s^2 + v_A^2)(\mathbf{k} \cdot \mathbf{v})\mathbf{k}.$$

Taking the scalar product of both sides of this expression with **k** yields

$$\frac{\omega^2}{k^2} = (v_s^2 + v_A^2). \tag{14.71}$$

The left-hand side of eq. 14.71 is the square of the phase velocity of the longitudinal wave.   This phase velocity depends on both the fluid pressure through v_s and the magnetic pressure through v_A.

If **k** is parallel to $\mathbf{v}_A$, eq. 14.70 simplifies somewhat.   By writing $\mathbf{k} = (k/v_A)\mathbf{v}_A$, eq. 14.70 may be rewritten in the form

$$(\omega^2 - v_A^2 k^2)\mathbf{v} = \left(\frac{v_s^2}{v_A^2} - 1\right)k^2(\mathbf{v}_A \cdot \mathbf{v})\mathbf{v}_A. \tag{14.72}$$

There are two different kinds of solutions to eq. 14.72.   The first is a longitudinal wave in which **k** is parallel to **v** (and also to $\mathbf{B}_0$).   The phase velocity of the longitudinal wave obtained from eq. 14.72 is

$$\frac{\omega}{k} = v_s \tag{14.73}$$

that is, the phase velocity of the longitudinal wave is just equal to the velocity of sound in the medium.   However, there also exists a solution to eq. 14.72 in which $\mathbf{k} \perp \mathbf{v}_A$ and which is therefore a transverse wave. The phase velocity of this transverse wave obtained from eq. 14.72 is

$$\frac{\omega}{k} = v_A \tag{14.74}$$

Such a wave, that is, a transverse MHD wave, is called an Alfvén wave; a noncurrent-carrying fluid cannot maintain such a wave since it is purely a MHD phenomenon.

The **B**-fields associated with the various MHD waves discussed above can be obtained from eq. 14.66c.   For the longitudinal wave in which

$\omega/k = \sqrt{v_s^2 + v_A^2}$, (i.e. $\mathbf{k} \parallel \mathbf{v}$, $\mathbf{k} \perp \mathbf{B}_0$)

$$\delta\mathbf{B} = \frac{v}{(v_s^2 + v_A^2)^{1/2}} \mathbf{B}_0 \exp\{i(\mathbf{k} \cdot \mathbf{r} - \omega t)\}.$$

This corresponds to a compressional wave in **B** without distortion of the lines of force since $\delta\mathbf{B} \parallel \mathbf{B}_0$ and $\mathbf{k} \parallel \mathbf{B}_0$.   For the longitudinal wave in which $\omega/k = v_s$, intuitively it is expected that there is no magnetic wave since the phase velocity does not depend on $\mathbf{B}_0$. This is verified by eq. 14.66c, which yields for $(\mathbf{k} \parallel \mathbf{v}, \mathbf{k} \parallel \mathbf{B}_0)$:

$$\delta\mathbf{B} = 0.$$

For the Alfvén wave $(\omega/k = v_A, \mathbf{k} \perp \mathbf{v}, \mathbf{k} \parallel \mathbf{B}_0)$, eq. 14.66c yields

$$\delta\mathbf{B} = -B_0\left(\frac{\mathbf{v}}{v_A}\right) \exp\{i(\mathbf{k} \cdot \mathbf{r} - \omega t)\}.$$

In such a wave the magnetic lines of force are distorted since

$$\delta\mathbf{B} \perp \mathbf{B}_0 \quad \text{but} \quad \mathbf{k} \parallel \mathbf{B}_0.$$

In a plasma of finite conductivity there will be dissipative effects and these MHD waves will be damped, that is, the phase velocity will be complex. Such effects will not be discussed here.

14.10 Plasma Oscillations

The previous discussion has concerned itself entirely with low frequency or MHD phenomena in a conducting fluid. Here the opposite limit will be examined, namely, the high frequency or plasma limit. In this limit the electrons and positive ions are assumed to move independently. The local fluctuations in the charge density cannot be ignored in the plasma limit; these fluctuations will introduce electrostatic effects which will dominate the behavior of the plasma. For simplicity, it will be assumed that the positive ions of the fluid are sufficiently massive compared to the electrons that they do not react to rapidly fluctuating fields and consequently provide a static electrostatic background field in which the electrons move.

Calling n the number density of the electron fluid, e the electron charge, and m the electron mass, the continuity and force equations may be written

$$\frac{\partial n}{\partial t} + \text{div}\,(n\mathbf{v}) = 0, \tag{14.75}$$

$$nm\left[\frac{\partial \mathbf{v}}{\partial t} + (\mathbf{v} \cdot \nabla)\mathbf{v}\right] = ne(\mathbf{E} + \mathbf{v} \times \mathbf{B}) - \text{grad}\, p, \tag{14.76}$$

where $p = $ pressure of the electron fluid. This pressure is caused by the internal motion of the electrons in the electron fluid and is a phenomenological way to describe to a first approximation the effects of this internal motion. The equilibrium configuration of the electron gas is assumed to be one in which

$$n(\mathbf{r}, t) = n_0 \qquad \mathbf{B}(\mathbf{r}, t) = 0$$
$$\mathbf{v}(\mathbf{r}, t) = 0 \qquad \mathbf{E}(\mathbf{r}, t) = 0.$$

The effects of small departures of the mechanical and electromagnetic quantities from these equilibrium values will be investigated:

$$n(\mathbf{r}, t) = n_0 + \delta n(\mathbf{r}, t)$$
$$\mathbf{v}(\mathbf{r}, t) = \delta \mathbf{v}(\mathbf{r}, t)$$
$$\mathbf{B}(\mathbf{r}, t) = \delta \mathbf{B}(\mathbf{r}, t)$$
$$\mathbf{E}(\mathbf{r}, t) = \delta \mathbf{E}(\mathbf{r}, t)$$

and
$$p(\mathbf{r}, t) = p_0 + \left(\frac{\partial p}{\partial n}\right)_0 \delta n(\mathbf{r}, t)$$

Substituting these values into eqs. 14.75 and 14.76 and neglecting all terms which are of quadratic or higher order in small quantities yields

$$\frac{\partial}{\partial t}(\delta n) + n_0 \operatorname{div}(\delta \mathbf{v}) = 0, \tag{14.77}$$

$$\frac{\partial}{\partial t}(\delta \mathbf{v}) = \frac{e}{m}(\delta \mathbf{E}) - \frac{1}{mn_0}\left(\frac{\partial p}{\partial n}\right)_0 \operatorname{grad}(\delta n). \tag{14.78}$$

The magnetic field does not appear in these equations because both $\mathbf{v}$ and $\mathbf{B}$ of the equilibrium configuration were assumed to vanish. If oscillatory solutions exist for these equations, they will be electric oscillations. These equations can be converted into a second order equation involving the density fluctuation δn by taking the time derivative of eq. 14.77 and the divergence of eq. 14.78 and eliminating the term involving $\delta \mathbf{v}$; this yields

$$\left[\frac{\partial^2}{\partial t^2} - \frac{1}{m}\left(\frac{\partial p}{\partial n}\right)_0 \nabla^2\right](\delta n) + \frac{en_0}{m}\operatorname{div}(\delta \mathbf{E}) = 0. \tag{14.79}$$

The fluctuation in $\mathbf{E}$ may be removed from eq. 14.79, using Gauss's law:

$$\operatorname{div}(\delta \mathbf{E}) = \left(\frac{1}{4\pi\epsilon_0}\right) 4\pi e \, \delta n.$$

Consequently the equation describing the behavior of the density fluctuations is

$$\left[\frac{\partial^2}{\partial t^2} - \frac{1}{m}\left(\frac{\partial p}{\partial n}\right)_0 \nabla^2 + \left(\frac{1}{4\pi\epsilon_0}\right)\frac{4\pi n_0 e^2}{m}\right]\delta n = 0. \tag{14.80}$$

Solutions to eq. 14.80 exist of the plane wave form

$$\delta n = n \exp\{i(\mathbf{k}\cdot\mathbf{r} - \omega t)\}.$$

The relationship between the wave number and the frequency obtained by substitution into eq. 14.80 is

$$\omega^2 = \omega_p^2 + \frac{k^2}{m}\left(\frac{\partial p}{\partial n}\right)_0 \tag{14.81}$$

where $\omega_p \equiv \sqrt{\left(\dfrac{1}{4\pi\epsilon_0}\right)\dfrac{4\pi n_0 e^2}{m}}$ = plasma angular frequency.

In order to determine the phase velocity (ω/k) and group velocity ($d\omega/dk$) of such density fluctuations, it is necessary to know the value of

$$\frac{1}{m}\left(\frac{\partial p}{\partial n}\right)_0$$

which plays the role of the square of the sound velocity in the electron fluid. This quantity depends on the equation of state of the electron fluid and to an excellent approximation can be shown by microscopic arguments to be

$$\frac{1}{m}\left(\frac{\partial p}{\partial n}\right)_0 = 3\langle u^2\rangle$$

where $\langle u^2\rangle$ = mean square of the velocity of internal motion of the electrons.

Using Maxwell's equations and the force equation (eq. 14.76), it is possible to show that $\delta\mathbf{E}$ satisfies an equation similar in form to that satisfied by δn. Solutions to this equation exist in which the behavior of $\delta\mathbf{E}$ corresponds to longitudinal oscillations with the frequency of eq. 14.81. Such longitudinal oscillations cannot dissipate energy via radiation. Other modes of oscillation for a plasma exist in which all mechanical and field quantities oscillate with the same frequency. Such a mode of oscillation contains both longitudinal and transverse waves and in such a mode the plasma can radiate. (A proof of the above statements is contained in Problems 14.9 and 14.10.)

PROBLEMS

14.1   A particle of charge q and mass m is accelerated through a potential difference $\Delta\varphi$ and enters a region of uniform magnetic field B_0 perpendicular to the field. Calculate the radius of curvature of the orbit of the particle after it has entered the magnetic field region. Calculate the effective magnetic moment of the particle due to its orbital motion.

14.2   A particle of charge q and mass m moves in a two-dimensional electrostatic potential given by the expression $\varphi = (m/2q)\omega_0^2(x^2 - y^2)$. Set up and solve the equations of motion for the particle, assuming that the particle is at rest and is located at the point $(x_0, 0)$ at the time $t = 0$. Give a physical interpretation of the constant ω_0 in the expression for φ.

14.3   Two concentric conducting cylinders of radius r_1 and r_2 ($r_2 > r_1$) have a potential difference of $\Delta\varphi$ between them. A uniform B-field exists in the region between the cylinders and parallel to the cylinder axis. (This is called a *magnetron*.) A particle of charge q and mass m starts out at rest from the inner cylinder and is accelerated toward the outer cylinder. Calculate the angular velocity and the kinetic energy of the particle at an arbitrary point in the region between the conducting cylinders. For a given value of $\Delta\varphi$, there is a maximum value of B for which the particle can reach the outer cylinder. Calculate this critical or "cut-off" value of B.

14.4   Assuming that the potential difference between the plates of a cylindrical magnetron and the magnetic field satisfy the "cut-off" relation (see previous problem), show that the angular velocity attained by the charged particle when it reaches the outer plate is

$$\omega = \frac{1}{r_1}\sqrt{\frac{2q}{m}\Delta\varphi}.$$

Show further that the potential difference between the plates and the cut-off magnetic field satisfy the following relation:

$$\Delta\varphi = \frac{m\omega_c^2 r_2^2}{8q}\left[1 - \left(\frac{r_1}{r_2}\right)^2\right]^2\left(\frac{1}{4\pi\epsilon_0}\right)$$

where ω_c = cyclotron frequency.

14.5   A particle moves in a region of "crossed" uniform fields, i.e., $\mathbf{E} = E\mathbf{z}$ and $\mathbf{B} = B\mathbf{x}$ (see Example 14.2). If the particle is initially at rest at the origin of coordinates, calculate the Cartesian components of its position vector after a time t has elapsed.

14.6   The angular velocity of a charged particle in an axially symmetric magnetic lens is the particle's Larmor frequency. A beam of particles enters the lens moving parallel to the axis after having been accelerated through a potential difference $\Delta\varphi$. Show that the angle through which the beam has been twisted after it emerges from the lens is given by

$$\Delta\theta = \sqrt{\frac{q}{8m\,\Delta\varphi}}\int_{x_1}^{x_2} B_x\,dx$$

where (x_1, x_2) are axial positions at which the beam enters and leaves the lens. If the lens consists of a short solenoid of N turns carrying a current I, use Ampère's law to show that

$$\Delta\theta = \mu_0\sqrt{\frac{q}{8m\,\Delta\varphi}}\,NI.$$

14.7   Consider a particle of charge q and mass m moving in the neighborhood of a long straight wire of radius a carrying a current I. At time $t = 0$, the particle is at position R, the component of its velocity parallel to the wire is v_0, and its motion in the plane perpendicular to the wire is characterized by an angular momentum l. Calculate the component of its velocity parallel to the wire at some time later when it is at a distance ρ from the wire; also calculate its radial acceleration at this position.

14.8   Consider a plasma confined to a cylindrical sheath of radius R. Assuming that the current density is constant within the plasma, show that the pressure at the cylindrical axis, p_0, is twice the average pressure within the plasma.

14.9 Develop the differential equation satisfied by the E-field for an electron gas in the plasma limit. Employ the same equilibrium conditions that were used in deriving eq. 14.80. Assuming that the B-field never departs appreciably from its equilibrium value, prove that solutions to this equation exist which correspond to longitudinal oscillations in E.

14.10 Consider a plasma in which the departure of all mechanical and field quantities from their equilibrium values vary as $\exp\{i(\mathbf{k} \cdot \mathbf{r} - \omega t)\}$. Show that solutions to the equations of motion exist in which $\delta \mathbf{E}$ satisfies the relation

$$[\omega^2 - \omega_p^2 - c^2 k^2]\, \delta\mathbf{E} - \left[c^2 - \frac{1}{m}\left(\frac{\partial p}{\partial n}\right)_0\right](\mathbf{k} \cdot \delta\mathbf{E})\mathbf{k} = 0.$$

If $\delta\mathbf{E}$ is written as $\delta\mathbf{E} \equiv \delta\mathbf{E}_{\parallel} + \delta\mathbf{E}_{\perp}$, where $\mathbf{k} \cdot \delta\mathbf{E}_{\perp} = 0$, show that $\delta\mathbf{E}_{\perp}$ (the transverse oscillation) satisfies the equation

$$(\omega^2 - \omega_p^2 - c^2 k^2)\, \delta\mathbf{E}_{\perp} = 0.$$

15 | *Electric and Magnetic Properties of Matter*

The preceding chapters have concerned themselves with the properties of electric and magnetic fields. Although it has been necessary to refer to the behavior of matter in the presence of electric charge and current, the emphasis has been upon the effects of matter on the fields produced by the charges and currents rather than on a detailed discussion of the structure of matter. Here a brief discussion will be presented on the structure of matter, with special attention being given to those aspects of the structure that are salient in determining the electric and magnetic behavior of matter. The discussion will be selective rather than inclusive since any attempt at completeness even at an elementary level would in itself require a lengthy book.

The basic elements of matter—atoms—have electric and magnetic properties. These atomic properties are directly measurable in dilute atomic gases. In the other extreme, namely solids, these atomic properties are masked by the interaction effects between closely packed atoms and the resulting cooperative effects. The constituents of an atom, namely the nucleus and the cloud of electrons, are charged, the nucleus having a positive charge of Ze (Z = atomic number or number of electrons in the extranuclear electronic cloud; e = magnitude of the electron charge) and the electronic cloud carrying a negative charge equal to $-Ze$. Atoms are electrostatically neutral. It is not possible using classical arguments alone to understand the stability of atoms. In any simple classical picture, the *mechanical* stability of the electronic orbits about the nucleus is produced by the opposite effects of the attractive Coulomb force between the nucleus and the electron and the effective repulsive force, the centrifugal force. However, an electron moving in these force fields has a centripetal acceleration and consequently, according to the classical theory of electromagnetism, will radiate electromagnetic energy. A classical atom is therefore *electromagnetically* unstable.

In order to understand the stability of atoms, it is necessary to invoke the ideas of quantum mechanics. Quantum mechanically, a system composed of a nucleus of charge $+Ze$ and a cloud of electrons of charge

−*Ze* has a lowest energy state. This lowest energy state is called the *ground state* of the atom and is electromagnetically stable, i.e., it cannot radiate. There are other *bound states*, i.e., states of negative total energy, of the atom which are of higher energy than the ground state. A stable atom may be "excited" into a higher energy state by absorption of energy through collision processes (conversion of kinetic energy into internal or excitation energy), radiative absorption processes, etc. These states are electromagnetically unstable and eventually decay with characteristic life times to the ground state emitting quantized electromagnetic energy, namely photons.

An atom in its ground state cannot possess an (E1) moment. However, in an externally applied electric field, it is possible to induce a dipole moment in the atom. The induction of an electric dipole in an atom is referred to as the Stark effect.

The elementary particle constituents of an atom (electrons in the negatively charged extranuclear cloud, protons and neutrons in the nucleus) all possess permanent magnetic dipole moments associated with their intrinsic angular momentum or *spin*. This spin angular momentum is independent of the motion of the particle involved; it is quantum mechanical in origin. The magnetic moments of the elementary particle constituents of an atom are

$$\mu = \begin{cases} -2\mu_B & \text{electron} \\ 2.79\left(\dfrac{m}{M_p}\right)\mu_B & \text{proton} \\ -1.91\left(\dfrac{m}{M_p}\right)\mu_B & \text{neutron} \end{cases}$$

where m = electron mass

M_p = proton mass

$\mu_B = \dfrac{e\hbar}{2mc}$ = one Bohr magneton = 0.927×10^{-23} amp − m^2

or 0.927×10^{-20} erg/gauss.

The electronic (M1) moment is about 2×10^3 larger than the nucleonic dipole moment, and consequently the electronic (M1) moment dominates that due to the nucleus unless the electronic (M1) moment of the electron cloud vanishes identically. The electronic contribution to the (M1) moment of the atom also contains terms associated with the electronic currents, sometimes referred to as the orbital contributions. In atoms with an even number of electrons, the electronic angular momenta are coupled or paired in such a way that the total angular momentum and as a consequence the (M1) moment vanishes. For an atom with an odd number of electrons, the angular momentum of the electronic cloud and the resultant (M1) moment is nonvanishing. A similar situation exists for a positive ion in which there is at least one "unpaired" electron. Since the angular momentum of an electron has two distinct origins, an intrinsic and an orbital contribution, the magnetic moment of the electron is not simply related to its total angular momentum. The relationship between the magnetic moment μ and the angular momentum can be derived by simple quantum mechanical arguments and is

$$\mu = g(J, L)\mu_B \tag{15.1}$$

where $\qquad g(J, L) = 1 + \dfrac{J(J + 1) + 3/4 - L(L + 1)}{2J(J + 1)}$

where J, L are the total and orbital angular momentum quantum numbers of the electron: $J = L \pm 1/2$; $L = 0, 1, 2, \ldots$. The constant $g(J, L)$ is called the Landé g-factor and was originally introduced empirically before the advent of quantum mechanics to account for certain features of the electromagnetic emission and absorption spectra of atoms.

The (M1) moment of a nucleus is small because of the factor (m/M_p) which appears in the expression for the nucleonic (M1) moments. For atoms in which the electrons are all paired so that $\mu_{\text{electronic}} = 0$, the nucleus may have an odd number of nucleons (although Z must be even) and therefore a nonvanishing moment. However, this nuclear moment is effectively screened from an externally applied magnetic field by the electronic cloud. The electronic cloud can be considered as a gas of high conductivity which repels an applied field through the Meissner effect.

The formation of compound structures from atoms of which simple molecules are the most elementary examples is only understandable on quantum mechanical grounds. A simple diatomic molecule has a stable state or ground state because of the net attraction between the two electron clouds as the two atoms are brought close together. This attraction is not of electromagnetic origin but is brought about by the "sharing" or "exchanging" of electrons by the two atoms. The "exchange" interaction between two or more atoms is attractive in some cases and these are the molecules which are bound. The exchange interaction between two H atoms is sufficiently strong to cause the H_2 molecule to be stable under ordinary conditions whereas the exchange interaction between two He atoms does not produce He_2 under ordinary conditions. The formation of complex collective ensembles of atoms, large molecules and solids, is attributable not only to electromagnetic effects but also these "exchange" and equivalent interactions which are quantum mechanical in origin.

15.1   Susceptibilities of Paramagnetic and Polar Substances

For the purposes of this discussion of electric and magnetic suscepti-bility of materials, it is useful to invoke the following procedure which has its origin in statistical mechanics: suppose a neutral molecule or an ion of a system can exist in any one of a number of discrete states which are characterized by an energy w_j at temperature Θ. Up to a normaliza-tion factor, the *partition function* for the system is defined as

$$Z(\Theta) \equiv \sum_j \exp\left\{\frac{-w_j}{k\Theta}\right\} \qquad (15.2)$$

where the subscript j runs over all the possible energy states of the molecule or ion; $k =$ Boltzmann's constant $= 1.38 \times 10^{-23}$ joules per degree Kelvin.

For a typical molecule or ion there are several contributions to the energy of a state, namely—translational kinetic energy, energy of rotation, energy of vibration, and various interaction energies with the various constituents and with external agencies. Of particular interest to this discussion is the interaction of polar molecules with an applied E-field and para-magnetic ions or molecules with an applied B-field. For certain molecules the center of charge of the positively charged nuclei is not coincident with the center of charge of the negatively charged electronic cloud. Con-sequently these molecules have an intrinsic (E1) moment and are called polar molecules. Any molecule composed of like atoms (e.g., H_2, O_2, etc.) cannot be polar since in the ground state the molecule is symmetric with respect to the interchange of like atoms. Paramagnetic molecules and ions exist because of the (M1) moments associated with unpaired electrons in the electronic clouds of the molecules and ions.

For a polar molecule of (E1) moment $\mathbf{p}$ the interaction energy with an applied field is:

$$w_{\text{int}} = -\mathbf{p} \cdot \mathbf{E}$$

whereas for a paramagnetic entity of (M1) moment $\boldsymbol{\mu}$, the interaction energy with an applied field is

$$w_{\text{int}} = -\boldsymbol{\mu} \cdot \mathbf{B}.$$

In both cases the interaction energy may be expressed as the negative product of the strength of the field, the strength of the moment, and the cosine of the angle between the moment and the field. Therefore the classical theories of the electric susceptibility of a gas of polar molecules and the magnetic susceptibility of a material composed of paramagnetic molecules or ions have precisely the same formulation and structure. It is only necessary to discuss one of the cases in any detail. The discussion that follows will be of the magnetic case and is sometimes referred to as the Langevin theory of paramagnetism.

In the Langevin theory, that part of the energy of the paramagnetic molecule or ion which is due to its interaction with the applied field is taken as $-\mu B \cos \theta$. The total energy of the molecule is then $w = w' - \mu B \cos \theta$ where w' is that part of the molecular energy which is of other physical origin; that is, it contains the kinetic energy, the internal energy, and the interaction among the molecules. The prescription to be used in calculating the magnetic susceptibility is as follows: in statistical mechanics, the average value of any quantity ψ for a molecule or ion of a material at temperature Θ is written in terms of the partition function as

$$\langle \psi \rangle \equiv \frac{\sum_j \psi_j \exp\left\{\frac{-w_j}{k\Theta}\right\}}{\sum_j \exp\left\{\frac{-w_j}{k\Theta}\right\}}. \tag{15.3}$$

In determining the magnetic susceptibility, the relevant quantity is

$$\langle \mu \cos \theta \rangle = \mu \langle \cos \theta \rangle = \mu \frac{\sum_j \cos \theta_j \exp\left\{\frac{-w_j}{k\Theta}\right\}}{\sum_j \exp\left\{\frac{-w_j}{k\Theta}\right\}}. \tag{15.4}$$

Equation 15.4 may be simplified as follows: it should be noted that $\exp(x + y) = \exp(x) \exp(y)$, and therefore the right-hand side of eq. 15.4 reduces after some cancellations to

$$\langle \mu \cos \theta \rangle = \mu \frac{\sum_j \cos \theta_j \exp\left\{\frac{\mu B}{k\Theta} \cos \theta_j\right\}}{\sum_j \exp\left\{\frac{\mu B}{k\Theta} \cos \theta_j\right\}}.$$

In a classical theory, $\sum_j \cdots$ is symbolic for an integral over all possible orientations of the magnetic moment of the molecule:

$$\sum_j \cos \theta_j \exp\left\{\frac{\mu B}{k\Theta} \cos \theta_j\right\} \Rightarrow \int_0^{2\pi} d\phi \int_{\theta=0}^{\theta=\pi} \cos \theta \exp\left\{\frac{\mu B}{k\Theta} \cos \theta\right\} d(\cos \theta).$$

Consequently

$$\langle \mu \cos \theta \rangle = \mu \frac{\int_{-1}^{1} x \exp\left\{\frac{\mu B}{k\Theta} x\right\} dx}{\int_{-1}^{1} \exp\left\{\frac{\mu B}{k\Theta} x\right\} dx} = \mu\left(\coth \frac{\mu B}{k\Theta} - \frac{k\Theta}{\mu B}\right). \tag{15.5}$$

The function $\coth y - (1/y)$ is called the Langevin function. It is linear in y for small y and *saturates*, approaches the limiting value of 1, for large y. For high temperatures and/or low fields ($y \ll 1$)

$$\coth y - \frac{1}{y} \approx \frac{1}{3} \frac{\mu B}{k\Theta}. \qquad (15.6)$$

The magnitude of the magnetization M of the gas is given by the expression $M = n\mu\langle\cos\theta\rangle$, where $n =$ number of molecules per unit volume, which in the high temperature, low field limit reduces to

$$M = \frac{n\mu^2 B}{3k\Theta}. \qquad (15.7)$$

Equation 15.7 is known as Curie's law; the Langevin theory leads to an inverse dependence of the magnetization upon the temperature in the high temperature, low field limit. In the high field limit, the magnetization saturates at the value $M_{\text{sat}} = n\mu$. Consequently for a paramagnetic gas which obeys Curie's law

$$\frac{M}{M_{\text{sat}}} = \frac{1}{3} \frac{\mu B}{k\Theta}.$$

A paramagnetic gas such as oxygen obeys Curie's law at room temperature. In addition, the paramagnetic moment of an oxygen molecule is about $3\mu_B$. For field strengths of the order of 1 weber/meter^2 or 10^4 gauss at room temperature

$$\frac{M}{M_{\text{sat}}} \approx 2 \times 10^{-3}.$$

A field of the order of 1 weber/meter^2 is relatively large, but the thermal motion of the oxygen molecules at room temperature is sufficient to destroy a major fraction of the alignment due to the interaction with the field. On the average, only about one molecule per thousand is oriented along the field. Even for oxygen in which the molecules have intrinsically large magnetic moments, the paramagnetic susceptibility is expected to be quite small.

The above discussion although reasonably accurate in a qualitative sense is beset with one major difficulty—that molecules do not behave classically in a magnetic field. In particular, the orientation angle θ cannot take on a continuum of values between 0 and π, but $\cos\theta$ is restricted to certain discrete values. In quantum theory this is called *space quantization*. The necessary quantum mechanical modification can be introduced in our elementary discussion as follows. For simplicity, it will be assumed that there are two orientations allowed by quantum mechanics, i.e., parallel and antiparallel to the field. The two resulting orientation energies are μB and $-\mu B$. Consequently that part of the partition function associated with the orientation energy is simply

$$Z = \exp\left\{\frac{\mu B}{k\Theta}\right\} + \exp\left\{\frac{-\mu B}{k\Theta}\right\} = 2\cosh\left(\frac{\mu B}{k\Theta}\right), \tag{15.8}$$

and therefore

$$\langle \boldsymbol{\mu} \cdot \mathbf{B} \rangle = \mu B \frac{\exp\left\{\dfrac{-\mu B}{k\Theta}\right\} - \exp\left\{\dfrac{\mu B}{k\Theta}\right\}}{2\cosh\left(\dfrac{\mu B}{k\Theta}\right)}$$

or

$$\langle \boldsymbol{\mu} \cdot \mathbf{B} \rangle = \mu B \tanh\left(\frac{\mu B}{k\Theta}\right).$$

The magnitude of the resultant magnetization is

$$M = n\mu \tanh\left(\frac{\mu B}{k\Theta}\right). \tag{15.9}$$

For large values of $y = (\mu B/k\Theta)$, M approaches $n\mu$ the saturation value predicted by the Langevin theory. On the other hand, for small y $\tanh y \approx y$ and

$$M \approx \frac{n\mu^2 B}{k\Theta}. \tag{15.10}$$

The considerations of space quantization yield the same qualitative values for the paramagnetic susceptibility as the Langevin theory except for a multiplication constant of the order of 1 in the Curie region. The argument given above for two possible orientations of the magnetic moment of a molecule with respect to the applied field can be generalized as follows. An elementary atomic structure with angular momentum $J\hbar(J = $ any integer or half integer) has $(2J + 1)$ equally spaced energy states in an applied field corresponding to $(2J + 1)$ possible orientations of the magnetic moment in a magnetic field. The resulting magnetization can be shown to be

$$M = ngJ\mu_B\left\{\frac{2J + 1}{2J}\operatorname{ctnh}\left(\frac{2J + 1}{2J}y_J\right) - \frac{1}{2J}\operatorname{ctnh}\left(\frac{1}{2J}y_J\right)\right\} \tag{15.11}$$

where $y_J = gJ\mu_e B/k\Theta$

$g = $ Landé g-factor ≈ 1.

In the Curie limit (high temperature, low field) this reduces to

$$M = \frac{nJ(J + 1)g^2\mu_B^2}{3k\Theta}. \tag{15.12}$$

Therefore in the Curie limit the classical Langevin theory gives results in good agreement with the quantum mechanical theory.

As mentioned previously, the Langevin theory for a gas of polar molecules yields results similar to those derived for a paramagnetic gas. The most common situation encountered experimentally for polar molecules is the case $pE/k\Theta \ll 1$. For polar gases at room temperature, $pE/k\Theta \approx 2 \times 10^{-4}$ and the polarization of the material is then approximately

$$P = \frac{np^2 E}{3k\Theta}. \tag{15.13}$$

The *dipolar polarizability* α_1 per molecule is defined as

$$\alpha_1 = \frac{P}{nE} = \frac{p^2}{3k\Theta} \approx 10^{-29} \text{ meter}^3. \tag{15.14}$$

The dipolar polarizability per molecule is to be compared in magnitude with the electronic polarizability per atom.   The electronic polarizability of a gas has been discussed previously in this text but it is instructive to repeat the argument here.   A bound electron acted upon by an E-field of angular frequency ω satisfies the equation of motion:

$$x'' + \omega_0^2 x = \frac{e}{m} E_0 \exp(i\omega t)$$

where ω_0 = angular frequency associated with the binding energy of the electron in the atom or molecule.   Writing $x = x_0 \exp(i\omega t)$, the equation of motion has the solution

$$x_0 = \frac{\dfrac{q}{m} E_0}{(\omega_0^2 - \omega^2)}$$

The resulting induced dipole moment is $p_0 \exp(i\omega t)$ with

$$p_0 = ex_0 = \frac{\dfrac{e^2}{m} E_0}{(\omega_0^2 - \omega^2)}.$$

The electronic polarizability α_0 is then:

$$\alpha_0 = \frac{e^2}{m(\omega_0^2 - \omega^2)}.$$

Since there are electrons with different binding energies and therefore different ω_0's, the above equation can be generalized to read in the low frequency limit $\omega \ll \omega_0$

$$\alpha_0 = \sum_k n_k \frac{e^2}{m\omega_{0k}^2} \tag{15.15}$$

where n_k = number of electrons per atom with resonance frequency ω_{0k}.

Equation 15.15 is only approximate since the model employed to obtain α_0 is very crude. However, eq. 15.15 yields the correct order of magnitude for α_0 which is about 10^{-30} meter³. Consequently the dipolar and the electronic polarizabilities are of the same order of magnitude for polar molecules.

Although the above discussion has been applied to gases, it can equally well be applied to a liquid or a solid. In a solid the situation is much more complex than in a gas, since the positive ions are relatively much closer together and thus interact very strongly. This can lead to such abnormal behavior as ferromagnetism, ferroelectricity, antiferromagnetism, etc.

15.2   Ferromagnetism and Related Properties

Perhaps the most striking cooperative effect of ions in a material is the existence of ferromagnetism, antiferromagnetism, and the related electric phenomenon, ferroelectricity. Ferromagnetism is the most commonly experienced of these phenomena, and thus the discussion will center mainly on ferromagnetism. Ions of iron and the iron group in the periodic table of the elements are paramagnetic and at highly elevated temperatures, materials composed of these ions exhibit normal paramagnetic behavior. Below a certain critical temperature Θ_c called the *Curie point*, these materials behave abnormally. In particular, they maintain a magnetization even when there is no applied field. This magnetization which occurs in the absence of an applied field below the Curie point is called the spontaneous or permanent magnetization. In essence, the paramagnetic ions align themselves as if an applied field were present.

A phenomenological model for spontaneous magnetization was suggested by Weiss. In this model a field B_W is assumed to be acting on the paramagnetic ion independent of any applied field. The field B_W, the *Weiss field*, is able to align ionic moments below Θ_c. It is possible to obtain an order of magnitude estimate of the Weiss field as follows. At the critical point the relaxation energy (the energy tending to disalign the ionic moments) is approximately $k\Theta_c$ which in turn is of the same order of magnitude as μB_W. The Curie point for iron is approximately $10^3\,°K$, from which it follows that $B_W \approx 10^3$ webers/meter² or 10^7 gauss. This is a very strong field compared to that produced by one paramagnetic ion at a neighboring ion site which is approximately 1 weber/meter² or 10^4 gauss.

Although the Weiss field model makes it possible to understand the phenomenon of ferromagnetism, it says nothing about the origin of the

Weiss field.   In ferromagnetic material, the spontaneous magnetization is not due to a direct interaction between the magnetic moments of the ions.   This direct interaction is too small by a very large factor since the magnetic field associated with this interaction is three to four orders of magnitude too small.   The interaction from which ferromagnetism results is the so-called *exchange interaction*—a concept introduced by Frenkel and Heisenberg who pointed out that reversing the magnetic moment of one ion in the presence of an identical ion must be accompanied by a change in the Coulomb interaction energy between the ions.   This is a purely quantum mechanical effect although it results in a change in a classical quantity, the Coulomb energy.   The Coulomb interaction energy between two ions therefore depends on the *relative orientation* of the two moments and is not correlated with any other direction.   It allows for spontaneous magnetization (i.e., a preferred direction in the material) even though the material itself has no apparent physical anisotropy.

The exchange interaction between two paramagnetic ions i and j of angular momentum $J_i\hbar$ and $J_j\hbar$ can be shown to lead to an energy contribution of the form

$$w_{\text{exch}}^{ij} = -K\mathbf{J}_i \cdot \mathbf{J}_j. \tag{15.16}$$

The factor K is called the *exchange integral* and is positive for ions which form ferromagnetic materials.   The specific form of eq. 15.16 illustrates that the interaction which leads to ferromagnetism depends on the relative orientation of the ionic moments.

The exchange interaction is a long-range interaction in that ionic moments are aligned over macroscopic distances.   In a ferromagnetic material which has been prepared in a field free environment, this long-range order extends over distances of the order of 10^{-4}–10^{-5} meters. This leads to the so-called *domain* model of a ferromagnetic in which a macroscopic sample under normal conditions possesses a spontaneous magnetization much below the saturation value (all ionic moments aligned). The sample is considered to be divided into small regions or domains each of which possesses the saturation value of the magnetization but these domains are randomly oriented with respect to each other.   Under the application of an applied field, the magnetization can be increased over its spontaneous value by either flipping the spins of individual ions causing the domains to increase in size or by alignment of all the domains by rotation of the moment of entire domains.   The former process is dominant for weak fields whereas the latter is the primary mechanism for attaining saturation at high fields.   (See Fig. 15.1.)

In the absence of an applied magnetic field, the structure in which a macroscopic sample is found is one which is characterized in many magnetic

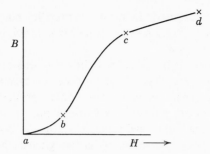

Fig. 15.1 The curve plotted is the history of B vs. H for a ferromagnetic material whose spontaneous magnetization vanishes initially. For that segment of the curve a-b, the dominant process is growth in size of domains; b-c corresponds to domain rotation. For segment c-d, the material is saturated and acts as a single domain.

domains rather than a single magnetic domain. This can be understood as follows: a material with several uncorrelated domains has a lower effective magnetic moment than the same material in the form of a single domain. Therefore, the multidomain structure produces a weaker field than the single domain structure from which it follows that the magnetic field energy associated with the multidomain structure is less than that associated with the single domain. This effect favors the multidomain structure since it has lower energy. However, there is another effect which acts in the opposite sense. Whenever the number of domains in a sample is increased by one, there is at least one other domain interface produced across which the magnetic moments are no longer aligned. The basic exchange interaction between ions causes ionic moments to be aligned (the energy for alignment is negative). However, the creation of a domain interface causes ions in the neighborhood of the interface to be disaligned, thereby increasing the interaction energy for these ions. The stable domain structure is, therefore, determined by the optimum minimization of the field energy associated with increasing the number of domains and the minimization of the domain interfaces. There are several experimental techniques available which vividly display the domains in a ferromagnetic material.

Antiferromagnetism is a phenomenon similar to that of ferromagnetism in that an antiferromagnetic substance exhibits long range ionic order of the paramagnetic ions below the Curie point. However, in an antiferromagnet, the spontaneous magnetization vanishes since neighboring ionic moments are aligned antiparallel to one another. The origin of antiferromagnetism is the quantum mechanical exchange energy between ions displayed in eq. 15.16. For an antiferromagnetic material, the exchange integral is negative favoring antiparallel alignment of ionic moments. Such relatively common substances as MnO, $NiCl_2$, NiO, etc., exhibit antiferromagnetism.

Ferroelectricity outwardly resembles ferromagnetism in that certain physical properties of ferroelectrics mirror those of ferromagnetics. In a ferroelectric, there is a spontaneous electrical polarization which disappears above a characteristic temperature or Curie point. In addition, in the absence of an applied field, the ferroelectric has a domain structure. However, the basic physical cause of ferromagnetism is different from that in ferroelectricity. It is the exchange interaction which is not correlated in any way with any physical anisotropies in the material which produces ferromagnetism. Ferroelectricity, on the other hand, is possible whenever the interaction between ions in a crystal lattice is anisotropic; as a consequence, the spontaneous electric polarization is correlated with characteristic crystalline axes. Crystalline dielectrics which do not have appropriate anisotropies cannot exhibit ferroelectric behavior; in particular, a cubic crystal is nonferroelectric.[1]

15.3   Electrical Conductivity

When a potential difference is applied across many materials, a measurable macroscopic electric current ensues; the current vanishes whenever the potential difference is removed. Materials which behave in this manner are called "conductors." The fact that conductors can maintain an electrical current implies that there is a measurable number of "current carriers" or relatively free charges per unit volume. A conductor is, of course, electrically neutral but its crystalline structure is such that some of the electrons from each of the constituent atoms are shared among all the atoms. The binding energy of these free or "conduction" electrons to any of the ionic sites is negligibly small. These conduction electrons can be viewed as a gas moving in the potential field supplied by the immobile positive ions. When no macroscopic electric field exists within the conductor, the velocities of the conduction electrons are randomly oriented and there is no net flow of charge. If an E-field is applied to the conductor, the conduction electrons experience an acceleration opposite in direction to the applied field. For a constant field, this would result in a current which increased linearly with time as long as the E-field was present. This is not the situation which exists experimentally. For most

---

[1] An exhaustive list of crystalline types in which ferroelectric behavior is possible is contained in Landau and Lifshitz, *Electrodynamics of Continuous Media*, Addison-Wesley, 1960, p. 61.

conductors and moderate **E**-fields, the current density **j** is proportional to **E**. This is known as Ohm's law.

A very simple model for the dynamical behavior of the conduction electrons can account quite accurately for the experimentally observed dependence of **j** upon **E**. Although the conduction electrons are not bound to lattice sites, they are not perfectly free to move within the conductor. They "collide" frequently with the lattice ions, that is they transfer energy to the lattice as they move through the potential provided by the lattice ions. The effective force associated with these electron-ion collisions can be taken to a first approximation as a viscous drag force proportional to the electron velocity.

In writing down the equation of motion for the conduction electrons, the thermal velocity will be ignored. The velocity associated with the applied field is called the *drift velocity* and shall be designated by the symbol $\mathbf{v}_d$. Actually, since the collision mechanism is represented in such a crude way by a damping force, the drift velocity must be thought of as the velocity averaged over many collisions. The drift velocity is therefore a macroscopic quantity. The equation of motion for a conduction electron is then

$$m \frac{d\mathbf{v}_d}{dt} + \gamma \mathbf{v}_d = e E.$$

For a constant macroscopic **E**, the equation has the solution:

$$\mathbf{v}_d = \frac{e\mathbf{E}}{\gamma}$$

corresponding to a constant drift velocity (i.e., $d\mathbf{v}_d/dt = 0$). The current density associated with this velocity is

$$\mathbf{j} = \frac{Ne^2}{\gamma} \mathbf{E} \quad \text{(Ohm's law)} \tag{15.17}$$

where N = number of conduction electrons per unit volume leading to a value of the conductivity

$$\sigma = \frac{Ne^2}{\gamma}. \tag{15.18}$$

Treating the conduction electrons in this phenomenological manner ignores the fact that an electron must be thought of as quantum mechanical particle obeying Fermi–Dirac statistics. It is far beyond the scope of this text to attempt a discussion of the electrical conductivity of a Fermi–Dirac gas.[2] It suffices here to remark that such a discussion leads to the

[2] A discussion of this type is carried out in C. Kittel, *Elementary Solid State Physics*, Chapter 5.

same value of σ as is contained in the classical discussion with, however, a physical interpretation of the constant γ more appropriate to a quantum mechanical gas. In a quantum mechanical treatment, the constant γ is written as:

$$\gamma = \frac{m}{\tau} \tag{15.19}$$

where τ is the *relaxation time*. The relaxation time is the time governing the reestablishment of equilibrium in a Fermi gas after a field $\mathbf{E}$ has been applied. In introducing the relaxation time, it is necessary that $\mathbf{E}$ be small enough so that departures from equilibrium in the electron gas are small. This is equivalent to the statement that only effects linear in the applied field are considered.

15.4   Thermodynamics of Magnetic Materials

Many interesting physical phenomena associated with magnetic materials involve striking temperature dependent effects. The abrupt transition that occurs between the normal (paramagnetic) and the abnormal (ferromagnetic) phases of a paramagnetic material, the transition between the normal (conducting) and the abnormal (superconducting) phases of a conducting material, the production of low temperatures by adiabatic demagnetization are among the physical processes which are associated with the temperature concept. These phenomena can all be understood using simple thermodynamic arguments.

In Chapter 9 it was shown that the work done *on* a magnetic material in a cycling of the currents producing a magnetic field could be written as:

$$w_M = \left(\frac{\mu_0}{4\pi}\right) 4\pi \oint \mathbf{H} \cdot \delta\mathbf{M}$$

where the integral is to be taken over the values of $\mathbf{H}$ and $\mathbf{M}$ during the cycling of the currents producing $\mathbf{H}$ and $\mathbf{M}$. In thermodynamics, the quantity of interest is the infinitesimal work done *by* the material on its environment during a small change in the quantities characterizing the state of the material. This quantity is

$$\delta w_M = -\left(\frac{\mu_0}{4\pi}\right) 4\pi \mathbf{H} \cdot \delta\mathbf{M}. \tag{15.20}$$

Of course, a term could be added to the right-hand side of eq. 15.20 which integrates to zero in a cyclic process. However, eq. 15.20 is the conventional form for δw_M. In addition to the magnetic work, a system can do mechanical work on its environment. The increment of mechanical work is simply

$$dw = p\, dV.$$

Restricting the present discussion to magnetic and mechanical work only, the first law of thermodynamics can be written as

$$\delta Q = dU + p\, dV - \left(\frac{\mu_0}{4\pi}\right) H\, dM, \quad \text{(first law)}. \tag{15.21}$$

(To avoid unnecessary algebraic complications the discussion will be restricted *ab initio* to situations in which **H** is parallel to **M**.) In eq. 15.21 δQ is the infinitesimal amount of heat *added to* the system and dU is the change in the internal energy of the system. It should be noted that M (magnetization) plays the same role in thermodynamics as V (volume) and $-(\mu_0/4\pi)H$ plays the same role as p (pressure).

If heat is added to the system in a *reversible* fashion, then it is possible to define a thermodynamic quantity,[3] the *entropy S*, which is related to Q via the relation

$$dQ = \Theta\, dS \tag{15.22}$$

where Θ is the temperature of the system. In terms of the entropy function, the first law of thermodynamics is

$$\Theta\, dS = dU + p\, dV - \left(\frac{\mu_0}{4\pi}\right) H\, dM. \tag{15.23}$$

Equation 15.23 will be used in connection with the equation of state of a paramagnetic material, namely Curie's law for low temperatures, to show that adiabatic demagnetization (decreasing H with no heat exchange) results in a lowering of the temperature Θ. To accomplish this, it will be assumed that volume changes associated with the physical processes are negligible. The entropy of the system will be considered as a function of the temperature and H only; under these assumptions

$$dS = \left(\frac{\partial S}{\partial \Theta}\right) d\Theta + \left(\frac{\partial S}{\partial H}\right) dH$$

which, when multiplied by Θ, yields

$$\Theta\, dS = C_H\, d\Theta + \Theta\left(\frac{\partial S}{\partial H}\right) dH \tag{15.24}$$

since $\Theta(\partial S/\partial \Theta)$ for fixed H is just the definition of the *specific heat* at

---

[3] A full discussion of the entropy is contained in any elementary thermodynamics text. See, for example, M. Zemansky, *Heat and Thermodynamics*, McGraw-Hill, 1957.

constant H. $(\partial S/\partial H)$ can be expressed in terms of physical quantities which appear directly in the equations of state for the paramagnetic material. This is accomplished by introducing the thermodynamic function called the Gibbs function G. The Gibbs function for a magnetic material can be defined as

$$G = U - \Theta S - \left(\frac{\mu_0}{4\pi}\right) 4\pi\, HM. \tag{15.25}$$

Equation 15.25 is a so-called Legendre transformation. Infinitesimal changes in the Gibbs function are evaluated as follows:

$$dG = dU - S\, d\Theta - \Theta\, dS - \left(\frac{\mu_0}{4\pi}\right) 4\pi M\, dH - \left(\frac{\mu_0}{4\pi}\right) 4\pi H\, dM. \tag{15.26}$$

dG can be simplified using the first law, namely, eq. 15.23:

$$dG = -S\, d\Theta - \left(\frac{\mu_0}{4\pi}\right) 4\pi M\, dH = \left(\frac{\partial G}{\partial \Theta}\right) d\Theta + \left(\frac{\partial G}{\partial H}\right) dH. \tag{15.27}$$

Since $\partial^2 G/\partial\Theta\partial H = \partial^2 G/\partial H\partial\Theta$, it follows from eq. 15.27 that

$$\frac{\partial S}{\partial H} = \left(\frac{\mu_0}{4\pi}\right) 4\pi\left(\frac{\partial M}{\partial \Theta}\right)$$

which, when substituted into eq. 15.24, yields

$$dS = C_H\, d\Theta + \left(\frac{\mu_0}{4\pi}\right) 4\pi\Theta\left(\frac{\partial M}{\partial \Theta}\right) dH. \tag{15.28}$$

The quantity $(\partial M/\partial \Theta)$ can be evaluated directly from Curie's law (eq. 15.7), yielding

$$\frac{\partial M}{\partial \Theta} = -\frac{KH}{\Theta^2} \tag{15.29}$$

where $K =$ Curie's constant for the material in question.

For a reversible adiabatic process, $dS = 0$, and therefore:

$$d\Theta = \left(\frac{\mu_0}{4\pi}\right) 4\pi\, \frac{K}{C_H \Theta}\, H\, dH.$$

This relation can be converted into one involving finite temperature changes if the dependence of C_H upon Θ is known. For many materials at low temperature C_H varies inversely with Θ^2, i.e.,

$$C_H = A\Theta^{-2}$$

from which it follows that

$$\ln\left(\frac{\Theta_f}{\Theta_0}\right) = \left(\frac{\mu_0}{4\pi}\right) \frac{4\pi K}{A}\, (H_f^2 - H_0^2).$$

If $H_f < H_0$ (demagnetization), it is noted that $\Delta\Theta = \Theta_f - \Theta_0 < 0$. The cooling that is brought about by adiabatic demagnetization of a paramagnetic material is a practical way of producing extremely low temperatures in small samples.

15.5   Superconductors

In Chapter 9 the existence of so-called superconductors was introduced. The salient physical attribute of a superconductor is its *perfect diamagnetism*, i.e., $B = 0$ although $H \neq 0$, within a superconductor. In a normal paramagnetic material $\mathbf{B} = \mu\mathbf{H}$. A paramagnetic material can become perfectly diamagnetic under appropriate conditions of temperature and H. Figure 15.2 is a *phase diagram* for a material which can become superconducting. The curve on the phase diagram separates the normal and superconducting phases. A superconductor can carry out a transition to the normal state by either increasing Θ, keeping H fixed (line A) or increasing H, keeping Θ fixed (line B). Note that there is a certain critical value of both H and Θ above which the superconducting state cannot exist.

Figure 15.3 illustrates the Meissner effect. It is a plot of B vs. H for fixed Θ for a material which has both a normal and a superconducting phase. A phase transition occurs at the field H_c. This phase transition

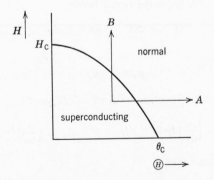

Fig. 15.2   The transition curve indicated separates the normal and superconducting regions on an H vs. Θ plot. The material which starts out in the superconducting region may carry out a transition to the normal state along path A by increasing Θ, and along path B by increasing H. Θ_c and H_c are the critical temperature and field above which the superconducting state cannot exist.

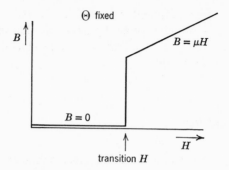

Fig. 15.3   The curve indicated is the plot of B vs. H for fixed Θ for a material which can have both a normal and superconducting phase at temperature Θ.

can be discussed using thermodynamics arguments. According to eq. 15.27, changes in the Gibbs function for the material can be written as

$$dG = -S\, d\Theta - \left(\frac{\mu_0}{4\pi}\right)4\pi M\, dH.$$

For an isothermal phase transition between the normal and superconducting states, $d\Theta = dH = 0$, and therefore the phase transition is characterized by

$$G^{(n)} = G^{(s)} \tag{15.30}$$

where the superscripts (n) and (s) stand for normal and superconducting phases, respectively. For a phase transition at a somewhat different temperature $\Theta + d\Theta$, the same result holds;

$$G^{(n)} + dG^{(n)} = G^{(s)} + dG^{(s)}$$

and consequently

$$dG^{(n)} = dG^{(s)}.$$

Using this result in conjunction with eq. 15.27 yields:

$$S^{(n)}\, d\Theta + \left(\frac{\mu_0}{4\pi}\right)4\pi M^{(n)}\, dH = S^{(s)}\, d\Theta + \left(\frac{\mu_0}{4\pi}\right)4\pi M^{(s)}\, dH$$

from which it follows that

$$-\left(\frac{dH}{d\Theta}\right) = \left(\frac{4\pi}{\mu_0}\right)\frac{1}{4\pi}\frac{S^{(n)} - S^{(s)}}{M^{(n)} - M^{(s)}}.$$

However, $S^{(n)} - S^{(s)} = L/\Theta$ where L is the latent heat of the phase transition (i.e., the heat that must be added at constant Θ to produce the transition). In addition, to a good approximation $M^{(n)} \approx 0$, and by definition $M^{(s)} = -H^{(s)}$. These relationships substituted in the above expression yields

$$L = -\left(\frac{\mu_0}{4\pi}\right)4\pi\Theta\left(H\frac{dH}{d\Theta}\right) \qquad (15.31)$$

where the quantities on the right-hand side are to be evaluated at the transition field at the temperature Θ.

The physical origin of superconductivity has only recently been understood. Although a phenomenological model for superconductivity was proposed some time ago by Fritz London,[4] a macroscopic quantum mechanical model of superconductivity has only recently been developed by Bardeen, Cooper, and Schrieffer. It should be remembered that the conduction electrons in a normal conductor are relatively free to move but attain a finite drift velocity under the application of an E-field through energy exchanging collisions with the ionic lattice. This interaction is "weak" in the sense that to a first approximation, the conduction electrons move in a potential field which has the lattice ions as its source. In a superconductor the interaction between the conduction electrons and the lattice is "strong." In particular, the lattice ions can be visualized as the source of two distinct phenomena: (1) the ions produce a weak potential in which the conduction electrons move, (2) the ions can be excited into certain quantum mechanically allowed states of vibration which are called *phonons*. Under certain conditions, the interaction between the electrons and the ions is so large (that part which leads to ionic vibration excitation sometimes called the electron-phonon interaction) that the conduction electrons cannot be considered to be moving independently of one another but rather exist in certain kinds of collective states which are called "excitations" of the electron system or "quasi-particles." The strong interaction between the electrons and the ionic lattice can cause the interaction between electrons, which is normally weak and repulsive, to become large and attractive producing strong collective motion in the electron gas. What Bardeen, Cooper, and Schrieffer were able to show was that if this effective interaction between electrons is a pair-interaction (interaction strong only if the electrons are moving in opposite directions, with their intrinsic angular momenta antiparallel) that the energy spectrum of the "excitations" has a "gap," that is, the difference in energy between the ground state of the electron gas and the first excited state is much larger than this energy difference for a normal electron gas. In a normal conductor, it is the transfer of small amounts of energy between the

---

[4] See, for example, F. London, *Superfluids*, Vol. I, Dover, 1961.

conduction electrons and the lattice which leads to a drift velocity proportional to the applied E (Ohm's law).   In a superconductor, such small energy transfers between the electrons and the lattice are not allowed as long as $k\Theta <$ energy gap leading to a breakdown of Ohm's law and to essentially zero resistivity.   The electromagnetic connection between superconductivity and perfect diamagnetism has already been discussed in Chapter 9.

Appendix A | Mathematical Appendix

Certain mathematical relationships and identities have been employed throughout the text. Many of these expressions have been discussed when first introduced, but those more frequently used are collected together in this Appendix.

A.1 Vector Algebra

ADDITION: $\mathbf{A} + \mathbf{B} = \mathbf{C}$

$$(A_x\hat{\mathbf{x}} + A_y\hat{\mathbf{y}} + A_z\hat{\mathbf{z}}) + (B_x\hat{\mathbf{x}} + B_y\hat{\mathbf{y}} + B_z\hat{\mathbf{z}}) = C_x\hat{\mathbf{x}} + C_y\hat{\mathbf{y}} + C_z\hat{\mathbf{z}}$$

with
$$C_x = A_x + B_x$$
$$C_y = A_y + B_y$$
$$C_z = A_z + B_z.$$

SCALAR PRODUCT:

$$\mathbf{A} \cdot \mathbf{B} \equiv |\mathbf{A}||\mathbf{B}| \cos \theta = \mathbf{B} \cdot \mathbf{A}$$

where θ = angle between $\mathbf{A}$ and $\mathbf{B}$.

In Cartesian representation:

$$\mathbf{A} \cdot \mathbf{B} = A_x B_x + A_y B_y + A_z B_z.$$

Scalar product of unit basis vectors:

$$\hat{\mathbf{x}} \cdot \hat{\mathbf{x}} = \hat{\mathbf{y}} \cdot \hat{\mathbf{y}} = \hat{\mathbf{z}} \cdot \hat{\mathbf{z}} = 1$$
$$\hat{\mathbf{x}} \cdot \hat{\mathbf{y}} = \hat{\mathbf{y}} \cdot \hat{\mathbf{z}} = \hat{\mathbf{z}} \cdot \hat{\mathbf{x}} = 0.$$

Geometrical interpretation:

From the law of cosines $\mathbf{A} \cdot \mathbf{B} = \dfrac{A^2 + B^2 - C^2}{2}$

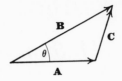

VECTOR PRODUCT:

$$\mathbf{A} \times \mathbf{B} = |\mathbf{A}| |\mathbf{B}| \sin \theta \hat{\mathbf{n}} = -\mathbf{B} \times \mathbf{A}$$

where $\hat{\mathbf{n}}$ is the unit vector normal to the plane defined by the vectors $\mathbf{A}$ and $\mathbf{B}$.

In Cartesian representation:

$$\mathbf{A} \times \mathbf{B} = (A_y B_z - A_z B_y)\hat{\mathbf{x}} + (A_z B_x - A_x B_z)\hat{\mathbf{y}} + (A_x B_y - A_y B_x)\hat{\mathbf{z}}.$$

Vector product of unit basis vectors:

$$\hat{\mathbf{x}} \times \hat{\mathbf{x}} = \hat{\mathbf{y}} \times \hat{\mathbf{y}} = \hat{\mathbf{z}} \times \hat{\mathbf{z}} = 0$$

$$\hat{\mathbf{x}} \times \hat{\mathbf{y}} = \hat{\mathbf{z}}, \quad \hat{\mathbf{y}} \times \hat{\mathbf{z}} = \hat{\mathbf{x}}, \quad \hat{\mathbf{z}} \times \hat{\mathbf{x}} = \hat{\mathbf{y}}.$$

Geometrical interpretation:

$|\mathbf{A} \times \mathbf{B}|$ is numerically equal to the area of the parallelogram sketched.

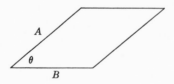

VECTOR ALGEBRA IDENTITIES:

$$\mathbf{A} \cdot (\mathbf{B} \times \mathbf{C}) \equiv (\mathbf{A} \times \mathbf{B}) \cdot \mathbf{C}$$

$$(\mathbf{A} \times \mathbf{B}) \cdot (\mathbf{C} \times \mathbf{D}) \equiv (\mathbf{A} \cdot \mathbf{C})(\mathbf{B} \cdot \mathbf{D}) - (\mathbf{A} \cdot \mathbf{D})(\mathbf{B} \cdot \mathbf{C})$$

$$\mathbf{A} \times (\mathbf{B} \times \mathbf{C}) \equiv (\mathbf{A} \cdot \mathbf{C})\mathbf{B} - (\mathbf{A} \cdot \mathbf{B})\mathbf{C}$$

$$(\mathbf{A} \times \mathbf{B}) \times (\mathbf{C} \times \mathbf{D}) \equiv [(\mathbf{A} \times \mathbf{B}) \cdot \mathbf{D}]\mathbf{C} - [(\mathbf{A} \times \mathbf{B}) \cdot \mathbf{C}]\mathbf{D}$$

A.2 Vector Differential Calculus

(1) Differentiation of a vector function of a single variable s:

$$\frac{d}{ds} \mathbf{A}(s) = \hat{\mathbf{x}} \frac{d}{ds} A_x(s) + \hat{\mathbf{y}} \frac{d}{ds} A_y(s) + \hat{\mathbf{z}} \frac{d}{ds} A_z(s).$$

(2) Differentiation with respect to time of a vector function of **r** and t:

$$\frac{d}{dt} \mathbf{A}(\mathbf{r}, t) = \frac{\partial}{\partial t} \mathbf{A} + \left(\frac{dx}{dt}\frac{\partial}{\partial x} + \frac{dy}{dt}\frac{\partial}{\partial y} + \frac{dz}{dt}\frac{\partial}{\partial z}\right) \mathbf{A}$$

$$= \frac{\partial}{\partial t} \mathbf{A} + \sum_{j=1}^{3} \frac{dx_j}{dt}\frac{\partial}{\partial x_j} \mathbf{A}$$

(3) Directional derivative of a vector point function:

$$\frac{\partial}{\partial n} \mathbf{A} = (\hat{\mathbf{n}} \cdot \mathbf{\nabla})\mathbf{A} = \left[(\hat{\mathbf{n}} \cdot \hat{\mathbf{x}}) \frac{\partial}{\partial x} + (\hat{\mathbf{n}} \cdot \hat{\mathbf{y}}) \frac{\partial}{\partial y} + (\hat{\mathbf{n}} \cdot \hat{\mathbf{z}}) \frac{\partial}{\partial z}\right] \mathbf{A}$$

(4) Gradient of a scalar point function:
   (a) Definition:

$$\text{gradient of } \varphi(\mathbf{r}) = \text{grad } \varphi = \nabla\varphi = \left(\hat{\mathbf{x}} \frac{\partial}{\partial x} + \hat{\mathbf{y}} \frac{\partial}{\partial y} + \hat{\mathbf{z}} \frac{\partial}{\partial z}\right)\varphi$$

   (b) Gradient in cylindrical coordinates (ρ, ϕ, z):

$$\text{grad } \varphi = \left(\hat{\boldsymbol{\rho}} \frac{\partial}{\partial \rho} + \hat{\boldsymbol{\phi}} \frac{1}{\rho} \frac{\partial}{\partial \phi} + \mathbf{z} \frac{\partial}{\partial z}\right)\varphi$$

   (c) Gradient in spherical polar coordinates (r, θ, ϕ):

$$\text{grad } \varphi = \left(\hat{\mathbf{r}} \frac{\partial}{\partial r} + \hat{\boldsymbol{\theta}} \frac{1}{r} \frac{\partial}{\partial \theta} + \hat{\boldsymbol{\phi}} \frac{1}{r \sin \theta} \frac{\partial}{\partial \phi}\right)\varphi$$

(5) Divergence of a vector point function:
   (a) Definition:

$$\text{divergence of } \mathbf{A}(\mathbf{r}) = \text{div } \mathbf{A} = \mathbf{\nabla} \cdot \mathbf{A} = \frac{\partial}{\partial x} A_x + \frac{\partial}{\partial y} A_y + \frac{\partial}{\partial z} A_z$$

   (b) Divergence in cylindrical coordinates (ρ, ϕ, z):

$$\text{div } \mathbf{A} = \frac{1}{\rho} \frac{\partial}{\partial \rho} (\rho A_\rho) + \frac{1}{\rho} \frac{\partial}{\partial \phi} A_\phi + \frac{\partial}{\partial z} A_z$$

   (c) Divergence in spherical polar coordinates (r, θ, ϕ):

$$\text{div } A = \frac{1}{r^2} \frac{\partial}{\partial r} (r^2 A_r) + \frac{1}{r \sin \theta} \frac{\partial}{\partial \theta} (\sin \theta A_\theta) + \frac{1}{r \sin \theta} \frac{\partial}{\partial \phi} A_\phi$$

(6) Curl of a vector point function:

  (a) Definition:

curl of $\mathbf{A(r)}$ = curl $\mathbf{A} = \nabla \times \mathbf{A}$

$$= \left(\frac{\partial}{\partial y} A_z - \frac{\partial}{\partial z} A_y\right)\hat{\mathbf{x}} + \left(\frac{\partial}{\partial z} A_x - \frac{\partial}{\partial x} A_z\right)\hat{\mathbf{y}} + \left(\frac{\partial}{\partial x} A_y - \frac{\partial}{\partial y} A_x\right)\hat{\mathbf{z}}$$

  (b) Curl in cylindrical coordinates (ρ, ϕ, z)

$$\text{curl } \mathbf{A} = \left(\frac{1}{\rho}\frac{\partial A_z}{\partial \phi} - \frac{\partial A_\phi}{\partial z}\right)\hat{\boldsymbol{\rho}} + \left(\frac{\partial A_\rho}{\partial z} - \frac{\partial A_z}{\partial \rho}\right)\hat{\boldsymbol{\phi}}$$

$$+ \left[\frac{1}{\rho}\frac{\partial}{\partial \rho}(\rho A_\phi) - \frac{1}{\rho}\frac{\partial A_\rho}{\partial \phi}\right]\hat{\mathbf{z}}$$

  (c) Curl in spherical polar coordinates (r, θ, ϕ):

$$\text{curl } \mathbf{A} = \frac{1}{r \sin \theta}\left[\frac{\partial}{\partial \theta}(\sin \theta A_\phi) - \frac{\partial A_\theta}{\partial \phi}\right]\hat{\mathbf{r}}$$

$$+ \frac{1}{r}\left[\frac{1}{\sin \theta}\frac{\partial A_r}{\partial \phi} - \frac{\partial}{\partial r}(r A_\phi)\right]\hat{\boldsymbol{\theta}} + \frac{1}{r}\left[\frac{\partial}{\partial r}(r A_\theta) - \frac{\partial A_r}{\partial \theta}\right]\hat{\boldsymbol{\phi}}$$

(7) Laplacian of a scalar point function:

  (a) Definition:

$$\text{Laplacian of } \varphi(\mathbf{r}) = \nabla^2\varphi = \left(\frac{\partial^2}{\partial x^2} + \frac{\partial^2}{\partial y^2} + \frac{\partial^2}{\partial z^2}\right)\varphi$$

  (b) Laplacian in cylindrical coordinates (ρ, ϕ, z):

$$\nabla^2\varphi = \left\{\frac{1}{\rho}\frac{\partial}{\partial \rho}\left(\rho \frac{\partial}{\partial \rho}\right) + \frac{1}{\rho^2}\frac{\partial^2}{\partial \phi^2} + \frac{\partial^2}{\partial z^2}\right\}\varphi$$

  (c) Laplacian in spherical polar coordinates (r, θ, ϕ):

$$\nabla^2\varphi = \left\{\frac{1}{r^2}\frac{\partial}{\partial r}\left(r^2 \frac{\partial}{\partial r}\right) + \frac{1}{r^2 \sin \theta}\frac{\partial}{\partial \theta}\left(\sin \theta \frac{\partial}{\partial \theta}\right) + \frac{1}{r^2 \sin^2 \theta}\frac{\partial^2}{\partial \phi^2}\right\}\varphi.$$

(8) Useful vector differential calculus identities:

grad $(\phi\psi) = \phi$ grad $\psi + \psi$ grad ϕ

div $(\phi\mathbf{A}) = \mathbf{A} \cdot$ grad $\phi + \phi$ div $\mathbf{A}$

curl $(\phi\mathbf{A}) =$ grad $\phi \times \mathbf{A} + \phi$ curl $\mathbf{A}$

div $(\mathbf{A} \cdot \mathbf{B}) = (\mathbf{A} \cdot \nabla)\mathbf{B} + (\mathbf{B} \cdot \nabla)\mathbf{A} + \mathbf{A} \times$ curl $\mathbf{B} + \mathbf{B} \times$ curl $\mathbf{A}$

grad $(\mathbf{A} \times \mathbf{B}) = \mathbf{B} \cdot$ curl $\mathbf{A} - \mathbf{A} \cdot$ curl $\mathbf{B}$

curl $\mathbf{A} \times \mathbf{B} = \mathbf{A}$ div $\mathbf{B} - \mathbf{B}$ div $\mathbf{A} + (\mathbf{B} \cdot \nabla)\mathbf{A} - (\mathbf{A} \cdot \nabla)\mathbf{B}$

curl grad $\phi = 0$

div curl $\mathbf{A} = 0$.

A.3 Vector Integral Calculus

Listed in this section are certain integral relationships satisfied by scalar and vector point functions and their derivatives. τ represents the volume over which an integral is to be performed and Σ the closed surface enveloping τ. Γ is a closed contour and S an open surface capping the contour. $d\tau$ is an element of τ, $\hat{n}\, dS$ a vector element of Σ or S, $\mathbf{dl}$ a vector element of Γ.

(1) Divergence theorem:

$$\oiint_{\Sigma} \mathbf{A} \cdot \hat{n}\, dS = \int_{\tau} d\tau \, \mathrm{div}\, \mathbf{A}$$

(2) Stokes's theorem:

$$\oint_{\Gamma} \mathbf{A} \cdot \mathbf{dl} = \iint_{S} \mathrm{curl}\, \mathbf{A} \cdot \hat{n}\, dS$$

(3) A related integral theorem:

$$\oiint_{\Sigma} \hat{n} \times \mathbf{A}\, dS = \int_{\tau} d\tau \, \mathrm{curl}\, \mathbf{A}$$

(4) Green's identities:

$$\int_{\tau} d\tau [\phi \nabla^2 \psi + \mathrm{grad}\, \phi \cdot \mathrm{grad}\, \psi] = \oiint_{\Sigma} \phi \, \mathrm{grad}\, \psi \cdot \hat{n}\, dS$$

$$\int_{\tau} d\tau [\phi \nabla^2 \psi - \psi \nabla^2 \phi] = \oiint_{\Sigma} (\phi \, \mathrm{grad}\, \psi - \psi \, \mathrm{grad}\, \phi) \cdot \hat{n}\, dS$$

Appendix B | Units and Dimensions

In any treatment of electricity and magnetism, it is impossible to avoid a discussion of the units and dimensions in which electromagnetic quantities are expressed. Very little attention has been given to this matter in the body of the text simply because the main emphasis has been placed on the structure of the theory of electromagnetism. In this appendix, units and dimensions will be discussed in a concise fashion; very little attempt will be made to argue for the virtue of one set of units out of the plethora of existing sets. Nor will any attempt be made at a discussion of the historical development of the standards for measurement of the various physical quantities.

The units used throughout this text are the "rationalized mks" units. This choice has been dictated by the current vogue experienced by this set of units. However, there still remains a considerable fraction of the practicing physicists who, for one reason or another, prefer the so-called "Gaussian" units. All important formulas in this text are written in such a manner that factors of $(4\pi\epsilon_0)$ and $(4\pi/\mu_0)$ may be replaced by unity and the expressions which result from this replacement are then in Gaussian units. (The previous statement does not apply to all formulas which appear incidentally in the mathematical development of a given final result.) This procedure will not prove satisfactory to those who prefer electrostatic, electromagnetic, Heaviside–Lorentz, or other infrequently employed sets of units. Table B.1 allows for the immediate conversion of any electromagnetic quantities into the various other sets of units.

In mechanics the basic quantities are mass, length, and time. All other physical quantities introduced into the discussion of mechanics can be expressed in terms of products of powers of these fundamental quantities. There are two systems of units in common use in mechanics: (1) cgs (length expressed in centimeters, mass in grams, and time in seconds); (2) mks (length expressed in meters, mass in kilograms, and time in seconds). Other systems of units in common use at one time, such as the English system, have all but disappeared in contemporary treatises on classical mechanics. There is no great problem in adopting a consistent and simple set of units in mechanics.

This situation does not obtain in electromagnetism primarily for

376

historical reasons. Much work had been done in both electricity and magnetism before the full impact of the Maxwell–Lorentz theory of electromagnetism was felt. Consequently it was quite natural that different sets of units became adopted in electricity and in magnetism and no unique way presented itself for bringing the two fields into harmony with respect to units and dimensions. The arbitrariness of units and dimensions can be simply illustrated by examining the two force equations from electricity and magnetism written in terms of the fields, these are:

$$\mathbf{f}_E = q\mathbf{E} \tag{B.1}$$

$$\mathbf{f}_B = q'\mathbf{v} \times \mathbf{B}. \tag{B.2}$$

The left-hand side of both equations contains a mechanical entity, namely, force, and as far as dimensions are concerned is not arbitrary; that is, $\mathbf{f}_E$ and $\mathbf{f}_B$ must be expressed as $[(\text{mass}) \cdot (\text{length})(\text{time})^{-2}]$. However, the dimensions of q and E are arbitrary as long as their product has the dimensions of a force. In addition, the right-hand side of eq. B.1 could be multiplied by a constant with dimensions further increasing the arbitrariness of the assignment of dimensions to q and E. The situation with respect to eq. B.2 is just as arbitrary with the additional complication that the charge of the particle called q in B.1 and q' in B.2 need not have the same dimensions. In fact, if the quantities on the right-hand side of eq. B.1 are expressed in electrostatic units (esu) and on the right-hand side of eq. B.2 in electromagnetic units (emu), then

$$q'(\text{emu}) = \frac{1}{c} q(\text{esu}) \tag{B.3}$$

where c = velocity of light in vacuum in centimeters per second; q' and q do not even have the same dimensions. (In both esu and emu systems, f_E and f_B are expressed in the cgs system of mechanical units, i.e., dynes.) In rationalized mks units q and q' are given the same dimensions and are taken to be numerically equal; in addition, in this system both f_E and f_B are expressed in the mks system of mechanical units, i.e., newtons. (Note: 1 newton = 10^5 dynes.) In the mks system E and B therefore do not have the same dimensions, but differ by a factor of the dimensions of velocity. In Gaussian units, on the other hand, E and B are taken to have the same dimensions. It is then conventional to express q' in terms of the charge q. As a consequence

	mks	*Gaussian*
$\mathbf{f}_E$	$q\mathbf{E}$	$q\mathbf{E}$
$\mathbf{f}_B$	$q\mathbf{v} \times \mathbf{B}$	$\frac{q}{c} \mathbf{v} \times \mathbf{B}$

At this stage in the discussion, the mks units have the apparent advantage of not having the constant c appearing in the equation for the magnetic force; however, this advantage is garnered at the expense of requiring E and B, the fundamental field quantities, to be expressed in units having different dimensions.

To specify the dimensions and units of the two fundamental field quantities (E and B) and the two physical sources of the fields (ρ and $\mathbf{j}$), it is convenient to base the discussion upon the Maxwell equations themselves. The magnetic Gaussian law, div $\mathbf{B} = 0$, is of no use in this respect. The electric Gaussian law may be written as

$$\text{div } \mathbf{E} = K_1 \rho \tag{B.4}$$

and serves as a way to choose the dimensions of both $\mathbf{E}$ and ρ when coupled with eq. B.1. Faraday's law is a relationship between $\mathbf{E}$ and $\mathbf{B}$ which does not involve ρ and $\mathbf{j}$; it can be written as

$$\text{curl } \mathbf{E} + K_2 \frac{\partial}{\partial t} \mathbf{B} = 0. \tag{B.5}$$

Finally, both $\mathbf{j}$ and a time-varying $\mathbf{E}$-field serve as sources of $\mathbf{B}$, which can be expressed via Ampère's law as

$$K_5 \text{ curl } \mathbf{B} = K_3 \mathbf{j} + K_4 \frac{\partial}{\partial t} \mathbf{E}. \tag{B.6}$$

The set of five constants (K_j) which appears in these equations must be specified in order to determine the units and dimensions of $\mathbf{E}$, $\mathbf{B}$, ρ, and $\mathbf{j}$.

The equation of continuity is of some help in this regard since it yields an algebraic relationship among some of the (K_j). The continuity relation is obtained by taking $\partial/\partial t$ of eq. B.4 and div of eq. B.6, yielding

$$K_3 \text{ div } \mathbf{j} + K_1 K_4 \frac{\partial}{\partial t} \rho = 0. \tag{B.7}$$

Taking conventional relationship between current (I) and charge (q), which serves as a definition of I, namely, $I = dq/dt$, then eq. B.7 reduces to the algebraic identity

$$K_3 = K_1 K_4. \tag{B.8}$$

An additional algebraic relationship among the constants is obtained from the vacuum wave equations for $\mathbf{E}$ and $\mathbf{B}$ obtained from eqs. B.5 and B.6. These wave equations are

$$\left[\nabla^2 - \frac{K_2 K_4}{K_5} \frac{\partial^2}{\partial t^2} \right] \binom{\mathbf{B}}{\mathbf{E}} = 0.$$

It is known experimentally that electromagnetic waves of constant phase travel with phase velocity c in vacuum, and consequently

$$K_2 K_4 = \frac{K_5}{c^2} \tag{B.9}$$

where $c = 2.997930 \pm 0.000003 \times 10^{10}$ cm/sec (10^8 m/sec). Equations B.8 and B.9 may be expressed in the related form

$$\frac{K_2 K_3}{K_1} = \frac{K_5}{c^2}. \tag{B.10}$$

One other piece of experimental information can be invoked to yield another relationship between the K_j's. In principle at least, it is possible to measure the electrostatic force between two slowly moving charged particles and the magnetic force between them. This is equivalent to determining a relationship between the constants preceding ρ and $\mathbf{j}$ in eqs. B.4 and B.6. The result, without going through the necessary steps in the argument, is

$$\frac{K_1}{K_3} = c. \tag{B.11}$$

There are no other relationships among the K_j's that can be obtained from experiment. In order to specify the system of units, it is necessary to assign values to two of the five constants. The constant K_5 serves to determine the relative dimensions of the two fundamental field quantities, $\mathbf{E}$ and $\mathbf{B}$, in a given system of units.

B.1 Gaussian System

In the Gaussian system $\mathbf{E}$ and $\mathbf{B}$ are measured in the same units ($K_5 = 1$), and K_1 is chosen to be 4π. (In this sense the Gaussian system is *unrationalized*.) Consequently, according to eq. B.11, K_3 is $4\pi/c$. Further, with this value of K_3 substituted into eq. B.10, K_2 becomes equal to $1/c$, via eq. B.9 K_4 is equal to $1/c$. Summarizing these results,

$$K_1 = 4\pi$$

$$K_2 = c^{-1}$$

$$K_3 = 4\pi c^{-1} \tag{B.12}$$

$$K_4 = c^{-1}$$

$$K_5 = 1.$$

In this system, the Maxwell equations are

$$\text{div } \mathbf{E} = 4\pi\rho$$

$$\text{div } \mathbf{B} = 0$$

$$\text{curl } \mathbf{E} + \frac{1}{c}\frac{\partial}{\partial t}\mathbf{B} = 0 \tag{B.13}$$

$$\text{curl } B = \frac{4\pi\mathbf{j}}{c} + \frac{1}{c}\frac{\partial}{\partial t}\mathbf{E},$$

and the Lorentz force law is

$$\mathbf{f} = q\mathbf{E} + \frac{q}{c}\mathbf{v} \times \mathbf{B}. \tag{B.14}$$

It is evident from eqs. B.13 and B.14 that **E** and **B** are expressed in the same units and dimensions. It is only necessary to specify the unit of charge and all other quantities are determined from eqs. B.13 and B.14. The unit charge is defined as follows. If two equal charges are separated by a distance of one centimeter and experience a force of one dyne, the charges are said to be of unit magnitude. A unit charge is called the esu or statcoulomb. A statcoulomb is an extremely small charge by practical standards, and for problems involving macroscopic charges statcoulomb is inconvenient. In the Gaussian system the unit of current is the statcoulomb per second or statampere. For practical problems involving macroscopic currents, this is also an inconvenient unit of current.

B.2   Rationalized mks Units

In the rationalized mks system, K_1 is chosen to be $\epsilon_0{}^{-1}$ where $4\pi\epsilon_0 = 10^7 c^{-2}$ and c is expressed in meters per second. The dimensions of ϵ_0 are $[(\text{charge})^2(\text{time})^2(\text{mass})^{-1}(\text{length})^{-3}]$. Consequently, according to eq. B.11, $K_3 = (c\epsilon_0)^{-1}$. In this system K_5 is chosen to be c, from which it follows that **E** and **B** have different dimensions. This is a specific drawback of the rationalized mks units. From eq. B.10 it then follows that $K_2 = 1$, and eq. B.9 yields $K_4 = c^{-1}$. To summarize these results in rationalized mks units:

$$K_1 = \epsilon_0{}^{-1}$$

$$K_2 = 1$$

$$K_3 = (c\epsilon_0)^{-1} \tag{B.15}$$

$$K_4 = c^{-1}$$

$$K_5 = c.$$

It is conventional to express the velocity of light in vacuum in terms of a related constant μ_0 through the equation $\mu_0\epsilon_0 = c^{-2}$, and to express the Maxwell equations in terms of the constants (ϵ_0, μ_0). $(4\pi\mu_0)$ has the value 10^{-7} and the dimensions $[(\text{mass})(\text{length})(\text{charge})^{-2}]$. The field equations are

$$\text{div } \mathbf{E} = \frac{1}{\epsilon_0} \rho$$

$$\text{div } \mathbf{B} = 0$$

$$\text{curl } \mathbf{E} + \frac{\partial}{\partial t} \mathbf{B} = 0$$

$$\text{curl } \mathbf{B} = \mu_0\left(\mathbf{j} + \epsilon_0 \frac{\partial}{\partial t} \mathbf{E}\right).$$

(B.16)

The equations are rationalized in the sense that no factors of (4π) appear explicitly. The Lorentz force law in these units is

$$\mathbf{f} = q\mathbf{E} + q\mathbf{v} \times \mathbf{B}. \tag{B.17}$$

The unit of charge in the mks system is defined as follows. If two equal charges of unit magnitude are separated by a distance of one meter, the force acting between them will be $10^7|c|^{-2}$ newtons, where $|c|$ is the numerical value of c. The unit of charge is called the coulomb. In this system the unit of current is the coulomb per second or ampere. The rationalized mks system is convenient for those problems involving macroscopic charge and current. But it is an inconvenient system for microscopic vacuum problems because of the appearance of the constants ϵ_0 and μ_0 in the Maxwell equations. It is a completely unnatural system for atomic and nuclear physics where the famous "fine structure constant" must be expressed as

$$\frac{1}{(4\pi\epsilon_0)} \frac{e^2}{\hbar c} = \frac{1}{137}.$$

B.3 The Macroscopic Field Quantities

The above discussion of units and dimensions refers to the microscopic fields $\mathbf{E}$ and $\mathbf{B}$. It also applies to the time and space averages of these fields or the macroscopic $\mathbf{E}$ and $\mathbf{B}$. In a macroscopic theory, four other field quantities are introduced, namely, $\mathbf{D}$, $\mathbf{H}$, $\mathbf{P}$, and $\mathbf{M}$. In all systems the relationship that exists between $\mathbf{D}$ and $\mathbf{E}$ and $\mathbf{H}$ and $\mathbf{B}$ for linear homogeneous material is:

$$\mathbf{D} = \epsilon\mathbf{E}$$

$$\mathbf{B} = \mu\mathbf{H}.$$

(B.18)

The various systems differ in the values that ϵ and μ assume for vacuum. In vacuum, for the Gaussian system $\epsilon = \mu = 1$, whereas for the rationalized mks system $\epsilon = \epsilon_0$, and $\mu = \mu_0$. In the Gaussian system the dielectric constant is equal to the electric permittivity ϵ, and the permeability is equal to the magnetic permittivity μ. In the mks system the dielectric constant is (ϵ/ϵ_0), and the permeability is (μ/μ_0). The relationship between $\mathbf{P}$ and the set $\mathbf{E}$, $\mathbf{D}$, and $\mathbf{M}$ and the set $\mathbf{B}$, $\mathbf{H}$ for the various systems of units is shown in Table B.1, which also serves to summarize the above remarks on units and dimensions.

System	Relationships among the macroscopic fields	Macroscopic Maxwell equations		Force per unit charge
mks (rationalized)	$\mathbf{D} = \epsilon_0\mathbf{E} + \mathbf{P}$	$\text{div } \mathbf{D} = \rho$	$\text{curl } \mathbf{E} + \dfrac{\partial}{\partial t}\mathbf{B} = 0$	$\mathbf{E} + \mathbf{v} \times \mathbf{B}$
	$\mathbf{H} = \dfrac{1}{\mu_0}\mathbf{B} - \mathbf{M}$	$\text{div } \mathbf{B} = 0$	$\text{curl } \mathbf{H} = \mathbf{j} + \dfrac{\partial}{\partial t}\mathbf{D}$	
Gaussian	$\mathbf{D} = \mathbf{E} + 4\pi\mathbf{P}$	$\text{div } \mathbf{D} = 4\pi\rho$	$\text{curl } \mathbf{E} + \dfrac{1}{c}\dfrac{\partial}{\partial t}\mathbf{B} = 0$	$\mathbf{E} + \dfrac{\mathbf{v}}{c} \times \mathbf{B}$
	$\mathbf{H} = \mathbf{B} - 4\pi\mathbf{M}$	$\text{div } \mathbf{B} = 0$	$\text{curl } \mathbf{H} = \dfrac{4\pi}{c}\mathbf{j} + \dfrac{1}{c}\dfrac{\partial\mathbf{D}}{\partial t}$	
Electrostatic	$\mathbf{D} = \mathbf{E} + 4\pi\mathbf{P}$	$\text{div } \mathbf{D} = 4\pi\rho$	$\text{curl } \mathbf{E} + \dfrac{\partial\mathbf{B}}{\partial t} = 0$	$\mathbf{E} + \mathbf{v} \times \mathbf{B}$
	$\mathbf{H} = c^2\mathbf{B} - 4\pi\mathbf{M}$	$\text{div } \mathbf{B} = 0$	$\text{curl } \mathbf{H} = 4\pi\mathbf{j} + \dfrac{\partial\mathbf{D}}{\partial t}$	
Electromagnetic	$\mathbf{D} = \dfrac{1}{c^2}\mathbf{E} + 4\pi\mathbf{P}$	$\text{div } \mathbf{D} = 4\pi\rho$	$\text{curl } \mathbf{E} + \dfrac{\partial\mathbf{B}}{\partial t} = 0$	$\mathbf{E} + \mathbf{v} \times \mathbf{B}$
	$\mathbf{H} = \mathbf{B} - 4\pi\mathbf{M}$	$\text{div } \mathbf{B} = 0$	$\text{curl } \mathbf{H} = 4\pi\mathbf{j} + \dfrac{\partial\mathbf{D}}{\partial t}$	
Heaviside–Lorentz	$\mathbf{D} = \mathbf{E} + \mathbf{P}$	$\text{div } \mathbf{D} = \rho$	$\text{curl } \mathbf{E} + \dfrac{1}{c}\dfrac{\partial\mathbf{B}}{\partial t} = 0$	$\mathbf{E} + \dfrac{\mathbf{v}}{c} \times \mathbf{B}$
	$\mathbf{H} = \mathbf{B} - \mathbf{M}$	$\text{div } \mathbf{B} = 0$	$\text{curl } \mathbf{H} = \dfrac{\mathbf{j}}{c} + \dfrac{1}{c}\dfrac{\partial}{\partial t}\mathbf{D}$	

Appendix C | *Answers*

The following answers are provided for certain of the odd-numbered problems, which appear at the end of each chapter.

1.1 $\mathbf{A} \cdot \hat{\mathbf{x}}_b = (\mathbf{A} \cdot \hat{\mathbf{x}}_a) \cos \beta + (\mathbf{A} \cdot \hat{\mathbf{y}}_a) \sin \beta$

$\mathbf{A} \cdot \hat{\mathbf{y}}_b = -(\mathbf{A} \cdot \hat{\mathbf{x}}_a) \sin \beta + (\mathbf{A} \cdot \hat{\mathbf{y}}_a) \cos \beta$

$\mathbf{A} \cdot \hat{\mathbf{z}}_b = \mathbf{A} \cdot \hat{\mathbf{z}}_a$

1.9 cylindrical: $\dfrac{d^2 \mathbf{r}}{dt^2} = (\ddot{\rho} - \rho \dot{\phi}^2) \hat{\boldsymbol{\rho}} + (2 \dot{\rho} \dot{\phi} + \rho \ddot{\phi}) \hat{\boldsymbol{\phi}} + \ddot{z} \hat{\mathbf{z}}$

spherical: $\dfrac{d^2 \mathbf{r}}{dt^2} = (\ddot{r} - r \dot{\theta}^2 + r \sin^2 \theta \dot{\phi}^2) \hat{\mathbf{r}}$

$+ (2 \dot{r} \dot{\theta} + r \ddot{\theta} + r \sin \theta \cos \theta \dot{\phi}^2) \hat{\boldsymbol{\theta}}$

$+ (2 \dot{r} \dot{\phi} \sin \theta + 2r \cos \theta \, \dot{\theta} \dot{\phi} + r \sin \theta \ddot{\phi}) \hat{\boldsymbol{\phi}}$

1.19 (a) yes; $\varphi(x, y, z) = -\alpha xyz + \text{constant}$

(b) no

2.1 $\left(\dfrac{1}{4\pi\epsilon_0} \right) \sqrt{3} \dfrac{q^2}{s^2}$

2.3 (a) 1.17×10^{-10} m

(b) 1.20×10^{-10} m

2.7 $\left(\dfrac{1}{4\pi\epsilon_0} \right) \dfrac{q}{\sqrt{y^2 + R^2}}$, $\left(\dfrac{1}{4\pi\epsilon_0} \right) \dfrac{qy}{(y^2 + R^2)^{3/2}}$

2.9 $\left(\dfrac{1}{4\pi\epsilon_0} \right) \dfrac{Q}{3R^2}$

2.13 $v_{\text{final}}^2 = \left(\dfrac{1}{4\pi\epsilon_0} \right) \dfrac{2q^2}{ms}$

2.15 (a) 0

(b) $\left(\dfrac{1}{4\pi\epsilon_0} \right) \dfrac{qQ}{|r - R|}$

2.17 $\dfrac{4\pi}{3} \sigma_0 R^3$

2.21 (a) $\begin{pmatrix} 2ql^2 & 0 & 0 \\ 0 & 2ql^2 & 0 \\ 0 & 0 & -4ql^2 \end{pmatrix}$

(b) $\left(\dfrac{1}{4\pi\epsilon_0} \right) \dfrac{ql^2}{r^5} (r^2 - 3z^2)$

2.23 (a) $-\left(\dfrac{1}{4\pi\epsilon_0}\right)\left[\dfrac{\mathbf{p}_1 \times \mathbf{p}_2}{d^3} - \dfrac{3(\mathbf{p}_2 \cdot \hat{\mathbf{d}})(\mathbf{p}_1 \cdot \hat{\mathbf{d}})}{d^3}\right]$

(b) 0

3.1 $\sqrt{\left(\dfrac{1}{4\pi\epsilon_0}\right)\dfrac{e^2}{4\pi^2 m R^3}}$

3.3 $\rho = -\left(\dfrac{\alpha^2}{4\pi}\right)\dfrac{q}{r}\exp(-\alpha r)$ plus a point charge of magnitude $+q$ located at the origin

3.5 $\left(\dfrac{1}{4\pi\epsilon_0}\right)\dfrac{q}{r^2}\hat{\mathbf{r}},\quad r_1 < r < r_2$

$0,\qquad\qquad r > r_3$

3.7 $\left(\dfrac{1}{4\pi\epsilon_0}\right)\dfrac{\sigma}{2}\hat{\mathbf{n}},\quad$ nonconductor

$\left(\dfrac{1}{4\pi\epsilon_0}\right)\sigma\,\hat{\mathbf{n}},\quad$ conductor

3.11 $\left(\dfrac{1}{4\pi\epsilon_0}\right)\dfrac{2\pi}{3}p(1 - \cos^2\theta)$

3.15 (a) $\dfrac{2}{2l + 1}$

(b) $\dfrac{2}{2l + 1}\,\delta_{ll'}$

3.17 $\varphi_0\left[\dfrac{3}{2}\left(\dfrac{r}{a}\right)P_1(\cos\theta) - \dfrac{7}{8}\left(\dfrac{r}{a}\right)^3 P_3(\cos\theta)\right.$
$\left. + \dfrac{11}{16}\left(\dfrac{r}{a}\right)^5 P_5(\cos\theta) + \cdots\right],\quad r < a$

$\varphi_0\left[\dfrac{3}{2}\left(\dfrac{a}{r}\right)^2 P_1(\cos\theta) - \dfrac{7}{8}\left(\dfrac{a}{r}\right)^4 P_3(\cos\theta)\right.$
$\left. + \dfrac{11}{16}\left(\dfrac{a}{r}\right)^6 P_5(\cos\theta) + \cdots\right],\quad r > a$

3.19 $\varphi_0\left(\dfrac{r}{a}\right)\cos\theta,\quad$ inside

$\varphi_0\left(\dfrac{a}{r}\right)^2\cos\theta,\quad$ outside

4.3 $\left(\dfrac{1}{4\pi\epsilon_0}\right)\dfrac{3Q_1Q_2}{4r^5}\{1 + 2\cos^2\theta - 20\cos\phi_1\cos\phi_2\cos\theta$
$- 5(\cos^2\phi_1 + \cos^2\phi_2) + 35\cos^2\phi_1\cos^2\phi_2\}$

4.5 $\left(\dfrac{1}{4\pi\epsilon_0}\right)\dfrac{q^2}{s}(12 + 6\sqrt{2} + \tfrac{4}{3}\sqrt{3})$

4.7 $\left(\dfrac{1}{4\pi\epsilon_0}\right)\dfrac{p^2}{3R^3}$

4.9 $(2\pi\epsilon_0)\ln\left(\dfrac{r_2}{r_1}\right)$

5.1 P on cylinder face perpendicular to **P**
      $\frac{1}{2}P, -\frac{1}{2}P$ on other cylinder faces

5.3 $\left(\frac{1}{4\pi\epsilon_0}\right)2\pi P\left\{2 - \dfrac{x}{\sqrt{x^2 + R^2}} - \dfrac{L - x}{\sqrt{(L - x)^2 + R^2}}\right\}$

5.5 $\arctan\left(\dfrac{\epsilon_2}{\epsilon_1}\tan\theta\right)$

5.7   (a) $\dfrac{\sigma}{2\epsilon_0}$

    (b) $\dfrac{\sigma}{2\epsilon}$

    (c) $\dfrac{\sigma}{2}\left(1 + \dfrac{\epsilon_0}{\epsilon}\right), \quad \dfrac{\sigma}{2}\left(1 - \dfrac{\epsilon_0}{\epsilon}\right)$

5.9 $\dfrac{1}{2}\left(\dfrac{\epsilon}{\epsilon_0} - 1\right)C(\Delta\varphi)^2, \quad \dfrac{1}{2}\left(1 - \dfrac{\epsilon_0}{\epsilon}\right)C(\Delta\varphi)^2$

5.11 $\nabla^2\varphi = -\left(\dfrac{1}{4\pi\epsilon}\right)4\pi\rho_{\text{real}}$

5.13 $\dfrac{2A}{d}(\epsilon_2 - \epsilon_1)\dfrac{1}{\ln\left(\dfrac{\epsilon_2}{\epsilon_1}\right)}$

6.5 $B = \left(\dfrac{\mu_0}{4\pi}\right)\dfrac{16}{3}\pi^2 RK$
      $A = 0$

6.9 $\dfrac{f}{l} = \left(\dfrac{\mu_0}{4\pi}\right)\dfrac{2I_1 I_2}{d}$

6.11 $-\boldsymbol{\mu}\cdot\mathbf{B}$

7.1 $\left(\dfrac{\mu_0}{4\pi}\right)\dfrac{2I}{r},$ inside
           0,   outside

8.1 $\left(\dfrac{\mu_0}{4\pi}\right)4\pi^2 N^2 R^2$

8.3 $\left(\dfrac{\mu_0}{4\pi}\right)I^2\ln\left(\dfrac{a}{b}\right)$

8.5 $\left(\dfrac{\mu_0}{4\pi}\right)2\pi^2 a\left(\dfrac{a}{D}\right)^3$

8.7 $\left(\dfrac{\mu_0}{4\pi}\right)2\pi\left(\dfrac{R}{D}\right)^2 Iv\left[1 + \dfrac{3}{4}\left(\dfrac{R}{D}\right)^2 + \cdots\right]$

9.5 $B_\rho = \left[1 + \dfrac{\mu - \mu_0}{\mu + \mu_0} \dfrac{a^2}{\rho^2} \right] B_0 \cos \phi$

$B_\phi = \left[-1 + \dfrac{\mu - \mu_0}{\mu + \mu_0} \dfrac{a^2}{\rho^2} \right] B_0 \sin \phi$ } outside

$\mathbf{B} = \mu_0 \mathbf{H}$

$B_\rho = \dfrac{2\mu}{\mu + \mu_0} B_0 \cos \phi$

$B_\phi = \dfrac{-2\mu}{\mu + \mu_0} B_0 \sin \phi$ } inside

$\mathbf{B} = \mu \mathbf{H}$

11.13   for $l = 0$ mode:

$B_z = B_0 J_0(\xi_{0m}) \exp \{i(k_g z - \omega t)\}$

$B_\rho = \dfrac{ik_g}{k^2 - k_g{}^2} \gamma_{0m} J_1(\xi_{0m}) \exp \{i(k_g z - \omega t)\}$

$E_\phi = \dfrac{-ik/c}{k^2 - k_g{}^2} \gamma_{0m} J_1(\xi_{0m}) \exp \{i(k_g z - \omega t)\}$

$E_z = B_\phi = E_\rho = 0$

with $\xi_{0m} \equiv \gamma_{0m}\rho$

and $\gamma_{0m}a$ the roots of the equation $J_1(\gamma_{0m}a) = 0$.

11.15 $\omega_{lmn} = \pi c \sqrt{\dfrac{n^2}{h^2} - \left(\dfrac{\gamma_{lm}}{\pi} \right)^2}$

with $\gamma_{lm}a$ the zeros of J_l.

12.1 $\dfrac{W_e}{W_m} = 1$

12.3 $T = \dfrac{2\left(\dfrac{v_1}{v_2}\right) \cos \theta_i}{\left(\dfrac{v_1}{v_2}\right) \cos \theta_i + \sqrt{1 - \left(\dfrac{v_1}{v_2}\right)^2 \sin^2 \theta_i}}$

13.3 $\mathbf{E} = E\hat{\boldsymbol{\theta}}$ $E = \left(\dfrac{\mu_0}{4\pi}\right)\dfrac{1}{r}\ddot{p}\sin\vartheta$

     $\mathbf{B} = B\hat{\boldsymbol{\phi}}$ $cB = E$

13.5 $\dfrac{8\pi}{3}r_0{}^2$

13.7 $\dfrac{P_{E1}}{P_{M1}} = \dfrac{4c^2}{\omega^2 r_0{}^2}$

14.1 $\rho = \sqrt{\dfrac{2m\Delta\vartheta}{qB_0{}^2}}$

     $\mu = \dfrac{q\Delta\vartheta}{B_0}$

Index